8/4/59 S.K.V.

Genetics, Paleontology, and Evolution

Genetics, Paleontology, and Evolution

EDITED BY

Glenn L. Jepsen · Ernst Mayr
George Gaylord Simpson

FOR THE COMMITTEE ON COMMON PROBLEMS
OF GENETICS, PALEONTOLOGY, AND SYSTEMATICS,
OF THE NATIONAL RESEARCH COUNCIL

1949

PRINCETON UNIVERSITY PRESS

PRINCETON, NEW JERSEY

FOREWORD

Publication of this volume upon various aspects and implications of organic evolution signifies the formal completion of work by the Committee on Common Problems of Genetics, Paleontology, and Systematics which was established on February 6, 1943, as a joint or interdivisional committee by the Division of Geology and Geography and the Division of Biology and Agriculture of the National Research Council. The Committee itself made a number of minor changes (not detailed here) in title and personnel during the development of its work.

Throughout its existence, however, the Committee has adhered to its stated functions of trying to bring about a meeting of minds in the territory between the fields of genetics and paleontology, of furthering cooperation between students in the two and in other disciplines, and, by pooling knowledge and methods and resources, of outlining promising lines for future research. Information and ideas and speculations were exchanged by meetings of subgroups of the Committee, by writing and distributing bulletins, and by holding a final symposium to which many additional specialists in several geological and biological fields were invited.

No member of the Committee ever expected that its self-set task would be easily or completely accomplished. Habits of thought in the tradition of a science are not readily changed, it is not easy to deviate from the customary channels of accumulated experience in conventionalized subjects or to predict the extent of thought confluence when old channels are brought together.

Few committees can so accurately define the instant that the idea of their work was generated. In 1941, at the annual meeting of The Geological Society of America, Walter Bucher suggested that some of the riddles of evolution, the most significant and basic fact of biology and paleontology, might be solved by a synthesis of the two subjects. He remarked that geneticists "have little time for, and less interest in the body of solid fact which . . . morphology, taxonomy, and paleontology are accumulating," and that when paleontologists show interest in genetics "it is intermingled with distrust in the long range significance" of the findings of geneticists.

Informal discussion immediately followed (indeed, several paleontologists were waiting for him at the door) about means of correcting the situation he had described, and on October 17, 1942, a small group of geneticists, paleontologists, and systematists met in the library of the zoology department of Columbia University. They agreed that paleontologists should learn more about the techniques and the essential results of genetics, that geneticists should become better acquainted with the degree of reliability of stratigraphic and paleontologic methods and the validity of generalizations proposed by paleontologists, and that specialists in the several evolutionary disciplines should learn each other's languages.

It was further decided that workers in genetics and paleontology should be brought together in a large committee which could be divided into two geographical subcommittees, an eastern group and a western group, to be concerned respectively with zoological and with botanical aspects of the problems. Organization under the National Research Council followed, as reported above.

In June of 1943 the western group met for three days in Berkeley at the University of California and the eastern group convened for two days at the American Museum of Natural History in New York. A report of these meetings, including abstracts of the papers and discussions, was distributed to the Committee members and to other specialists. These discussions revealed some of the kinds of information which could be profitably exchanged between geneticists and paleontologists in the synthetic attack upon the common problems, and also showed what aspects of each field are crucial for coordinate research in the other.

Soon war conditions made it impossible to hold meetings, but a plan was developed whereby members exchanged questions and answers by letters, and the correspondence thus stimulated was mimeographed and distributed, under the editorship of Ernst Mayr, in four bulletins which totaled 115 pages.

These communications not only heightened the interest and increased the knowledge of the committee members and others but aided in still further defining the subjects which might most profitably receive cooperative attention and be the basis for this final symposial volume.

Reading lists in the three fields of the Committee's name were compiled and distributed in furtherance of the design of mutual education. These methods of exchanging information and ideas stimulated new research, and some synthetic studies of previous research resulted in several publications in scientific journals and bulletins.

In 1945 a committee member was reported missing in action in Germany. The annual report for the year carried the comment, "He continues to be listed as a committee member in the hope that he is a prisoner and may soon return." This hope was fulfilled. Later that year, however, the Committee was saddened by the death of Bruce L. Clark, an active and valued member, on September 23.

As plans advanced for the final conference and for the publication of the terminal volume the need became more obvious for a permanent organization to continue and expand the work of the Committee and for the establishment of a journal devoted to the field and to allied subjects.

In Chairman Simpson's annual report for 1946 he explained the need for a permanent organization: "Immediately before the war the Society for the Study of Speciation had been organized in a very informal way, with aims similar to but more limited than those of the Committee. This Society became dormant during the war. Under the stimulus of this Committee and as a result of plans made by its members and others, a new society was organized on 30 March 1946 at the St. Louis meeting of the A.A.A.S., under the name of the Society for the Study of Evolution. The new society is devoted to evolutionary problems on an inter-science basis, essentially covering the field of this Committee, broadening it still further but retaining its focal aims. At the same meeting the Society for the Study of Speciation, the aims of which are also included in the new Society, was dissolved and its records, mailing list, and treasury were turned over to the Society for the Study of Evolution." In 1947 Simpson reported: "The Society held a successful First Annual Meeting at Boston in December, 1946, and its success and permanence seem to be assured. With the assistance of a grant from the American Philosophical Society, the Society for the Study of Evolution has established an international journal titled *Evolution*."

In 1946 the Committee received and accepted an invitation from Princeton to hold the final symposium under the sponsorship of the University in connection with one of a series of Bicentennial Conferences. This logical combination of the work of the Committee and the desire of the University to advance research in the field of the Committee resulted in the international Conference on Genetics, Paleontology, and Evolution which was held at the Princeton Inn on January 2-4, 1947. Princeton invited each member of the Committee and other active workers in the various fields of evolutionary studies to be its guests for the Conference and also contributed transportation expenses for foreign guests and for American principal speakers who came from areas west of the eastern seaboard.

Under the title of the Conference Princeton published a brochure which summarized the proceedings and discussions and was distributed to members of the Society for the Study of Evolution and other organizations. The brochure also listed all Conference participants.

For the record a brief formal meeting of the Committee was held in Princeton on January 4, 1947, with the chairman presiding and twenty-three other Committee members in attendance.

All authors contributing to this book attended the Conference. Fourteen of them served on the Committee. Membership of the Committee, as it has been since 1945, is listed on page *xi*.

To complete the assembly and editing of this volume an editorial subcommittee consisting of Ernst Mayr, George Gaylord Simpson, and Glenn L. Jepsen, as chairman, was appointed.

Indexing a book of this sort is a difficult job, and the editorial subcommittee here expresses its gratitude to members of the Lunch Club of the Chicago Natural History Museum for doing it.

This volume is not a single synthesis of its three titular subjects, but is, rather, a compound of data, of ideas, and of conclusions. Researchers who realize the magnitude and significance of the work still to be done in their own fields usually need active and even aggressive encouragement to stray beyond the conventionalized limits of their subjects. To this end, each author in this book was subjected to close association with practitioners in other fields during the period of the Conference, and many critical, penetrating, and sometimes embarrassing questions and comments were exchanged in an attempt at mutual education.

Such interchange of the concepts, which sometimes arise in one field of research and develop their greatest meaning in another, may be observed in the book's various sections which, in this sense, are individual syntheses. Synthesis of diverse subject matter is a process which must of course occur in minds before it does in books.

Not only do the authors herein view the subject of evolution from different directions, but the method of treatment varies from the specific to the general. Some sections contain the results of new and detailed original research; in others the authors present speculations and reflections upon many decades of effort toward the common goal.

Genetics is concerned largely with a small number of concepts or "laws" whose manipulation results in the derivation of many deductive propositions which may be tested by the way they fit observed situations in the field or in the laboratory. According to a member of the Committee, ". . . learning genetics involves not only (or not so much) memorizing a body of facts but also acquisition of a habit of thinking in terms of certain genetic concepts." Among its subdivisions modern genetics includes developmental or physiological genetics and population genetics. In physiological genetics the role of the gene in ontogeny is the principal subject for attention; whole individual organisms and their aggregates in populations are but terminal results of genic and environmental action. Population genetics is the study of the behavior of genes in populations and of the means by which genes are distributed in populations. It deals with multiples of individual organisms; its focus is phyletic, and it attempts to predict and to test the consequences of various genetic situations to gene frequencies and to species. In the studies undertaken by the Committee these and other subdivisions of genetics have contributed evidences for mathematical regularities and for hypotheses concerning the mechanisms and processes by which men and fruit flies may have developed from the organic magma.

Paleontology supplies the annals of morphologic and ecologic events and their time and space relationships for five million centuries of the adaptive organizations of protoplasm; it historifies the geological records of life. Comparative anatomy and time and the means of describing individuals and groups of individuals have classically occupied the attention of paleontologists who thus, perforce, must be skilled in comparative anatomy and in taxonomy.

From morphological and stratigraphic and taxonomic data a species' phylogenetic history, our knowledge of its ancestral stages and their sequence in time, may be established. Details of the time dimension were not treated as very significant elements in phylogenetic studies until an enormous fund of paleontological facts had been accumulated. Anatomists, including paleontologists, formerly arrayed species in the order of their complexity and assumed that the more "primitive" forms represented older stages in morphologic history and were thus structural ancestors of the "higher" types. Unfortunately no truly definitive criteria for primitiveness and complexity could be devised and, as paleontological records frequently proved, the order postulated for some anatomical sequences was the reverse of the actual historical sequences.

In modern studies of phylogeny relative time forms a coordinate system with estimates of morphologic or genetic status. Although we will never have the complete geological record of evolution, the principal outline of the histories of many living and many extinct groups is now at hand, and is plotted against fairly satisfactory estimates of time in years.

Systematics or taxonomy is the most obvious link between genetics and paleontology because it attempts to provide a universally recognized system of perceiving and symbolizing the groups of organisms which receive attention in paleontology and in population genetics. In modern evolutionary studies concern has shifted from the organism as a describable object to the more sophisticated view of it as a morphological expression of the genetic and environmental status of an evolving population.

This revision in attitude emphasizes the limitations and the multiple character of our taxonomic practices. Names and classifications of organisms formerly presented no intricate problems of manipulation or symbolism. As long as species were believed to be immutable and anatomically as static as the names by which they are symbolized, species had no history of change. However, when paleontological discoveries proved evolutionary transformation as a historical fact, the sempiternal problem of classification arose to new heights in biology—the problem of developing a satisfactory device to reconcile the frozen mechanics of the Linnean system with the concept of a species' modification in time. Numerous and widely-discussed attempts have been made to harmonize vertical and horizontal (or transverse) taxonomic schemes, but as yet the proposed solutions are incomplete and unsatisfactory.

Recently another perplexing puzzle has developed from the differences between paleontology and genetics in the methods and motives for classifying organisms. This also is a problem of deciding when and how to use one or the other of two systems for taxonomy, one based upon gross morphology and one (called "genetic" or "biological") upon breeding habits and the distribution and behavior of genic materials. The latter species-concept separates species upon the basis of tested or assumed genetic discontinuity. It has considerable use in describing and postulating genetic and distributional situations and in making decisions about specific allocation of living individuals. This criterion of discontinuity, however, is inapplicable in most paleontological or phylogenetic studies, which must be based upon morphological conditions, and it represses or ignores the principle that genetic continuity is the *sine qua non* in the vertical or time sequence of species in phylogeny.

Many such differences in materials, methods, and logics are revealed in the writings of the authors of this book. Each evolutionary discipline, as herein represented, holds a mirror for self-observation in the light radiated from other lines of study.

GLENN L. JEPSEN
*Sinclair Professor of
Vertebrate Paleontology*

Princeton, N.J.

THE COMMITTEE ON
COMMON PROBLEMS OF GENETICS, PALEONTOLOGY,
AND SYSTEMATICS

CONTENTS

{ *xiii* }

CONTENTS

VI. ADAPTATION

VII. HUMAN EVOLUTION

VIII. SUMMATION

PART I

GEOLOGICAL TIME

· 1 ·

TIME IN EARTH HISTORY

BY ADOLPH KNOPF[1]

DURING the past two decades the length of geologic time and its subdivisions as measured by radiogenic lead has become the standard against
which all other estimates are compared. These measurements, demanding
a twenty-fold extension of our ideas of the length of geologic time (2),
were received with profound skepticism at first, but since 1931 (13) they
have gradually become orthodox. The method based on the amount of
lead generated in a radioactive mineral by atomic disintegration was first
proposed by Boltwood (3) in 1907, when the science of radioactivity was
in its infancy. As the years have gone by, the lead method of measuring
geologic time, as it has come to be known, has grown steadily in strength,
until it now appears to be impregnable. It has grown in versatility too, so
that it can now step over its earlier limitations and use not only fresh
unaltered minerals but also altered, oxidized minerals. Since most radioactive minerals contain three radioactive elements—U^{238}, U^{235}, and
thorium—and all three produce leads of differing atomic weights and at
differing rates, it is now possible by proper quantitative analysis to obtain
three independent determinations of age on one and the same mineral.
One determination is based on the ratio between U^{238} and the radiogenic
lead derived from it; the second, on the radiogenic lead derived from Th;
and the third is based on the ratio between the radiogenic lead derived
from U^{235} and that derived from U^{238}. If all three age determinations agree,
assurance is rendered trebly sure. As the most ancient minerals were
formed as much as 2000 million years ago, such a three-fold check on
determinations of age is highly welcome in view of the enormous extrapolation backward in time.

Three other methods based on radioactivity have been used to measure
absolute time. One of these is based on radiohalos, on the intensity of the
color produced around minute particles of radioactive minerals inclosed in
certain minerals. The alpha-particles emitted from the radioactive centers
crash through the space-lattice of the host mineral and cause the color of
the host mineral to deepen. The depth of color thus caused is determined
by the intensity and the duration of the bombardment by the alpha-
particles, which is a function of the radioactive content of the enclosed
mineral and the length of time. To translate this color effect into time in

[1] Sterling Professor of Geology, Yale University.

years is a difficult feat. So difficult, in fact, that only one investigator, Henderson of Dalhousie University, has continued to work on the problem during the last two decades. The usable halos so far found are scarce and have been found only in very ancient rocks, about 960 million years old. No great future in measuring geologic time by means of radiohalos is yet in sight.

The second method, strontium method, based on the transformation of rubidium 87 to strontium 87, is currently being developed and holds great promise (1, 8). Because rubidium transforms so slowly into strontium—in 900 million years only one per cent of the active rubidium (Rb^{87}) will have changed to Sr^{87}—the strontium method will most likely be useful in determining the ages of the most ancient rocks.

A third method of measuring time is based on the accumulation of radiogenic helium. The helium method, as it is called, has had a curious history. It was the first method based on radioactivity to be applied to measure geologic time. The pioneer attempt in 1909 gave astonishingly high figures, much higher than had been considered probable. For example, a Precambrian zircon gave an age of 700 million years. The great age thus indicated was a minimum, because the zircon was able to hold within itself only a third or at most a half of the helium generated from the uranium contained in it. As the lead method grew in strength, the helium method was abandoned.

In 1928 a new form of the helium method was devised. It was based on the fact that a remarkable new technique had just been developed, whereby quantities of helium as small as one-millionth of a cubic cm. could be accurately measured. The new form of the helium method, then, was not to take strongly radioactive minerals, which accordingly contained large amounts of radiogenic helium, but to take minerals that contain a minute quantity of radioactive matter, one might say an almost infinitesimally small quantity. In the course of geologic time this small quantity generated an extremely small amount of helium, so minute in fact, so the hope was, that it was all retained in the mineral in which it had formed; none had leaked away. The great advantage of the new helium method was that it could be applied to rocks, since all rocks contain radioactive matter. Consequently, what was of immense importance to geology, the new helium method could be applied to rocks whose geologic age is precisely known. Rocks of known geologic age can be obtained in abundance and can therefore be subjected to the new procedure. The great desideratum—measuring geologic time in years—seemed to be within our grasp. A large number of rocks were examined and their ages in years determined: Unicoi basalt in the Early Cambrian beds of North Carolina, 430 million years; late Triassic dolerite, at New Haven, Connecticut, 160 million years; and many others. These numerous determinations are now doing duty in the literature, and many are being used by geologists to prove that their estimates of the length of the geologic periods or portions thereof obtained by other than the methods based on radioactivity must be right, because the estimates agree with the figures "obtained from radioactive data."

Suddenly in 1939 the new helium method collapsed (7). It collapsed for a number of reasons, but chiefly because it was shown that if a rock is separated into its constituent minerals, each mineral gives highly different values for its age. The Cape Ann granite of Massachusetts, for example, was separated into its component feldspar, quartz, and dark minerals: the feldspar gave an "age" of 59 million years; the quartz 94, and the dark minerals 159 million years. The Palisade diabase was broken down into its constituents—plagioclase, pyroxene and magnetite; the plagioclase indicated an age of 36 million years, the pyroxene 103 million years, and the magnetite 134 million years. Manifestly the three minerals have greatly differing retentivities; the magnetite retains the helium generated within it three times as well as does the feldspar.

To salvage the helium method if possible was the next step. Much work along this line has been done by Clark Goodman and P. M. Hurley (12) and is being continued by Hurley. The fundamental assumption in this work is that all the helium generated in the magnetite is retained in the magnetite. Consequently the age of the magnetite can be determined by separating the magnetite from the rock in which it occurs and cleaning it completely of all adherent minerals and measuring the helium, uranium, and thorium content, and from these data computing the age. Preliminary determinations on a series of magnetites thus investigated agree fairly well with the ages as found by means of the lead method. But occasionally some highly disconcerting results are obtained, as when a Keweenawan lava gives an age of 36,000 million years, instead of the usual 550 millions. This new form of the helium method—the magnetite-helium method—is therefore insecure and needs to be greatly strengthened in order to inspire confidence. Another fundamental assumption underlying the magnetite-helium method, in addition to the assumption that the radiogenic helium is completely retained in the magnetite, is that all the helium is derived from uranium and thorium. If, for example, some of the other radioactive elements such as ionium should have been deposited in the magnetite as well as uranium and thorium, the age determinations will bear no relation to the real age of the magnetite.

Of the three methods for measuring geologic time based on atomic disintegration we are therefore forced to rely entirely on the lead method. As I have already emphasized, it has grown enormously in strength since it was first proposed by Boltwood. It can now use oxidized minerals; it can evaluate the amount of ordinary lead deposited in a mineral at the time the mineral was formed; and on an unaltered mineral it gives three independent values for the age.

A considerable number of determinations of the ages of minerals based on the lead method have now been made. To evaluate their reliability they can be divided into four classes: Class I, in which U, Th, and Pb have been determined by standard gravimetric chemical analyses and the isotopic composition of the lead has been determined by means of the mass spectrograph; Class II, in which U, Th, and Pb have been determined by standard gravimetric methods and the atomic weight of the lead has been determined chemically; Class III, in which U, Th, and Pb have been determined by standard gravimetric methods; and Class IV, in which a few milligrams of mineral have been analyzed for their U, Th, and Pb content by microanalytic methods.

About 25 Class I determinations have so far been made, 21 of them by A. O. Nier (18) alone. They represent 18 localities scattered over the globe. The oldest indicate ages of about 2000 million years. As these minerals occur in pegmatites that cut older rocks, and these older rocks themselves record a long history, it follows that the age of the Earth is considerably more than 2000 million years. The youngest mineral determined by Class I measurements is a pitchblende, from Central City, Colorado; its absolute age is 58 million years; and the youngest minerals as determined by the lead method, Class III determinations, are a uraninite from Chihuahua, Mexico, which is 35 million years old, and brannerite, from Idaho, also 35 million years old.

One of the tasks of geology is to build up an absolute time scale, to determine the length in years of the major divisions and of the subdivisions of the established geologic time scale. How long was the Ice Age? Was it 600,000 years, as some astronomers think, or 1,350,000 years, as other astronomers think, or 3 million years, as some geologists think? How long was the world's principal coal-forming period, the Carboniferous? And so on, for all the divisions of the geologic time scale. The importance of such absolute time measures to studies of the rates of organic evolution is very great.

Two severe limitations have retarded the use of the lead method in building up the absolute geologic time-scale. First, the highly radioactive minerals, uraninite and other minerals rich in uranium and thorium, are restricted almost exclusively to pegmatites. Pegmatites are not common, however, and only a few of them carry radioactive minerals. Secondly, from their nature, most pegmatite masses cannot be accurately dated in the geologic time-scale. To illustrate, pegmatite dikes or veins occur at Branchville near Danbury, Conn., and others occur near Middletown, Conn. The radioactive evidence tells us that the Branchville pegmatite is 350 million years old, and those at Middletown are 260 million years old.

Geologically, however, all that can be positively ascertained as to their ages is that they are older than Late Triassic, but how much older we cannot determine because nature has failed to supply the necessary evidence in the rocks themselves. Consequently the ages of these pegmatites, although conclusively established by the lead method, cannot be used directly in building up the absolute geologic time-scale.

So far only three Class I determinations are precisely dated by geologic evidence. One is the remarkable marine oil shale from Sweden known as kolm; it carries trilobites and other fossils, which date it as being very late Cambrian in age. The kolm contains 0.45 per cent of uranium, which appears to have been precipitated out of the sea water and incorporated into the kolm at the time the kolm was forming. The isotopic composition of the radiogenic lead in the kolm was determined by Nier. Very disconcertingly, it yielded the result that the age based on RaG/U^{238} is 380 million years, whereas that based on AcD/RaG is 770 million years. Now Nier, it must be recalled, regarded the figure given by the AcD/RaG ratio as the least subject to error and hence the most reliable. For the kolm, however, the figure 770 million years is manifestly too large. No answer to this paradox was forthcoming; but recently Wickman (21), a Swedish investigator, has proposed a solution. During the transformation of U to lead, one of the intermediate radioactive products is radon, a gas of half-value period of 3.82 days. Consequently the possibility exists that some of the gas may escape. If some of the radon diffuses away, the amount of radiogenic lead (RaG) ultimately formed will be too small. Therefore the age given by the ratio AcD/RaG is too large, and the age given by the ratio RaG/U^{238} is too small. By solving two simultaneous equations involving these quantities, the probable real age is found to be 440 million years.

The other precisely dated age determination is the end of Early Permian time. Remarkably enough, we have two localities where this has been done: one based on pitchblende from Joachimstal, Bohemia, which gives 230 million years, and the other, based on thorite from near Oslo, Norway, also gives 230 million years. From these figures I infer that the end of the Paleozoic was in round numbers 200 million years ago.

The youngest Class I absolute age determination is based on pitchblende from Central City, in the Front Range, Colorado. The mean of two closely concordant results by Nier in 1942 gives an age of 58 million years, or in round numbers 60 million years. This figure is identical with the long-accepted figure based on Hillebrand's analysis, a Class III determination. This figure of 60 million years has long done duty as dating the Laramide Revolution and the beginning of Tertiary time. The Laramide Revolution, however, is now known to comprise eight or more orogenic phases. These orogenic phases took place from Middle

Cretaceous time until Oligocene or later. The problem as we now see it is which phase of the Laramide Revolution is it that is dated by the pitchblende of Central City. According to Dr. T. S. Lovering (16), who has made a special study of that part of Colorado, the pitchblende veins are related in origin to the intrusion of a porphyry stock that cuts through a great thrust 50 miles long, known as the Williams Range thrust. This thrust has affected strata as young as Fort Union, of Paleocene age. The pitchblende is therefore post-Paleocene and is regarded as marking the diastrophism and igneous activity that took place at or near the end of Paleocene time. If the length of the Paleocene is 10 million years, for which we have no assured evidence, then the length of Tertiary time is 60 + 10 million years, or 70 million years.

Remembering that all helium age determinations before 1943 must be discarded, we have only a few apparently reliable magnetite-helium age determinations for all of Tertiary time. The geologic ages corresponding to these determinations rest on slender evidence, which may or may not prove to be correct. The best magnetite-helium age determinations are based on material from the Iron Springs district, Utah—four determinations ranging from 15 to 21 million years and averaging 17 million. The geological age is given as doubtfully Miocene (15), and recent detailed field work has not yet turned up definitive evidence (17).

Summarizing the age evidence based on the radioactive minerals, we find that the oldest minerals are 2000 million years old. At least three-fourths of geologic time, 1500 million years, had passed before the beginning of Cambrian time, when life other than algae first became abundant on this planet, or at least left records in the rocks. The first accurately dated strata are the Late Cambrian of Sweden, 440 million years old. The end of Early Permian time is accurately dated by radioactive and geologic evidence, from two localities, Joachimstal, Bohemia (5), and Oslo, Norway (10, 11). These independent determinations gratifyingly agree in establishing that the end of Early Permian time was 230 million years ago.

The indicated length of the Paleozoic era is 300± million years, of the Mesozoic era 130± million years, and of Cenozoic time 70± million years. No secure evidence is yet at hand from radioactivity on the length of any of the periods. We have made only a beginning in establishing an absolute geologic time scale.

Let us now examine the rocks themselves to see what evidence they give as to the length of geologic time and of its subdivisions. The thickness of the strata have long been used in estimates of this kind. The strata consist of rocks of various kinds—sandstones, limestones and shales, each of which had not only an inherently different rate of accumulation, but also had rates that differed during the different geologic periods and the subdivisions thereof and in the various parts of the world. But these rates cannot in general be determined. Hence the thicknesses of strata afford no reliable measures of time. The conclusion has recently been reached by Twenhofel (20) that estimates of time based on thicknesses of strata are hardly worth the paper they are written on, and this judgment is unfortunately in the main true. Average rates at which one foot of sedimentary rock was formed have been frequently used in the effort to translate thicknesses of strata into years.

A more promising mode of attack on the problem is to examine the rocks themselves to see what internal evidence they give as to the rate at which they were formed. Some stratified rocks show a thin layering, or lamination, and these laminae suggest that each one represents a year, like the rings of a tree. Such annual layers, as is well known, are the varves of the Swedish geologists, a term now in international use. It is an interesting fact that the finest example of varves, and affording the clearest evidence of their annual nature, was the first deposit ever suggested to have been built up of recognizably annual layers. It was described by the paleobotanist Heer (9) in 1865 long before the present great interest in varves. In certain Miocene shales at Oeningen, Switzerland, layer upon layer repeat the following sequence: at the bottom of each layer are blossoms of poplar and camphor trees, indicating the spring of the year; above this is a thin zone containing winged ants and fruits of the elm and the poplar, indicating summer, and the summer zone in turn is overlaid by a zone containing fruits of the camphor tree, wild grape, and date-plum, indicating autumn. The three zones together constitute a varve in which the progression of the season is thus marvelously recorded. In the perfection of the evidence the shales at Oeningen are still a unique example.

To obtain criteria by which laminated rocks believed to be built up of varves can be proved to be actually varved is the present urgent task of geology. The most thorough study of rocks thought to be varved are the Green River shales of Eocene age in Wyoming and Colorado. These shales have been intensively investigated because they contain a potential supply of oil far greater than all the oil so far taken out of the rocks of the United States. As a by-product of these investigations Bradley (4) has made a penetrating study of the chronology of the oil shales. The shales are very thinly layered; and each layer consists of two laminae, one of which contains considerably more carbonaceous matter than the other. The paired laminae are interpreted as representing the sediment laid down during one year, in short a varve, an interpretation which is strengthened by the fact that the varves fluctuate in thickness in a cycle corresponding to the sunspot cycle. The varves average less than 1/2000 of a foot in thickness, and as the Green River shales are 2,600 feet thick, the time represented by their accumulation is about 6 million years. Green River time, which is possibly one-third of the Eocene, is the longest span of time so far measured by means of data obtained from the rocks themselves. While this span of 6 million years is compatible with estimates based on radioactive evidence, there is however *no direct evidence* for the length of Green River time based on radioactivity, i.e. on the lead method or even on the helium-magnetite method, by which this estimate of 6 million years can be rigorously checked. No one has yet measured the beginning of the Eocene and the end of the Eocene by methods based on radioactivity. Until that is done, rigorous comparison of the length of the Eocene as obtained by geologic methods is of course impossible.

At present the best estimates of the lengths of the several subdivisions of the Tertiary are based on the evolution of the horses. This method was first used by Matthew in 1914 and was recently employed in somewhat different form by G. G. Simpson (19), who took into account the adverse criticisms leveled at Matthew, as well as the newer knowledge about the horses. Furthermore, Simpson took the total length of time required to evolve from *Eohippus* (or *Hyracotherium*) to *Equus* as given by radioactivity data. However, he took the time involved, namely from the beginning of the Eocene to the present as 45 million years instead of 60 millions which as previously shown in this paper is demanded by the geologic and radioactive evidence. Incidentally, the figure 45 million years has obviously been obtained by subtracting 15 million years from the 60 million years, which has long been held to be the orthodox measure of the whole of Tertiary time, including the Paleocene. Fifteen million years is therefore the estimate of the vertebrate paleontologist as to the length of Paleocene time, based on the amount of mammalian evolution. If then we take as the proper value 60 million years for the time involved in the evolution of the nine genera of horses from *Hyracotherium* to *Equus* from the beginning of the Eocene to the present, Simpson's figures must be increased by a factor of 60/45, or 1 1/3 times. The estimates for the durations of the Tertiary epochs younger than the Paleocene become then as follows:

Pleistocene	1 million
Pliocene	11
Miocene	17
Oligocene	11
Eocene	20
	—
Total	60

At present there appears to be no objective evidence by which these figures for the individual epochs can be checked. That interesting task remains yet to be done.

In conclusion, we can say that a solid framework for the absolute length of geologic time and its major divisions has been constructed by the combined labors of geologists, chemists, and physicists. The highly important details, such as the lengths of the subdivisions from Cambrian through Pliocene, not a single one of which has yet been determined, remain as tasks for the future.

REFERENCES

1. Ahrens, L. H. Determination of the age of minerals by means of the radioactivity of rubidium. *Nature*, Vol. 157, p. 269, 1946.
2. Barrell, J. Rhythms and the measurement of geologic time. *Geol. Soc. Am., Bull.*, Vol. 28, pp. 745-904, 1917.
3. Boltwood, B. B. On the ultimate disintegration products of the radioactive elements. Part II, The disintegration products of uranium. *Am Jour. Sci.*, Vol. 23, pp. 77-88, 1907.
4. Bradley, W. H. The varves and climate of the Green River epoch. *U.S. Geol. Survey, Prof. Paper 158*, pp. 87-110, 1929.
5. von Bubnoff, S. *Geologie von Europa*, Bd. 2, pt. 1, pp. 588, 618, 625-626, 1930.
6. Committee on Measurement of Geologic Time, A. C. Lane, chairman, Nat. Research Council, Washington. *Annual Reports*, 1930 to 1945.
7. Evans, R. D., Clark Goodman, N. B. Keevil, A. C. Lane, and W. D. Urry. Intercalibration and comparison in two laboratories of measurements incident to the determination of the geological ages of rocks. *Phys. Review*, Vol. 55, pp. 931-946, 1939. In this paper the many age determinations made by W. D. Urry by means of the helium method are acknowledged to be erroneous.
8. Hahn, Otto. Geologische Altersbestimmungen nach der Strontiummethode. *Geol. För. Förh.*, Bd. 66, pp. 90-97, 1944.
9. Heer, O. *Die Urwelt der Schweiz*, pp. 453-455, 468, 1865.
10. Hoeg, O. A. The Lower Permian flora of the Oslo region. *Norsk Geol. Tids.*, Bd. 16, pp. 1-43, 1936.
11. Holtedahl, O. Jungpaläozische Fossilien im Oslogebiet. *Norsk Geol. Tids.*, Bd. 12, pp. 323-339, 1931.
12. Hurley, P. M., and Clark Goodman. Helium age measurement. I, Preliminary magnetite index. *Geol. Soc. Am., Bull.*, Vol. 54, pp. 305-324, 1943.
13. Knopf, Adolph (editor), *Age of the Earth*, Nat. Research Council Bull. 80, 487 pp., 1931. On the basis of radioactivity and geologic data, the age of the Earth was shown to be at least 2000 million years.
14. Lane, A. C., Rating the geologic clock. 16th Internat. Geol. Congress, Washington, 1933, *Reports*, Vol. 1, pp. 145-167, 1936. Contains a bibliography of 246 titles.
15. Leith, C. K., and E. C. Harder. The iron ores of the Iron Springs district, southern Utah. *U.S. Geol. Survey, Bull.* 338, 1908.
16. Lovering, T. S. Geology and ore deposits of the Montezuma quadrangle, Colorado. *U.S. Geol. Survey, Prof. Paper 178*, 1935; also personal communication.
17. Mackin, J. H. Personal communication.
18. Nier, A. O. The isotopic constitution of radiogenic leads and the measurement of geological time. II: *Phys. Review*, Vol. 55, pp. 153-163, 1939; III, *op. cit.*, Vol. 60, pp. 112-116, 1941.
19. Simpson, G. G. *Tempo and Mode in Evolution*. Columbia Univ. Press, pp. 17-19, 1944.
20. Twenhofel, W. H. Marine unconformities, marine conglomerates, and thicknesses of strata. *American Assoc. Petrol. Geol., Bull.*, Vol. 20, p. 701, 1936.
21. Wickman, F. E. On the emanating power and the measurement of geological time. *Geol. För. Förh.*, Vol. 64, pp. 465-476, 1943.

PART II

VIEWPOINTS ON EVOLUTION

· 2 ·

GENE AND CHARACTER

BY CURT STERN[1]

THE speculations of the last and of preceding centuries often implied a rather close connection between hereditary elements and external characters. Even the earlier Mendelians' concept of unit characters determined by unit factors was reminiscent of the idea of particles in the germ plasm representative of the external properties. These ideas have gradually faded out. The localization of genes inside the cell nucleus, the realization of their large numbers and the limitations thus imposed on them in respect to size related them to the lines of thought which are characterized by the concept of "molecular biology." This term, "molecular biology," is to be taken in a wider sense than that of the chemical molecule. Molecular biology may deal with the smaller entities, atoms and ions, and the energy changes impinging on them or the larger structures met with in protein- and other macro-molecular chemistry. Genic action then involves aspects of cellular physiology, the biological field par excellence in which the molecular approach has found its successful application. On the other hand genic action, too, often transcends the molecular level. Many biological processes, functional and morphologic, while being based upon the planes of biochemistry and biophysics, extend to new, different planes of organization. The effects of genes in development lead most frequently to these more strictly biological levels. To study the interrelations of genes and characters, in ontogeny and phylogeny, requires thus many-sided approaches.

A character may be defined as any observable product of genic action. If immediate genic action is thought of in terms of molecular interaction of a chromosomal gene with its protoplasmatic environment, then a character may be the product of this immediate interaction itself, or may be removed from it by several or by numerous steps in a chain of reactions. Some of these steps may again be molecular in an elementary sense, that is, minute amounts of reagents participate in them and no biological phenomena in terms of new functions or changes in form are involved. Other steps may have consequences beyond the elementary ones. The production, at a suitable period in the life of cells, of new molecular species, or of old ones in different quantities, may be the beginning of far-reaching developmental processes which may best be described in such biological

[1] Professor of Zoology, University of California, Berkeley.

terms as determination, differentiation, and organ formation; organ function and regulation; in terms of behavior and of ecological interrelations. It is well known how the introduction of an organized assembly of genes in the form of the goat onto an oceanic island may completely change its flora, fauna, and physiography. Changes of comparable extent may well be brought about by the occurrence of a single gene change in a plant which causes increased production of an alkaloid that protects it from a hitherto limiting predator. In reality no sharp boundary can be expected between occurrences at the elementary and the higher levels since the latter are nothing but aspects of the former.

It is possible that we know of characters that are the immediate products of genic action. It has been suggested that antigens belong to this group (see Irwin, 1946). The facts underlying this hypothesis consist of the genetic demonstration that certain antigens are always found when a given genic variety, a specific allele, is present. This is true irrespective of all kinds of genetic backgrounds tested hitherto, and it comprises the interesting fact of additive phenotype of heterozygotes between two different antigen-causing alleles A and A'. The heterozygote AA', instead of showing the usual phenomenon of dominance or intermediacy, may possess *both* antigens controlled by the two alleles. A long known example is furnished by the human blood groups. Whenever the alleles I^A or I^B are present in an individual, antigens A or B develop, respectively, and the heterozygote $I^A I^B$ forms both antigens simultaneously. More recently antigenic properties of a similar kind have been found in various other organisms. In pigeons simply inherited antigens exist which are species-specific, and others which certain species have in common and which differentiate them from other species. It is possible without hybridization to clarify the genetic interrelations between different species by means of agglutination tests. Thus characters of interest to the systematist may be very closely linked in their origin to immediate gene action.

Even more may this be true in microorganisms where ontogenetic changes are limited. In the fungus *Neurospora* and in yeasts enzymatic differences were found to be intimately related to genic differences. It would not be surprising to discover that different enzymatic systems based on perhaps few genetic differences would furnish isolating mechanisms which in turn would favor further speciation. In this connection the case of the American and Russian lines of *Paramecium bursaria* may be cited (Jennings and Opitz, 1944; Chen, 1946). Apparently due to a reaction between their cytoplasms, conjugation between these lines leads to death of the conjugants. Nothing is known yet about the genetic basis of this reaction. It may conceivably be due to a simple allelic difference. If this were true then this case would provide a model for the initiation of sympatric speciation in an organism with alternating asexual and bisexual mode of reproduction. A mutant gene which during conjugation with a member of its own strain would make its carrier liable to death, would become extinct soon after it originated, if sexuality were a necessary part of reproduction. Asexual fission, however, would lead to existence of many individuals with the new gene and subsequent conjugation among the descendants of the first mutant individual would be harmless while back-crosses to the original type remain fatal. To complete such speciation further events are needed which eliminate attempts of hybridization before they are fatal. What these "further events" may be is a subject of speculation. It may be surmised that in some cases antigenic properties by themselves can prevent the initiation of conjugation or gametic fusion in asexual-sexual species without any fatal effects being involved.

For most characters of multicellular organisms the relation between genes and character is not that of "one-to-one" but that of a long multidimensional network of interrelations between numerous genes and their interweaving reaction sequences. Consequently, changes in many genes may affect the "same" character. Thus, in corn (*Zea mays*) at least 50 genic loci in chromosomes have been discovered all of which are concerned with the production of chlorophyll. A change in any of these loci may result in absence or abnormality of pigment. In *Drosophila* more than 40 loci are known to affect eye color, and at least 43 jointly to be responsible for normal, flat wings. Reduction in wing size, an evolutionary important trait, has been found to be caused by each one of 34 different loci. In mice, shortness of tail is known to be due to any one of 10 different loci. The list could be continued far, since these examples are typical for any one of the more thoroughly investigated organisms. The paleontologist and systematist who finds similar character changes in different groups, be they different isolates of the same species or be they members of different larger taxonomic units, cannot with certainty, and need not, attribute such phenotypic similarities to similar genetic changes in the different groups.

Another consequence of the network-like relation between genes and characters is that a change in a simple locus may result in changes in more than one seemingly related character. Dobzhansky (1927; see also Dobzhansky and Holz, 1943) showed many years ago that alleles in *Drosophila* known only for their effects on eye- or body-color had also diverse influences on the proportions of an internal organ, the female spermathecae, chosen at random for study. Such cases of multiple effects of genes are probably the rule. Often the developmental connection between the different characters is obscure. In some cases it is known how the different manifestations all depend on some primary effect. Thus, in mice dwarfness and sterility due to the allele *d* are both consequences of the gene-controlled absence of eosinophile cells in the anterior pituitary and the consequent lack of production of pituitary growth hormone (Smith and MacDowell, 1930). In fowl, the allele frizzled leads to a peculiar curliness of the feathers which makes them wear off quickly, and in homozygous birds results in more or less complete bareness. This initial character has far-reaching consequences. The lack of insulation against loss of body heat causes "subnormal body temperature, stimulation of cellular oxidation and increased metabolic rate. From here, one chain of adaptations leads to acceleration of heart rate, ventricular hypertrophy, enlarged blood volume, and excessive size of spleen. In order to sustain the acceleration of these vital processes more food is consumed and this, in turn, produces enlargement of the intestinal parts, hypertrophy of the pancreas and of the kidneys. A heavy burden falls on the adrenals and thyroid and they show corresponding changes" (Landauer, 1946).

It is likely that most cases of multiple effects of genic conditions will resolve themselves as consequences of a single primary event, but frequently we lack knowledge. Thus, it is not known how in *Drosophila* the numerous mutants known as "Minutes," which in many cases have been shown to be due to cytologically visible losses of short chromosomal sections, influence such diverse characters as size of bristles, smoothness of eye surface, contour of wings, female fertility, and length of larval development. Nor is it understood how the genic condition for the Laurence-Moon-Biedl syndrome in man leads simultaneously to polydactyly, obesity, and mental deficiency. It may turn out that some cases like these are independent consequences of truly multiple primary action of the complex genic particles. Others may be due to identical primary gene action in different parts of the developing organism. These different parts, as a result of their ontogenetic differentiation, would react differentially to the same primary event within their cells ("repetitive gene action," Stern and Schaeffer, 1943a).

It is interesting to contemplate that striking evolutionary trends may be due to the secondary effects of gene changes, that is, those that are only distantly related to the more immediate ones. Important properties of the classes Aves and Mammalia may have emerged "spontaneously" when mutations changed the reptilian scales into feathers and hairs, and adaptations to land-living modes of life may have been "unexpected" consequences of minor genetic modifications. Just as the loss of feathers in the frizzle fowl has its far-reaching consequences on metabolism, and organ structure and function, so would the acquisition of heat insulating body coverings result in complex internal changes. In the frizzle fowl many of these changes consist of regulations, more or less successful attempts to adapt the organism to its changed status. Similarly, in evolution, the organism can draw upon its physiologic and morphologic plasticity with which it can adjust to a new situation either of environmental or genetic nature. An example among plants may be found in the numerous species which have turned out to be allopolyploid hybrids of preexisting species. Without immediate internal regulations in forms and functions the bringing together of widely different genomes could hardly have led to the establishment of evolutionary successful new entities.

The perfection of all new structures and functions certainly is due to selection of genes which permitted the most adaptive response to the new setup initiated by the primary gene. This polishing-off function of selection is a well-founded concept and its Neo-Darwinian extension to cover evolution in general is a fruitful approach. It is doubtful, however, whether we are forced to rely exclusively on the slow elaboration of all organic properties or whether "the potentialities of development" which Goldschmidt (1940) urges us to consider do not present us with a needed phenomenon without which our understanding of the more revolutionary events in evolution will remain inadequate. Experimental morphogenesis suggests that minor changes in the physio-chemical status of cells, caused by changes within them or in their cellular environment, may result in widely different responses such as the formation of nervous versus epidermal tissue, or of epidermis versus lens. Must we assume that the ability to respond so strikingly to slight differences is the result of many accumulated small mutational steps or could it not have been inherent in some cellular organizations that they would respond this way if a single mutation provided the right differential? May not a mutational change of a gene become amplified beyond expectation in its developmental effect and thus make a cataclysmic origin of strikingly new characters be compatible with typical gene mutations?

In this connection it is obvious that terms such as large or small gene changes are without precise meaning. Character changes may perhaps be classified in this way, but the differences between alleles are on a different level from those of characters. If we knew in physico-chemical terms what the difference between two alleles of a gene is, we would probably find that some such differences, slight in molecular configuration, cause striking effects while others which consist of more important structural differences of the gene become hardly expressed in the phenotype. An analogy may be found in the experiences of the organic chemist who finds the biological activity of related groups of compounds greatly affected by some changes of his molecules and little by others. As so often in passing from a lower to a higher level of organization new properties may arise which could not have been foreseen—though a later analysis shows, of course, that they are rationally understandable consequences of the properties of the lower level's elements.

Another frequent and misleading term is "defective gene." Generally the term is meant to designate an allele which does not result, partly or completely, in a phenotype which another allele makes possible. Obviously, even at the character level the term defective is only relative. The two-wingedness of flies is not a defect in spite of their typical insect ancestors having had four wings, nor is the lack of gills a defect in the Amniota, though fishes and amphibians are endowed with them. An allele which in contrast to another one results in a decreased expression or absence of a character does so by means of a changed reaction sequence— a *different* sequence, hardly to be called a defective one. Muller's (1932) terms hypomorph and amorph refer only to the decreased or lost *action* of a gene whose allele makes a certain character possible, but these terms do not imply a gene defect. Sometimes insufficient effect on one character may be accompanied by destructive effect on another one, as in the case of a gene in *Drosophila* which affects the presence or absence of different bristles in such a fashion as to behave as a hypomorph in some respects and an antimorph in others (Tsubina, 1935). Evolution consists of simultaneous character losses and gains; it makes constant use of "defective genes," thus reducing this term *ad absurdum*.

Genes are intracellular physiological agents and their developmental and finally evolutionary significance emerges after the question of their activity has passed the test of intracellular fitness. Selection of new alleles must be accomplished not only on the basis of the final character or the multicellular developmental interactions but already on the intracellular level. If we assume for simplicity that a gene interacts with only one specific intracellular component, its substrate, then experimental results may be interpreted in terms of competition for the substrate between different alleles of a locus (Stern, 1943). Thus, a "normal" allele of the ci (cubitus interruptus) locus in *Drosophila melanogaster* if present alone, in single dose causes slight interruptions in the cubital vein, in double dose leads to uninterrupted veins. The mutant allele ci itself, in single dose, causes wide interruptions, in double dose lesser interruptions, and in triple dose still smaller ones. Both alleles, if like is added to like, act cumulatively toward normality. That indicates that their substrate is present in larger amount than can be acted on by either one normal allele or one or two mutant ones. Yet, the substrate is limited. If a mutant allele is added to a normal, that is, if a heterozygote is produced, the resulting venation is less complete than if the normal allele had been present alone. It appears that the two kinds of alleles compete for the not inexhaustible supply of the substrate, with the mutant allele causing a less efficient product in terms of full venation than the normal allele. A study of several alleles, both normal and mutant, may be described in terms of independently varying "combining powers" for the substrate and "efficiencies";

one allele may have both higher combining and efficiency properties than another, or one allele may be higher in one but lower in the other respect.

It is possible to use alternative explanations for the phenotypic effect of different doses and combinations at the ci locus. The general concepts of specific substrates of genic action, of their limited amounts within the small volume of the nucleus or cell and of different combining powers of different alleles remain valid in any case. It may also be regarded as likely that not only different alleles of one locus may compete for a given substrate, but that different loci share in such a substrate. No such case is known with certainty, but no search has been made yet. At a slightly different stage of cellular metabolism, the formation of enzymes in yeast active in the fermentation of different sugars, a competition for their building blocks has been demonstrated; adaptive formation of galactozymase in the absence of exogenous nitrogen leads to decrease and final disappearance of the amount of maltase present originally (Spiegelmann, 1946).

This intracellular interplay of gene activity may account for limiting factors in evolution which could not be suspected from a consideration of derived characters. The curious "Minute" phenomenon in various species of *Drosophila* may possibly be related to such an intracellular limit. As mentioned earlier, many rather frequently occurring mutants are known which reduce the size of the bristles on various parts of the body surface. Why did this small bristle size never become established in nature? It has been found that the "Minute" bristle character is generally accompanied by reduced female fertility and greatly prolonged development of the individual, and Sturtevant (1924) has suggested that the ecological disadvantages of these characters are the limiting factors which have tended to keep bristle size larger. May it not be possible that the retarded rate of ontogeny itself is an outcome of insufficiency of some important intracellular reaction? Such supposition may be difficult of proof at present, but its possibility should be recognized in evolutionary discussions. The adaptations of organisms include not only fitness of organs, tissues and cells as wholes but also the intranuclear adjustment of gene activities. If, for instance, an external morphological character depends in its development on high activity of a certain gene, the limiting factor in the evolution of that character may lie in an intranuclear situation.

On the other hand, the multiple dependence of characters on the genic reaction network makes it possible to have certain successful external characters preserved despite evolutionary processes which have changed the genic conditioners of these characters. In general, the work of geneticists has been concerned with allelic differences which cause striking external effects. There are, however, many allelic differences which cause no or hardly any phenotypic differences. That such "isoalleles" (Stern and Schaeffer, 1943b) exist, can be shown by special experiments in which the external effects are accentuated through combination with unusual genetic or environmental conditions. In spite of their similar phenotypic expression, different iso-alleles will hardly have identical selective values on the intracellular level. They will make use of different substrates, or of different quantities of a substrate, and thus change the reactions between the substrates and other loci. To retain highest efficiency, selection will tend to associate a given iso-allele at one locus with specific iso-alleles on other loci, while a different iso-allele on the first locus will become incorporated within a harmonious system of different iso-alleles on the other loci. Consequently, given sufficient isolation for the evolution of such different systems of iso-alleles, two or more populations may exhibit the same façade of external characters, yet based on genic interiors which have undergone considerable remodeling since the groups became separated. The frequent occurrence of the very similar "sibling species" of the systematist (Mayr, 1942) seem to be results of conservative retention of external characters under cover of which different genic systems have evolved. That crosses between sibling species lead to sterility, or to morphological features different from those of the nearly identical parents, indicates the internal divergence of their genetic bases. In the formalism of genetics these facts have long been expressed in terms of complimentary factors whose presence, in different species, becomes obvious only when a cross joins them in a hybrid.[2]

Characters due to mutant genes are often different from those long established by being more variable in expression and by having a lowered adaptive value. Thus, in *Drosophila*, the eye size of the wild type varies within narrow limits but many mutants which reduce eye size lead to extreme variability from individual to individual or even from the left to the right eye of the same specimen. Similarly, mutants which increase the number of dorsocentral bristles above the highly constant number four characteristic for wild-type will cause a whole range of phenotypes, from that of the typical number of four to more than ten bristles. In mammals the variability of coat pattern is often extreme in domestic or laboratory forms in contrast to the constancy of wild patterns. Such variability is not exclusive to the geneticist's mutants. Taxonomists and paleontologists, too, are familiar with such cases, as, for instance, the variations in number and kind of vertebral elements in the posterior body region of reptiles which are in the process of changing from a walking to a crawling locomotion (Severtzoff, 1931), or the presence or absence of a ridge on the teeth of condylarths (Simpson, 1944). The variability of such characters has been regarded by Simpson as due to variability in the genetic background in which mutations have to work, while Goldschmidt (1946) has stressed the intrinsic variability of many developmental reactions as exemplified

---

[2] These considerations follow the trend of thoughts expressed by Muller (1939).

particularly well in the asymmetrical expression of mutants which on the two sides of the same individual obviously act within identical genotypes. It seems that the cell-physiological and developmental processes influenced by mutant genes are not sufficiently "buffered" to yield constant results, and that selection of genetic modifiers which narrow down the variability of these processes is an important part of evolution.

There may be an initial advantage in the variable expression of new mutants, a variability which may in some individuals overlap the non-mutant type, i.e. lack expression altogether (so-called "lack of penetrance"). A strikingly expressed initial appearance of a mutant character will have little prospect of occurring within a genetic background or at an ecological niche which permits it to be sufficiently well adapted for survival. In contrast, low expression or even lack of penetrance will permit the character to spread more or less invisibly and to crop up phenotypically in diverse genetic backgrounds or ecological niches, some of which may happen to harmonize with the mutant toward higher adaptiveness. Variable penetrance thus may accomplish for dominant genes what recessiveness does for recessive genes, namely, spread under cover of unchanged phenotypes. Even the establishment of recessive genes, in homozygous state, may be helped by their variable expression.

Once the exploration of genetic or environmental backgrounds has led to a well-adapted configuration, the variability and low penetrance of a mutant becomes a hindrance rather than a help in the final establishment of the character. Selection will then tend to reduce variability around the new phenotype till it becomes stabilized as a constant normal one. Reversal in the selective value of gene-controlled developmental properties is an interesting example of the complex interrelations between gene and character.

REFERENCES

Chen, T. T. 1946. Conjugation in Paramecium bursaria. II. Nuclear phenomena in lethal conjugation between varieties. *J. Morph.*, 79:125-262.

Dobzhansky, Th. 1927. Studies on the manifold effect of certain genes in Drosophila melanogaster. *Z.I.A.V.*, 43:330-388.

Dobzhansky, Th., and A. M. Holz. 1943. A re-examination of the problem of manifold effects of genes in Drosophila melanogaster. *Genetics*, 28:295-303.

Goldschmidt, R. 1940. *The Material Basis of Evolution.* New Haven, Yale University Press.

——. 1946. "An empirical evolutionary generalisation" viewed from the standpoint of phenogenetics. *Am. Nat.*, 80:305-317.

Irwin, M. R. 1946. Antigens, antibodies and genes. *Biol. Reviews*, 21:93-100.

Jennings, H. S., and Pauline Opitz. 1944. Genetics of Paramecium bursaria. IV. A fourth variety from Russia. Lethal crosses with an American variety. *Genetics*, 29: 576-583.

Landauer, Walter. 1946. Form and function in frizzle fowl: The interaction of hereditary potentialities and environmental temperature. *Biol. Symposia*, 6:127-166.

Mayr, Ernst. 1942. *Systematics and the Origin of Species.* New York, Columbia University Press.

Muller, H. J. 1932. Further studies on the nature and causes of gene mutations. *Proc. 6th Int. Congr. Genet.* (Ithaca), 1:213-255.

——. 1939. Reversibility in evolution considered from the standpoint of genetics. *Biol. Reviews,* 14:261-280.

Severtzoff, A. N. 1931. *Morphologische Gesetzmässigkeiten der Evolution.* Jena, Gustav Fischer.

Simpson, G. G. 1944. *Tempo and Mode in Evolution.* New York, Columbia University Press.

Smith, P. E., and E. C. MacDowell. 1930. An hereditary anterior-pituitary deficiency in the mouse. *Anat. Rec.,* 46:249-257.

Spiegelmann, S. 1946. Nuclear and cytoplasmatic factors controlling enzymatic constitution. *Cold Spring Harbor Symp. Quant. Biology,* 11:256-277.

Stern, C. 1943. Genic action as studied by means of the effects of different doses and combinations of alleles. *Genetics,* 28:441-475.

Stern, C., and E. W. Schaeffer. 1943a. On primary attributes of alleles in Drosophila melanogaster. *Proc. Nat. Ac. Sc.,* 29:351-361.

——. 1943b. On wild-type iso-alleles in Drosophila melanogaster. *Proc. Nat. Ac. Sc.,* 29: 361-367.

Sturtevant, A. H. 1924. An interpretation of orthogenesis. *Science,* 59:579-580.

Tsubina, M. G. 1935. Hypomorphic and antimorphic genes (Russian with English summary). *Biol. Zb.* (Mosc.), 4:997-1004.

· 3 ·

GENE HOMOLOGIES AND THE MUTANTS
OF *DROSOPHILA HYDEI*

BY WARREN P. SPENCER[1]

In recent years the general concepts of homology and analogy have been the subjects of critical reviews by several authors (for a bibliography see Boyden, 1947). Hubbs (1944) has clearly stated the difficulties involved in adhering to exact definitions in the light of modern work in genetics, embryology, and micro-evolution. He concludes with: "Both concepts—of homology and analogy—should be recognized as involving grave complexities. These ideas involve the same sort of inexactitude that is inherent in such principles as those expressed in Haeckel's biogenetic law and Dollo's law of irreversible evolution. Precision in any of these concepts should not be allowed to transcend the complexities that exist. Despite these difficulties, the concepts of homology and analogy retain, in their evolved, modern meaning, a place of importance and value in biology."

Most studies of homology have dealt with organs or parts of organs, the structure of which must certainly be conditioned by a complex of genetic factors. In summarizing his views on homology Boyden (1947) states: "The original and necessary concept in homology is essential structural similarity. The secondary meaning for homology of common phylogenetic origin has no place in serial homology and a role of secondary importance in special homology because in special homology essential similarities must be recognized first before ancestry can be assumed and always special homologues are not only required to show such essential similarities but they must be of such a nature as to leave no real doubt of their structural correspondence." This would seem to minimize the basic concept of the common ancestral origin of homologous structures. Boyden rightly emphasizes the importance of careful comparative anatomical studies, but seems to minimize the role of embryological and, where possible, paleontological evidence.

To some, who deal with the grand strategy of evolution as evidenced by structural similarities and continuities in organs and organ systems, the consideration of gene homologies may seem trivial or at most of secondary importance. In any case it is a study of homology at quite a different level from that of organs and organ systems. In considering the course of evolution one is forced to conclude that there has been a progressive in-

[1] Department of Biology, The College of Wooster.

crease in the numbers and kinds of genes as life has evolved from the simple to the complex. Many recent studies on the nature of the gene and its action and on the origins of chromosomal and gene diversities have been instituted and vigorously pursued. A corollary of such studies is a recognition that those organisms which have diverged from a common stock still retain in recognizable form a large group of common or homologous genes.

One might define homologous genes as those which, in a common genetic background, behave as alleles. Obviously, except in forms capable of crossing and producing hybrid offspring, this criterion is not experimentally verifiable. We are therefore forced to rely upon their "structural correspondence," to use Boyden's phrase. This structural correspondence is deduced indirectly from the allelic forms which a gene may assume and the changes in the character complex conditioned in the organism by these alleles. Another important structural correspondence deals with the spatial relations of genes in the chromatin complex.

In the genus *Drosophila* considerable material has been accumulated for the study of gene homologies. The present paper deals with a comparative study of the mutant genes in *Drosophila hydei* in respect to their possible homologies with genes in *D. melanogaster* and other species.

FORMER WORK ON GENE HOMOLOGIES IN DROSOPHILA

Sturtevant and Novitski (1941) have summarized data published up to that time on gene homologies in about fifteen species of *Drosophila*. On the basis of a considerable number of parallel mutations and the distribution of these in the chromosomes they have come to the conclusion that the six elements of chromosome limbs found in *D. melanogaster* have remained largely intact in the five other species for which they give extensive data, namely *simulans, pseudoobscura, affinis, ananassae,* and *virilis*. They have followed the suggestion of Muller (1940) on symbols for designating these elements. The *X* of *melanogaster* is designated *A*, *II L* as *B*, *II R* as *C*, *III L* as *D*, *III R* as *E*, and *IV* as *F*. These authors clearly recognize the possibility of interchange of euchromatic material from one element to another, either through translocation or pericentric inversion involving two elements in a *V*-shaped chromosome. They mention, furthermore, the one case of pericentric inversion known at that time to occur in natural populations, that found by Miller (1939) in *D. algonquin*. But on comparative cytological grounds they consider that only the element *E* is involved, this element having acquired a median rather than a terminal centromere. They also point out that the end of element *A* in *ananassae*, containing the "bobbed" locus, has become attached to element *F* (Kikkawa, 1938).

Wharton (1943) has made an extensive study of the cytology, both metaphase and salivary chromosomes, of 80 species and three additional subspecies of *Drosophila*. She finds evidence that in several cases pericentric inversions must have occurred in the process of speciation. From her studies she concludes that "in the course of the divergence and evolution of *Drosophila* species some widespread alterations have changed the original six chromosome elements in species of the genus. It is futile to assume the integrity of chromosome 'elements' in the light of the evidence presented by fusions, translocations and pericentric inversions, which have been shown to occur throughout the genus. Homology in terms of whole chromosome elements has doubtless been disrupted by such events. There must be, in some instances, particularly in closely related species or species groups, some, or even extensive homologies, but this is not an indication of stable and inviolable linkage relationships." In conjunction with her comprehensive work on the cytology of the genus these conclusions of Miss Wharton are likely to cast doubt on the validity or expediency of attempts at establishing gene and chromosome element homologies. The writer considers that, on the basis of the data, she has overstated the case. Actually most of the cases which she has interpreted as pericentric inversions might well involve only one of the six chromosome elements, and still leave these as continuous structures with median or sub-median centromeres.

It should be pointed out, however, that Carson and Stalker (1947) have recently reported two cases of pericentric inversions in *D. robusta*. One of these is in chromosome *II* and widely spread through the geographic range of the species. The other is in chromosome *III* and has only been recovered once. They report that the species contains three pairs of V-shaped chromosomes, one large, one intermediate, and one small, and a pair of dots. The salivary chromosomes show six arms and a small chromosome. The largest V has been identified as the sex chromosome, the intermediate V has been designated chromosome *II*, the small V chromosome *III*, and the dot chromosome *IV*. Thus, on the postulate that there were six elements corresponding to the six elements of *melanogaster*, at least one of these pericentric inversions must represent an exchange of chromatin material between two of the original elements. These facts establish beyond a doubt that within this species the six postulated elements for the genus do not always remain intact. It seems likely that, should similar large-scale cytological studies of many other species of *Drosophila* be undertaken, other such cases may appear. However, the evidence summarized by Sturtevant and Novitski and that to be presented in this paper indicate that many species within the genus have retained these six chromosome elements sufficiently intact that a study of their homologies may be profitably pursued.

It should further be noted that some species apparently show relatively few paracentric inversions within their chromosomes. Warters (1944) reports only one such inversion in *D. hydei* in a study of 518 chromosomes from stocks collected from 28 widely separated localities. However, in view of the many paracentric inversions found in such species as *pseudo-obscura, funebris, robusta,* and *affinis,* linkage relations within elements must certainly have undergone wide variations both intraspecifically and interspecifically. In any case, even with translocations, paracentric and pericentric inversions occurring, extensive studies might show chromatin blocks containing pairs or groups of homologous genes maintaining their linkage relations intact even in widely divergent species within the genus. A comparative study, both genetic and cytological, should throw new light on the evolution of the gene complex.

With the data at hand any study of gene homologies in the genus *Drosophila* must start with *D. melanogaster* as a base of reference. In a comprehensive monograph (Bridges and Brehme, 1944) several thousand gene mutations in this species have been described and many of these illustrated. By far the most extensive chromosome maps of mutant loci for any species of plant or animal are given here. This work, containing a vast amount of exact data both on the description of mutants and their linkage relations has been accumulated over a long period of years, through the efforts of many workers and particularly through the life-long studies of Dr. Calvin Bridges.

It may well be asked whether mutations in one species may be recognized with any degree of accuracy, even if they do arise in another species. Fortunately Sturtevant (1929) has made an extensive study of mutations arising in *D. simulans,* a species which hybridizes with *D. melanogaster.* Sturtevant made the requisite tests for allelism and demonstrated that in two hybridizing species many mutants can be recognized as alleles, and this judgment was vindicated by hybrid tests. It should, however, be emphasized that such judgments can be made with accuracy only by individuals who have had considerable training in the study of mutant types.

CRITERIA FOR ESTABLISHING HOMOLOGIES

We may now consider the criteria to be set up for establishing homologies in two or more species which do not hybridize. Before such studies can have much significance a large number of mutant loci must have been observed in the species being compared. The difficulties involved have been discussed by Sturtevant (1921) and by Morgan, Bridges, and Sturtevant (1925). Thus in *D. melanogaster,* where thousands of mutants have been observed in hundreds of loci, there are numerous cases of 'mimic' mutations occurring in different loci and yet distinguishable in slight degree or not at all in their phenotypic expression. The dominant 'Minutes,' occurring at many loci, and some of the eye colors are examples. Obviously these loci are of little value in establishing homologies, even though homologous mutations may occur in other species. On the other hand, if only one or two loci in this species have given mutants of a distinct phenotype, these loci furnish good material for establishing homologies. The locus par excellence for comparison is one which has given mutations marked by a unique complex of phenotypic characters, a polymorphic mutant locus. The spineless-aristapedia complex is a good example. In this connection it should be emphasized that mutant types often show subsidiary characters likely to be overlooked unless carefully studied. Such character complexes strengthen the case for homologies. Sometimes the subsidiary characters have been overlooked in the first species in which the mutation has occurred, only later to be found when they appear, possibly in an exaggerated form or against a different background, and are observed in a second species.

In the great majority of *Drosophila* species there are five long arms or elements and a short element of euchromatic material in the salivary chromosomes. If, then, mutant types which meet the above criteria are found to be associated in six linkage groups corresponding to these elements, as shown by Sturtevant and Novitski (1941) for the species on which most genetic data have accumulated, the evidence for gene homologies is strengthened. In spite of fusion of certain elements and in other cases shifts in the centromere from a terminal to a subterminal or median position, the elements appeared to have remained largely intact as judged by their gene contents. A strong case for homologies can be established where groups of similar mutant genes appear in species after species, always associated with some chromosome element having a distinctive position in the chromosome complex, as the sex chromosome, or recognized by its size, as the dot or short element. Finally, if two distinctive genes are so closely linked in one species that they give little or no crossing-over and the same condition is met with in another species, the case for homology seems established beyond a reasonable doubt. More cases of this kind may be found as genetic data accumulate on species other than *melanogaster*. If the present evidence justifies the conclusion that these comparative studies can be profitably undertaken, then a study of very closely linked genes should give valuable evidence on the evolution of the chromatin complex in the genus.

GENE AND ELEMENT HOMOLOGIES IN THE X-CHROMOSOME OF D. HYDEI

Preliminary accounts of the origin and linkage relations of vermilion, Extra-scutellars, white, Notch, miniature, and bobbed mutants of *D. hydei* have been published (Clausen, 1923; Spencer, 1927, 1932a). A description of the sex-linked mutants known in this species, with a discussion of their homologies in other species, follows.

Highly Probable Homologues of Mutant Loci in Other Species

(1) bobbed; locus 116. (Clausen, 1923; Spencer, 1927, 1930, 1938, 1944, 1945). A large series of alleles found in many wild strains from California, Kansas, Ohio, New York, and Tennessee. Males, except when *XO*, are normal, due to strong wild-type allele in the *Y*. Females show a complex of characters, alleles differing in respect to the grade of character expression; abnormal abdominal sclerites; reduction in bristle size; lowered fertility; late emergence; late sexual maturation after emergence. Clearly a parallel of sex-linked bobbed in *D. melanogaster* (Bridges and Brehme, 1944); *simulans* (Sturtevant, 1929); *pseudoobscura* (Sturtevant and Tan, 1937); *virilis* (Chino, 1936); *funebris* (Luers, 1937); *affinis* (Sturtevant, 1940); *subobscura* (Jermyn, Philip, Rendel, and Spurway, 1943); and of the *IV*th chromosome mutant, bobbed, in *ananassae* (Kikkawa, 1938).

(2) cut; locus 77.3. Seven cut males found in a cross of vermilion scute miniature jauntex *x* garnet light. Margin of wing nicked. Better expression in males and at high temperature. The large series of cut alleles in *melanogaster* makes it easier to establish the parallel. Resembles closely the cut-notch allele found by Ives (Plough and Ives, 1935). Probable homologues in other species—beaded, *D. pseudoobscura* (Sturtevant and Tan, 1937); beaded, *persimilis* (Beers, 1937); cut, *affinis* (Sturtevant, 1940); cut, *ananassae* (Kikkawa, 1938); cut, *simulans* (Sturtevant, 1929); cut, *subobscura* (Spurway, 1939).

(3) dusky; locus 55.8. Found by R. E. Clausen. Small, dark wings; female sterile. Probable homologues of same name—frequently recurring mutant in *melanogaster*; *simulans*; *pseudoobscura*; *virilis*; *ananassae*. (See description and linkage relations with miniature below.)

(4) flared; locus 0.0 Found by R. E. Clausen. Deltoid areas at distal ends of longitudinal veins, best developed at end of second longitudinal; wings spread. A good parallel of deltex in *melanogaster*, with character expression intermediate to the two alleles known in that species. To the author's knowledge these are the only two species in which this good homologue has been reported. This situation may well be explained as due to a low mutation frequency at this locus. Only two occurrences of deltex are recorded in *melanogaster* (Bridges and Brehme, 1944), while most of the good homologues have been recorded several to many times in this species.

(5) miniature; locus 59.6. Found in one male in a stock culture. Small, dark wings; wings tend to be stringy in moist cultures. The locus of this gene and that of dusky, which has a very similar phenotype, are 3.8 units apart on our map. However, as these loci have been determined in refer-

ence to other genes and no direct linkage tests on the two are available, they may lie even closer together. Two very closely linked, but non-allelic loci, giving similar phenotypes have been found in *melanogaster, pseudo-obscura, affinis, virilis,* and *ananassae.* This is one of the strongest cases for homologous genes and is of additional interest in that two closely linked loci give mutants which are phenotypically alike. Grüneberg (1937) has reviewed cases of such gene doublets in *Drosophila.* Lewis (1945) has made an extensive study of the relations of two such closely linked genes, Star and asteroid, in *melanogaster.* Dunn and Caspari (1945) report a case in mice where five closely linked genes all have similar phenotypic effects. In addition to the doublet homologues mentioned above, mutation at one locus, either miniature or dusky, has occurred in *busckii* (Krivshenko, 1939), *affinis, algonquin,* and *takahashii* (Sturtevant and Novitski, 1941), *immigrans* (Spencer, 1947), and *subobscura* (Spurway, 1946).

(6) Notch; locus 22.3 (Spencer, 1927). One female in a large stock bottle. Not a deficiency for the white locus. Another Notch found by R. E. Clausen was a deficiency for white. Two other Notches found by the author were not white deficiencies. Wings notched; this character quite variable; wing veins thickened, a constant character; eyes often reduced in old and dry cultures; homozygous lethal. Clearly a homologue of Notch in *melanogaster* and like the alleles in that species variable in the size of the deficiency. Parallel mutants have been recorded in *pseudoobscura, virilis, ananassae, busckii, funebris* (Sturtevant, 1918; Kiil, 1946); *subobscura;* and *montium* (Osima, 1940).

(7) sable; locus 35.8. Several males in the F_2 generation of a cross of wild male from Gatlinburg, Tennessee, to scarlet, gray, pearly, javelin. Dark body color, obscuring the thoracic spotting; pollinose sheen when viewed obliquely; fair viability. Probable parallel of sable in *melanogaster.* Only two mutations at this locus are recorded by Bridges and Brehme (1944). As this is the only dark body color known in the X of *melanogaster* it seems fairly safe to consider it a homologue. Its absence among observed mutants in other species may be due to low mutation frequency; but in dark species as *pseudoobscura* and *virilis* it might be difficult to distinguish.

(8) scute; locus 15.6. Scute-1 found as one male in a cherry stock. Scute-2, one male collected at a citrus dump near Azusa, California. Scute-1 always removes anterior orbital and posterior sterno-pleural; effect on scutellars and other bristle groups variable. Scute-2, more extreme, removes all scutellars and several other bristles; variable effect on other bristle groups. This is a clear parallel of the scute locus in *melanogaster,* at which a large series of alleles has been found. Scute has also been

recorded in *simulans, pseudoobscura, affinis, ananassae, willistoni* (Lancefield and Metz, 1922), *subobscura, virilis* and *busckii.*

(9) singed; locus 31.4. First found by R. E. Clausen; recurrence as about half the males in progeny of one female in a laboratory culture. Both alleles produce short, gnarled bristles and hairs; female sterile. This locus has mutated many times in *melanogaster* and many of these mutations are female sterile in contrast to the phenotypically similar forked mutants, all of which are female fertile. Homologues in *simulans, pseudoobscura, ananassae, willistoni, subobscura, virilis, immigrans* (Spencer, 1940), and *busckii.*

(10) vermilion; locus 7.4. (Clausen, 1923). Clausen found a second vermilion mutant associated with an *X-V* translocation. Vermilion could be recovered for some years from populations in and near Wooster, Ohio (Spencer, 1932b). Also found in one male collected from citrus dump, Azusa, California. A brilliant, scarlet-like eye-color. Only one sex-linked locus in *melanogaster* gives such an eye-color and many mutations have been recorded at this locus. Additional evidence for homology was secured through interspecific eye-disc transplantation tests made by G. W. Beadle. For the method used see Beadle and Ephrussi (1936). Most of the homologues in other species have been determined by these interspecific transplants. The mutant has been found at least once in *simulans, pseudoobscura, affinis, ananassae, willistoni, montium, subobscura, busckii, virilis,* and *funebris.*

(11) white; locus 19.0. (Clausen, 1923). A second mutation to white was found in one male in a linkage test involving several Vth chromosome mutants. In *melanogaster* only one locus, and that always in the X-chromosome has given a white eye mutation. This mutant has been recorded many times in *melanogaster* and repeatedly in several other species. It is known in *simulans, pseudoobscura, affinis, ananassae, montium, subobscura, persimilis, busckii, virilis* and *funebris.*

(12) yellow; locus 38.8. Found twice by R. E. Clausen. The two mutant alleles are identical. Wild-type spotted thoracic pattern is obscured; body, wings, and bristles yellow. Even in species as different in color as *hydei* and *melanogaster* the mutant is readily recognized as a probable homologue. The yellow locus in *melanogaster* has mutated many times and there are no other loci which give similar mutations. Good parallels have been found in *simulans, pseudoobscura, affinis, ananassae, willistoni, subobscura, busckii, virilis* and *immigrans* (Spencer, unpublished).

Possible Homologues of Mutant Loci in Other Species

(13) cherry; locus 115.7. One male in a miniature, vermilion stock. In addition one female, heterozygous for this mutant, was collected in Wooster, Ohio. Dark, cherry eye-color. The name cherry has been used

for a white allele in *melanogaster*. However, it seems unnecessary to restrict the names applied to a large multiple allelic series at the white locus in *melanogaster* only to alleles at this locus in other species. In addition to white and vermilion there are seven other eye-color loci known in the X of *melanogaster*, carmine, carnation, garnet, raspberry, ruby, prune, and bordeaux. With the range in color of alleles at a given locus and the similarity in phenotype of certain alleles at one locus with those at another it is not safe to determine eye-color homologies on the basis of similar phenotype alone, unless these are distinctive as in white and vermilion. Cherry might be a homologue of ruby, garnet, carmine, carnation, or raspberry, but probably not of prune or bordeaux. Garnet and ruby are the most frequently recurring mutants of the five in *melanogaster* and thus most likely to be represented in other species. Possibly eye-color interaction and hormone studies may eventually assist in establishing these homologies.

(14) garnet; locus 32.5. Wild female collected in Wooster, Ohio, was heterozygous for this eye-color. Purplish ruby, translucent eye-color, darkening with age. Nearest to garnet of *melanogaster*, but the same reservations hold here as stated above for cherry in determining homologue. In any case it is not unlikely that both of these mutants have their homologues at two of the five loci mentioned above in the *melanogaster* X.

(15) jauntex; locus 112.0. Found by R. E. Clausen. Wings imperfectly unfolded, or with a wavy surface; wing tips turning up or down and lateral margin kinked. Closely resembles wavy in the *melanogaster* X, but here there are some other mutants which produce irregular wing surface.

(16) russett; locus 94.5. Found by R. E. Clausen. Pale, light brownish body color; legs pale. Viability and fertility low, but males become sexually mature earlier than in most wild stocks. Resembles silver of *melanogaster*; might, however, be a parallel of chlorotic or lemon.

It is apparent that the four mutants, cherry, garnet, jauntex, and russett in *hydei* resemble certain mutants in the X of *melanogaster*, but owing to similar phenotypes at different loci in this species it is not advisable to draw conclusions on their homologues without further study. It is therefore not profitable to look for their homologues in other species.

Mutant Loci with no Recognizable Homologues in melanogaster

The six mutants described below are not sufficiently similar to any known mutants in the X of *melanogaster* to warrant comparisons. Neither is there evidence that they are homologues of specific autosomal mutants in this species. While most of the frequently mutating loci in *melanogaster* have certainly been discovered, there are undoubtedly many loci in this species in which mutations are still to be found. In his limited work on *melanogaster* the author has found several such loci. It is thus not surprising that the investigation of a new species uncovers some mutant loci which are not yet represented by mutations in *melanogaster*. Furthermore, owing to the widely different appearance of *hydei* and *melanogaster*, there should be some mutants in one species, which, even if they appeared in the other, would not be recognizable against the new phenotypic background. Finally, with the genetic divergence of two species, there may well be loci in one not represented in the other.

(17) Extra; locus 16.5. Two females and one male in a vermilion stock. From one to four extra scutellar bristles present; normal overlaps in many cultures; semi-dominant. Linkage determined by counts of Extra males only. While there are several mutants in *melanogaster* characterized by extra bristles and hairs, none resembles this mutant in bristle distribution.

(18) Light; locus 39.0. One male collected at Azusa, California, citrus dump. Dark thoracic spots reduced; semi-dominant. This mutant illustrates the masking effect of the phenotype in certain species. *D. hydei* has a thoracic pattern marked by dark spots on a light gray background. Obviously such a mutant would not be recognizable in a species lacking this color pattern. A sex-linked semi-dominant has been repeatedly found in wild collections of *D. repleta*, a closely related species with a similar thoracic color pattern (Sturtevant, 1915). It appears that this locus mutates more frequently in *repleta* as the mutant has only been found once in hundreds of thousands of *hydei*. As there are many species in the *repleta-hydei* group light should be found in some of these if they are thoroughly investigated.

(19) rusty; locus 88.9. Found by R. E. Clausen. A modifier of vermilion eye, changing it to a yellowish color. Owing to the dark mahogany eye-color of the wild-type in *hydei* it is possible that certain mutants, which are easily recognized in species with lighter eyes, may have little or no phenotypic effect alone but may act as modifiers of mutant eye colors. There is no locus in *melanogaster* which can be considered a homologue of rusty.

(20) scaloid; in X, locus unknown. Found by R. E. Clausen. Imperfect abdominal banding. Possible homologue of Abnormal in the X of *melanogaster*.

(21) scaly; locus 47.3. Found by R. E. Clausen. Similar to scaloid but not an allele. Either of these mutants might be a homologue of Abnormal. There are also several mutants of this type in the autosomes of *hydei* and *melanogaster*.

(22) tiny wing; locus 47.4. Several males in a stock culture. Wings of normal shape but scarcely half normal length. Much smaller than miniature or dusky; viability poor. No mutant in *melanogaster* resembles tiny wing.

Comparison of the X of melanogaster, Element A, with the X of hydei

The metaphase chromosomes of *D. hydei* in the female consist of a pair of large V's, four pairs of rods and a pair of dots. In the male one large V and a J, one limb of which is quite short, take the place of the pair of large V's in the female (Wharton, 1943). The V's are the X-chromosomes, but one limb is entirely heterochromatic. The salivary chromosomes consist of five long strands and a very short strand. On the basis of the gene comparisons made above we may now consider whether the euchromatic limb of the X in *hydei* is the homologue of element A, the X of *melanogaster*. The linkage map of the X of *D. hydei* is shown in Figure 1. This map is based on approximately 295,000 cross-over determinations. Figure 1 also includes a map of the X in *D. melanogaster*, containing those loci which are probable or possible homologues. Inspection of the two maps will show that genes reasonably interpreted as homologues are scattered the length of both maps. The longest distances containing none of these are 21.6 units between garnet and bobbed in *melanogaster* and 17.5 units between russett and jauntex in *hydei*. There seems little doubt that in the main the euchromatic limb of the X in *hydei* is homologous to the X or element A of *melanogaster*. The question as to whether the X of either species has gained or lost a sizeable block of euchromatic material must be left for future study.

The order of the genes indicates numerous paracentric inversions in one or both phylogenies since the time of origin from a common ancestral stock. *D. melanogaster* belongs to the subgenus *Sophophora* and *D. hydei* to the subgenus *Drosophila* (Sturtevant, 1942). Considering the number of intraspecific paracentric inversions found in the chromosomes of populations of some *Drosophila* species, this realignment of the genes within a chromosome element for two species as distantly related as these appear to be may not be surprising. It should be pointed out, however, that neither species shows this tendency to undergo inversion in the X at the present time. In this connection it might be mentioned that Sturtevant's extensive study of *D. simulans* has shown that in this species, which hybridizes with *melanogaster*, homologous genes both in the X and the autosomes have maintained their order largely intact in the divergence of the two forms. It would be of interest to make a similar study of one of the close relatives of *hydei*.

Examination of the linkage maps will show that in some of the clearest cases of homology, such as yellow and scute, two genes very closely linked in one species are widely separated in the other. Scute, white and Notch and miniature and dusky have retained their linkage relations intact in the course of the divergence of *hydei* and *melanogaster*. Of the 22 loci in which visible mutants have been found in *hydei* 12 seem clearly to be homologues of loci in the X of *melanogaster*; for four more there are possible homologies; the remaining six are doubtful, although there is no reason for considering them homologous with autosomal loci in *melanogaster*.

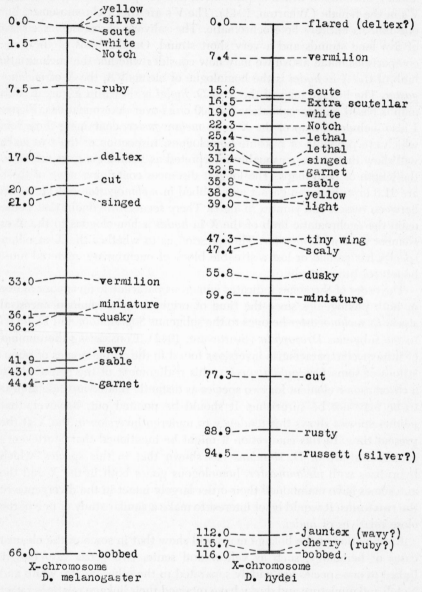

Figure 1. Linkage maps of *Drosophila melanogaster* and *Drosophila hydei*; probable homologues shown on *melanogaster* map; all known loci shown on *hydei* map.

AUTOSOMAL HOMOLOGIES

We turn now to the more difficult study of autosomal homologies. In the first place the visible mutations in the X are more easily discovered owing to the fact that the male carries only one X and any visible present in this X, even though it be recessive, will be expressed in the phenotype. There is some evidence that mutation rates are higher in the autosomes than in the X, a mechanism which would protect the species against deleterious sex-linked mutants. In spite of this mechanism in D. melanogaster there are more loci known for the X than for any of the other elements, although four of these are comparable to the X in length. The discrepancy shows even more clearly when a tabulation is made of those loci in which mutants have been found three or more times. An approximate count from Bridges and Brehme (1944) showed 36 such loci in the X and only 23 for the second and 21 for the third chromosomes. This would mean that roughly three times as many such loci are known for the X as for each of the other long elements.

In D. hydei autosomal mutants at approximately 130 loci have been found, and repeatedly in some of these loci. However, most of these autosomal mutants have been found by inbreeding flies taken as samples of three populations. The mutants extracted from a few thousand flies from a few localities would hardly be expected to give a true picture of the mutating loci in the species. Due to genetic drift (Spencer, 1947) even rare mutants may have a high local frequency and conversely many common mutants will be absent from the samples taken. In considering the data presented the inadequacy of the mutant samples, particularly of D. hydei, should be kept in mind. Of the autosomal mutants found in hydei 81 have been identified to chromosome, 26 in the IInd, 20 in the IIIrd, 15 in the IVth, 14 in the Vth, and 6 in the VIth. Most of the remainder were either semi-lethal or sterile types not easily studied. Maps of the autosomes will not be presented here. Apparently homologous genes show the same lack of order in the autosomes as in the X when compared with melanogaster mutants.

PROBABLE HOMOLOGIES IN CHROMOSOME VI

We shall first consider the dot-like chromosome VI, because it represents a small distinctive block of autosomal chromatin, presumably carrying relatively few genes, a highly localized segment. Sturtevant (1946) has presented a discussion of the homologies of the dot chromosome in D. hydei and D. repleta. The following mutants have been found in the VIth chromosome of D. hydei.

(1) Cubitus interruptus. A dominant found in a male collected in Wooster, Ohio. In heterozygotes part of the fifth longitudinal vein is

missing. The character is variable, but with no normal overlaps. In homozygous form the character is more extreme and the fourth vein may also be affected. Sturtevant questions the homology of this mutant with cubitus interruptus of *melanogaster*. However, two of the four alleles recorded in Bridges and Brehme affect the fifth as well as the fourth vein. It is apparently a homologue of Gap in *D. virilis*. Fortunately in this species a large series of alleles has been found. Most of these affect the fifth vein but Gap[10] acts on both the fourth and fifth veins. It therefore seems probable that Cubitus interruptus is homologous to Gap of *virilis* and to Cubitus interruptus of *melanogaster*.

(2) grooveless. The wild fly carrying Cubitus interruptus also carried the recessive, grooveless, in the same VIth chromosome. Groove between the scutellum and thorax obliterated; black excrescences at sides of scutellum. A clear parallel of grooveless in *melanogaster* and several other species. In fairly extensive tests it has never been separated from Cubitus interruptus by crossing-over.

(3) tibia bent. Recessive in wild fly from Azusa, California. Hind tibia bent; hind femur broken; wings inflated.

(4) bent. Recessive in wild fly from Azusa. Tarsal joints short; legs misshapen. Hind legs most affected. An allele of tibia bent, but with no effect on wings. The locus of these two mutants appears to be homologous to the bent locus in *melanogaster IV*. In *melanogaster* the bent alleles produce leg effects shown in *hydei*. Tibia bent in *hydei* also affects wings, though somewhat different from *melanogaster* bent. Both *hydei* and *melanogaster* bents show a tendency for wing character to become less extreme as stock is maintained. This is a good case to show variation in alleles in both species.

(5) Extension; semi-dominant. Found in wild fly from Azusa, California. In heterozygote the dark thoracic spots, particularly on sides, are enlarged. Always identified by a dark spot around the humeral bristles. In homozygote spotted pattern of the thorax is obliterated by evenly distributed dark brown pigment; head bristles lie flat and thorax is humpy. Extension has crossed over with Cubitus interruptus-grooveless so does not lie between these two genes.

(6) lethal. A recessive lethal or semi-lethal has occurred in the Cubitus interruptus-grooveless chromosome, which was carried in stock in heterozygous form over Extension. The stock is now Cubitus interruptus-grooveless-lethal/Extension. Consequently grooveless flies are seldom seen.

Of the five visibles which have been found in the VIth chromosome of *D. hydei*, four of them, lying in three loci, are apparent homologues of mutants known in chromosome *IV*, element *F*, of *melanogaster*.

PROBABLE HOMOLOGIES IN CHROMOSOME II

Of the 26 mutants which have been found in chromosome *II* of *D. hydei* three of them, each with a distinctive and unique phenotypic complex, show a striking resemblance to three mutants in *III R*, element *E*, of *melanogaster*.

(1) spineless-aristapedia. A fly collected in Wooster, Ohio, was heterozygous for this recessive gene. An extreme spineless-aristapedia complex; sterile in both sexes; low viability; antennae changed into legs of three or more joints with well defined terminal claws; all three pairs of legs shortened, with the tarsal joints fused into a club-shaped structure with a heavy knot near the distal end; all bristles reduced to tiny hairs no larger than the microchaetae; groove between scutellum and thorax missing as in grooveless; wings thin textured. A good homologue of the spineless-aristapedia locus in *melanogaster* and several other species; the most extreme allele found in any species.

(2) ebony. Recessive found by R. E. Clausen and named black. Body and legs dark; golden brown bristles on rear tarsi of wild flies are black in the mutant; larval spiracles are black in contrast to brown spiracles of the wild-type. Both larval and adult characters identify this as a homologue of ebony in *melanogaster*. Black and ebony of *melanogaster* may be distinguished by the black larval spiracles of the latter.

(3) warped. Wild fly collected in Wooster, Ohio, was heterozygous for this recessive. Wings saddle-shaped, divergent, waxy textured and dark. An excellent homologue of warped in *melanogaster*.

Seven other mutants appear to be good parallels with mutants in *III R* of *melanogaster*, although they are not distinctive enough to make identification certain and could, in some cases, be compared with mutants in other elements. They are cardinal eye color with cardinal; peach eye color with pink locus; pink eye color with the maroon locus; scarlet eye color (Hyde, 1915) with karmoisin; taxi wing with taxi; water wings with blistery; rough eye-*II* with rough. Of the remaining mutants several have mimics in other *hydei* chromosomes, several are not similar to any of the described mutants in *melanogaster*, and none show a clear-cut and unique phenotype parallel to that of any mutant in *III R* or any other element of *melanogaster*.

PROBABLE HOMOLOGUES IN CHROMOSOME III

Of the 20 mutants in the third chromosome of *D. hydei* four are excellent parallels of mutants in *II R*, element *C*, of *melanogaster*.

(1) cinnabar. Fly heterozygous for this recessive collected at Azusa. A brilliant scarlet-like eye color. Interspecific transplants between *hydei* and *melanogaster*, made by G. W. Beadle, showed this to be a homologue of cinnabar in *melanogaster*.

(2) engrailed. Heterozygous in a fly from Azusa. This recessive has a polymorphic character expression including nicked scutellum or split thorax; wing veins altered, with sections missing or extra venation; rounded, broad, and thin textured wings; all these characters also present in *melanogaster* engrailed. At high temperatures the *hydei* engrailed shows other characters, as bifurcated antennae; shortened tarsi, sometimes branched; eyes bulging or reduced and roughened; and pupal lethal at 30 *C* (Spencer, 1942).

(3) scabrous; formerly named roughest. Heterozygous in a fly from Gatlinburg, Tennessee. This recessive shows large, bulging eyes; some facets very large, rounded and irregularly distributed; extra acrostichal rows of microchaetae. An excellent parallel of scabrous in *melanogaster*.

(4) vestigial. Heterozygous in a wild fly from Gatlinburg, Tennessee. This recessive shows wings with varying degrees of scalloping and nicking of margins; no normal overlaps. A good parallel of some of the intermediate alleles of vestigial in *melanogaster*.

There are several eye colors which may well be homologues of eye colors in *II R* of *melanogaster*. Orange and orange-like, not alleles, are similar to light and lightoid, and purple is like purploid. Brown of *hydei* is phenotypically similar to brown of *melanogaster*. Most brown alleles of *melanogaster* in homozygous combination with vermilion, scarlet, or cinnabar give an almost white eye, but brown^{37g}, found by Clancy (Bridges and Brehme, 1944) gives a yellowish eye color with vermilion. Brown *hydei* in combination with the vermilion-like eye colors gives a yellowish color in young flies, darkening with age. Red in the *IIIrd* chromosome of *hydei* seems to have no known parallel in *II R* of *melanogaster*. However, it resembles closely the wild-type eye of *melanogaster* and might well be a homologue of such a mutant as pinkish in that species, by itself not classifiable, but a dilutor of eosin. Red dilutes the orange-like eye colors of *hydei* but has no effect on the vermilion-like group. Taken together, the *IIIrd* chromosome eye colors of *hydei*, even excluding the clear homologue of cinnabar, resemble more closely the known eye colors in *II R* of *melanogaster* than those in any other element in this species.

EVIDENCE OF TRANSLOCATION OR DUPLICATION IN III OF D. HYDEI

There are two mutants in the third chromosome of *D. hydei* which do not fit the scheme of homologies with *II R* of *melanogaster*. A wild fly collected in Pasadena, California, was heterozygous for the third chromosome mutant, shaven. This recessive reduces many bristles to the size of hairs. There are bristles varying in size to normal in an irregular mosaic pattern, but no normal overlaps. Females are sterile. The mutant resembles closely alleles at the shaven locus in chromosome *IV*, element *F*, of *melanogaster*.

Another mutant, sanded, a recessive carried in heterozygous form in a fly collected at Azusa, resembles the *IV*th chromosome dominant, Cataract, in *melanogaster*. In both mutants a part of the eye is quite rough, with facets irregularly arranged. In Cataract the disturbance is in the posterior part of the eye; in sanded the upper part is affected. According to the most recent revision of the cytological and genetic maps of *melanogaster IV* (Slizynski, 1944) bent lies in the tiny left limb, cubitus interruptus and grooveless in the right limb near the spindle attachment, shaven and Cataract in the distal end of the right limb. Sparkling, which affects the entire surface of the eye, is a recessive allele of Cataract.

It seemed that a reciprocal translocation might have occurred between element *C*, (*II R* of *melanogaster* and *III* of *hydei*), and element *F*, (the dot), in the course of the divergent evolution of these two species. Extension, which is far enough from Cubitus-interruptus-grooveless in *hydei* to give some crossing-over might, therefore, be found in *II R* of *melanogaster*. An inspection of the *II R* mutants in Bridges and Brehme (1944) reveals a dominant body color, Blackoid, found by Goldschmidt and localized by Braun. In view of the very different wild phenotypes in the two species Blackoid is a good parallel for the body color part of the Extension complex. The fact that these are the only two dominant body colors in either species lends weight to the argument. In considering the Extension mutant as a complex of a dominant body color and recessive body shape, possibly capable of separation by separate mutation either in *hydei* or *melanogaster*, it must be remembered that the Cubitus-interruptus-grooveless mutants in *hydei* arose as a complex, not yet separated but clearly parallels of two separate loci in *melanogaster*. Furthermore, when mutants in the dot chromosome of other species are examined, the mutant, hump, in *D. virilis* of the subgenus *Drosophila*, described and figured by Chino (1936) compares closely in body shape to the recessive expression of Extension in *hydei*. The head bristle character, however, seems to be absent in the *virilis* mutant. Chino's chromosome map of the dot in *virilis* shows that hump lies toward the distal end of the chromosome from Gap. The author suggests that there may have been a reciprocal translocation in the process of speciation by which a chromosome block carrying the shaven and Cataract loci exchanged places with the block carrying the Extension complex. Evidence for such translocations would more likely be found in the dot where a group of genes are tied into a small chromatin block, not capable of wide dispersion through paracentric inversions.

A good case can be made for an alternative hypothesis that the dot, element *F*, represents duplicated material carried also in element *C*, *II R*, of *melanogaster*. Thus Malformed is a dominant eye mutant depending for its expression on genes in *II R* and the dot. Gap of *II R* is a good parallel for Cubitus interruptus; knot for Cell; engrailed for Scutenick; and possibly roof for bent. On this hypothesis Blackoid-like should eventually be found in the *melanogaster* dot, and grooveless-like, Cataract-like, and shaven-like in *II R*. This hypothesis, if established, would suggest a mechanism through duplication of chromatin blocks whereby additional genes might be added to the chromatin complex. At the present stage in the investigation the question may be left open and neither hypothesis accepted.

Probable Homologies in Chromosome IV

Of the fourteen mutant loci known in this chromosome three are good parallels of mutants in *II L* of melanogaster and several others are possible parallels.

(1) irregular-IV. A fly heterozygous for this mutant was collected in Coffeyville, Kansas. In this recessive the bristles and hairs on the wing and abdomen are disarranged; the marginal hairs on the wing stand out at a wide angle. This is a good parallel of fuzzy in *II L* of *melanogaster*.

(2) squatty. Recovered from a laboratory stock. Cross-veins close together; wings short and wide; abdomen and legs chunky; posterior cross-vein broken. This is an excellent parallel of dachsous alleles in *II L* of *melanogaster*.

(3) short. Recovered from the same laboratory stock which gave squatty. Fifth longitudinal vein does not meet the margin; character somewhat variable. A good parallel of abrupt in *II L* of *melanogaster*.

Wavy, a recessive mutant in which the wing surface undulates, was carried in heterozygous form in a fly from Azusa. The mutant resembles jaunty in *II L* of *melanogaster*. Three rough eye loci are known and might correspond to rough eye loci in *II L*, although this type of mutant, unless accompanied by some unique expression, is not favorable for comparisons. Grooveless-*IV* is similar in phenotype to grooveless in the sixth chromosome. There are no mutants recorded for *II L* of *melanogaster* which compare with this; however, ascute in *III L* is similar. This seems to constitute another exception to the hypothesis that the elements have remained intact. The other mutants in *hydei IV* are not readily comparable with *melanogaster* mutants or are of types too general in phenotype to be of value for establishing homologies. It is of interest to note that no eye colors have yet been found in *hydei IV*; the same holds for mutants reported by Chino (1936) in *IV* of *virilis*, the chromosome in that species which Sturtevant and Novitski (1941) consider the homologue of *II L* in *melanogaster*.

Probable Homologies in Chromosome V

Of the fourteen mutants known for this chromosome several are good parallels of mutants in *III L* of *melanogaster*.

(1) irregular-V. Found in a stock culture. Phenotype almost identical with irregular-*IV*. This is a good parallel of frizzled in *III L*. Thus fuzzy in *II L* and frizzled in *III L*, which are rather distinctive mimic mutations in *melanogaster*, have their parallels in the fourth and fifth chromosomes of *hydei*, the apparent homologous elements.

(2) javelin. A recessive recovered from a wild fly collected at Azusa. Bristles long, not tapering at ends, often hooked. A good parallel of javelin in *III L*.

(3) sepia. A recessive recovered from a wild fly from Gatlinburg, Tennessee. Dark brown eye-color changing to black in old flies. An excellent parallel of sepia in *III L*.

(4) incomplete. Recessive recovered from an Azusa wild fly. Second and fifth longitudinal veins incomplete distally or gap in the second longitudinal; wings slightly warped. A good parallel of radius incompletus in *III L*.

(5) rose. Recessive recovered from Wooster wild fly. A deep purplish pink eye color; variable; better classification in old flies when eyes become translucent although darker in color. A good parallel of rose in *III L*. In *hydei* rose sepia homozygotes go through a striking cycle as the fly ages. Comparison with *melanogaster* might be helpful in establishing homology.

(6) blister. A recessive recovered from an Azusa wild fly. A blister between fourth and fifth longitudinal veins and posterior to posterior cross-vein. Generally in only one wing though few normal overlaps; wings a little smaller than normal; often held out at an angle. This seems a good parallel of divergent in *III L*. The blister character is shown in the figure illustrating this character though not otherwise mentioned in the description (Bridges and Brehme, 1944).

Three semi-lethal or poorly viable mutants, one from a Gatlinburg, Tennessee, fly, and the other two from wild flies from Alabama, resemble abdominal, ragged and tiny wing of *melanogaster III L*. A good cross-veinless-*V* found by R. E. Clausen has no known parallel in *III L*. There are, however, two cross-veinless loci in *III R* and one in the *X* of *melanogaster*. The presence of these three mimics suggests that the character is of doubtful value for comparative purposes.

Table I presents a summary of probable parallel or homologous genes in the autosomes of *D. hydei* and *D. melanogaster*.

Discussion and Conclusions

Drosophila hydei and *D. virilis* are the two species in the subgenus *Drosophila* on which sufficient genetic work has been done to justify a tentative study of gene homologies with those species in the subgenus *Sophophora* on which extensive genetic studies have been made.

The data presented here indicate that there is a large series of gene loci in the X-chromosome of *hydei*, which like those in the *virilis* X, are almost certainly homologues of loci in element A of *melanogaster, simulans, pseudoobscura* and other members of the subgenus *Sophophora*. One may conclude that in the main these elements are homologous from species to species.

It is obvious that significant comparative data have accumulated and will continue to accumulate more slowly for autosomal elements, owing to the technical difficulties involved in discovering and locating new autosomal mutants. With the limited material already at hand it is clear that there are a considerable number of autosomal loci which give mutants so distinctive in character in species after species, even in different subgenera, that their homologies can be established with a high degree of probability.

TABLE I

Probable parallel loci in the autosomes of *D. melanogaster* and *D. hydei*

D. melanogaster	*D. hydei*	*D. melanogaster*	*D. hydei*
Element B		*Element E*	
II L	*IV*	*III R*	*II*
dachsous	squatty	warped	warped
fuzzy	irregular-IV	pink	peach?
abrupt	short	blistery	water wing?
jaunty	wavy	maroon	pink?
		karmoisin	scarlet?
Element C		spineless	spineless
II R	*III*	ebony	ebony
light	orange?	cardinal	cardinal?
lightoid	orange-like?	taxi	taxi?
cinnabar	cinnabar	rough	rough-II?
engrailed	engrailed		
scabrous	scabrous		
vestigial	vestigial	*Element F*	
brown	brown?	*IV*	*VI*
purploid	purple?	cubitus inter.	cubitus inter.
		grooveless	grooveless
Element D		bent	bent; tibia bent
III L	*V*		
javelin	javelin		
divergent	blister		
sepia	sepia		
rose	rose?		
frizzled	frizzled		
radius incompletus	radius incomp.		

The present study indicates that the transposition and rearrangement of autosomal chromatin has not gone too far in the evolution of the

Drosophila subgenera to make profitable an attempt to study element homologies. The data presented indicate that for the most part the autosomal elements have remained sufficiently intact in the divergence of *hydei* and *melanogaster* so that they can still be recognized. However, there is evidence that translocation or duplication of some material has taken place. The same criteria and judgments used in establishing element homologies indicate exchange or duplication of material in the study of the third and sixth chromosomes of *hydei* and the right limb of the second chromosome and the fourth chromosomes of *melanogaster*.

ACKNOWLEDGMENTS

The author wishes to thank Dr. R. E. Clausen for his generous permission to publish descriptions of numerous *D. hydei* mutants found in his laboratory and to use his very extensive linkage data on sex-linked mutants in constructing the genetic map of the X-chromosome and Dr. G. W. Beadle, who kindly made the interspecific transplants which established the vermilion and cinnabar homologies. A part of this work was done at the California Institute of Technology, where the interest and advice of Dr. A. H. Sturtevant were a constant stimulus.

REFERENCES

Beadle, G. W., and B. Ephrussi. 1936. The differentiation of eye pigments in Drosophila as studied by transplantation. *Genetics*, 21:225-247.

Beers, C. V. 1937. *Drosophila Information Service*, 7:70-71.

Boyden, Alan. 1947. Homology and analogy. A critical review of the meanings and implications of these concepts in biology. *Amer. Midl. Nat.*, 37:648-669.

Bridges, C. B., and K. S. Brehme. 1944. *The mutants of Drosophila melanogaster.* Carnegie Inst. Washington, Publ. 552. 257 pp.

Carson, H. L., and H. D. Stalker. 1947. Gene arrangements in natural populations of Drosophila robusta Sturtevant. *Evolution*, 1:113-133.

Chino, M. 1936. The genetics of Drosophila virilis. *Japan. J. Genet.* 12:257-277.

Clausen, R. E. 1923. Inheritance in Drosophila hydei. *Amer. Nat.*, 57:52-58.

Dunn, L. C., and Ernst Caspari. 1945. A case of neighboring loci with similar effects. *Genetics*, 30:543-568.

Grüneberg, H. 1937. Gene doublets as evidence for adjacent small duplications in Drosophila. *Nature*, 140:952.

Hubbs, C. 1944. Concepts of homology and analogy. *Amer. Nat.*, 78:289-307.

Hyde, R. R. 1915. The origin of a new eye-color in Drosophila repleta and its behavior in heredity. *Amer. Nat.*, 49:183-185.

Jermyn, J. E., U. Philip, J. M. Rendel, and H. Spurway. 1943. *Drosophila Information Service*, 17:52-53.

Kikkawa, H. 1938. Studies in the genetics and cytology of Drosophila ananassae. *Genetica*, 20:458-516.

Kiil, V. 1946. *Drosophila Information Service*, 20:77-78.

Krivshenko, Y. D. 1939. A comparative genetic study on Drosophila busckii and Drosophila melanogaster. Acad. Sci. Ukrainian SSR, Inst. Zool., *Memoirs on Genetics*, 3:15-89.

Lancefield, R. C., and C. W. Metz. 1922. The sex-linked group of mutant characters in Drosophila willistoni. *Amer. Nat.*, 56:211-241.

Lewis, E. B. 1945. The relation of repeats to position effect in Drosophila melanogaster. *Genetics*, 30:137-166.

Luers, H. 1937. Ein Beitrag zur vergleichenden Genetik an Hand des dominanten Bobbed im Y-Chromosome von Drosophila funebris. *Z.i.A.V.*, 74:70-90.

Miller, D. D. 1939. Structure and variation of the chromosomes in Drosophila algonquin. *Genetics*, 24:699-708.

Morgan, T. H., C. B. Bridges, and A. H. Sturtevant. 1925. The genetics of Drosophila. *Bibliogr. Genet.*, 2:1-262.

Muller, H. J. 1940. Bearings of the Drosophila work on systematics. *The New Systematics*, pp. 185-268. Oxford, Clarendon Press.

Osima, T. 1940. Cyto-genetic studies of Drosophila montium. *Cytologia*, 10:450-457.

Plough, H. H., and P. T. Ives. 1935. Induction of mutations by high temperature in Drosophila. *Genetics*, 20:42-69.

Slizynski, B. M. 1944. A revised map of salivary chromosome 4. *J. Hered.*, 35: 323-324.

Spencer, W. P. 1927. The X chromosome of Drosophila hydei. *J. Exp. Zool.*, 47:441-466.

——. 1930. Primary non-disjunction in Drosophila hydei. *Ohio J. Sci.*, 221-228.

——. 1932a. Sex-linked inheritance in Drosophila. *Proc. Sixth Int. Cong. Genetics*, 2:188-190.

——. 1932b. The vermilion mutant of Drosophila hydei breeding in nature. *Amer. Nat.*, 66:474-479.

——. 1938. Multiple alleles at the bobbed locus in populations of Drosophila hydei. *Genetics*, 23:170.

——. 1940. On the biology of Drosophila immigrans Sturtevant with special reference to the genetic structure of populations. *Ohio J. Sci.*, 40:345-361.

——. 1942. Engrailed, a pupal lethal at high temperatures in Drosophila hydei. *Amer. Nat.*, 76:325-329.

——. 1944. Iso-alleles at the bobbed locus in Drosophila hydei populations. *Genetics*, 29: 520-536.

——. 1945. Interaction of alleles at the bobbed locus in Drosophila hydei. *Amer. Nat.*, 79:85-88.

——. 1947. Genetic drift in a population of Drosophila immigrans. *Evolution*, 1:103-110.

Spurway, H. 1939. *Drosophila Information Service*, 11:29-32.

——. 1946. *Drosophila Information Service*, 20:82-83.

Sturtevant, A. H. 1915. A sex-linked character in Drosophila repleta. *Amer. Nat.*, 49:189-192.

——. 1918. A parallel mutation in Drosophila funebris. *Science*, 48:72-73.

——. 1921. Genetic studies on Drosophila simulans. II. Sex-linked group of genes. *Genetics*, 6:43-64.

——. 1929. *The genetics of Drosophila simulans.* Carnegie Inst. Washington, Publ. 399:1-62.

——. 1940. Genetic data on Drosophila affinis, with a discussion of the relationships in the subgenus Sophophora. *Genetics*, 25:337-353.

——. 1942. The classification of the genus Drosophila, with descriptions of nine new species. *Univ. Texas Publ.*, 4213:5-51.

——. 1946. On the dot chromosomes of Drosophila repleta and D. hydei. *Genetics*, 31:259-268.

Sturtevant, A. H. and E. Novitski. 1941. The homologies of the chromosome elements in the genus Drosophila. *Genetics*, 26:517-541.

Sturtevant, A. H., and C. C. Tan. 1937. The comparative genetics of Drosophila pseudoobscura and D. melanogaster. *J. Genet.*, 34:415-432.

Warters, M. 1944. Chromosomal aberrations in wild populations of Drosophila. *Univ. Texas Publ.*, 4445:129-174.

Wharton, L. T. 1943. Analysis of the metaphase and salivary chromosome morphology within the genus Drosophila. *Univ. Texas Publ.*, 4313:282-319.

· 4 ·

THE EVIDENCE AFFORDED BY FOSSIL VERTEBRATES ON THE NATURE OF EVOLUTION

BY D. M. S. WATSON[1]

BEFORE entering on the consideration of actual evolutionary series it is desirable to consider in a simple and generalized manner the nature of the evidence bearing on the process of evolution which may be derived from the study of fossils. Paleontological procedure is as follows: it begins with the collection of the fossil remains, in general only skeletal elements of animals, from beds of rock whose relative ages can be established, funda-mentally by superposition, but in practice largely (and in the case of rocks in disconnected areas entirely) by the use of "characteristic fossils." All experience since William Smith in 1812 shows that this procedure is reliable; it enables predictions to be made which can be (and very often have been) confirmed by subsequent discoveries. The whole of the technical exploitation of coal and oilfields depends on such work. The material, then, consists of groups of fossils found together, or shown to be of the same age, which stand in a known time relation to one another. The first process of examination of such groups is the determination of the species represented. It is taxonomist's work carried out by the methods used by morphologists in the investigation of the structure, and of the classification based upon that structure of recent animals. The methods of morphology have never been precisely stated and discussed. They are known traditionally and by example to working zoologists, and they also have been justified by the confirmation by later discoveries of the solutions reached by morphologists of such recondite problems as the segmentation of the head in vertebrates, or the determination of the morphological nature of the ear ossicles of mammals.

The classification of animals is thus based on similarities of structure between two or more allied forms, the similarities being judged according to an order of importance established by experience in the application of morphological principles. Thus it is possible to classify the animals contained in a series of successive faunas into smaller groups and ultimately into species. It was recognized by William Smith and by Cuvier that species have only a limited persistence in time; on this limitation rests the power of recognizing "strata by the organised fossils which they contain." Very often in those cases where we possess a succession of faunas of the

---

[1] Jodrell Professor of Zoology and Comparative Anatomy, University College, London.

same ecological type, for example inhabitants of sea floors of the same grade of sediment at the same depth of water, we find that genera may persist over considerable periods, species having shorter ranges, and it is then possible to pick out a series of species occurring in successive beds and to claim that they are ancestral to one another, the differences between them having been brought about by evolution. Such evolutionary series among invertebrate animals have repeatedly been brought forward and it is useful to consider on what basis the forms included in them have been selected.

Probably the most perfect of such evolutionary series amongst invertebrates is that of *Micraster* in the English Chalk. Here we are dealing with an echinoid which lived burrowing in the mud of a sea floor which is now chalk. Chalk in general contains very little detrital material which has been derived from the land, pure chalk may have less than 1% of material other than calcium carbonate, and the only common constituent is silica as flint formed *in situ*, presumably from the skeletons of sponges and radiolaria which are themselves taken from sea water. The uniformity of chalk is probably due to the aridity and lack of river discharge from the neighboring lands, but it was clearly laid down in comparatively deep water and at a depth which varied. Specimens of *Micraster* are scattered through this chalk, more abundantly at certain horizons than at others, but they can be found in southern England in Cenomanian and Senonian times and clearly inhabited the area continuously. These animals, like all echinoids, have a test of very elaborate structure which is perfectly preserved in the fossils. They were first satisfactorily discussed by Dr. A. W. Rowe in a classical paper and he found it convenient to divide them into five species, each of which has a limited range in time, although these ranges overlap. Rowe was able to show that eleven apparently independent qualities of the test change with time, the direction of the change not running constantly in the same direction throughout the whole period, and that it is possible to date a series of *Micraster* found together rather accurately. In this particular case there is no possibility of confusing *Micraster* with any other form of echinoid found with it except for "*Epiaster*," which by definition differs from *Micraster* by not possessing a sub-anal fasciole.

In these circumstances it is natural to suppose that the differences between the earliest and the latest members of this series depend on an evolutionary change which has gone on in the area which is now southern England. It would be conceivable that the change had been brought about by immigration of new types into the area from somewhere else. The story as it is shown in north France appears to be identical with that in England. *Micraster* occurs also in north Germany and has been recorded from Italy, the Caucasus, and Madagascar, with very uncertain reliability.

But so far as present materials allow one to judge, the courses of change are so similar all over the known distribution of *Micraster* as to make an explanation of the English conditions by immigration impracticable. We have thus in *Micraster* what is to all appearance a perfectly well-established record of the process of evolutionary change. Evolutionary series comparable in their apparent reliability with that of *Micraster* are exceedingly rare; many such have been put forward, for example among ammonites, but these have involved very much more difficult problems of selection. Most of the richly fossiliferous ammonite horizons contain forms belonging to many genera, some of which are closely similar, and the genera themselves have often been divided into numerous species. The number of recognizable qualities to be found in the ammonite shell is much less than that in an echinoid, so that those persistent characters on which we depend for recognition that species B in a later horizon is closely related to species A, which lived earlier, are few and often "small," and the possibility of error is thereby disproportionately increased. It is therefore exceedingly difficult to discover material which can throw light on the problem of the evolution of species in a convincing manner. Most of the casual suggestions that B is the descendant of A cannot be established on evidence which is at all adequate. In the case of fossil mammals, where the structure is extraordinarily intricate and in which the recognizable characters are very numerous, it is evident that persistent characters on which we depend for the selection of the individuals of which our series is composed may be so numerous that the probability of their existence in association with one another throughout the term of the series, except in a true line of descent, is very small and may be negligible.

It should therefore be possible to find true evolutionary series illustrating the origin of species of mammals. The chief difficulties arise from the rarity of cases in which we have a series of successive forms representing the same ecological niche. None the less in such cases, for example the species of *Siphneus* described by Teilhard de Chardin from North China, we are probably near the truth. This case might have the special importance that the latest members of these series are still living and thus available for investigation by geneticists and cytologists. There are, however, evolutionary series of fossils of a different character and of much greater reliability. It will be appreciated that the doubts presented by series purporting to show specific changes of character arise from the fact that the process of selection of the materials which compose the series necessarily depends on small qualities, and generally on very few of such. If we can avoid these difficulties by dealing with groups which at the particular horizons concerned are sharply marked off from all others, and use the whole of the available material, we are in a much stronger position. Thus it is possible to consider the relatively large structural changes which are common to all members of a relatively large group, a family or sub-family, over a prolonged period by making use of everything wherever it be found, in a continent or over the world, as the basis of our series.

The classical case is of course that of the horses. W. Kowalevski, writing in 1873, presented an evolutionary series of horses from the Late Eocene to today in which the Eocene horses were represented by the palaeotheres and paloplotheres, those from the Miocene by *Anchitherium*. *Hipparion* was his Pliocene horse, and *Equus* was the final term. From these materials, which represented the whole group of equine perissodactyls then known (the relationship of *Hyracotherium* being then unrecognized), Kowalevsky made out an essentially correct story of the mechanical evolution of the horse foot and dentition. But none of these forms is on the direct line of descent of *Equus*, indeed all represent side branches of aberrant structure. Consideration of the very large literature of Tertiary horses, or still better of actual materials of such things, shows that it is relatively easy to distinguish the members of such side lines by comparison of a totality of qualities and by their possession of characteristic features which persist for some time. Thus the "true" Late Eocene horses of North America and Europe are usually less than half the size of the Eocene palaeotheres, as measured in any linear dimension, and are distinguished by many qualities of the teeth, and so for all later stages. But within the true horse line, although we can recognize the existence of several species of hyracotheres, *Orohippus*, etc., even if we consider only specimens found at the same horizon and in the same region, it is as yet impossible to be certain that any given species of *Orohippus* has descended from any nameable species of hyracothere, though the absence of all other genera of true horses in the Early and Middle Eocene rocks of America makes it certain that the later is derived from the earlier genus. Thus the fact that the horse series lacks specific detail is associated with a very much greater reliability of the fundamental facts of horse evolution than exists in the case of most series which are supposed to show the origin of one species from another.

Let us then consider in outline the kind of information which may be drawn from the evolutionary story of the horse, using that group as it is very familiar to general zoologists as well as to palaeontologists, is well based, and remarkably complete. It is one among many; Dr. W. D. Matthew told me that he believed that materials existed which would allow a history of camels, even more complete than that of the horse, to be written by a man who could visit the very large number of museums in which it is contained. Dr. Thorpe's monograph of the oreodonts shows that that group also would provide a complete though much less spectacular story, and there must be other groups equally profitable. May I therefore consider the horse story. Freed from the palaeotheres, the

Equidae begin in Europe and North America in the form *Hyracotherium*, small with three- and four-toed feet, with cheek teeth extremely brachyodont and of a simple sex-tubercular pattern. It passes on through *Orohippus, Epihippus, Mesohippus, Miohippus, Parahippus, Merychippus, Pliohippus, Plesippus* to *Equus*, and from *Merychippus* direct to *Hipparion*. With the partial exception of the very few known specimens of *Epihippus*, this series shows a steady increase in size through the whole history, although at various times dwarf members occur. (*Archaeohippus* is a dwarf *Parahippus, Nannippus* is a dwarf *Hipparion*, the Shetland pony is a dwarf *Equus* and the dwarfs in a very curious way retain the characters of the normal sized horses from which they were derived.) Throughout the series of horses, from its beginning to its termination in *Equus* and *Hipparion*, we find a tendency to increase the area of the grinding dentition of the two jaws by an increasing size and by further elaboration of the premolars, and we find concurrently an increase in the depth of the teeth to the extreme presented by the African Pleistocene *Hipparion*. These changes proceed steadily in the normal horses but in the side branch *Anchitherium, Hypohippus*, etc., in which there is a very marked increase in size, although the premolars increase in size relatively to the molars, and in complexity, their relative height does not increase. The same series of animals shows an increase in the transverse sectional area, and ultimately in the length of the third metapodial, in comparison with its neighbours on either side. The process in *Equus* is carried to the stage at which the lateral metapodials are only about two-thirds the length of the median bone with which they lie in contact. The story has long been known, and can be followed in very great detail, of addition of cusps to the teeth and of their remodelling, and the whole has long been regarded as the classical example of orthogenesis as it is understood by paleontologists. This orthogenesis is sometimes supposed to have been brought about by some mechanism inherent in the animal which would ensure that changes proceeded, as it were, automatically with time, and that they proceed in a definite direction. This conception, which is not by any means impossible, demands very serious consideration and criticism.

It is evident and has long been realized that the effect of these changes is to secure an improvement in mechanical efficiency. The horses are now galloping animals; when moving at the highest speed of which they are capable—somewhat of the order of 40 miles per hour—they gallop, all the feet at a certain stage of the stride being off the ground at the same time, the whole weight of the animal very little later being received on one hind foot, the leg flexing to take up the shock. The magnitude of the impulsive forces acting, in the case of a large horse, is very great indeed and it is clear that only extremely good design in an engineering sense enables the whole structure of the leg to take up the initial shock and to control the subsequent movement of the horse. In general in such circumstances the fewer moving parts the better, and it is clear that the disappearance of the lateral hooves greatly reduces the probability of damage to the whole structure. I have been told by a veterinary surgeon that racing greyhounds, which run at very high speeds, quite commonly break individual toes, and I have seen such cases of healed fractures in the lateral toes of *Mesohippus*, an animal in which the lateral hooves were in contact with the ground. Such fractures, until healed, must seriously reduce the speed of the animals and thus their viability. We do not know what gaits were possible to *Hyracotherium*, but it seems to me in every way probable that it galloped as does a modern horse, for I have seen an African black rhinoceros in the London Zoo galloping round a paddock in a typical horse manner.

The effect of increasing size on the structure of the limbs of an animal is evident in the area of transverse section of a metatarsal, which (if the increased size did not involve proportional changes) would increase as the square of a linear dimension; if we ignore shape changes the weight of the animal which possessed it would increase as the cube of a linear increase. In other words to be adequate the area of transverse section of a limb bone should increase as the cube of a linear dimension, the bone becoming proportionally thicker. To this process there is an obvious limit although the horses do not reach it, but it seems reasonably clear that to replace three smaller bones by a single larger one is economical in material, a given increase in strength being attained by a smaller increase in weight. Thus it seems in every way probable that the changes which take place in the limbs of horses are adaptive in that they enable a large and heavy animal to move as fast as its small and slender ancestor with the smallest utilization of material.

The development of the grinding dentition may have the same end. The food requirements of every animal may be divided into two parts—the maintenance ration, representing the amount of foods of varied chemical natures necessarily consumed in order that the animal may remain alive, that its heart may continue to beat, its respiratory movements to take place, that the necessary enzymes be secreted, the minimum necessary excretion be provided for, the constant cost of maintaining tone in muscles met, and that inevitable continuous breakdown of living materials may be made good. This amount contains the basal metabolism but is somewhat larger in the case of animals living a normal life. To this maintenance ration must be added an amount, which the agricultural physiologists call the production ration, which provides the energy needed for activities of all kinds, locomotion, growth, reproduction, and the production of milk. In an animal like the horse the greater part of this production ration will be spent in running about. The maintenance ration is related to the weight of the animal but is not proportionate to it. It increases roughly as the animal's surface area, that is as the two-thirds power of the weight (in the case of domestic cattle the figure is more accurately the 0.73 power of the weight). The production ration, on the other hand, varies in strict accordance with the amount and kind of the materials produced or, in the case of locomotion, as the amount of energy used in these movements, which will clearly vary in some direct proportion to the animal's own weight. Thus the total food consumption of an animal is built up by a maintenance ration, varying roughly as the square of a linear dimension, plus a production ration varying as its cube. In domestic animals, for example cows producing a gallon of milk a day, the maintenance and production rations are of the same order of magnitude, as they are in horses doing heavy work.

In the case of an animal which feeds on vegetable food the area of the cheek teeth and the character of their surface must be related to the total daily food consumption, for the object of the cheek dentition is to cut up and triturate the food sufficiently to disrupt any cell walls and thus make the contents of the cells, both living protoplasm and food stored in the form of starch or of fat, accessible to the enzymes in the digestive juices. It is evident that, other things being equal, the amount of vegetable material which can be reduced to a standard degree of preparation will be related to the surface area of the teeth over a unit period. But plant materials vary very greatly in character and it is probable that grasses, with their narrow hard stems and leaves, need very different treatment from the leafy twigs which are eaten by browsing animals. Grass stalks are not adequately disrupted by mere pressure between bunodont teeth, they must be cut into short lengths before swallowing and this can only be done by a scissor-like action of an enamel ridge in a lower molar being drawn across a similar ridge in an upper molar. This process implies that the amount of food prepared in a given time will be related not to the surface area of the dentition but to the length of the enamel ridge presented by it. This would imply that with increase in size the total superficial area of the crowns of the grinding teeth should increase disproportionately, and that at the same time the length of the enamel ridge on the surface should increase even more rapidly than the surface area. We have here an explanation in functional terms of the increase in area of the cheek dentition represented by the greater molarization of the premolars in the Eocene horses, and subsequent enlargement of the premolars, and indeed of the cheek teeth in general, in later horses, and of the great complexity ultimately obtained in the enamel pattern in such animals as *Hipparion*. The size of the face is determined by the size of the teeth which it carries, but brain size does not increase proportionately to increased weight, it varies much more nearly as the two-thirds power of the weight, and it is brain size which determines that of the cranium which contains it. Thus it is evident that the face of a horse will increase in size relatively to the cranium, with increasing weight of the horse, and such an increase has long been recognized, but Robb first showed that the increase was systematic and that the ratio of length of face to length of cranium could be represented by a regression equation which conforms to the equation of heterogonic or allometric growth discovered by Huxley. Robb has shown that the equation for such growth applies not only to growth stages of recent horses, and to recent adult horses of varying size, but to the approximately direct evolutionary series from *Hyracotherium* to *Equus*. The only weakness in Robb's examination of the problem is that he related facial length to total skull length, which, though it establishes that the proportional changes do take place in accordance with a definite law, does not enable us to go much further with an analysis of the significance of the phenomenon; for both total skull length, which is the face and the cranium, and the cranial length are independently related to the animal's size as judged by its weight; and the existence of a regression equation connecting skull length and cranial length is thus a secondary phenomenon dependent on the existence of two other series of proportional changes, each of which could obviously be expressed as a regression on weight, which is the fundamental quality with which all other measurements should be compared. None the less it is obvious that all or at least the great majority of characters in horses whose evolutionary change is known are (or may be) due to the effect of increasing size and the necessary food and mechanical requirements that go with it. In some cases at any rate they seem to depend on the carrying on, from generation to generation over some fifty million years, of the mechanism, whatever it may be, which determined the changes in proportion in the skeleton which took place during the growth of a new born *Hyracotherium* to its adult size. It is not however clear that this explanation in terms of a hereditary mechanism is adequate for all cases; it is possible that the molarization of the premolars, for instance, has been brought about by natural selection acting upon the limited variations thrown up by mutations.

It therefore appears that much of the change which distinguishes *Equus* from *Hyracotherium* is not orthogenetic in the esoteric sense that that term has sometimes acquired. It depends in some cases on a lack of evolutionary change in a mechanism controlling development and in other cases may have been brought about by natural selection retaining and directing changes made necessary by a steadily increasing size of the animals during the evolutionary series.

A steady increase in size is very commonly found in evolutionary series of fossil mammals. It is for example general in artiodactyls, perissodactyls and Proboscidea; it is not, however, characteristic of carnivores in general nor of rodents and insectivores. Indeed modern insectivores are no larger than their Oligocene and Eocene forerunners, and the pygmy shrew is probably the smallest of all known mammals, recent or fossil. It is therefore impossible to regard a steady increase in size as a phenomenon characteristic of mammals as a whole, and it is useful to consider how it may have arisen. The analysis of food intake discussed above shows that if the activity, meaning the distance run per day at a given speed, be constant through an evolutionary story, the thermodynamic efficiency of the large animals is greater than that of the small to an amount which may be very material, and is certainly sufficient to give to these larger animals an advantage great enough to afford the basis for natural selection. In addition, beyond a certain point increase in size may well reduce the incidence of the attacks of predators.

Thus it seems probable that the whole story of horse evolution, which is orthogenetic in the actual etymological significance of the word, may be accounted for entirely by the bringing about of an increase in size by natural selection, this increase in size at once producing a need for alterations in proportions in order that the body as a whole may remain a workable machine, able to stand up to the mechanical forces which act on it when running, and able to provide an adequate amount of properly masticated food for its maintenance. It seems quite clear that similar considerations lie at the base of the apparent orthogenesis to be seen in other groups of perissodactyls, in artiodactyls and Proboscidea, and it is important to try to find any example of an orthogenetic change which cannot be accounted for in terms of natural selection.

One such case appears to be presented by the character of the ossification of many lower vertebrates. In cephalaspids, osteolepids, coelacanths, Dipnoi, and the series from palaeoniscids to sturgeons we find regularly occurring a reduction in the amount of cartilage bone in the skeleton taking place with time, and without, in very many cases, an equivalent reduction of membrane bones. Many of the facts have been recorded by Professor Stensiö, who has called attention to the wide existence of the phenomenon. It presents itself in a way which may be set out in comparatively few words. The neural cranium is known in many palaeoniscids from the Late Devonian Cleveland shale, the Early Carboniferous of Scotland, the Coal Measures of North America and of England. In all cases in adults the separate bones, which are present in young individuals, fuse completely and indeed become unrecognizable. In the Triassic palaeoniscids of Greenland, which Stensiö has described, such a complete fusion does not occur, although it does in the perleidids of Greenland and of Madagascar which are descendants of palaeoniscids. In the Liassic *Chondrosteus*, ossifications in the neural cranium are very much reduced, and in the living sturgeons they make their appearance only in old age. Similarly in the earliest coelacanths from the Late Devonian of Wildungen the whole neural cranium, although, as in osteolepids, it is divided into two parts, is fully ossified. Carboniferous coelacanths, where the conditions are not well known, have certainly much less completely ossified brain cases. Stensiö has shown that the conditions in his Spitzbergen Triassic forms are similar to those in the Carboniferous genera, although probably the ossification is even less complete. In the Late Cretaceous *Macropoma*, although several bones are present in the brain case, they are always exceedingly lightly ossified, and the living coelacanth shows still further reduction. In Dipnoi we have the same story, *Dipterus* from the Middle Old Red Sandstone of Scotland has a very well ossified brain case which still lacks complete description. *Phaneropleuron* from the Upper Old Red Sandstone has little bone in its brain case and the living *Ceratodus*, like the living sturgeon, only produces replacement bone in the skull in old age. Thus the phenomenon of a reduction of cartilage bone, which occurs throughout the entire skeleton, is very widespread, and it occurs in fish from the sea as well as in those which lived in fresh water. *Dipterus* and all other dipnoans lived in streams and lakes, the early palaeoniscids were fresh water forms, those from the Trias marine, *Chondrosteus* is a relatively shallow water sea fish, the sturgeon is both marine and fresh water. The earliest coelacanths are found in a marine deposit, Carboniferous forms are predominantly fresh water, those known from the Trias are shallow water marine, while *Macropoma* occurs in relatively deep sea.

It is thus very difficult to account for this steady reduction of cartilage bone by any process dependent on the environment in which the animal lived. Reduction of cartilage bone is vividly shown in the labyrinthodont Amphibia. All the labyrinthodonts in which conditions are known, occurring in the "Lower Carboniferous" of Scotland (much of which is probably of Namurian age), and all those occurring in the productive Coal Measures of Great Britain possess fully ossified brain cases and well developed ossifications in the postcranial skeleton. The embolomerous vertebral columns associated with them contain relatively massive bones, the ribs are long, and where remains of the limbs are known these bones are really well-finished, recalling those of Permian reptiles. Membrane bone in the head covers very large areas but the bones themselves are thin, the pits of the ornamented external surface leaving only a thin layer of continuous bone below them. These animals were all inhabitants of a Coal Measure type of country, that is, they lived in or near the shallow streams and ponds on a land surface at sea level on which the great forests which provided the materials now forming coal seams stretched over vast and scarcely interrupted areas.

Later, in Late Carboniferous times, for example in South Joggins, Nova

Scotia, there are labyrinthodonts of a different type, in some at least of which the brain case is still well ossified. In the Texas Red Beds it is evident, if we consider the Labyrinthodonts as a whole (excluding perhaps the form *Archeria* [*Cricotus*] which is in effect a carry-over from Carboniferous times), we find that the brain case, although it still contains a good deal of cartilage bone, is much less completely ossified than it was in the Carboniferous labyrinthodonts and that the ossifications appeared to have been a good deal less solid. Relatively few labyrinthodonts are known in later Permian rocks, but those that are appear to have less cartilage bone than those from the Texan Early Permian.

When we pass on to the labyrinthodonts of the Early Trias it is evident that a very great reduction in the amount and postponement of the time of appearance of cartilage bones has taken place. Large, obviously nearly full grown specimens of *Capitosaurus* and *Trematosaurus* may show very little ossification in the brain case other than the functionally necessary ex-occipital condyles, and even the most completely bony specimens show very little cartilage bone. The Late Triassic labyrinthodonts, even in the case of relatively gigantic skulls, often show no ossification other than the ex-occipitals in the neural cranium. Meanwhile the dermal bones and the membrane bones of the palate, on which increased demands for strength are made, become thicker until in the large Late Triassic labyrinthodonts they may be immensely massive, a centimeter or more thickness of continuous dense bone occurring in *Cyclotosaurus*.

We have then, in the same animals, a thickening of membrane bones, which assures us that ample supplies of calcium and phosphatase were available, going on side by side with a great reduction and final complete loss of cartilage bones, of immensely smaller total volume. The conditions are in fact completely parallel to those occurring in those groups of fish I have mentioned above and they take place among animals the early forms of which were certainly aquatic. The Early Permian forms were generally terrestrial, the Early Triassic forms aquatic, some living in fresh waters and others in the sea, while the Late Triassic animals are certainly restricted to life in fresh water pools and streams.

There is another series of changes in labyrinthodonts which can be brought out by a consideration of the whole available materials of such animals from the Scotch Early Carboniferous to the Rhaetic of Scania. The one completely undistorted skull of a Carboniferous labyrinthodont, that of *Megalocephalus* from Coalbrookdale, shows the remarkable condition of having an extremely deep occipital region, while the anterior part of the skull in the region of the nostrils is much depressed and very low indeed in proportion to its width. This shape occurs in an exaggerated form in all or nearly all labyrinthodont skulls, the dorso-ventral depression which it presents proceeding further and further backward until in the Late Triassic labyrinthodonts the whole skull is very shallow, even in the occipital region. This reduction in the height of the skull seems to have proceeded at very different rates in different stocks of labyrinthodonts, but taking the group as a whole the change from first to last is obvious. The dorso-ventral depression is recognizable in a highly developed condition throughout the skull even in such Early Permian creatures as *Eryops*, which were certainly inhabitants of the land. It is thus difficult to believe that its occurrence was induced by environmental influences, although its effect, when carried to an extreme, is to render the animal incapable of progress on land and thus to compel it to live throughout its life on the floor of a pond or river. But this dorso-ventral depression has many mechanical sequels and is associated with a series of changes in the basi-cranial region which are made necessary in part also by the deficient cartilage ossification.

One of the most easily discussed of all the changes which take place in very many of the labyrinthodont stocks is the development and steady exaggeration of the retro-articular process. In all the labyrinthodonts of the British Carboniferous, whether they be anthracosaurs or loxommids, there is a complete absence of any trace whatsoever of any protuberance behind the articular facet on the articular bone; the crest which marks the hinder edge of the articulation of the quadrate descends smoothly and uninterruptedly to curve round into the lower border of the jaw; even in later labyrinthodonts from the Texan Permian the retro-articular process is still little developed. In *Eryops* it may perhaps be said to exist, in the much flattened *Trimerorachis* it is relatively rather larger, in *Cacops* (as shown by a photograph published by Case) it is relatively well developed. When we go to the later forms we find that in *Capitosaurus*, for example, it is a considerable projection which is further exaggerated in *Cyclotosaurus*. In the brachiopids it is present as a small projection in the Late Permian *Dwinasaurus*. It is relatively somewhat larger in *Bothriceps australis*, in the Middle Triassic *Plagiosuchus* it is a remarkably large and powerful process, while the Rhaetic *Gerathorax* has an enormous greatly elongated retro-articular process. The function of this process is very evident. It gives attachment to the depressor mandibulae muscle which arises from the posterior surface of the upper border of the skull, from tabulars and post-parietals, dorsal and internal to the otic notch. This muscle passes downward and outward to be inserted on the posterior extremity of the retro-articular process; its function is to open the mouth by depressing the lower jaw. In animals whose legs are so short that the body habitually lies in contact with the ground, and the lower jaw is thus in contact with the soil, the mouth can only be opened by raising the head, leaving the lower jaw where it was; this condition is very familiar in crocodiles. The raising of the head is normally brought about by the contraction of those muscles which are inserted on the occiput and pass backward to the dorsal parts of the vertebral column. In the case of the very flattened amphibia, such as *Cyclotosaurus* and *Gerathorax*, these muscles are inserted very inadvantageously, for in a large amphibian such as *Metoposaurus*, where the skull is 22.5 cm. wide, the upper border of the occiput lies only 3.75 of a centimeter above the centre of curvature of the condyle, and such a skull is 28.5 cm. in length. It is therefore obvious that the epiaxial musculature, when flattening is excessively developed, will be inadequate; hence the musculus depressor mandibulae is enlarged and its point of application removed as far as possible from the fulcrum represented by the quadrate condyle. Hence as the skull becomes more and more flattened the retro-articular process tends to lengthen as a direct adaptation to enable the mouth to be opened by raising the head while the lower jaw remains in contact with the ground.

In all the early labyrinthodonts the occipital condyles lie much in front of the quadrate condyles and hence, if the head be raised so as to open the mouth with the lower jaw in contact with the ground, not only must the head be raised but the anterior part of the vertebral column (which is articulated with the occipital condyle) must also be pulled up, greatly increasing the weight which has to be lifted and the tension necessary in the muscles to bring the movement about. In the large late labyrinthodonts with exceedingly flattened skulls the shape is so changed that the occipital condyles come to lie in the same transverse plane as the quadrate condyles and are even lowered so that the two condyles are surfaces of rotation about the same axis. In these circumstances the head can be raised while the lower jaw remains in contact with the ground without any displacement of the anterior part of the body behind the skull. The process is indeed carried beyond this point in brachyopid forms, where the occipital condyles actually lie posterior to the quadrate condyles and considerably above them, and hence when the skull is raised the lower jaw is automatically pushed forward.

It seems perfectly obvious that these changes in the relative positions of the quadrate and occipital condyles, and the development of the retro-articular process, serve a functional end and meet a need that has arisen through the flattening of the anterior part of the animal which places the fore limbs in such a position that they could certainly not have raised the head from the ground on land, and could have done so only very ineffectively under water. Furthermore the fore limbs of later labyrinthodonts are considerably reduced in comparison with *Eryops* and other Early Permian land living amphibia, and their feebleness may perhaps be related (at any rate in part) to the decrease of cartilage bone in such forms, not only in the skull but in the post-cranial skeleton.

It is possible to give a functional explanation of many of the other changes which are seen to take place with time, all the labyrinthodonts of early being compared with all those of later time, for example the change in the basi-cranial connection of the pterygo-palatine cartilage, and its functional replacement by a sutural union of the pterygoid with the parasphenoid. These changes may all be shown to be of such a nature that they secure the mechanical strength of the skull despite the dorso-ventral compression of the animals and the decline in cartilage bone. It is in fact possible to explain the whole evolution of the labyrinthodonts (apart from that which is clearly related to such matters of habit as the nature of the animal's food) as the effect of natural selection so altering the structure that the skull, and indeed other parts of the skeleton, remain mechanically competent despite the flattening and the loss of cartilage bone which appears to have provided the drive which called natural selection into effect.

So far the case is parallel to that of the horses, where it is possible to explain the majority of all those changes in the dentition and feet which seem to present an orthogenetic change as due directly to natural selection in some cases, in others to the working out of a hereditary mechanism, persisting throughout the whole history of horses, which determines the proportions of the animal. In both cases the changes ultimately depend on the increase in size; this increase can itself be explained as a product of natural selection because an increase in size automatically increases the overall thermodynamic efficiency of a mammal.

I have been able to find no advantage that an animal can obtain by a reduction in the amount of cartilage bone. The cartilages which then remain functional in the adult are weaker than the bones which would usually have replaced them, and where specially great stresses have to be met, as in the occipital condyles, cartilage bone is retained. It cannot be due to lack of calcium, phosphate or a general inability to produce phosphatase, for the weight of membrane bone in the skeleton probably increases. The condition does in fact recall the disease phocomelia, shown characteristically in the Scotch Dumpy or Creeper fowl, where there is a similar decline in cartilage ossification without the corresponding decrease in membrane bone. As their name indicates, these abnormal fowls have very short limbs, as do the late labyrinthodonts, and the condition in the fowls is heritable; it is indeed produced by a single recessive gene. No one has yet suggested that mutation is directed, although it may be evoked by external conditions.

Thus considering the labyrinthodonts as a group, neglecting none of the existing material and thus freeing ourselves from the danger inevitable in the selection from a larger material of those individuals which we believe to belong to a narrow line of descent, we can recognize a series of changes which exhibit an orthogenetic evolution and show that these more visible and obvious changes may be adaptive, not to any circumstances external to the animal, but in relation to other changes going on in the animals which continue, to all appearances, throughout the whole history of the group. And these basal changes which evoke those which are easily recognizable are not of such a character that it is at present possible to explain their occurrence as an adaptation and hence their appearance as a result of natural selection.

If I am correct in regarding the decrease of cartilage bone and the progress of a dorso-ventral compression backwards from the anterior part of the skull (which can be observed from the whole material of labyrinthodonts) as phenomena not imposed by any environmental influences, and hence incapable of explanation by natural selection, but produced in response to some continuing internal condition, it is obviously desirable to consider whether any other examples of the same strange type can be found. It is only in fossil material forming a continuous series relatively well known, and representing a large group, that we could expect to recognize a parallel. The idea of the occasional occurrence of such changes has long been present in my mind and when, about thirty years ago, I was actively examining mammal-like reptiles, I reached the conclusion on the materials then available that those animals exhibited a decrease in height (and subsequently in size) of the quadrate which could be associated with a general reduction in depth of all parts of the skull in the region of the brain case which lie below the brain. Since then our knowledge of mammal-like reptiles, especially of the beginnings of the group in the Pelycosauria, has increased enormously and our understanding of the interrelationships of the independent stocks within the order or superorder has become much more precise. So far as I can judge without a very lengthy new investigation, the phenomenon is genuine if we take as the end terms the typical cynodonts (*Cynognathus*, etc.) and the later bauriamorphs (*Bauria* itself). In these two lines, which are quite independent of one another, the quadrate does become a very small bone and the whole of the skull laterally to the occiput is much less deep than it is in the earlier Deinocephalia and in the sphenacodonts. It is thus possible that my original view that these changes in structure existed and exhibited an orthogenetic evolution is justified.

The next stage in the argument is to try to discover some way in which they can be shown to be mechanically advantageous or, if not desirable on mechanical grounds, have been forced on the animals exhibiting them by some requirement of head shape, itself desirable functionally, which can be brought about only if the quadrates and the hinder part of the lower jaws suffer such reduction. I have not been able to discover any such explanation and am thus still inclined to regard the evolution of these groups of mammal-like reptiles as having been induced by an internal mechanism. I expect further light on this matter from the study of the tritylodonts, which are descendants of cynodonts of some kind not remotely related to *Diademodon*. The Anomodontia, although they seem to have followed the same course between the time of their origin from early Deinocephalia to the establishment of a typical dicynodont structure, show no steady changes from this time in the *Tapinocephalus* zone to the disappearance of the group some time in the Late Trias.

I may perhaps summarize the evidence which paleontology may contribute to the study of the mode and the machinery of evolution as follows. The establishment of the smallest recognizable groups of individuals in the animal kingdom, geographical varieties or subspecies, may be due to one of two things, or to both. If we consider a population of one species with a wide geographical range we may expect to find differences, which can only be expressed in statistical terms, between populations from separate regions. These differences may be due to direct environmental effects. If one area affords a more adequate food supply than another, the individuals inhabiting it will tend to be larger, the curves representing the distribution of weight in the populations having different means or modes. But in the case of mammals, change in size may actually bring about changes in proportion which owe their appearance to the nature of the hereditary mechanism which determines the mode of growth of an animal. Indeed the matter is even more complex, for Hammond has shown in the case of domesticated pigs that if two animals be fed so that they reach the same weight on the same day, one having been well fed in its early days and poorly fed subsequently, and the other subjected to the reverse of this treatment, they will differ very greatly in appearance and in all their bodily proportions. And Hammond has shown also that sheep and cattle seem to show a similar condition. Thus changed conditions of nutritional level may bring about large proportional changes in the bodies of mammals of a kind which would mark out a geographical race or a subspecies. But it seems evident that populations of different character have arisen within a species in groups separated from one another, either geographically or in any other way which does not permit free breeding between the separated groups, simply because the initial group contained few individuals. It is probable that these individuals, chosen by hazard, will contain different associations of genes and with interbreeding among the individuals of the group in isolation these will spread through an enlarging population until something near a steady state is achieved, so that viewed statistically the isolated populations will differ in their visible characters even if natural selection has not come into operation.

If these be the two extreme ways in which geographical races or subspecies have come into existence, it seems evident that paleontology can very seldom, if ever, contribute much of importance to the matter. In the case of the species, which is perhaps the only real group with a theoretical strict limitation, paleontology could perhaps do rather more, but could only do so under the very rare conditions of an abundance of material fit for statistical treatment, collected from a series of horizons in the same district not far separated from one another, and representing a continuous and unvaried (or if varied then regularly varied) ecological condition. In these circumstances it should be possible to determine whether recognizable and statistically significant changes do occur and whether the character of the whole population exhibits a change of character with time. It is possible theoretically that structural changes could go on for some distance without any true new species being established, that is, without such modifications of the chromosomal pattern or otherwise as would prevent interbreeding from taking place, but the conditions are rare and very few of the evolutionary stories among invertebrates are based on materials which comply with them. In the case of vertebrates such series will be rare and can only be expected to be found in mammals, and perhaps only in small mammals. If they could be discovered in Late Pleistocene and Holocene deposits they would be extremely important because the possibility would then exist of breeding of the still surviving animals and thus affording the opportunity of comparing the conclusions drawn from two entirely different kinds of evidence.

Paleontological evidence as to the nature of evolution is really of importance in the consideration of relatively large groups, families, orders, and even larger units. It is to the consideration of such cases that the present paper is devoted. Paleontology is indeed our only mode of study of such major evolution, the results it obtains rest ultimately on the validity of the morphological methods worked out by the zoologists of the past. They require the selection from the whole mass of fossils, found on each of successive horizons, of particular animals which are shown to be related to one another on a basis of the common occurrence of particular structural features, and this process becomes more and more precarious as the line of assumed descent becomes narrower. If we deal with species we are dealing inevitably with a discrimination of animals which differ only in minute qualities. If we deal with families we may be concerned, as we are in the case of the horses, with a sharply delimited group of forms. If we treat an order we may be able to use all the materials which have been collected falling within it, and setting bounds to our material will, except perhaps in the most primitive members of the order, be easy. The case of the labyrinthodonts considered above falls into this class; there can be no real doubt in any case that a well-preserved skull of an adult is, or is not, a labyrinthodont. If I am right in the conclusions I have drawn as to the evolution of this group we have exhibited in it a new phenomenon, the existence of structural changes which proceed with time brought about not by any environmental influences (adaptations in the ordinary sense) but dependent upon some internal quality common to all members of the group, which survives from its introduction to its disappearance. The changes so produced may make necessary a whole series of consequential modifications carried out in order that the animal may remain a working whole, all the mechanical requirements of the skeleton being met, and these consequential changes (in as much as they are not carried out in exactly the same way in different stocks within the large group and are adaptive in nature) may well have been produced by natural selection acting on variability in the form of mutants which occurs in all animals.

It is interesting to attempt to find out how far through a large group changes of the kind which I believe to be produced by internal conditions in the animals concerned may extend, and this may conveniently be done in the case of the Amphibia. There is now a very large number of genera of labyrinthodonts known; Romer in his most useful review lists 130, some of which may perhaps not be labyrinthodonts, and many are very incompletely known. From this vast mass it seems to me possible to select, on a basis of characters which persist over considerable periods of time, a certain number of series which appear to represent more or less closely true phylogenetic lines. Comparison of these with one another shows that the reduced ossification and flattening proceed at very different rates in different lines, and that the mechanical rearrangements in the skull rendered necessary are met in a variety of different ways; this is indeed the basis of my belief that these consequential changes have been brought about by natural selection. When we go to other of the great groups of Amphibia we can, I think, find traces of a similar change in progress in them. Of these the clearest is that presented by the group including the Coal Measure *Ceraterpeton* and *Batrachiderpeton* and the Early Permian *Diplocaulus*. These animals are very sharply separated from all labyrinthodonts by the structure of their vertebral columns, but they certainly show a progressive flattening, *Diplocaulus* being perhaps the most extreme example of this change known in the whole of the amphibia, and they seem also to exhibit the customary reduction of cartilage bone. Actually *Diplocaulus* is remarkably like a Late Triassic labyrinthodont in the structure of its basicranial region, whilst *Ceraterpeton* recalls a Late Carboniferous labyrinthodont such as *Dendrerpeton*, but on the other hand the very incompletely known true Microsauria, Adelospondyli, do not show any clear evidence of such changes. The frogs are of labyrinthodont ancestry, and in them extreme forms such as *Pipa* are obviously highly flattened, and in some cases at any rate are deficient in cartilage ossifications. The urodeles, whose ancestry is still unknown, are clearly a group exhibiting flattening and loss of cartilage bone, though here the conditions are not so readily recognized, there are so many neotenic species which retain a larval skull. The Gymnophiona, on the other hand, with their bodies of circular transverse section, present no trace whatsoever of flattening, which may be due to the fact that they never possessed the mechanism which produces such a change, or may merely mean that their burrowing habits inhibit any such development. They are on the whole well-ossified forms, a solid and massive skull being a necessity in any creature which burrows in the earth presumably by using its nose as a ram. Thus the two independent phenomena are not exhibited throughout the whole range of the amphibia, but some conditions which may reasonably be interpreted as representing them are widely spread through that group.

The various stocks of labyrinthodonts clearly exhibit an adaptive radiation; they are fitted for different kinds of life and especially for different feeding habits. It now seems evident that differences of this kind can, in principle at any rate, be brought about by natural selection. Indeed there are in animals very few changes of such a character that natural selection is excluded as an explanation, and those which are of such a nature seem to me to be of small importance, matters which characterize species and not greater groups. Such characters may well be without adaptive significance, that is their possession or lack does not affect the viability of the animals under their natural conditions and hence will not be affected by natural selection. One possible case is presented by the existence in England of the two shrews Sorex vulgaris and S. minutus; these animals differ only in that one is half the weight of the other, they may live in the same district feeding on identical food and having, so far as is known, identical habits and behavior, and both are relatively common. In such a case it is exceedingly difficult to believe that the differences have any adaptive significance whatsoever, and they may have arisen, perhaps, as a single chance mutation.

· 5 ·

COMPARATIVE ANATOMY AND THE EVOLUTION
OF VERTEBRATES

BY D. DWIGHT DAVIS[1]

THE past ten years have witnessed a striking rapprochement of various biological disciplines in the study of evolution and allied problems. A convergence of interests scarcely dreamed of a decade ago has been discovered between such once divergent fields as genetics and paleontology.

Recent syntheses of current evolutionary thought have, almost without exception, ignored comparative anatomy completely or considered it only very obliquely. This is an amazing change from seventy years ago, when comparative anatomy (with descriptive embryology) was quite generally regarded as the only productive approach to evolutionary problems. Many non-morphologists believe that the morphological sciences, because they are "descriptive" rather than "experimental," are excluded from effective participation in the essentially dynamic modern assault on the problems of evolution. Paleontology, however, is certainly no less descriptive than any other morphological science, yet in the hands of Simpson and others it has yielded conclusions whose importance the experimentalists would probably be the last to deny. It is difficult to escape the conviction that the undistinguished role that comparative anatomy has played in modern evolutionary studies results from failure on the part of comparative anatomists rather than of their science.

The basic aims of comparative anatomy have changed more during the past half century than is generally realized. The newer concepts are not yet fully crystallized, and many of the statements made below are doubtless grossly oversimplified or even erroneous generalizations. The conclusions as to the relation between comparative anatomy and adaptation are admittedly inadequately documented. Nevertheless it seems desirable to try to set forth the relation, actual and potential, between modern comparative anatomy and neo-Darwinian ideas of evolution. Naturally only those aspects of comparative anatomy that seem to me to bear directly on this question are considered here.

I. COMPARATIVE ANATOMY, OLD AND NEW

In the years following 1859, when the fact of evolution was still being debated, comparative anatomy quickly became the most influential of

[1] Curator, Division of Vertebrate Anatomy, Chicago Natural History Museum.

the biological sciences and certainly contributed the bulk of the "proof" that led to general acceptance of the theory. Carl Gegenbaur typified and largely fathered the morphological research of this era—comparative anatomy based on the theory of descent. Its proponents maintained that the fundamental problem of biology is to discover the history of the *structural elements* of the animal body. Gegenbaur himself regarded the elasmobranchs as the structural prototypes of all vertebrates, and tried to derive all vertebrate structure from the conditions seen in sharks. The Gegenbaurian school thus aimed at documenting the concept that Julian Huxley has recently called "evolutionary progress," a general improvement in all-around biological efficiency, such as is implied in the terms "lower" and "higher." This is indeed the most obvious manifestation of evolution, but the facts of paleontology demonstrate evolutionary progress far more convincingly than do the inferences of comparative anatomy.

The need for further proof of the fact of evolution soon passed, and the decline of comparative anatomy from its position as the leading biological discipline in the 1880's was, if anything, more rapid than its rise. Darwin's emphasis on individual variations and the development of modern cytology, plus the rediscovery of Mendel's work at the turn of the century, revolutionized the formulation of the fundamental problems of biology. Interest shifted from observation of the major phenomena of evolution to observation of individual variations on the one hand and experimentation with the minute random mutations (genetics) and "natural selection within the organism" (developmental mechanics) on the other. The era of the speculative phylogenist was ended, although the methods developed during this period are still among the basic tools of taxonomy.

During the first quarter of the present century morphologists were largely occupied with trying to reorient their science toward the new biological outlook. Two major schools, extremely divergent in outlook and aims, eventually emerged. A third school, that of the statics and mechanics of morphological elements, has been more active than either of the others, but such studies are not usually comparative and have as yet contributed little to evolutionary thought.

The Neo-Classicists

A neo-classical school of idealistic or "pure" morphology, led by Jakobshagen, Naef, and Kälin, has returned to the non-phylogenetic type concept of Goethe. Goethe's *morphological type* (which has no relation to the type concept of taxonomists) is an abstraction arrived at by combining the fundamental structural features of all representatives of a given taxonomic category. What is achieved is regarded as the basic structural plan of that category, its morphological "theme," of which each of the subsumed categories is merely a variation. Hierarchies of such morphological types, corresponding to the taxonomic hierarchies, can be set up.

The most characteristic feature of this concept is that it is devoid of phylogenetic implications, and deals only with structure as such. This thesis has been developed with great skill by Kälin (1935, 1941). It is easy to dismiss such thinking as a quaint sort of atavism, a return to pre-evolutionary ideas, but its full implications have yet to be explored. Certainly the interpretation of homology that Kälin has developed is far more logical than the recent crop of illogical and poorly thought-out suggestions by non-morphologists.

The Functional Comparative Anatomists

A second morphological school, represented especially by Hans Böker, is founded on the interdependence of form, function, and environmental factors. Morphology is regarded, correctly I believe, as merely one facet of the dynamic organism-environment relationship that directs evolution. It is further maintained that the organism as a whole, or at least its major functional units (locomotor apparatus, nutrition apparatus, etc.), are subjected to selection, and not genetic characters or the usual artifically segregated morphological units. Conclusions as to major evolutionary phenomena based on isolated morphological characters are therefore regarded as suspect. The detailed operations of genetic mechanisms underlying such holistic adaptation are of course unknown at present. But this does not preclude profitable study of the phenomenon any more than incomplete understanding of the genetical details involved in species formation invalidates the study of speciation.

This genuinely dynamic approach to comparative anatomy is at present in a rather amorphous state. Its proponents have adopted an uncompromisingly hostile attitude toward genetics, and have retreated into metaphysical assumptions that explain without explaining. Böker, for example, repeatedly and emphatically affirmed his belief in contrasting "active" and "passive" forces that maintain "equilibrium" between a species and its environment and thus determine structure. This gives a superficial appearance of naïveté to such studies, but it is only the interpretations that are naive; the method is sound. The neo-Darwinians, by assigning the decisive role in evolution to selection, have focused attention on adaptation. The importance of morphological adaptation may be debated at the population or subspecies level, as it has been *ad nauseam*, but at higher taxonomic levels adaptation is so obvious that it cannot be denied. Adaptation at these supraspecific levels is precisely the problem of functional comparative anatomy. As I shall attempt to show below, it actually aims at reducing the generalized abstractions represented by the mathematical models of Wright and Simpson to concrete cases.

II. GENETICS AND COMPARATIVE ANATOMY

Geneticists have made their position with respect to evolution abundantly clear. The voluminous evidence and the conclusions derived therefrom have been reviewed so often that they need be repeated here only in briefest outline. Genes and gene systems control phenotypic characters. Small random mutations of the genes and structural and numerical chromosome changes produce corresponding changes in the phenotype. No other agency is known to produce heritable changes in the phenotype. Under the directive influence of selection, new genetic systems arise gradually as a result of these chromosomal changes. Thus distinctive populations, subspecies, species, and finally genera and the higher categories evolve in an orderly and successive manner by the accumulation of small mutations, rigidly screened by selection. The creative role in evolution is thus assigned to selection.

As long as geneticists were concerned solely with the mechanism underlying the transmission of inherited characters there was virtually no contact between genetics and the morphological sciences. But geneticists have recently turned to questions of how the genetic mechanism achieves its phenotypic expression (physiological genetics), and how gene frequencies behave in breeding populations (population genetics), and their conclusions are of distinct and immediate concern to morphologists. On the other hand, morphology is the most tangible embodiment of what has actually been achieved by these processes, not in a few experimental animals but in the whole extent of nature. Therefore conclusions resulting from properly oriented morphological research should likewise be useful to geneticists.

Physiological genetics comes into contact with morphology via embryology, and its implications for comparative anatomy are considered briefly in the next section. Physiological genetics deals with the mechanisms whereby genetic differences are translated into differences in the phenotype. Thus it actually does not come to grips with the basic problem of evolution, which is how these differences become established.

Population geneticists seek to answer precisely that question. Evolution, they maintain, is not primarily a question of the nature or origin of mutations, or of how they are brought to expression in the organism, but of their fates in breeding populations. "A mutation, chromosomal or genic, major or minor, must undergo a virtually continuous process of change in frequency before becoming characteristic of a population. The elementary evolutionary process is therefore change of gene (or chromosome) frequency" (Wright, 1945). The expected behavior of gene frequencies under various conditions has been demonstrated by means of mathematical models, employing statistical concepts. In addition to speciation—

the mere multiplication of subspecies and species by processes that are either non-adaptive or adaptive only to minor ecological zones—it is recognized that "under certain conditions the processes considered in the statistical theory may lead to a very rapid, almost explosive, origin of higher categories" (Wright, 1941a). Simpson (1944) recognizes a third mode, phyletic evolution, the sustained directional shift in average direction of evolution that is particularly apparent in sequences of fossil forms. Simpson points out that speciation is the only mode of evolution that is open to investigation by experimental biology and genetics, although it is not necessarily the most important from the evolutionary standpoint.

The mathematical models set up by population geneticists are statistical abstractions, and the conclusions based on them are extremely broad generalizations. Such concepts are useful only if they can be documented. Experimental biology, and especially field studies of actual breeding populations, may be expected to supply such documentation for the phenomena of speciation. As Simpson has stated, phyletic evolution is a peculiarly paleontological problem. But the origin of new major adaptive types (Simpson's "quantum evolution") is a problem that is not amenable to the methods of either experimental biology or (for reasons given below) of paleontology. This central problem of evolution can, I believe, be documented only by the data of functional comparative anatomy.

III. EMBRYOLOGY AND COMPARATIVE ANATOMY

Embryology, as represented by modern concepts of developmental mechanics and the genetical control of developmental processes, differs greatly from the descriptive and comparative embryology of the era of Haeckel. Descriptive embryology was essentially an adjunct of comparative anatomy, confirming and extending the conclusions as to phylogeny that were derived from study of adult organisms. Thus its role, like that of Gegenbaurian comparative anatomy, was chiefly a historical one.

Many modern embryologists claim that ontogeny plays a part in evolution that is in no way less important or less fundamental than that played by the genes.[2] Every adult animal, they point out, is a product of an individual ontogeny. This ontogeny is the resultant of a large number of correlated reactions proceeding at definite relative velocities. It is the timing and integration of these reactions that determine the differentiation of originally indifferent cells and their subsequent fates in the individual. Goldschmidt (1927) suggested twenty years ago that the rates of these

[2] The school of embryologists, of which Weiss (1939) is a typical example, that is attempting to reduce development to a set of physico-chemical systems, is not considered here. Even if this work succeeds in its aim it will have little direct bearing on evolutionary problems, since evolution is not a matter of ultimate mechanisms in the organism, but the mechanisms of change.

processes are gene controlled, and that mutation may alter the velocity of one or several such reactions. Such a change would shift the whole subsequent course of the ontogenetic reaction involved, or of its rate relative to the rates of the other integrating processes of differentiation. On the model of the chain reaction, this involves change in the character of a large number of tissues, combined with a considerable capacity for self-differentiation in individual tissues, and the resulting difference is not in a few crude respects but a permeating change in general facies.

This concept has since been verified by numerous experimental studies. It changed greatly our ideas of the nature of the available raw materials on which natural selection can act, although opinions as to the actual evolutionary efficacy of such a mechanism have varied widely. Goldschmidt (1940) argued that changes of such magnitude would provide natural selection with material for saltatory evolution, since a relatively simple genetic alteration could condition a more or less thorough repatterning of adult morphology. Thus the detailed and, to Goldschmidt, otherwise unaccountable differences in morphological pattern between genera, families, orders, etc. would rest on a relatively simple genetic basis, with natural selection (1) seizing upon a potentially successful new adaptive type so produced, and (2) refining the crude pre-adaptation by a process of post-adaptation. A residue of "neutral" morphological features, not directly affected by selection but an incidental product of the altered ontogenetic velocities, would help account for the permeating differences (the "unbridgeable gaps") between representatives of different taxonomic categories.

Goldschmidt himself was interested chiefly in the mechanism whereby developmental rates could be altered, and suggested that chromatin rearrangements were responsible for such "systemic mutations." This relatively non-essential feature of his theory has been the chief target of criticisms. As Waddington (1941) has pointed out, however, this highly speculative suggestion is not to the point so far as evolution is concerned, since what evolutionary theory requires is "a picture of the possible kinds of inter-actions between developmental processes," rather than a hypothesis of the ultimate physico-chemical mechanisms of development. Waddington points to the fact that adult tissues fall into a few quite sharply defined kinds rather than varying continuously from one type to another, and postulates a succession of "branching points" during ontogeny, at each of which development can move into one or another of a few alternative paths. Ontogeny is thus envisaged as a "set of branching developmental paths along each of which a certain part of the egg moves during its development." Changes in ontogeny would then be (1) in the pattern of the developmental paths, or (2) in the actual course of the paths, or (3) combinations of the two, and qualitative discontinuous differences in adult organization would be accounted for.

It is apparent that Goldschmidt and Waddington are concerned with the same concept as the neo-classical morphologists. The "morphological type" of the latter is the correlative of Goldschmidt's "unbridgeable gap."

Homeosis

Homeosis was defined by Bateson as the alteration of one organ of a segmental series from its own characteristic form to that of some homologous member of the series. Villee's recent review (1942) of the observational and experimental evidence for this phenomenon, plus his rather naive interpretation of the evolutionary importance of isolated features characteristic of another family or order, have drawn attention to this type of mutation and have contributed to misunderstanding (e.g. Simpson, 1944, p. 52). It is evident that homeosis represents a special case of the reaction rate concept of ontogeny, and that its particular interest is based on the relative abundance of experimental evidence. The data considered by Villee all relate to arthropods, mostly dipterans. But Sawin (1945, 1946) and Sawin and Hull (1946) have interpreted displacements of the thoraco-lumbar and lumbo-sacral borders (i.e. variations in vertebral formula) in rabbits as due to genes having generalized regional rather than a specific field of action. The genes are visualized as controlling growth and differentiation gradients during ontogeny and thus determining the position and magnitude of the thoracic and lumbar regions. Butler (1939, 1946) has argued that the teeth of mammals have evolved as part of a system rather than as individual units, and that a common morphogenetic cause must have acted on more than one tooth germ to account for the close similarity between adjacent teeth. The concept of homeosis with its genetic and ontogenetic background is implied throughout Butler's work, although he does not mention it specifically.

From the morphological standpoint homeosis is intimately related to the concept of serial homology. Old ideas of serially repeated structures, in which each adult unit in the series was regarded as a distinct structural entity that under certain circumstances became "transformed" into an entity characteristic of an adjacent region, are no longer tenable. The adaptive evolution of the vertebral column, for example, is not explained by the genetical control of fields, but the mechanism involved in such evolution is enormously simplified.

In some cases, at least, there is a similar field effect on non-serial (non-homeotic) structures, with a common genetical control of functional rather than morphological units. This is seen in Washburn's (1943, 1946) interpretation of the sequence of epiphyseal union in mammals. Washburn found that the epiphyses of a region, such as the shoulder or knee, unite at more nearly the same time than epiphyses in general or than the epiphyses of a single bone. He further points out that acceleration or deceleration of maturity tends to affect a whole region (involving some epiphyses of several bones) rather than the epiphyses of a single bone, or a single epiphysis.

Modern Descriptive Embryology and Evolution

Another school of embryologists has continued embryological investigation in the Gegenbaur tradition, i.e. from the standpoint of comparative morphology. Franz and Naef in Germany, Sewertzoff in the Soviet Union, and de Beer in England have been particularly active in this field. It is of the utmost interest that this purely morphological work has independently derived a set of empirical "principles" that often amount to a restatement of the conclusions of the genetically-minded experimental embryologists. These rules have been derived quite independently and are based on a wholly different type of data. A well-documented review was recently presented by de Beer (1940), although somewhat colored by his preoccupation with refuting the old Haeckelian idea of recapitulation. Morphological embryologists are agreed on recognizing a principle of *heterochrony*, alteration of the sequence of ontogenetic stages in the phylogeny of a structure. Obviously this is merely a morphologist's phrasing of the geneticists' conclusion that mutation may alter the relative velocity of ontogenetic processes. Heterochrony may be expressed in a variety of ways, depending on the time during ontogeny when its effects become manifest. Thus de Beer recognizes eight principles of heterochrony, the names of which are largely self-explanatory: caenogenesis, deviation, paedogenesis, reduction, adult variation, retardation, hypermorphosis, and acceleration. Haldane earlier (1932) discussed this question and recognized three "ontogenetic tendencies": acceleration, retardation, and caenogenesis (embryonic and larval adaptations not affecting the adult). It is illuminating and instructive to compare de Beer's "descriptive historical" account with the "causal analytic" account given by Goldschmidt (1940, 341 ff.). The convergence of concepts is evident and striking.

Thus the most important effect that embryological work has had on morphological thinking is the altered notion of the mechanics underlying morphological change. Morphologists a generation ago were thinking in terms of the transformation of an *adult* structure in one organism into an *adult* structure in another organism. The assumptions demanded by such an interpretation often strained credulity beyond the breaking point. A far simpler mechanism, consonant with genetical ideas, is supplied by the concept of reaction velocity or "ontogenetic field" development under genetic control. Statisticians deny that profound changes could have arisen as abruptly as postulated by Goldschmidt and have therefore dismissed his theory. It is apparent, however, that evolution via alteration of ontogenetic rates has taken place on lower levels, involving less drastic changes in morphological pattern, and from the standpoint of mechanics this is a quantitative and not a qualitative difference from the type of change suggested by Goldschmidt. In the final analysis, of course, any genetic change can achieve phenotypic expression only via a change in ontogeny.

Important as this interpretation is, however, it fails to get at the core of adaptive evolution. Embryologists may explain post facto the changes in the mechanics of ontogeny that are reflected in an adult adaptation, but evolution demands an explanation of *why* a given course has been followed far more than it demands detailed clarification of the course actually followed.

IV. VERTEBRATE PALEONTOLOGY AND COMPARATIVE ANATOMY

Vertebrate paleontology is comparative osteology in the time dimension. What is implied in this statement? First, that paleontological data are essentially limited to a single *morphological* system, the skeleton.[3] And second, that paleontologists have at their disposal a succession of samples of this one system extending backward into time. The factual data of vertebrate paleontology therefore relate to (1) the actual rate of change in the skeleton, and (2) the pattern of phyletic change in the skeleton. All other factors, both as to organism and as to environment, must largely be inferred.

Comparative osteology is one of the several subdivisions of comparative anatomy, and this suggests a critical reexamination of the relationships between paleontology and comparative anatomy.

Subdivisions of the Organism

An organism can be subdivided into systems on the basis of several widely different criteria. The classical division into morphological systems (skeletal, muscular, circulatory, etc.) has logical validity and is a convenient subdivision for practical study. No one today believes that these various systems evolved as separate entities, however, although such a view is implied in much of the comparative anatomy of the past century. With equal propriety the organism can be divided into physiological systems, and such a division is useful for certain types of study. This criterion has the additional merit of associating tissues on a functional

---

[3] In some cases data are available on individual variation in the skeleton. Brain casts give information on the evolution of the brain, but still via the skeleton. The dentition is functionally a part of the digestive system. These exceptions, however, do not alter the generalization.

basis, regardless of their topographical relations, as is admirably illustrated by the endocrine system.

A division on the basis of the major functions of the organism is also possible, involving such basic activities as locomotion, nutrition, reproduction, and self-defense. In the end, each of such functional systems involves the whole organism, and finally not only the organism but the organism plus its environment. It is obvious that it is these functional systems as wholes that were subjected to selection during evolution, and not their component parts. It is logically inconsistent to speak of the "evolution of the dentition," for example, unless it is kept firmly in mind that the teeth are an integral part, quite artificially segregated for purposes of study, of the nutrition apparatus of the organism as a whole. This seeming truism deserves emphasis because the arbitrary nature of the segregation is all too often lost sight of.

The neobiologist's knowledge of the structure, functioning, activities, and environmental relationships of members of the contemporary fauna is potentially unlimited. It can embrace the total existing fauna in one direction and can extend down to the very molecules of the individual in the other. Of the history of these organisms he knows nothing, except what paleontology can tell him of the history of their skeletons plus what can be inferred by comparing "primitive" with "specialized" forms. The paleontologist, by contrast, must infer the major part of each functional system, the functioning of those systems, and the conditions under which they functioned. These limitations are extremely severe, often insurmountable. The difficulty is dramatically illustrated in the case of forms that have no existing counterparts or of lines that died out completely. The chalicotheres, to cite a single example, were perissodactyl ungulates with an undistinguished ungulate dentition and huge claws on the feet, a combination not found in any existing mammal. Numerous careful studies by competent students have failed to produce any even remotely probable explanation of the biology of these animals. Yet they were no more bizarre than many existing types are.

It is evident not only that the paleontologist and the comparative anatomist are studying evolutionary phenomena in different dimensions, one in time and the other in space, but also that their basic data differ. The two dimensions are by no means wholly complementary. The comparative anatomist has at his disposal a complete cross section of a given moment in time, containing all the results of evolution as of that moment. He likewise has available all the factors, both organismic and environmental, that are contributing to evolution as of that moment. The paleontologist has threads of this cross section, disconnected and fragmentary because of deficiencies in the record and further limited by being restricted to a single morphological system, extending backward into time. Both depend upon observation of the static results of evolution for inferring the dynamic processes of evolution, but the inferences differ, sometimes in scope and sometimes in nature.

Paleontology and Evolution

Paleontology is unique in being a factual record, however defective, of evolution. This record reveals, as Simpson (1944, 1946) has emphasized, that evolution is gradual, that it is often sustained and directional, that progressive adaptation is typical, and that major adaptations often appear suddenly. These are major features of the mode of evolution that could hardly have been demonstrated in any other way, and it is curious that it was precisely these facts that were largely responsible for the antagonism that long existed between genetics and paleontology. Only recently have attempts to reconcile such empirical paleontological facts with the data of genetics met with approval from both sides.

Neo-Darwinism, with its emphasis on environmental selection of small mutations as the directing force in evolution, explained most of these evolutionary modes to the satisfaction of nearly all paleontologists. The sudden emergence of major adaptive types, as seen in the abrupt appearance in the fossil record of families and orders, continued to give trouble. The phenomenon lay in the genetical no man's land beyond the limits of experimentation. A few paleontologists even today cling to the idea that these gaps will be closed by further collecting, i.e. that they are accidents of sampling; but most regard the observed discontinuities as real and have sought an explanation for them.

The origin of new adaptive types, as opposed to their subsequent evolution, is the crux of the whole adaptation question, whether from the standpoint of paleontology or of neobiology. This fact has been clearly recognized by paleontologists for a decade. Two attempts, in some respects from widely different viewpoints, have been made to extend genetical concepts to cover them.

Schindewolf (1936) was influenced by the concept of "morphological types" of the neo-classical morphologists. These basic patterns obviously correspond to the complexes of morphological features characterizing the taxonomic categories, from phyla down to genera (logically to species and even subspecies). The observed discontinuities between these patterns led many German morphologists in the 1930's to question the validity of the evolutionary theory, or to limit its operation to the confines of a given morphological type. These limits were drawn by different authors at various levels: at phyla, at classes, in extreme cases even at genera. Schindewolf noted that the morphological discontinuities correspond to the observed discontinuities in the fossil record, which he accepted as representing abrupt transitions from one major adaptive type to another, rather than as deficiencies of record. He suggested that new morphological types (new major adaptive types, in current terminology) stemming from such discontinuities are attributable to disturbances in ontogenetic processes, which can produce abrupt and profound changes in adult organization. He argued that such changes would occasionally, by chance, produce a form that was basically preadapted to a new way of life, and that this basic type would then be "shaped" or "perfected" (ausgestaltet) by selection. According to this view transitional stages between one basic type and another never existed, since the fundamental determining features of the new type arise instantaneously during ontogeny. Schindewolf postulated two successive phases in the origin of a new adaptive type: "(1) a usually short phase of discontinuous, explosive origin of types, and (2) a succeeding, usually longer phase of continuous, gradual, orthogenetic shaping of the type complex." With respect to environmental relationships these are designated "preadaptive" and "adaptive" phases. A mechanism capable of producing changes in the manner postulated, through alteration of ontogenetic processes, has been demonstrated experimentally (see above). Schindewolf's theory is practically identical with that of Goldschmidt.

Nearly a decade later, Simpson (1944) attempted another synthesis of paleontological and genetical data, utilizing the newer concepts of population genetics as developed especially by Wright. Simpson rejected any method of saltatory evolution as an important evolutionary factor[4] and embraced the completely neo-Darwinian thesis of Wright (1941b) that new adaptive types normally arise via the action of strong selection pressure on small mutations. Simpson describes the typical pattern for such a change in adaptive direction as follows: ". . . a large population is fragmented into numerous small isolated[5] lines of descent. Within these, inadaptive differentiation and random fixation of mutations occur. Among many such inadaptive lines, one or a few are preadaptive, i.e. some of their characters tend to fit them for available ecological stations quite different from those occupied by their immediate ancestors. Such groups are subjected to strong selection pressure and evolve rapidly in the further direction of adaptation to the new status. The very few lines that success-

[4] Simpson's list of the various means by which saltation might occur (p. 52) does not include the most likely of all, mutations affecting developmental velocities, and there is no evidence that he has considered it. This is one of the weakest points in his whole argument. Origin of the "raw materials" for the higher categories via this means is the core of the theories of Schindewolf, Goldschmidt, and most recent embryologists. It certainly deserves more consideration than it has been given by geneticists.

[5] Wright (1945) points out that mutation rate is the limiting factor if small populations are completely isolated, but that if numerous small populations are not quite isolated, there is available "an enormous store of potential, easily available but not actually manifested, variability," and the mutation rate can then be largely ignored.

fully achieve this perfected adaptation then become abundant and expand widely at the same time becoming differentiated and specialized on lower levels within the broad new ecological zone." Thus the origin of a new adaptive type (Simpson's "quantum evolution") involves three successive phases: (1) an inadaptive phase, during which the population loses its former adaptive equilibrium with its environment, (2) a preadaptive phase, during which the population moves toward a new equilibrium, and (3) an adaptive phase, during which a new equilibrium is reached. Simpson admits the possibility of preadaptation arising in the absence of any positive inadaptation (which would virtually eliminate phase 1) and becoming fixed through a threshold effect of selection pressure.

These two views have long been argued back and forth as contrasting and more or less mutually exclusive explanations of major evolutionary phenomena. It is usually urged that one postulates discontinuous saltatory origin of new adaptive types, the other transition from one type to another by a continuous process occurring at extremely rapid but finite rates. Both agree that, once initiated, adaptation is carried on by selection. Thus disagreement actually involves only the initial preadaptive phase. But any mutation or combination of mutations is discontinuous too, and therefore the question is merely as to the magnitude or degree of the initial preadaptation visualized in the two systems. Geneticists often assume that the "new type" referred to by morphologists is a fully equipped new form, that the first bird quite literally hatched from a reptile egg, and have with reason ridiculed such an idea. Schindewolf (among others) has pointed out, however, that it is the *determining* features, the basic structure or combination of structures deciding the direction of the new adaptive type, that are postulated. What is actually visualized is a morphological threshold effect. The magnitude of the initial change would vary from situation to situation (in some cases a very trivial morphological change would suffice), and the subsequent shaping or perfecting of the type follows by selection, perhaps interspersed with further saltatory changes. This view is hardly distinguishable from Simpson's concept of "quantum evolution"; indeed the analogy with the quanta of the physical sciences is even closer. It is true that morphologists have not thought in terms of populations, but in my opinion the final convergence of the ideas evolved by population geneticists and evolutionary morphologists is astonishingly complete. Disagreement can be attributed far more to mutual failure to understand concepts and terms than to differences in views.

Paleontology and Adaptation

More important than any fundamental similarity between the views of Schindewolf and those of Simpson is the fact that neither was derived from the data of paleontology. Each has taken a theory derived from neobiological data and superimposed it, so to speak, on the data of paleontology. The fact that the observed data of paleontology conform with the neobiological theory enhances the probable validity of the theory, and certainly no theory that does not so conform can be accepted. But the facts of paleontology conform equally well with other interpretations that have been discredited by neobiological work, e.g. divine creation, innate developmental processes, Lamarckism, etc., and paleontology by itself can neither prove nor refute such ideas.

The neo-Darwinian school, by emphasizing the role of selection on variations in populations, interprets evolution as a process of adaptation going on at various ecological levels. But adaptation can be demonstrated in fossil material only by the most oblique means. A few groups of living vertebrates (e.g. horses, elephants) have long well-documented histories of rectilinear evolution. The extant survivors show a high degree of adaptation and morphological specialization. Since the fossils indicate that the group was evolving in this direction during most or all of its history it is extremely probable that the history of the group is one of increasingly close adaptation. Non-skeletal (and even non-morphological) conditions, as known among the survivors, can be projected back along the evolutionary line, but with probability decreasing as the lineage recedes into time. In other cases, where there are no survivors, paleontologists infer by analogy with unrelated living forms that morphological specialization denotes adaptation, although the nature of the adaptation may be (and usually is) wholly unknown. Finally, in the case of forms that show no particular morphological specialization, it is inferred (again by analogy with similar but unrelated living forms) that some sort of adaptation did exist.

Adaptation can be studied to advantage only when the complex organism-environment interrelationship can be studied, even though from the evolutionary standpoint it is the morphological specialization of the organism that is of chief interest. The skeleton, recent or fossil, exhibits a part of the total *morphological change* of the organism, which in turn is only a part of the dynamic relationship that is adaptation. Evolution is measured in terms of morphological change, however, rather than in terms of dynamic relationships, and thus interest is ultimately in the agencies producing such changes. In the final analysis evolution is (except possibly on the very lowest levels) a shift in the direction or level of adaptation. The factors initiating such shifts are rarely, if ever, subject to fossilization, and here the paleontologist must depend upon the neobiologist. We have seen that both genetics and embryology supply some, but not all, of the required data. Paleontology supplies vitally important data on the rates and direction of (supposedly) adaptive changes. But none of the fields so far mentioned, nor all together, reveals how these various organismic and environmental factors have operated in specific cases to produce a new direction of morphological specialization.

V. Adaptation and Comparative Anatomy

One of the greatest biological controversies centers around the role of adaptation in evolution. The most casual examination of the literature shows, however, that differences of opinion are confined almost entirely to the question of adaptation at the lowest taxonomic levels, the subspecies and species. This is the level at which the tremendously active experimental attack on evolutionary problems is being carried on, and for this reason the controversy assumes an importance that is largely fictitious. Among the higher vertebrate categories adaptation is an empirical fact, and here the problem is not whether adaptation exists, but how and why adaptations arose, and what part they have played in evolution.

There can be no doubt that unadaptive (neutral), and even adverse, characters can arise in and spread through breeding populations, nor can there be much doubt that many of the morphological characters used to distinguish subspecies are of this type. It is equally obvious, however, that the basic morphology of most and probably all vertebrate orders, such as the rodents, the carnivores, or the hawks and falcons, is in each case a major adaptation to a particular way of life. And the basic functional adaptation of the cats or the eagles, for example, must either have started as a minimal departure from the parent stock, or have appeared suddenly, essentially full-blown.

The Nature of Adaptation

Adaptation means many things to many different people. Both Lamarck and Darwin regarded adaptation as indicated in any change in the structure of an animal that better fitted it to its organic or inorganic environment. Thus a general increase in the efficiency of an animal is an adaptation. Gegenbaur defined adaptation as "gradual, but steadily progressive, changes in the organisation," which is equivalent to Julian Huxley's "evolutionary progress"—the all-around improvement in functional efficiency that is implied in the terms "lower" and "higher." Experimental embryologists, since Roux's attempt to extend the concept of natural selection to a "struggle of the parts" in the developing organism, have spoken of "adaptation" of the developing parts to the roles they are destined to play in the mature individual. This is akin to the physiologists' definition of adaptation as the adjustment of one part of the organism to other parts.

Modern evolutionary biologists define adaptation in various ways, usually emphasizing the "fitness" between the organism and its environment. Such definitions are accurate as far as they go, but they lack the preciseness, especially the quantitative exactness, that is required of a genuinely usable concept. This has led to attempts to demonstrate the existence and degree of adaptation by various oblique and logically invalid criteria, such as increase in numbers relative to supposedly worse adapted forms (Gause) or by the "power conferred over the environment" (Robson and Richards, 1936, p. 353).

Population geneticists (Wright, 1932, 1937; Simpson, 1944) have emphasized the adaptive aspect of the population-environment relationship. Wright visualizes the genetic structure of a population as a number of adaptive peaks separated by inadaptive valleys, with selection tending to keep the population closely clustered around the adaptive peaks. Simpson, on the other hand, has emphasized the environmental aspect of the relationship, visualizing the environment as a set of discontinuous adaptive zones and subzones into which populations can deploy under the guidance of natural selection. These are useful concepts for establishing general principles of adaptation. They reduce the unmanageable facts of adaptive relations to a system that is amenable to statistical analysis. But at supraspecific levels adaptation almost invariably involves gross morphological, physiological, and psychological specializations. Interest is accordingly focused on the adapted organism (as a sample of the adapted population), rather than on the genetic structure of the population or on the environment to which the population is adapted. For example, statistical treatment would be required to demonstrate the differential adaptive value of a character in subspecies of *Peromyscus,* but any rodent individual would exhibit the basic morphological adaptation of the order Rodentia. A method of defining adaptation from the standpoint of the organism which would complement the environmental concept and supplement the mathematical models is clearly needed if adaptation is to be studied from the standpoint of functional morphology.

By implication (though to my knowledge it has never been so expressed), most modern biologists regard adaptation as exemplified in any deviation from the basic plan of any taxonomic category when such deviation is associated with some special and characteristic mode of life. The "basic plan"[6] logically includes not only the morphology but also the physiology and psychology of the unit—in short, the total biology. Thus adaptation is actually a hierarchy of increasingly restricted or less inclusive features as we move down the scale from class to species. This may be illustrated by selecting one (out of the many) adaptive feature at each level of a taxonomic sequence. Homoiothermy is an adaptation within the phylum Chordata, appearing in the classes Aves and Mammalia. Carnassial teeth

[6] The concept of the basic plan has been developed chiefly by the German morphologists, who refer to it as the "type." Choice of the term *type* is unfortunate because of its very different and much older use by taxonomists.

involving P^4 and M_I are an adaptation within the class Mammalia, appearing in the suborder Fissipedia of the order Carnivora. Remodelling of these carnassial teeth into flat-crowned crushing teeth is an adaptation within the order Carnivora, appearing in the family Ursidae. Reduction of the entire dental battery, in correlation with fish-eating habits, is an adaptation within the family Ursidae, appearing in the genus *Thalarctos* (the polar bear). *Thalarctos* also exhibits all the more inclusive adaptations of modified carnassial teeth and homoiothermy, but none of these is a polar bear adaptation.

The basic morphological plan can be determined at any taxonomic level (Naef, 1919; Kälin, 1935, 1941) for an organ, an organ system, or the total organism. The direction and magnitude of any deviation from the basic plan can likewise be determined and measured quantitatively. This, of course, is a valid measure of adaptation only if a close correlation can be demonstrated between environmental relations and these deviations from the norm. At any supergeneric level such a correlation can probably be safely assumed in most if not all cases because of the generally adaptive nature of superspecific variation. Many mechanical and physiological relations are amenable to experimental analysis, and their functional importance, if not their adaptive value, can be measured directly. But the convergent appearance of similar conditions in more or less remotely related organisms under similar or identical environmental conditions is the most readily available proof of adaptive value. Hence the shift of morphological interest from homology to analogy.

Embryological processes and psychological and physiological traits are doubtless subject to the same adaptive hierarchy, although existing technics do not permit its demonstration. Logically they cannot be divorced from morphology in the complex factors that combine to make up adaptation from the standpoint of the organism.

The greatest difficulty in the way of studying adaptation as an evolutionary phenomenon of the organism (except in the restricted sense possible in the few adequately documented cases of progressive adaptation known to paleontology) has long been the lack of any valid method of estimating degree of adaptation. If degree of divergence from an established norm is a valid criterion of degree of adaptation, then it should be an extremely useful tool for attacking this most obvious but at the same time most refractory of evolutionary phenomena.

The Origin of Adaptations

Adaptations may appear at any taxonomic level, and obviously not all adaptations are of equal value or have the same prospective outlook. Wright (1941a) proposed a useful distinction between *adaptations of general importance*, which relax selective processes that have previously restrained variation and so set the stage for deployment into numerous environmental niches via selection for accessory mechanisms; and *specializing adaptations*, which have the reverse effect of restricting selection. It can be determined only *a posteriori* to which of these categories a given adaptation belongs. The basic rodent adaptation was obviously a tremendously successful adaptation of general importance, and the basic adaptation of the anteaters an equally successful specializing adaptation.[7] On the other hand, the basic specialization of the snakes would surely appear *a priori* to be a specializing adaptation, but actually it has been exploited almost as successfully as that of the rodents. In general, though by no means invariably, adaptations of general importance are associated with classes and orders, and specializing adaptations with families, genera, and occasionally species.

Neo-classical morphologists have emphasized the deep-seated permeating morphological individuality of classes, orders, families etc., each within the framework of the next higher category. This they express in the term "morphological type." The Rodentia, for example, are not merely mammals supplied with chisel-like incisor teeth, nor are they a conglomeration of "diagnostic characters." Rather the Rodentia, like any other mammalian order, represent a recasting of the features of the class Mammalia. Neo-Darwinians, on the other hand, have emphasized the fact that each of such categories is equipped to exploit a major adaptive zone, and would regard the numerous supposedly neutral or non-adaptive morphological features associated with each category as an incidental result of genetic divergence. The crucial point in any theory of adaptation is the origin of a new adaptive type, which is an essentially discontinuous process, usually involving an abrupt change in direction of adaptation. Practically all students of evolution agree in recognizing an element of real or seeming discontinuity in the origin of a major adaptation.

Disregarding the frankly metaphysical explanations of Böker, Beurlen, and others, there are three major theories that attempt to account for this discontinuity. Goldschmidt regards the discontinuities (his "bridgeless gaps") as real, and postulated a special type of "systemic mutation" resulting from chromatin rearrangements to account for them. Waddington and Schindewolf represent a second school that considers the discontinuities as real, but accounts for them via alterations of ontogenetic processes through orthodox mutations. Population geneticists (Wright, Simpson), on the other hand, interpret the discontinuities as artifacts resulting from extremely short and rapid evolution during a phase of

---

[7] Anteaters have survived essentially unchanged since at least the Early Pliocene, and there is no reason to believe that their numerical position ever differed much from the humble one that it is today.

adaptive instability, with a resulting reduced probability that individuals would be observed in this stage.

Comparative Anatomy and the Origin of Adaptations

It was pointed out above that the critical preadaptive phase initiating a new adaptive type would rarely, perhaps never, be accessible to pale-ontologists. It is also unlikely that embryonic changes of the type postulated by some morphologists to account for the origin of radically different adaptive types will be observed, or that they would be recognized if they were observed. It was further pointed out that if the nature of adaptation is to become more than a statistical abstraction it must be verified on individuals as samples of populations.

Naturally, features are not likely to be observed in the actual pre-adaptive phase among existing organisms. Nor would they be likely to be recognized if observed, because a feature is seen to have been preadaptive only after it has become adaptive. But it is entirely possible to segregate preadaptations (but not the order of their appearance if more than one is involved, as is almost invariably the case) by a proper synthesis of morphological, embryological, and ecological evidence. From the morphological side this involves meticulous analysis of deviations from the basic pattern of the taxonomic category to which the adapted type belongs. Such studies offer a rich and almost untouched field for comparative anatomy, and one that can hardly be approached from any other standpoint.

The most promising situation for detecting morphological preadaptation should be in a form or group of related forms showing some specialized habit or other environmental relation that would be reflected in its morphology. The generic or family levels are most likely; at the ordinal or class levels any basic preadaptation would be irretrievably masked by postadaptation, and functionally correlated morphological features are rarely shown by species. A further requirement is that the adapted type belong to a taxonomic group large enough to exhibit a range of morphological variation, i.e. large enough that the basic morphological plan of the group as a whole can be determined. Finally, knowledge of the ecological relations of both the adapted type and its unadapted or differently adapted relatives must be sufficiently intimate and detailed to reveal the functional relations of the preadaptation.

Few comparative anatomists have been thinking along these lines. The most promising and ambitious work (Böker, 1935-1937) is marred by naive neo-Lamarckism and resort to mystical "active" and "passive" forces, although it contains a wealth of useful data. Examination of the scanty pertinent data shows, however, that the origin of a new adaptive type via preadaptation is not a simple mode of evolution, but that the preadaptive threshold may be achieved in several quite different ways. At least five "sub-modes" can be distinguished:

1. *Extension into a generally less favorable environment by selective extension of adaptive features already present in the parent population.* Certain existing adaptive features or combinations of features are pre-adaptive in the new environment and are then enhanced by selection. This is perhaps the commonest but least characteristic type of quantum origin of a new adaptive type. The crucial transition from one adaptation to another, the threshold or "quantum" effect, is least evident.

The case of Weddell's seal (*Leptonychotes weddelli*), which Simpson has cited, is an example of this type. Related seals exhibit a tendency for the upper lateral incisors to become enlarged and canine-like. In *Leptonychotes* this trend is carried further, and these teeth and the canines are used for cutting breathing holes in the ice. This seal is thus able to survive the Antarctic winter beyond latitudes where there are many natural breaks in the ice, and ranges farther south than any other mammal. The emperor penguin (*Aptenodytes forsteri*) provides a parallel case. This bird breeds at the edge of the Antarctic pack ice, where no nesting materials are available and temperatures range down to —80° F. (Murphy, 1936). A complex of adaptive behavioral features makes survival under these rigorous conditions possible, but most of these adaptations are also found in the closely related king penguin (*A. patagonicus*), which is found farther north.

2. *Deployment into a new environmental relation by altering the direction of an existing adaptation.* This mode is particularly useful for explaining the "pre-useful" stages of many adaptations, which have long been a favorite target of non-selectionists and even of non-evolutionists. An adaptive relation, carried forward in a given direction by selection, may quite fortuitously reach a threshold where it is preadaptive for an entirely different adaptive relation. Selection will then begin to operate in the new direction on the basis of features that are preadaptive in the new adaptive relation. The quantum effect is particularly evident in this mode.

No clear-cut examples of this mode are at hand. The origin of the rays from the sharks would theoretically fall in this class. Sharks are wide ranging pelagic forms, free swimming and predaceous. Most rays are littoral and bottom dwelling, feeding largely on inactive prey. The absence of a swim bladder in elasmobranchs conditions the hydrostatics and hydrodynamics, and thus the external morphology, of sharks (Harris, 1936). Some of the features correlated with equilibrium, such as the flattened belly and the fact that sharks must perforce rest on the bottom when they are not in motion, are "preadaptive" in the bottom dwelling littoral adaptive zone, and may have determined an abrupt shift in adaptive direction that culminated in the rays.

The flying lizards of the genus *Draco* are unique among living lizards in having the ribs greatly elongated and supporting a membrane used in gliding from tree to tree. Most arboreal lizards (including those of the family to which *Draco* belongs) have vertically compressed bodies, an adaptive direction quite different from the depressed body form of *Draco*. The body is depressed in many arboreal geckos, however, and these animals habitually mold themselves to a branch when at rest. In some geckos there are fringes along the sides of the body that efface the shadow of the resting animal. Such a condition can be visualized as reaching a threshold stage for gliding flight, thus precipitating an abrupt shift in adaptive direction. An entirely different, superimposed effect is seen in *Draco*, in the secondary use of the highly colored flight membrane for courtship display (Schmidt, 1935).

The ocean sunfishes (Molidae) are remarkably specialized, apparently for bottom feeding at great depths. The body is greatly shortened and deepened; the caudal fin has completely disappeared, and locomotion is by means of the hypertrophied dorsal and anal fins. The lateralis mass of metameric musculature, which composes 90% of the weight of a typical fish, has been entirely lost. Its locomotor function has been taken over by the erector and depressor muscles of the dorsal and anal fins, and these muscles are correspondingly hypertrophied (Raven, 1939a). One of the molids (*Ranzania*) has secondarily become elongated into a fast-swimming form, and its erector and depressor musculature and skeleton are further modified (Raven, 1939b). As Amadon (1943) has pointed out, it is entirely conceivable that the new pattern of musculature might give *Ranzania* a competitive advantage over other fishes with the old metameric musculature, with the result that molids would differentiate rapidly by displacing other fishes in various ecological zones. Similar examples of representatives of a group highly specialized in one direction re-invading another ecological zone via a morphological pattern radically different from the typical occupants of that zone are numerous. In the giant panda, for example, the carnivore morphology, with its numerous specializations, has been adapted to a completely herbivorous diet. And the tree kangaroos (*Dendrolagus*) represent a successful re-invasion of the arboreal environment by the extraordinarily specialized kangaroo stock.

3. *Deployment into new environmental relations when a neutral (fortuitous?) morphological structure is preadaptive.* A morphological feature or combination of features, of neutral selective value or carried in combination with other positively valuable features, becomes preadaptive under certain circumstances or in certain morphological and/or psychological combinations. When this adaptive threshold is reached, an abrupt shift in direction of adaptation ensues.

The thrashers (*Toxostoma*) show a marked tendency toward ground foraging, in contrast with the feeding habits of other mockingbirds. In the less specialized thrashers, this involves pecking, poking, and hammering the bill into the ground, while the more specialized forms habitually tunnel insects out of the ground. Certain peculiarities of the pterygoid musculature, common to all mimids, are apparently preadaptive for the digging habit of thrashers; strengthening and lengthening of the flexor muscles of the head and neck appear in all thrashers, and may be considered preadaptive for the tunneling behavior of the more specialized forms (Engels, 1940).

In the Carnivora the panniculus carnosus muscle inserts in the axilla, along with the pectoral musculature, as in other mammals. The mustelids (weasels and their allies) differ from all other carnivores in having a slip of the panniculus pass to the outer surface of the upper arm. No functional advantage can be assigned to this mustelid aberration. In the badger (*Taxidea*), which is a powerful burrowing mustelid, this slip is larger, ties the elbow down to the body, and inserts on the acromion process of the scapula. It thus aids in tying the scapula down, an important consideration in the absence of a clavicle. The condition of the panniculus in other mustelids is obviously preadaptive for the functional arrangement in the badger (Davis, unpublished).

4. *Mutations with conspicuous effects resulting from an alteration of relatively early ontogenetic processes* could conceivably produce a new type basically preadapted to a radically different ecological zone. Such a preadaptation would be an example of Goldschmidt's "hopeful monster." Despite the demands on chance involved, as compared with other modes of preadaptation, this mode cannot be disregarded entirely as a theoretical possibility. Among vertebrates at least, no examples are known that are not sheer speculations, explainable in alternative ways.

5. *Deployment into a generally less favorable environment as a result of predisposition.* Features that are neutral or even disadvantageous in one environment may be wholly neutral in another environment, into which the population is forced by competition, population pressure, or accidental transport. Preadaptation is negative in this mode, and positively adaptive features may secondarily arise in the new adaptive zone.

The cave fishes of Yucatan belong to four separate families, and thus represent a minimum of four incursions into this environment. All show various degrees of loss of eyes and pigment and increased development of tactile and other sense organs. In each case it can be shown that the cave forms were derived from non-cave dwelling forms that are nocturnal, burrowing, or crevice-seeking (Hubbs, 1938). These ancestral forms already have weakened vision and seemingly compensatory development of tactile and other senses, and often breeding habits suitable to reproduction in total darkness. Hubbs concludes that "only preadapted strays, if any, have evolved into typical cave forms."

Beurlen earlier (1931) came to exactly the same conclusions regarding the origin of deep-sea decapod crustaceans. He showed that during the geological history of this group only those that were preadapted to life in the deep sea were able to colonize this environment. Others fled to fresh water or to land, or became extinct when the littoral zone decreased. Preadaptation, supposedly evolved among mud inhabitants of the shallow-water zone, involved reduced eyes, elongate antennae, and reduced mouth parts (for detritus feeding).

All the examples cited above are at the generic, subgeneric, or specific levels. Nearly all (only the two Antarctic examples have not) have differentiated further on lower levels within the new adaptive zone, indicating that they are not examples of the severely specializing adaptations leading to monotypic families and genera.

It is, of course, improbable that differentiation at specific or generic levels is invariably, perhaps not even typically, adaptive, even among vertebrates. The characters used to distinguish many snake genera, for example, such as a single vs. a divided anal plate, are surely not adaptive, although these may merely represent the most conspicuous, not the most important, differences, and the less conspicuous differences may be adaptive. It is suggestive that the very few generalized forms that have been studied adequately do show divergent adaptive trends at these low levels, although these often resemble phyletic rather than quantum evolution. Howell (1926), for example, found such adaptive trends in the subgenera of the woodrat *Neotoma*, which is a very generalized cricetine rodent.

It is evident that quantum evolution, involving a typical threshold or "quantum" effect, is common even at the lower (macro-evolutionary, as opposed to mega-evolutionary) levels, where it may be studied to advantage on existing forms.

Population geneticists have postulated a condition of ecological disequilibrium (the "inadaptive phase") as the normal situation in which, through a process of trial and error, random mutations or combinations of mutations achieve a preadaptive status. Simpson (1944, p. 211) admits the possibility of preadaptation arising in the absence of any positive inadaptation (disequilibrium), but assigns to this a lesser role. But none of the examples given here suggests an inadaptive phase, although the threshold effect is evident in each. It seems likely that the supposed inadaptive phase is actually adaptive in some other direction oftener than population geneticists believe, i.e. that it is "inadaptive" only with reference to the adaptive relation that develops later.

The scanty data suggest that in many cases adaptation may be a succession of sudden, somewhat erratic, shifts in adaptive direction. This would produce an overall pattern quite different from the orthoselective pattern displayed, apparently at least, by many examples of phyletic evolution. In no instance do such shifts involve an inadaptive phase. The pattern appears rather to be: a structure, or combination of structures, carried forward in a given adaptive direction by selection, occasionally achieves a preadaptive threshold that permits selection to begin operating in a new adaptive direction. Each shift in direction sets the stage for the next shift, and little or no disequilibrium is involved.

VI. Summary and Conclusions

1. The phylogenetic comparative anatomy of the nineteenth century aimed at documenting the concept of *evolutionary progress* and thus demonstrating the fact of evolution. The truth of evolution was proved conclusively by paleontology, however, which has the tremendous advantage of being an actual time record. The phenomenon of evolutionary progress is farthest removed from the basic mechanics of evolution, and this type of comparative anatomy cannot contribute effectively to neo-Darwinian study of adaptive evolution.

2. Twentieth century comparative anatomy is divided between two main schools: (a) a neo-classical school of pure morphology attempting to prove that the "morphological type" of a given taxonomic category is its most basic quality, and (b) a school that regards morphology as merely the most tangible product of the dynamic organism-environment relationship, expressed in structural adaptation.

3. Neo-Darwinism has focused attention on adaptation, not only at the population and subspecies levels but also at the higher levels of families, orders, etc. The origin of new major adaptive types, such as characterize the higher taxonomic categories, is the most controversial feature of neo-Darwinian evolution.

4. The mathematical models of population geneticists are abstract generalizations of how such major adaptations may have arisen. Existing statistical techniques cannot, however, demonstrate how a specific adaptive relation has arisen.

5. Discoveries in physiological genetics and embryology have greatly simplified interpretations of the mechanisms underlying many kinds of morphological change. These interpretations have profoundly altered morphological thinking, but they relate to the mechanics of evolution only in so far as they imply revaluation of the raw materials on which natural selection can act.

6. Paleontology supplies factual data on the actual rates of change *in the skeleton* and the patterns of phyletic change in the skeleton. Because of the inherent limitations of paleontological data, however, it cannot

perceive the factors producing such changes. Attempts to do so merely represent a superimposition of neobiological concepts on paleontological data.

7. The hierarchies of "morphological types" of neo-classical morphology supply a set of norms against which morphological deviation can be measured. If such deviations are adaptive, as implied by neo-Darwinism, then it is possible to measure direction and relative amount of morphological adaptation.

8. Quantitative measurement of morphological deviation can be combined with analysis of the environmental relations of the organism. The morphological features peculiar to the adaptive relation are thus isolated. In some cases, at least, a hierarchy of successive morphological deviations, each dependent on what has gone before, can be demonstrated.

9. Existing data permit analysis of only a handful of specific cases, but these indicate that (a) the preliminary inadaptive phase of adaptive evolution that is postulated by population geneticists is not generally evident, and (b) adaptive evolution is often a succession of sudden shifts in adaptive direction, apparently resulting from attainment of a succession of adaptive thresholds.

REFERENCES

Amadon, Dean. 1943. Specialization and evolution. *Amer. Nat.*, 77, 133-141.

de Beer, G. R. 1940. *Embryos and Ancestors*. Oxford, Clarendon Press; x, 108 p., 18 figs.

Beurlen, K. 1931. Die Besiedlung der Tiefsee. *Natur und Mus.*, 61, 269-278, 11 figs.

——. 1937. *Die stammesgeschichtlichen Grundlagen der Abstammungslehre*. Jena, Fischer, viii, 264 p.

Böker, Hans. 1935-37. *Einführung in die vergleichende biologische Anatomie der Wirbeltiere*. Jena, Fischer; v.I, xi, 228 p., 225 figs.; v.II, xi, 258 p., 260 figs.

Butler, P. M. 1939. Studies of the mammalian dentition. Differentiation of the postcanine dentition. *Proc. Zool. Soc. London*, (B) 109, 1-36, 28 figs.

——. 1946. The evolution of carnassial dentitions in the Mammalia. *Proc. Zool. Soc. London*, 116, 198-220, 13 figs.

Engels, W. L. 1940. Structural adaptations in thrashers (Mimidae: genus *Toxostoma*) with comments on interspecific relationships. *Univ. Calif. Publ. Zool.*, 42, 341-400, 24 figs.

Franz, V. 1927. Ontogenie und Phylogenie. *Abh. Theorie Org. Entw.*, 3, 1-51.

Gegenbaur, Carl. 1878. *Elements of Comparative Anatomy* (translated by F. J. Bell). London, Macmillan; xxvi, 645 p., 356 figs.

——. 1898-1901. *Vergleichende Anatomie der Wirbeltiere*. 2 Vols. Leipzig, Engelmann; xiv, 978 p., 619 figs.; viii, 696 p., 355 figs.

Goldschmidt, Richard. 1927. *Physiologische Theorie der Vererbung*. Berlin, Springer; vi, 247 p., 59 figs.

——. 1940. *The Material Basis of Evolution*. New Haven, Yale Univ. Press; xi, 436 p., 83 figs.

Haldane, J. B. S. 1932. The time of action of genes, and its bearing on some evolutionary problems. *Amer. Nat.*, 66, 5-24.

Harris, J. E. 1936. The role of the fins in the equilibrium of the swimming fish.

I. Wind-tunnel tests on a model of *Mustelus canis* (Mitchill). *Jour. Exp. Biol.*, *13*, 476-493, 8 figs.

Howell, A. B. 1926. *Anatomy of the wood rat. Comparative anatomy of the subgenera of the American wood rat (genus Neotoma)*. Baltimore, Williams & Wilkins; x, 225 p., 37 figs., 3 pl.

Hubbs, C. L. 1938. Fishes from the caves of Yucatan. *Carnegie Inst. Wash. Publ.*, *491*, 261-295, 4 pl.

Huxley, J. S. 1942. *Evolution, the Modern Synthesis*. New York, Harper; 645 p.

Kälin, J. 1935. Ueber einige Grundbegriffe in der vergleichende Anatomie und ihre Bedeutung für die Erforschung der Baupläne im Tierreich. *C. R. 12th. Congr. Int. Zool.*, Lisbon, p. 647-664, 1 fig.

——. 1941. *Ganzheitliche Morphologie und Homologie*. Freiburg (Schweiz); Universitätsbuchhandlung; 1-41, 4 figs.

Murphy, R. C. 1936. *Oceanic Birds of South America*. Vol. 1, New York: Amer. Mus. Nat. Hist.; xxii, 640 p., illus.

Naef, Adolf. 1919. *Idealistische Morphologie und Phylogenetik*. Jena, Fischer; vi, 77 p., 4 figs.

——. 1931. Die Gestalt als Begriff und Idee. In: Bolk, Göppert, Kallius, Lubosch, *Handbuch der vergleichenden Anatomie der Wirbeltiere*, Vol. 1, p. 77-118, figs. 5-12. Berlin, Urban & Schwarzenberg.

Raven, H. C. 1939a. On the anatomy and evolution of the locomotor apparatus of the nipple-tailed ocean sunfish (*Masturus lanceolatus*). *Bull. Amer. Mus. Nat. Hist.*, *76*, 143-150, pl. 2.

——. 1939b. Notes on the anatomy of *Ranzania truncata*. *Amer. Mus. Nov.*, *1038*, 1-7, 3 figs.

Robson, G. C., and O. W. Richards. 1936. *The Variation of Animals in Nature*. London, Longmans, Green; xvi, 425 p., 30 figs., 2 pl.

Sawin, P. B. 1945. Morphogenetic studies of the rabbit. I. Regional specificity of hereditary factors affecting homoeotic variations in the axial skeleton. *Jour. Exper. Zool.*, *100*, 301-329, 3 figs.

——. 1946. Morphogenetic studies of the rabbit. III. Skeletal variations resulting from the interaction of gene determined growth forces. *Anat. Rec.*, *96*, 183-200, 3 figs.

Sawin, P. B., and I. B. Hull. 1946. Morphogenetic studies of the rabbit. II. Evidence of regionally specific hereditary factors influencing the extent of the lumbar region. *Jour. Morph.*, *78*, 1-26, 6 figs.

Schindewolf, O. H. 1936. *Paläontologie, Entwicklungslehre und Genetik*. Berlin, Borntraeger; v, 108 p., 34 figs.

Schmidt, K. P. 1935. Notes on the breeding behavior of lizards. *Field Mus. Nat. Hist.*, *Zool. Ser.*, *20*, 71-76, figs. 4-6.

Sewertzoff, A. N. 1931. *Morphologische Gesetzmässigkeiten der Evolution*. Jena, Fischer; xiv, 371 p., 131 figs.

Simpson, G. G. 1944. *Tempo and Mode in Evolution*. New York, Columbia Univ. Press; xviii, 237 p., 36 figs.

——. 1946. Tempo and mode in evolution. *Trans. N.Y. Acad. Sci.*, (2) 8, 45-60.

Waddington, C. H. 1941. Evolution of developmental systems. *Nature*, *147*, 108-110.

Washburn, S. L. 1943. The sequence of epiphyseal union in Old World monkeys. *Amer. Jour. Anat.*, *72*, 339-360.

——. 1946. The sequence of epiphyseal union in the opossum. *Anat. Rec.*, *95*, 353-363.

Wright, Sewall. 1932. The roles of mutation, inbreeding, crossbreeding, and selection in evolution. *Proc. 6th Internat. Congr. Gen.*, *1*, 356-366, 1 fig.

——. 1937. The distribution of gene frequencies in populations. *Proc. Nat. Acad. Sci.*, *23*, 307-320, 9 figs.

——. 1941a. The "age and area" concept extended. *Ecology*, *22*, 345-347.

——. 1941b. The material basis of evolution. *Sci. Mon.*, *53*, 165-170.

——. 1945. Tempo and mode in evolution: a critical review. *Ecology*, *26*, 415-419.

· 6 ·

SOME ASPECTS OF PLANT MORPHOLOGY
AND EVOLUTION

BY THEODOR JUST[1]

THE spectacular rise and development of modern genetics and the renewed interest in evolution promptly invite comparison with the attainments of the older biological sciences. The "new systematics" clearly shows what may be expected from such a comparison and reorientation. But has the "new morphology" been integrated with related fields to the same extent and with equally promising results, or is Berry (1945) correct in speaking about the "predicament of morphology" and in castigating the "folkways" of morphology?

FLORAL MORPHOLOGY

It has long been customary to distinguish between an old, idealistic, classical, pure (typological) or pre-evolutionary morphology and a new, dynamic (experimental), evolutionary (applied) or phylogenetic morphology (Arber, 1937; Bancroft, 1935; Thomas, 1933; Troll, 1935; Zimmermann, 1930; Zündorf, 1940). While the former is to all intents and purposes synonymous with comparative morphology using essentially contemporaneous plants, the latter aims to determine the true relationships of all living and fossil plant groups, even experimentally as far as possible. The more important viewpoints may be illustrated by those advanced in the interpretation of the angiosperm flower. The following scheme readily suggests the complexity of the problem and records the varied lines of investigation pursued to date. One group is conveniently referred to as (1) *neoclassical*, for the variants placed here are direct descendants of the old morphology and essentially descriptive or anatomical in character; they are the typological approach (or Gestalt morphology), organography, and carpel polymorphism; the second group is here called (2) *phylogenetic* and includes the theory of reduced branching systems (telome theory), the caytonialean theory, the bennettitalean theory, the gnetalean theory, etc.; the third group has been called "developmental" and is really (3) *ontogenetic* or histogenetic. Three theories should be mentioned here, the theory of the fundamental difference between vegetative and reproductive apices, the theory of acarpy or of the complete absence of carpels in the inferior ovary, and the theory of physiomorpho-

[1] Chief Curator, Department of Botany, Chicago Natural History Museum. Paper submitted: November 1947.

logical fields. The delimitation of these groups must of necessity be somewhat arbitrary. However, the very fact that these and other theories still hold the arena leaves little doubt "that, lacking fossil evidence, no theory of the origin of the flower can ever be established except on the basis of probability" (Wilson, 1941). As the details have been reviewed elsewhere (Arber, 1937; Bancroft, 1935; Chadefaud, 1946; Just, 1948; Matthews, 1941; Ozenda, 1946; Parkin, 1933; Thomas, 1936; Wilson and Just, 1939), the following comments can be limited to a discussion of fundamental differences in approach and methodology.

Peculiarly enough, groups (1) and (3) have at least one thing in common, i.e. "the reaction against phylogeny" (Arber, 1937). This is the more striking since the theory of acarpy is in reality more physiological than morphological, as is evident from its author's own words (McLean Thompson, *fide* Arber) "the real problem of floral morphology is that of the physiology of growth of a sporogenous axis." The second important ontogenetic theory was advanced by Grégoire, who thought he had found essential differences in the histogenesis of reproductive and vegetative apices. However, this distinction must now be discarded, since Philipson's (1947) careful histogenetic studies have proved that such differences actually do not exist. For he concluded that "the organization of the apical meristems should not be regarded as essentially different in the vegetative and the reproductive state." Engard's theory (1944), the third of this group, introduces from zoology the concept of physiomorphological fields. Based mainly on histogenetic data it represents an attempt to reconcile many conflicting viewpoints. According to it, the plant comprises two major morphogenetic fields, reproductive and vegetative, each finding expression in the various organs ranging from roots to carpels. In retrospect, modern ontogenetic botany dates from C. F. Wolff (1733-1794), who was the first to study the early developmental stages of plants and inquire into the processes and causes of development. As will be shown below, the other main lines of morphological study were initiated at about the same time.

Group (1), on the other hand, marks a return to "a standpoint not far removed from that of Goethe" (Arber, 1937). But in order to gain a proper perspective in this respect, a short historical digression may here be permissible. While it is generally accepted that the beginnings of modern plant morphology can be traced to the eighteenth century and beyond, it was Goethe who gave it its own methodology and concepts. This he accomplished by the introduction of the concept of morphological type, a concept which was to embrace all particular structures falling within its possible range, though obviously not according to their actual form. Arber (1946), who has contributed so much to our understanding of Goethe's botanical work and its neoclassical sequels, appraises it as follows: "The

Metamorphose must be judged, not as if it were a modern scientific treatise, but as a presentation of a nexus of ideas, much of the material for which was already in existence. These ideas Goethe alone succeeded in developing into a unified organic whole, by adjusting them to the living framework of his thought, and thus creating one of the minor classics of botany." Elsewhere she points out that the book really does not deal with the whole plant but rather with the appendicular organs of the stem only. Her studies of Goethe's botanical writings convinced her also of the need for a less strict application of some of the time-honored morphological concepts. For example, she proved convincingly that Goethe used the word "leaf" for want of a better general term when he probably should have referred to this "protean form" as a "hypothetical appendage." On this basis the carpel and foliage leaf would be regarded as "parallel developments . . . between parts of one and the same plant body." In her opinion, this version of parallelism is free from any implications derived from ontogeny or the "changing visions of phylogeny," and permits circumventing Goethe's type concept, should its abstract character prevent its use in modern work.

Though at first widely accepted and used, the concept of morphological type was also frequently misused and finally fell into disrepute with the advent of the theory of evolution and the reorientation of morphology following in its train. However, in recent years it has been restored and reapplied in the most extensive morphological treatise of the vascular plants ever undertaken. In this work, Troll, the leading exponent of this neoclassical morphology, simply defines morphology as the "doctrine of type" and, since comparison of forms has always been its method, synonymizes comparative morphology with "typology." The results of the application of the type concept to the interpretation of the flower are evident from two recent reviews (Arber, 1937; Wilson and Just, 1939), while other phases will be mentioned below under growth forms.

Parallel with Goethe's morphology and quite independent of it, A. P. De Candolle founded another field of morphological study. In his extensive taxonomic studies De Candolle used morphology as the sole basis of taxonomy (Baron, 1931). In this way he arrived at a number of morphological principles similar to those advanced by his great zoological contemporaries and as valid as in his day. An epitomist of botanical knowledge, he readily linked his morphological work with physiological (and ecological) data and thereby created the science of organography. Despite his vast contributions toward the establishment of a natural classification of plants, De Candolle never expressed any evolutionary ideas in his writings. Neither did he know or employ the concept of morphological type. Modern organography, as represented by Goebel's writings (1928-1933), deals with two groups of problems, i.e. the origin and interrelations of all morphological forms, and the origin of adaptations in plants. Goebel's general conclusions, applicable far beyond the domain of the flower will be discussed elsewhere in this paper.

While the beginning of organography is roughly contemporaneous with that of the old morphology, its modern version closely approaches experimental morphology, a direct descendant of classical morphology.

The tremendous impact of the theory of evolution and its far-reaching effects on morphology are well known and exemplified by the writings of W. Hofmeister. His classical studies on the homologies of the reproductive organs of the cormophytes appeared prior to the publication of Darwin's *On the Origin of Species* but were subsequently reinterpreted by others. The same treatment was afforded a large body of morphological knowledge accrued by the early morphologists. Meanwhile, Hofmeister himself extended his exemplary studies and laid the real foundations for modern "developmental" morphology (Sifton, 1944). With improved techniques and equipment there soon appeared also the healthy offspring of morphology in such new and revitalized fields as cytology, anatomy, and embryology. Developmental morphology is now often known as morphogenesis. Its aims have been defined by Sinnott (1937) and include the exact description of the progress of development, of the morphogenetic changes and their causes, and the formulation of the results obtained in quantitative terms. It is difficult to imagine the fragmentary character of our knowledge if causal or developmental morphology had never achieved its present prominence.

The phylogenetic theories, here referred to group (2), represent various attempts to reconstruct the evolution of the angiosperm flower (and of other structures) either on the basis of data assembled by the old morphology or by entirely new lines of approach (for details see the reviews cited above).

Presumably the final answer to the perplexing problem of the origin of the angiosperm flower may eventually come as the result of concerted effort such as suggested by Joshi (1947). "Any theory of floral morphology, if it is to hold the field, must attempt to reconcile evidence from all sources. It appears to the writer that even today the classical theory with few minor modifications, such as suggested by Arber (1937), Hunt (1937) and Wilson (1942), is able to do so." Accordingly, Joshi sums up the situation as follows: "We can safely conclude that the flower and the vegetable shoot are quite comparable structures. It may not be correct to say that the carpel is a modified leaf, but there is ample evidence to state that it is an appendicular structure of the stem like the leaf and is morphologically equivalent to or comparable to a leaf folded along its midrib and bearing the ovules along its margin."

MORPHOLOGY OF SHOOT AND ROOT

As in the case of the flower, the interpretation of the plant as a whole has been subjected to considerable study (Bower and Wardlaw, 1947; Browne, 1935; Emberger, 1944; Thoday, 1939; Thomas, 1947). Three important theories may be mentioned here. Troll and his school, following the classical tradition, accept root, stem, and leaf as "unanalysable categories." Arber (1941), on the other hand, elaborated A. P. De Candolle's theory of the partial-shoot nature of the leaf and now regards the leaf as a "partial shoot with an urge to whole-shoot characters." In conjunction with this new theory of the nature of the leaf, she also attempted to draw the root into "a unified picture of plant construction." The root, too, is regarded as a partial shoot, though in a different way. According to this interpretation the root would correspond to the "internal component" of the shoot which "is in some degree analogous to a periclinal chimaera." On these assumptions, the vegetative body of an angiospermous plant "consists entirely of shoots and partial-shoots." Allen (1947), who is apparently the first actually to have tested this hypothesis in *Pseudotsuga*, found it necessary to advance an alternative one. He regards the "stele of the primary root" as "homologous with the whole primary shoot; the peripheral tissues of the root, that is, the 'cortex' and the rhizodermis, have no counterpart in the shoot."

Finally, Engard's distinction of two "morphological domains," stem and root, as the "morphological units of organization" and the adoption of reproductive and vegetative fields, the two "physiological domains" of the stem, go beyond any other interpretation of plant construction. While all structures of the reproductive field are regarded as "homologous among themselves," the structures of the vegetative field are said to be *organa homologata* at the organismal level, although each group represents *organa sui generis* phylogenetically. Engard, then, aims to combine the important features of the other schools of morphology in his effort to interpret the structure of flowering plants as a whole.

MORPHOLOGY OF CRYPTOGAMS

The new and far more satisfactory classification of the lower plants, especially their pigmented groups, is the direct result of the great progress made in this branch of morphology (Smith, 1938; Schussnig, 1938). The old collective group commonly called Thallophyta has been broken up into several distinct phyla, all representing separate, though largely parallel, evolutionary lines. Each of these lines begins at the morphological level of a flagellated uni-cell and terminates with the production of complex multicellular members after passing various clearly marked levels of morphological differentiation. As the sequence of these levels was worked out in one phylum before all corresponding members of the other phyla were known, it was possible to predict their existence and eventual discovery. The missing members have, with few exceptions, been found and thus lend considerable credence to the new polyphyletic division of the thallophytes.

An interesting parallel is seen in the newer classifications of the vascular plants. Although they are customarily retained as a unit, their main groups apparently followed a similar course of evolution, each representing a separate line long isolated from the others (Bertrand, 1937; Bertrand and Corsin, 1937; Just, 1945).

These modern classifications of the lower and higher plants are bound to restrict further the limited applicability of the "biogenetic law" in the plant kingdom. For linear ascent, as postulated by it, is not a general evolutionary phenomenon, but characteristic only of special cases (Däniker, 1945).

GROWTH FORMS

In contrast to these more or less strictly morphological lines of investigation concerned with the interpretation of plant structure, classification, and phylogeny, botanists have always studied plants in their native environments and attempted to determine the kind and nature of their adaptations. Thus they came to distinguish with A. P. De Candolle between constitutive and nonconstitutive characters or, in current terminology, between indifferent, fortuitous, or karyogenetic and biological, epharmonic, adaptive, or organismal characters. On this basis, botanists have devised a number of systems of growth or life-forms of plants using mainly adaptive characters or a combination of such with certain morphological characters. These systems were used for the characterization of vegetation types as well as the study of the ecological relationships between the plants themselves. The varying emphasis placed by different authors on certain characters or sets of characters is clear from Du Rietz's exhaustive summary (1931). Of the available systems, that of Raunkiaer enjoys the widest acceptance, largely because of its great simplicity, even in its variously emended versions. Its value has been assessed by Adamson (1939) as follows: "A close parallel can be drawn with taxonomic classification; Raunkiaer's scheme might be compared with the Linnaean system." Actually Raunkiaer's system is based on the position of the rejuvenating buds and the protective devices of plants for overcoming unfavorable seasons, while the well-known Linnaean system is based on the nature and numbers of reproductive organs of plants. In this respect both systems have their obvious limitations.

As it seemed impossible to express in any one system all important criteria, Du Rietz finally adopted Hayata's "dynamic system" of reticulate relationships and proposed an extended scheme of six parallel systems of growth and life forms, viz., main life-forms, growth-forms, periodicity life-forms, bud-height life-forms, bud-type life-forms, and leaf life-forms. The immediate reason for this proposal can be traced to Du Rietz's refusal to recognize the old distinction of adaptive and indifferent characters since "life-forms should be founded simply upon the characters observed by us, and not upon what we believe about the probable origin of these characters. For anybody used to the inductive methodic of modern sociological ecology it must also be quite clear that *only life-forms delimited independently of any adaptation theory can be of any use at all as units for the inductive study of adaptation problems and of the actual correlation between life-form and environment.*" The full significance of this statement is apparent if Du Rietz's definition of life-form is kept in mind, namely: "the term 'life-form' is used by me . . . in the widest possible sense, i.e. as a general designation for any class of plants based upon any other point of view than those of idiobiological taxonomy."

One striking example may be given here. A very distinctive growth form is represented by the so-called cushion-plants. Many species of diverse systematic affinity are characterized by it and are known to occur under widely differing ecological conditions. Previous efforts to study and interpret the peculiar growth form of these plants from various ecological points of view proved inadequate. This problem has lately been restudied and resolved in essentially morphological terms. Rauh (1939) found that all species of cushion-plants possessed the same mode of branching regardless of their systematic affinity or ecological habitat. His results are doubly significant as they were obtained by the strict application of the methods of comparative morphology (typology). Likewise, the lists of species referred to other fundamental growth forms are made up of similar selections of plants of varied taxonomic affinity, indicating clearly the wide occurrence of convergent evolution among flowering plants.

ADAPTATION AND STANDARDIZATION

In Bower's (1931) opinion, convergent evolution "with a high degree of similarity" is a "frequent consequence of homoplastic adaptation," the "final result" of which may be standardization. The latter is "most remarkable" in the reproductive organs, viz. the uniformity of archegonia in bryophytes and pteridophytes (Bower, 1935), of the megaspores of heterosporous types, and of the embryo-sacs of angiosperms. Such standardized structures are convenient for purposes of classification, as in the case of the Archegoniatae. Modern schemes, however, place the emphasis on anatomical characters of the sporophyte. Consequently, standardization of one organ may bring about results suggesting relationships difficult to maintain in the presence of other standardized structures and neces-

sitating, in this case, the removal of the pteridophytes from the Archegoniatae to the vascular plants (Just, 1945). This and similar examples of
convergent evolution or standardization illustrate the results of evolution
as evident in contemporaneous groups. Morphologically speaking, convergences may either be homologous, affecting the same organs (Seybold,
1927) in widely separated groups, or analogous, affecting structures of
different organization either in related or unrelated groups, viz. resemblances between individual flowers and inflorescences, etc. (Troll, 1926,
1935). As the adaptive value of many morphological characters remains
to be demonstrated, provided this can ever be done, convergences must
for the time being be studied from the morphological point of view. It
is here that the typological approach will yield more and more significant
results through the analysis of growth forms, root systems, leaf types,
floral types, etc. If the conclusions of the neoclassical school are compared
with those of the leading student of organography, the following interesting result emerges. Goebel, from the organographic point of view,
claims that the variability of morphological types in plants far exceeds that
of the ecological conditions to which they are supposedly adapted. In fact,
morphological variants apparently radiate in all directions from the
principal organizational type. Rauh, who employed typological methods
in his study of cushion-plants, expresses his views as follows: "the real
morphogenetic principle is form," whereas the environment plays an important, though secondary role. A statement of this kind approaches
closely the zoological concept of preadaptation involving the "fixation
of characters that are inadaptive or at most nonadaptive in the circumstances under which they first appear" (Simpson, 1944).

In the light of such considerations it is readily understandable that
taxonomists are more and more inclined to include a wider selection and
combination of characters of the vegetative as well as reproductive region
in their systems of classification. Both Hutchinson (1926) and Willis
(1946) have prepared lists of taxonomic characters and their distribution
in the families of flowering plants, while others (Bessey, et al.) have tried
to formulate phylogenetic series or principles from such data (Just,
1948). For instance, Hutchinson (1946) now goes all the way in dividing
the Dicotyledons into two phyla, *Lignosae* and *Herbaceae*, separating
completely the "one fundamentally and remaining predominantly woody,"
from "the other fundamentally and remaining predominantly herbaceous."
In so doing he regards the woody phylum as "probably the older" though
both have apparently "evolved side by side." Hutchinson's phylogenetic
chart, like those prepared by others, quickly shows the great difficulty met
in any attempt to express the known and probable relationships of the
many families of flowering plants. In his words, "the more natural a system
becomes the more difficult it is to express on paper."

Although this difficulty has long been recognized, its possible reason was never as apparent as it seems to be today. In his discussion of the significance of polyploidy in plants, Stebbins (1947) suggests that a large proportion of genera and even higher groups of angiosperms may be polyploid and, therefore, largely of hybrid origin. If polyploidy is actually as widespread as we have reason to believe, the result would be a "pattern of relationships between genera of a family, and even between the families themselves" that is to a large extent reticulate. As this assumption is more likely to be substantiated than others proposed so far, an "explanation is at hand for the fact that plant systematists have never been able to construct a satisfactory system of relationships for the flowering plants."

On this basis, and in the light of other well-established genetical data, it is no longer necessary to postulate the occurrence in the past or present of large mutational steps, as was the opinion of some paleobotanists and botanists (fide Scott, 1924; Willis, 1940). For Stebbins has clearly shown that the main role of allopolyploidy lies in the fact that it provides new combinations of characters rather than new characters, even if new genera and families are concerned. If that is correct, the possible recombinations of available genetical characters through polyploidy should also provide an adequate basis for all morphological variants conceivable within the possible limits of any morphological type.

As previously shown, morphologists customarily compare various representatives of the same type and then aim to visualize the latter by abstraction of all specific characters. Geneticists establish the "modal points" (Dobzhansky, 1941) on the basis of mathematical data and by abstraction. Though theoretical, both concepts are as useful as those of modern physics. If experimental proof of the effect of the environment is furnished by transplant studies, the control gained thereby permits a consolidated yet objective analysis of the vexed problem of adaptation in plants.

SUMMARY

The present status of plant morphology, particularly that of the angiosperm flower, is characterized in terms of the accomplishments of various schools. The need for a coordinated attack involving all possible avenues of approach is demonstrated.

The growth forms of higher plants can be interpreted only by more extensive morphological (typological) study and without recourse to any special theory of adaptation.

Numerous convergences have been detected in modern angiosperm groups. A possible explanation of these (and other phenomena) may be

{ 98 }

seen in the presence and operation of polyploidy in a large proportion of the known families, genera, etc. Large scale mutations (saltations) are not required to explain these phenomena.

REFERENCES

Adamson, R. S. 1939. The Classification of Life-forms of Plants. *Bot. Rev.*, 5:546-561.

Allen, G. S. 1947. Embryogeny and the Development of the Apical Meristems of Pseudotsuga. III. Development of the Apical Meristems. *Amer. Jour. Bot.*, 34 (4): 204-211.

Arber, A. 1937. The Interpretation of the Flower: A Study of Some Aspects of Morphological Thought. *Biol. Rev.*, 12:157-184.

——. 1941. The Interpretation of Leaf and Root in the Angiosperms. *Biol. Rev.*, 16:81-105.

——. 1946. Goethe's Botany. *Chronica Botanica*, 10(2):63-124.

Bancroft, H. 1935. A Review of Researches Concerning Floral Morphology. *Bot. Rev.*, 1:77-99.

Baron, W. 1931. Die idealistische Morphologie Al. Brauns and A. P. de Candolles und ihr Verhältnis zur Deszendenzlehre. *Beih. Bot. Centralbl.*, Abt. 1, 48:314-334.

Bertrand, Paul. 1937. Isolement précoce de tous les grandes groupes de végétaux vasculaires. *Bull. Soc. Bot. France*, 84:713-720.

—— et P. Corsin. 1938. Phylogénie des végétaux vasculaires. *Bull. Soc. Bot. France*, 85:331-348.

Berry, E. W. 1945. *The Origin of Land Plants and Four Other Papers.* Johns Hopkins Univ. Stud. Geol. 14.

Bower, F. O. 1932. Morphology of Plants. *Britannica Booklet* 10:5-8.

——. 1935. *Primitive Land Plants also Known as the Archegoniatae.* London.

—— and C. W. Wardlaw. 1947. *Botany of the Living Plant.* Fourth ed., London.

Browne, Isabel M. P. 1935. Some Views on the Morphology and Phylogeny of the Leafy Vascular Sporophyte. *Bot. Rev.*, 1:383-404, 427-447.

Chadefaud, M. 1946. L'Origine et l'évolution de l'ovule des phanérogams. *Rev. Sci.*, 84:502-509.

Däniker, A. U. 1945. Die differenzierte Entwicklung. *Vorläufige Mitteilung. Archiv Julius Klaus-Stiftung* 20 (Suppl.): 252-267.

Dobzhansky, Th. 1941. *Genetics and the Origin of Species.* 2nd ed. New York.

Du Rietz, G. E. 1931. Life-forms of Terrestrial Flowering Plants. *Acta Phytogeogr. Suecica*, 3(1):1-95.

Emberger, L. 1944. *Les plantes fossiles dans leurs rapports avec les végétaux vivants.* Paris.

Engard, C. J. 1944. *Organogenesis in Rubus.* Univ. Hawaii Res. Publ. 21:234 pp.

Goebel, K. 1928-1933. *Organographie der Pflanzen.* Third ed., Jena.

Hunt, K. W. 1937. A Study of the Style and Stigma with Reference to the Nature of the Carpel. *Amer. Jour. Bot.*, 24:288-295.

Hutchinson, J. 1926. *The Families of Flowering Plants.* 1. Dicotyledons. London.

——. 1946. *A Botanist in Southern Africa.* London.

Joshi, A. C. 1947. Floral Histogenesis and Carpel Morphology. *Jour. Indian Bot. Soc.* 26(1):63-74.

Just, T. 1945. The Proper Designation of the Vascular Plants. *Bot. Rev.*, 11(6): 299-309.

——. 1948. Gymnosperms and the Origin of Angiosperms. *Bot Gaz.*, 110(1): 91-103.

Matthews, J. R. 1941. Floral Morphology and its Bearing on the Classification of Angiosperms. *Trans. Bot. Soc. Edinburgh*, 23(2):69-82.

Ozenda, Paul. 1946. La nature morphologique du carpelle. *Rev. Sci.*, 84:393-404.

Parkin, J. 1933. The Classical Carpel and Recent Attacks. *Reports Bot. Exch. Club*, pp. 598-606.

Philipson, W. R., 1947. Some Observations on the Apical Meristems of Leafy and Flowering Shoots. *Jour. Linn. Soc.*, Botany, 53(350): 187-193.

Rauh, W. 1939. Über polsterförmigen Wuchs. Ein Beitrag zur Kenntnis der Wuchsformen der höheren Pflanzen. *Nova Acta Leop.*, N.F., 7(49):267-508.

Schussnig, B. 1938. *Vergleichende Morphologie der niederen Pflanzen*. 1. Berlin.

Scott, D. H. 1924. *Extinct Plants and Problems of Evolution*. London.

Seybold, A. 1927. Untersuchungen über die Formgestaltung der Blätter der Angiospermen. *Biblioteca Genetica*, 12.

Sifton, H. B. 1944. Developmental Morphology of Vascular Plants. *New Phytol.*, 43(2):87-129.

Simpson, G. G. 1944. *Tempo and Mode in Evolution*. New York.

——. 1947. The Problem of Plan and Purpose in Nature. *Sci. Monthly*, 64(6):481-495.

Sinnott, E. W. 1937. Morphology as a Dynamic Science. *Science*, 85(2194):61-65.

Smith, G. M. 1938. *Cryptogamic Botany*. Vols. 1 and 2. New York.

Stebbins, G. L., Jr. 1947. Types of Polyploids: Their Classification and Significance. *Advances in Genetics*, 1:403-429.

Thoday, D. 1939. The Interpretation of Plant Structure. *Advancement of Science*, 1(1):84-104.

Thomas, H. H. 1933. The Old Morphology and the New. *Proc. Linn. Soc. London*, Session 145, 1932-33(1):17-46.

——. 1936. Paleobotany and the Origin of the Angiosperms. *Bot. Rev.*, 2:397-418.

——. 1947. The History of Plant Form. *Advancement of Science*, 4(15):243-254.

Troll, W. 1936. Organisation und Gestalt im Bereich der Blüte. *Monogr. Gesamtgeb. wiss. Bot.*, 1:xiii + 413 pp. Berlin.

——. 1935-1943. *Vergleichende Morphologie der höheren Pflanzen*. 1(1-3). Berlin.

Willis, J. C. 1940. *The Course of Evolution by Differentiation or Divergent Mutation Rather than by Selection*. Cambridge.

Wilson, C. L. 1941. The Evolution of the Stamen. *Chronica Botanica*, 6(11):245.

——. 1942. The Telome Theory and the Origin of the Stamen. *Amer. Jour. Bot.*, 29:759-764.

—— and T. Just. 1939. The Morphology of the Flower. *Bot. Rev.*, 5(2):97-131.

Zimmermann, W. 1930. *Die Phylogenie der Pflanzen*. Jena.

Zündorf, W. 1940. Phylogenetische oder idealistische Morphologie. *Der Biologe*, 9(½):10-24.

PART III

EVOLUTIONARY TRENDS

· 7 ·

TIME SERIES AND TRENDS IN ANIMAL EVOLUTION

BY ALFRED SHERWOOD ROMER[1]

In the study of evolution it is impossible to overemphasize the importance of the fossil record, the evolutionary lines apparent in this record, and the evidence of evolutionary processes and trends which is revealed by the study of these phyletic series. The study of living materials has furnished vital knowledge, unavailable to students of evolution in early days, of the nature of inheritable variations in organisms, and it continues to furnish significant data concerning the nature of selective processes. It is, however, too much to expect that such studies can give us positive and conclusive answers as to the actual, obviously complex, operation of the mechanisms concerned in major evolutionary developments. There are many disadvantages and imperfections to be encountered in the paleontological study of evolutionary series; nevertheless such series are the factual material against which any theoretical conclusion must be checked. I shall attempt here to discuss some of the more striking phenomena which are apparent in the study of evolutionary lines in animal groups.

ADAPTATION

Evolution as seen in the fossil record is in its entirety a study of continual adaptive processes, for any feature of mutational nature which becomes well enough established in a group to appear in the fossil record is surely sufficiently advantageous to be considered an adaptation or is associated genetically with adaptive features in other structures or in functions. Adaptation in general is being treated elsewhere in this volume by other authors; I shall here discuss only certain points pertinent to the fossil record.

Among fossil animals various structural features fall into categories familiar in living animals and are thus reasonably interpretable as adaptive in nature. But even among living animals not all features have obvious utility, and interpretation is far more difficult in the case of fossil groups, where structures are often built on unfamiliar patterns and where pertinent ecological conditions and life-habits are difficult to evaluate. Frequently the attempt at interpretation in terms of adaptation is abandoned, and odd and unusual structures are assumed to be non-adaptive or even harmful products of evolutionary development. It is,

[1] Alexander Agassiz Professor of Zoology and Director of the Museum of Comparative Zoology, Harvard University.

however, probable that fuller knowledge and more careful study will lead to the conclusion that most if not all of these unusual features are adaptive in nature.

A case in point is that of the development of long spines, connected in life by a web of skin, in the case of a number of Permian pelycosaurian reptiles (Romer, 1927; Romer and Price, 1940, 104-107, etc.). This sail was independently developed in at least three and perhaps five separate lines. Cope, who originally described these structures, jocularly suggested that they were for sailing on the lake. Despite numerous discussions, in and out of print, no more reasonable suggestions as to their use were brought forward for many years. Recently, however, Dr. Alfred C. Redfield suggested to the writer the possibility that the sail was a thermal regulating device, capable of absorbing or giving off heat, and Dr. Jepsen informs me that a similar suggestion was made to him in seminar discussion. It is of interest that the pelycosaurs were primitive members of the mammal-like reptile group, in the higher members of which a homoeothermous condition was apparently developing. That the sail may actually have been a primitive essay in this direction is suggested by the fact that in the larger species of *Dimetrodon* the sail height (and area) increases out of all proportion to the normal body parts. To keep pace, as a regulating device, with body volume, the length of the spines should grow at such a rate that the exponent of the length, in the equation $y=bx^k$, should be 1.5 (or somewhat in excess of this figure, since additional expansion here is necessary to compensate for the failure of the remainder of the body surface to increase proportionately to volume). The actual figure for three successively larger species of *Dimetrodon* is $k=1.6$. It is thus probable that this peculiar and puzzling feature of early reptiles may have been of a reasonably adaptive nature, and we need not have recourse to any mystical or mysterious evolutionary urge to explain this "spinescence." The same may prove to be true of many another puzzling phenomenon. We must not, however, expect to explain every feature of our fossil forms as directly adaptive; it is perfectly possible that certain structural features were not in themselves adaptive but tied genetically to other adaptive structures or functions. It is, however, almost impossible to prove such correlations in fossil material.

PALEONTOLOGY AND GENERAL EVOLUTIONARY THEORY, ORTHOGENESIS, "IRREVERSIBILITY."

Currently most paleontologists seriously interested in evolutionary processes subscribe, in common with their neozoological fellows, to a Neo-Darwinian doctrine. In the past, however, they tended to worship at other shrines—those of Lamarckianism, orthogenesis, and a variety of other mysterious and teleological cults. Backsliding is easy, for the Neo-

Darwinian point of view brought forward by neozoologists and geneticists gives a relatively simple explanation of the bulk of paleontological data and tends to render unnecessary other and less tangible hypotheses.

From time to time we are confronted with teleological evolutionary theories, evolved in general in the philosopher's cabinet or theologian's study, which base evolutionary events upon the "design" of some external force—a deity, or "Nature"—or upon some mysterious "inner urge" of the organism or its protoplasm.

A recent example is du Noüy's best-selling *Human Destiny* (1947), in which its author exhibits an amazing ignorance of both genetics and paleontology. He frankly admits that his thesis is based on "wishful thinking," as appear to be most arguments of this sort: "Evolution . . . is comprehensible only if we admit that it is dominated by a finality, a precise and distant goal. If we do not admit the reality of this orienting pole . . . the appearance of moral and spiritual ideas remains an absolute mystery. Mystery for mystery, it seems wiser, more logical and more intelligent to choose the one which explains, thus satisfying our need to comprehend; the one which opens the door to hope; rather than the one which closes those doors and explains nothing."

Argument for such theories is frequently to the effect that more materialistic bases are insufficient to explain the end results of evolutionary processes as seen today or the evolutionary developments seen in fossil forms.

In general the paleontologist can dispose of such theories by the application of Occam's razor. We may not fully understand the workings of the internal combustion engine which purrs beneath the hood of our car; but such facts as are known to the layman are interpretable in terms of ordinary physics and chemistry, and there is no reason to believe that the complications that we do not understand are not similarly explicable. If someone postulates that the workings of the engine are directed or influenced by a small demon dwelling therein, one cannot prove him wrong; but his theoretical demon is an unnecessary accretion. Many paleontological facts are reasonably interpreted in an essentially materialistic Neo-Darwinian fashion. Others are more obscure. But there seems little positive reason for a call upon teleology, particularly when an increasing number of puzzling and seemingly teleological questions, if critically examined, are capable of more rational explanation.

Teleology, or some mysterious "urge," is often appealed to for an explanation of the initial appearance, in a "rudimentary" state, of structures which, when fully developed, are obviously advantageous and of selective value. Thus, for example, Osborn (1929, 813-817, 834-843, etc.), in discussing the gradual phyletic development of horns as "rectigradations" in titanotheres, assumes that they have, in early stages, little or no selective value. Hence he concludes that their origin and growth is due to ill-defined "germinal potentialities" and exemplifies his syncretic but (despite his denial) essentially mystical "principle of tetrakinetic evolution." Recent genetic work, however, tends to show that even slight variants may be surprisingly effective as selective agents, and even a modest thickening of the bone in the potential horn region may have been, in the course of generations, influential in survival or (a field ripe for restudy) sexual selection.

Again, recourse is made to teleology to explain the development of features which (it is assumed) are evolved prior to a stage in which the animal can utilize them; here selection cannot operate and "design" appears to be definitely in the picture.

We may, however, question in cases of this sort whether development does actually precede utilization. As an illustration we may cite the general evolutionary sequence, bony fish–amphibian–reptile. The three most conspicuous developments in this transition are (1) lungs, (2) limbs, and (3) the amniote egg. These three structures, in the attainment of a true land stage in vertebrate history, are all of the utmost importance. It has been assumed that they would be of no use to an aquatic vertebrate, and hence that the appearance of these structures preceded their utilization.

This is not the case, as a consideration of the combined evidence from fossil and recent forms shows. (1) It now seems clear that lungs were present in the early bony fishes of the Devonian (Watson, 1926, 199-200; Romer, 1945, 84-85, etc.) and were of immediate functional importance under the conditions of drought then prevalent. (2) Limbs (Watson, 1926, 203; Romer, 1941, 47-48) were also of immediate use to water-dwellers living under similar drought conditions, enabling them, paradoxically, to remain in the water. (3) The amniote egg, instead of being "a transformation which does not confer an immediate advantage on the animal endowed with it" (du Noüy, 1947, 73-74) was obviously immediately advantageous to the aquatic ancestors of the reptiles among whom it appears to have arisen; a point which I have noted elsewhere (Romer, 1946a, 187) and hope to develop on another occasion.

Paleontologists, like other human beings, easily acquire a belief in Lamarckian doctrine; their willingness to abandon it in favor of a Neo-Darwinian explanation is due more to their acceptance of the neozoological Scotch verdict of "not proven" than upon the results of their own work. There is at present little available evidence from the paleontological data bearing upon the inheritance of acquired characteristics, although means might be devised to study it on a paleontological basis. Cope's theory of kinetogenesis (Cope, 1887), "a hypothesis that animal structures have been produced, directly or indirectly, by animal movements," was once widely accepted by vertebrate paleontologists; as a theory related to that of Lamarck, it has been generally abandoned.

Orthogenesis, the doctrine of "straight line" evolution, has played a prominent part in paleontological thought. This concept is a double-barreled one. It includes the belief, based upon a considerable body of evidence, that phyletic lines generally proceed in one direction in an essentially undeviating fashion throughout their course, and this belief is usually coupled with the supposition that some mysterious principle lies behind the observed phenomena.

Currently, however, paleontological interest in this doctrine is on the wane. There are probably few instances of long-continued phyletic lines which are unbranched and do not change their direction. In many groups which were thought to follow an orthogenetic pattern, fuller knowledge of fossils shows that branching does occur. The fossil horses, the Equidae, were once thought to be a prime example of orthogenetic phenomena, and early "family trees" of the group exhibited little but a direct succession of genera from "*Eohippus*" of the early Eocene to the surviving genus *Equus*, and few if any side branches. The story as known today is quite different (cf. Stirton, 1940). From "*Eohippus*" through its Eocene successors *Orohippus* and *Epihippus*, and *Mesohippus* and *Miohippus* of the Oligocene there is still, as far as we know, a one-for-one sequence of genera following in an unbranching, orthogenetic fashion. But at the beginning of the story there was, in the Old World, considerable branching, a variety of forms known collectively as paleotheres springing out from the basal "*Eohippus*" stock. And in the Miocene there again appears a rather complex branching pattern. Thus even the horses fail to exhibit the trim and proper orthogenetic pattern of an unbranching stem; and the related rhinoceroses (Wood, 1941, etc.) show no trunk whatever for their tree, but rather a straggling bushy effect.

Orthogenetic phenomena, then, are probably much less common than they were thought to be. But even in cases where straight-line phenomena are present, there is no need to postulate any teleological principle to explain them. Phyletic lines of this sort are reasonably to be considered as due to orthoselection, a process of increasingly improved adaptation to a relatively stable environment. Under such conditions any deviation from the "normal" line would be negative as to survival value, and would tend to be eliminated; the potential branches of the "tree" would tend to be pruned by selection before they became marked enough to become apparent in the fossil record.

It is thus possible to account for orthogenetic phenomena without recourse to any theoretical interpretation other than a Neo-Darwinian one; and it is perhaps better, as Simpson and others suggest, to use some such term as rectilinear evolution for this type of phenomenon and thus avoid the implications of teleology usually attached to the word orthogenesis.

As usual, of course, we cannot positively disprove the presence of some mysterious "principle" underlying the described facts. One can, however, bring forward evidence tending to minimize the necessity for the introduction of such a principle. The evolution of horse premolars is a case in point. The Eocene-Oligocene segment of the horse series is, we have noted, one which is still to be considered as "rectilinear" in nature. A notable event in equid evolution at this time was the expansion of the second to fourth upper premolars from originally small structures to a point where they attained a size (and structure) comparable to that of the true molars lying behind them. If there were some orthogenetic directive principle behind this process, one would not expect any great variation in the size of the teeth at any given stage, for, if "directed," all changes should be unidirectional. On the other hand, if the attainment of increased size had come about through the process of selection, one might reasonably expect to find wide variation during the time of increase, giving an abundance of material for selective processes. A study of all available horse material[2] shows that the latter of the two situations considered was the actual one. The data are presented in the accompanying table. The areas of premolars are stated in terms of percentages of the area of M^2 (as a "normal" member of the molar series) of the same individual; the "total" is the area of three premolars combined as a whole in terms of the percentage of the combined areas of the six grinding teeth. It will be noted that the coefficient of variation is markedly higher for each tooth at the beginning of this evolutionary series than at the end, when it has reached or approached its definitive size, and that in general a less fully developed tooth at any given stage is more variable than one which is closer to its definitive size. These facts are certainly not in accord with an orthogenetic interpretation of this phase in horse evolution; they are in accord with a Neo-Darwinian interpretation, although of course they do not offer positive proof for it.[3]

[2] As part of a more comprehensive study of equid evolution, not yet completed; this study was partially supported by a grant from the National Research Council.

[3] These data are unfortunately on a generic rather than a specific basis. Specific identification in fossil horses is a very dubious matter.

	Areas of tooth surfaces				Coefficient of variation			
	P2	P3	P4	total	P2	P3	P4	total
Eohippus	21	41	53	39.8	28.4	25.6	24.2	23.3
Orohippus	39	65	78	46.0	35.0	26.3	23.9	18.8
Epihippus	36	65	78	46.2	22.8	18.4	19.5	16.4
Mesohippus (E. Olig.)	75	95	99	55.6	20.2	19.6	19.3	14.5
					15.2	12.9	13.2	12.6
Mesohippus (M. Olig.)	74	92	98	54.7				

A special case of "orthogenesis" is the very common trend toward increasing body size seen in group after group. So often do we see this occurring in the fossil record that one gets the impression that this trend was universal. Actually, of course, this was not the case; if it had been, we would be living in a world of giants. There has been, it is sure, a persistent reservoir of smaller forms lying along the main branches of the evolutionary tree from which, in age after age, phyletic lines of larger forms have constantly arisen.

There are obvious advantages to size, in greater efficiency in energy conservation, greater safety from attack, and other features. But also, it would seem, there are major disadvantages, for lines of giant animals do not in general persist over long periods of time. Among the vertebrates many of those evolved during the Age of Reptiles have been long extinct, and the larger living mammals appear to be but the last futile survivors of Tertiary lines which for the most part did not outlive the Pleistocene. Large size appears to be accompanied by the development of a type of organization closely dependent upon a stable environment (i.e. specialized, to use an overworked term) and hence highly susceptible to environmental changes.

"The doctrine of the irreversibility of evolution" is a phrase which unfortunately has played an important part in shaping paleontological thought. This "doctrine" is, as stated in a broad sense, a corollary to that of orthogenesis. Literally interpreted it assumes that evolution does not reverse itself, that an animal does not, or cannot, turn back toward a former condition. It is usually interpreted in terms of organs. Structures once acquired, it is believed, are not reduced or lost; structures once reduced or lost are not redeveloped.

The phrase is an imposing one, but is obviously absurd in broad interpretation and contradictory if stated in terms of organs. It is today difficult to understand how any great degree of adherence to this "doctrine" came about. Adherence to this creed has made it difficult to develop reasonable phylogenies for various groups for which there is an abundance of fossil material, and it has been responsible in many cases for the supposition that successive representatives of a group have not descended one from another, but that the known types are a series of side branches from an unknown main line of "unspecialized" forms.

The late H. F. Osborn adhered strongly to this principle, although stating his evolutionary beliefs in other fashions, and his conclusions as to the phylogeny of the Proboscidea (Osborn, 1936, pls. X, XI) show the difficulties into which a fixed belief in irreversibility leads one. In his final "family tree" of the proboscideans shown on the plate cited, we see that a wealth of these forms was present in almost every stage of the Cenozoic from the Late Eocene to the Pleistocene. And yet, if one inspects this table, it will be discovered that in almost no instance is any known form considered to be descendant from any other known form; every subordinate group is assumed to have sprung quite separately, and usually without any known intermediate stage, from hypothetical common ancestors in the Early Eocene or Late Cretaceous. Despite the wealth of Tertiary mastodons, and the presence in the Pliocene of stegodonts which seem to bridge much of the structural gap, even the elephants of the Pleistocene are assumed to have emerged directly from these hypothetical ancestors, without any connection whatever with the other proboscideans! The reasons for this refusal to admit any earlier forms to the pedigree of the true elephants, or even to a position close to their line of descent, appears to be, basically, the fact that these forms possess characters (although in general minor ones) not found in later types. If evolution is irreversible, later forms which lack these characters cannot be descended from them, no matter how closely they may resemble them in every other way.

But evolution is definitely known to be reversible. Recent forms alone give strong evidence to that effect, and the paleontological evidence is conclusive. That structures once gained can be again lost is obvious from even a broad and superficial glance at the evolutionary story. We need only cite such examples as the loss in typical tetrapods of the bony armor of their piscine ancestors, and the loss in snakes of the typical tetrapod limbs present in their lacertilian ancestors.

Further, apart from organs, trends in phyletic development are frequently reversed. The equids are, as we have noted, a group exhibiting for the most part a rectilinear type of evolutionary progress. Among the notable trends in horse evolution is generally cited the increasing length of the lower segment of the limb (radius, tibia) as compared with the proximal segment (humerus, femur), a condition generally correlated with increasing speed (cf. for example, Osborn, 1929, 733-739 and passim). In the equids (cf. Fig. 1) the earlier genera show a rather steady increase in the relative length of radius and tibia, and in the front leg this tendency for increase continues on to the Pliocene. But *Equus* shows, on the data available to me, a sharp reversal of these trends. In the case of the tibia the reversal began earlier, and in *Equus* the tibia-femur ratio is actually lower than it was in the Eocene.

We have noted that increase in bodily size may be considered as a special case of "orthogenetic" evolution. This too may show reversal. Pleistocene and Recent mammals show a number of instances of pigmy species of elephants, hippopotami, etc., especially on the Mediterranean islands. These are definitely not a retention of a primitive diminutive size, but are to be considered as a secondary dwarfism—a very clear reversal of a definite evolutionary trend. In certain cases, at least, this appears to be

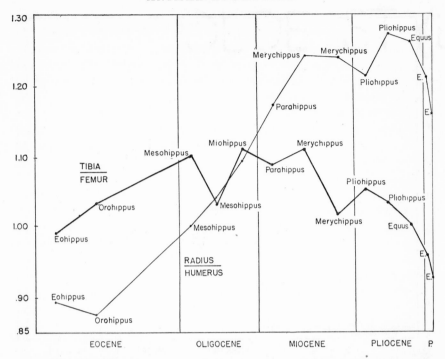

Figure 1. The ratio of lower to upper limb segment lengths in the horse series. The ratios given are the means of those obtained from all available specimens; the ratios for each genus are indicated for the various faunal zones in which it occurs. E. = *Equus*; P. = Pleistocene.

associated with selective processes peculiar to insular conditions. Even such a seemingly "orthogenetic" group as the horses, however, may show a reversal of the general trend without any evidence of insular isolation. In Figure 2 are plotted in chronological order the lengths of the upper cheek tooth series in the American equids, a measurement which appears to be fairly proportionate to bodily dimensions as a whole. As may be seen, the main line of horse evolution is one exhibiting on the whole a steady increase in size. But there are definite reversals. *Archaeohippus* is a tiny Miocene horse that is surely not primitive in its dimensions; in the Pliocene, *Calippus* and *Nannippus* are further dwarfs; and in the Pleistocene, dwarf horses, as yet incompletely known, were present in the Southwest and in Mexico.

It is moreover possible that the latest chapter in mammalian evolution may be a demonstration on a large scale of a reversal of the earlier general trend toward large size. Weidenreich (1946) suggests that the post-Tertiary evolution of the higher primates shows a strong trend toward reduction in size. He believes that this is exceptional. But Hooijer (1947)

{ *111* }

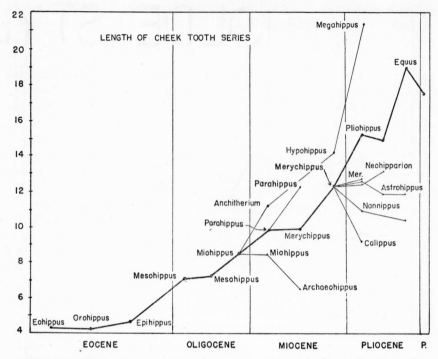

Figure 2. Changes in absolute size in the horse pedigree as indicated by the length of the cheek tooth series. Time, horizontal axis (P. = Pleistocene); Lengths of P^2-M^3 in cm., vertical axis. The figures used are means of all material available of each genus in each faunal zone.

points out that in a variety of cases Recent specimens of mammals are distinctly smaller than Pleistocene fossils representing the very same species. He further notes that their distribution shows that the phenomenon cannot be interpreted in terms of Bergman's principle.

In its literal interpretation, then, the "doctrine" of irreversibility is obviously untenable, and adherence to it, consciously or unconsciously, by many paleontologists has been an obstacle to reasonable interpretation of evolutionary events. The "doctrine" is usually ascribed to the late Louis Dollo as "Dollo's Law." This, however, is an undeserved slur on this distinguished Belgian paleontologist. His theory was one of a more modest sort (Dollo, 1893, 1922, etc., Gregory, 1936). An animal, he admits freely, may change the general course of its evolution and return, for example, to a former mode of life long since abandoned; but in doing this it does not revert precisely to its former structure. "Toute trace des étapes intermédiares ne disparaît jamais entirèment"; structures once lost are not regained. An ichthyosaur or a whale may return to purely aquatic life; but in doing so, gills never become functional again, the lateral line system does not appear. The limbs and tail are remodified into fin-like structures, but these are not at all closely comparable to the original fish fins, and show clearly the traces of the intermediate terrestrial phase.

In this original and limited sense, the doctrine of "irreversibility" seems, on the paleontological evidence, to be essentially a statement of fact. It seems further to be in reasonable accord with genetic theory. Since every complex structure is presumably produced ontogenetically by a considerable number of genes, the chance of reversion of a structure to a condition characteristic of a far earlier and far different stage is very small (Muller, 1939). It seems highly improbable that reverse mutations would take place to the extent and in the sequence which would be necessary for a true return to a former condition. Phenotypic disappearance of a structure may result from a single masking mutation (or even an environmental change in developmental conditions) and it may readily reappear after a few generations with the removal of the "block" to its expression. Wright (1934) has cited in the guinea pig the reappearance, in apparently normal form, of a digit which presumably had been lost far back in the ancestry of the species. But it is highly improbable that the redevelopment of a lost structure would often take place. Mutation would in general tend over an extended period of time to alter radically the genetic factors which could reproduce it. In Wright's example, most of the factors necessary for the reappearance of the lost digit are obviously present in the digital embryonic field, and little is needed except a reduplication factor for the addition of the absent digit.

PATTERNS OF DIVERSIFICATION

The essential picture of evolution under a Neo-Darwinian concept is that of a slow steady change through the gradual building up of minor modifications; over long periods of time animals become more perfectly adapted to a stable environment or change gently with slowly changing surroundings. The paleontological record of animal life is rich in examples of this sort, with species changing to species, genus gradually evolving into succeeding genus, together with a pattern of mild divergence, frequently with indications of parallelism. From a theoretical point of view, however, there have not been lacking concepts of evolutionary changes of more radical and abrupt nature. Such changes may be conceived of as either single major "saltations," as in the original (and still popularly held) concept of a mutation and the Goldschmidt hypothesis of macroevolution, or as due to a multiplicity of smaller changes accumulated in rapid fashion.

Abrupt evolutionary changes very definitely do occur in the fossil record, and Simpson (1944, 206-213) has recently discussed such phenomena under the term "quantum evolution."[4] There are numerous cases where it is obvious that there has been, in a relatively short time, an abrupt shift, the "sudden" development of a novel type; following this the new type may settle down into a more "normal" evolutionary pattern. Simpson reasonably interprets such a phenomenon as a shift from one adaptive "channel" to another, in the course of which there must be for survival a rapid change in adaptations toward a pattern suitable for the radically new environment.

There is, however, no positive reason to believe that in animals there is here any phenomenon in the nature of a "saltation." In plants polyploidy may occasionally produce immediate changes of considerable magnitude. This phenomenon, however, is generally believed to have been of little moment in animal evolution. In rapid evolutionary changes in animal lines the process may have been a typically Neo-Darwinian one of the accumulation of numerous small adaptive mutations, but an accumulation at an unusually rapid rate. Unfortunately there is in general little evidence on this point in the fossil record, for intermediate evolutionary forms representative of this phenomenon are extremely rare (a situation bringing smug satisfaction to the anti-evolutionist).

Reasons for the rarity of annectant forms may, as Simpson points out, be readily adduced. The time concerned was short; the size of the populations concerned was probably small. The chances of obtaining a complete graded series (if one existed) are hence obviously vastly less than in the case of more normal phyletic evolution. "Links" are missing just where we most fervently desire them, and it is all too probable that many "links" will continue to be missing.

Of a somewhat different nature is the phenomenon of "explosive evolution," particularly prominent in such invertebrate groups as the belemnites and terebratuloid brachiopods, etc. In such cases we see, at some period in the history of a group (frequently, but not always near its inception), a sudden development of a great variety of forms, a host of genera and species showing numerous variations of the central pattern of the group. Later most of these types disappear, and but a few phyla remain for the further history of the group.

Simpson (1944, 213) has interpreted this phenomenon in terms of a number of changes of the "quantum" type into a variety of adaptive channels. This is true if we include such large-scale phenomena as the "adaptive radiation" of Paleocene mammals and the subsequent radiation

---

[4] Some substitute should perhaps be found for this term (cf. Jepsen, *American Midland Naturalist*, 35, 540 [1946]). In one sense it is perfectly appropriate, as indicating (as in physics) a sharp shift from one orbit to another. However the implication usually attached to a "quantum" is that of something of the smallest possible magnitude; the term "quantum evolution" would be very appropriate for the results of a single mutation.

of various definitive placental orders. At least in the case of certain of the invertebrate groups, however, the phenomenon occurs in a more restricted adaptive area, perhaps, in a single broad zone; for numerous forms resulting from the "explosion" may be found in a single bed and show little evidence of variety in habits.

In many instances there is little evidence to explain the "explosion." In general it would appear that the balance between the organism and its environment of the moment has reached a point where the pressure of selection has been released and conformity to a narrow pattern is not a requisite. This condition may have been attained as the result of evolutionary progress in the organism itself, by entrance into a new environment where restrictive factors are not present, or by changes in the environment lessening unfavorable factors (enemies, rivals) or increasing favorable features (as food materials).

Parallelism appears to have played an important part in animal evolution. This phenomenon is one in which two or more forms, basically similar in pattern and related to one another, possess various common features which were lacking in their common ancestor and which they have acquired independently. Although parallelism is radically different from the concept of convergence, the two are so frequently confused in common usage that the contrast must be emphasized. In convergence, two forms with similarities in directly adaptive structures (as wolf and marsupial "wolf") have come from radically different ancestors with basically different patterns of organization; in Gregory's terminology, the habitus is similar, the heritage different.[5] In true parallelism, both habitus and heritage are similar; the ancestral types were closely related, and evolutionary progress, stage by stage, has been closely comparable in the two or more lines concerned.

Gregory has long emphasized the importance of parallelism in various vertebrate groups; Watson (1919, 1926, etc.) has commented repeatedly on its frequent occurrence in labyrinthodonts (loss of ossification in braincase, skull depression, palatal development, etc.) and therapsids (phalangeal formula, secondary palate). The known presence of parallelism in so many cases and its suspected presence in others suggests that it may have been an almost universal phenomenon. A close student of the subject may, if pressed, be driven to the logical though absurd admission of the possibility that two animals as closely related as, for example, chimpanzee and gorilla may have evolved in parallel fashion all the way from a piscine stage!

[5] Still further removed from parallelism is the purely superficial sort of resemblance, found in fossil as in recent examples, often referred to as mimicry, but for which the term homeomorphy, as lacking teleological implications, is preferable (Cloud, 1941).

No difficulty exists in explaining parallelism in evolution on a genetic basis. The phenomenon of parallel mutation was long ago observed in *Drosophila*. An accumulation in related species of favorable parallel mutations would eventually result in evolutionary parallelism, the production of forms with a genetic constitution very similar to one another although dissimilar in many regards to that of their common ancestor.

The recognition of parallelism leads to disturbing thoughts on classification and the homology concept.

We customarily define a group by the characters which its living members possess in common. But in many cases we suspect, and in certain cases we know, that part or all of these characters were not present in the ancestral forms. How, then, may we define such a group? May we not make our definition in terms of common trends, saying in effect that these forms all have a basically similar genetic constitution and hence are liable to similar modification?

The concept of homology implies that forms possessing structures thought to be homologous have inherited them from a common ancestor. Forms possessing structures evolved in parallel fashion have not so inherited them, but the complex of genes which are responsible for these structures may be identical or nearly so. Both phenotypic and genotypic identity may be present; shall we refuse application of the term homology?

The term phyletic drift may be applied to situations in which within the broad limits of a major group there have been great diversities in certain characters but parallel tendencies in others. Unfortunately no clear distinction can be drawn between phyletic drift and parallelism; our usage must depend on the relative dominance, in the group discussed, of divergent or parallel evolutionary tendencies. As an example of phyletic drift we may note that although the nectridian amphibian *Diplocaulus* has diverged markedly in most regards from the labyrinthodonts mentioned above, it has nevertheless paralleled them in skull flattening, development of large palatal vacuities, etc. (Watson, 1913). Again, most "modernized" placental mammals show common advanced brain characters which are generally assumed to have been inherited from a common ancestry, but recent work by Dr. Tilly Edinger (1948) shows that this is not the case. The brain of the common ancestor was organized on a lower, essentially marsupial, level, and the development of "modernized" placental brain patterns is due to a phyletic drift running counter to the development of diversity in other organs.

RACIAL OLD AGE; EXTINCTION

Processes antithetical to evolution should not pass without mention—evolutionary lines have failed to evolve; groups have become extinct.

There are various phyletic lines which have survived over long periods of time and yet show extremely little structural change. Among inverte-brates the linguloid brachiopods are commonly cited as examples, for Paleozoic shells are very similar to those of living forms.[6] Among verte-brates the chelonians, for example, have changed very little since their appearance. The attitude of students toward this phenomenon often has a moral tinge. Such groups are spoken of as exhibiting "racial sterility." The use of the term sterility implies an invalid comparison of a group with an individual. The term is often used in essentially a contemptuous sense, as if lack of change were a shameful thing. It is however equally possible to view this phenomenon from an opposite, approving, point of view—namely that of an essentially perfect (and hence laudable) adaptation to environment. Once a satisfactory adjustment to environment has been attained by an animal, evolutionary change is necessary only if that en-vironment itself changes; otherwise "evolution" is detrimental.

Degeneration is another term with derogatory implications often ap-plied to forms which exhibit a secondary simplification of structure. That such simplification has taken place has been reasonably deduced for many soft-bodied living invertebrates, particularly parasitic or semi-parasitic types, and the fossil record shows many examples of such degeneration. The term tends to imply a process antithetical to evolution. But there is no reason to assume that increasing complexity or addition of new parts are processes which have a copyright on the term evolution; simplification may equally be a change leading to survival, which is the only test of success. As regards, for example, dermal armor and squama-tion, almost the entire known history of vertebrates is one of reduction and simplification (Romer, 1942, 1946b). In many respects (such as jaws, jaw muscles, dentition) human evolution shows degenerate features which have not interfered with the success of mankind.

The phenomenon of extinction deserves greater consideration than is currently given it, although various authors have discussed the extinction of certain specific forms. It must be emphasized, however, that the major question is not so much why animals become extinct as why a certain favored few survive; for extinction is the common lot, survival the ex-ception. Entire major groups have been wiped out in the course of evolutionary history, and even in the case of surviving groups much extinction has occurred along the way. The horse family has survived and been plentiful in almost every stage of the Tertiary from the Early Eocene onward, and a majority of the genera have given rise to succeeding genera. But on the species level it is fairly certain that most of the species of any given stage have become extinct, and that only relatively few horse

[6] But the shells, upon which the belief as to lack of change is based, show but little "character" in any case; internal structure may possibly have changed to a considerable degree without being reflected in the shell.

species have given rise to descendants. Reptiles, birds, and mammals were all present in mid-Mesozoic days and have given rise to the dominant terrestrial land vertebrates of today, but the present continental faunas are derived from a very small percentage of the Mesozoic assemblages. As a liberal estimate one may guess that perhaps not more than one per cent of the tetrapod genera living in early Middle Mesozoic days have living descendants.

Like static conditions, extinction has been given a moral slant through the concept that end lines show a disgraceful "senescence," "racial old age." This strongly implies a comparison with an individual and its life history, a comparison which is without any reasonable foundation. The organs and protoplasm of an individual may age in one fashion or another, but it is obvious upon consideration that at a given stage in earth history no one type of animal is a whit older than any other. Unless animal life has come into existence more than once, each line has a pedigree just as long as every other, and should be no more senescent than any other. The senescent concept has arisen mainly in the study of invertebrates where in certain groups spinescence and other peculiarities appear shortly before the extinction; it has been especially developed by Beecher (1898. cf. Smith Woodward, 1910) and has tended to be an accepted tenet among many invertebrate paleontologists. In the vertebrates such phenomena are relatively rare, but there are some examples. The duckbills (hadrosaurs or trachodonts) of the Late Cretaceous, not long before the extinction of the dinosaurs, show grotesque variants in the development of bony crests on the skull, and the contemporary horned dinosaurs show great variations of horns and neck frills (Lull, 1933; Lull and Wright, 1942). But the last of ceratopsians, found in the Lance formation of the Late Cretaceous, are relatively normal in construction; the more "spinescent" forms are earlier. And among the duckbills the last representative in the Lance is a simple form without spinescence. Again, the long spines of Permian pelycosaurs have been considered as a "spinescent" condition. These types were doomed to early extinction; but so were numerous spineless relatives, and the spinescent forms were very flourishing groups for the time.

Extinction can in general be attributed not to change in the organism but to change in its environment. The animal is faced with changed conditions with which it cannot cope, conditions under which it cannot survive and reproduce successfully. In some cases the nature of the changes are fairly obvious; in others reasonable deductions can be made; in many instances satisfactory data are not available.

Obviously no single explanation is universally applicable (cf. Osborn, 1929, 859-894). Inorganic factors may have been responsible in many cases—changes in temperature, in water salinity, in rainfall, in physiographic conditions, etc. Failure of the food supply surely looms large in the picture. Competition with other forms for a common food supply may result in racial starvation; disappearance of the forms, animal or plant, upon which a group customarily feeds may have been a major factor in the extinctions of such varied types as Paleozoic predaceous sharks, ichthyosaurs and dinosaurs, both carnivorous and herbivorous. The appearance of new enemies may have been, for example, important in the disappearance of certain native South American herbivores in the Pleistocene, and a similar phenomenon is apparently under way in Australia today. Enemies in the form of disease may have been of importance (proof is almost out of the question in the fossil record) but Recent evidence suggests that this factor alone is unlikely to cause complete elimination. All these varied factors may be summarized as environmental changes too great or too rapid for the organism concerned to adjust itself to them.

One is tempted to explain extinction as the result of "specialization" which prevents escape of the forms concerned from the evolutionary blind alleys in which they find themselves. There is at least a modicum of truth in such a facile verbal explanation. Forms on the verge of extinction are frequently found to be individually large; abundant in numbers; and (in the case of terrestrial vertebrates) herbivorous rather than carnivorous in habits. Size itself may in some degree limit ability to readapt to changed conditions (but cf. Osborn, 1929, 878-880); numbers may imply an over-perfect adaptation to a particular mode of life, but may be merely a corollary of the fact that herbivores are likely to be more numerous than flesh-eaters. Herbivorous forms are usually more specialized in food-gathering and digestive mechanisms than carnivores.

But the terms "specialized" and "generalized" should be used with caution. It is said that the fossil record shows that generalized forms survive and specialized forms become extinct, but this is true only because extinct lines are *ipso facto* characterized as specialized; those which survived are labelled as generalized. These terms have little meaning otherwise. Were we living in the Jurassic we would have voted the ancestral mammals, with their "specialized" (aberrant) jaws, teeth, etc. as "least likely to succeed"; in the early Pleistocene, early man, as an ape no longer able to live in the trees, with aberrant cranial structure and a reduced pelt, might have appeared to an intelligent contemporary as highly specialized and doomed to speedy extinction.

REFERENCES

Beecher, C. E. 1898. The origin and significance of spines. A study in evolution. *Amer. Jour. Sci.* (4), VI, 1-20, 125-136, 249-268, 329-359.

Cloud, P. E. 1941. Homeomorphy, and a remarkable illustration. *Amer. Jour. Sci.*, CCXXXIX, 899-904.

Cope, E. D. 1887. *The Origin of the Fittest. Essays on Evolution.* 467 pp. New York.

Dollo, L. 1893. Les lois de l'évolution. *Bull. Soc. Belge Géol.*, VII, Proc.-Verb., 164-166.

——. 1922. Les céphalopodes déroulés et l'irréversibilité de l'évolution. *Bijdr. Dierk. Amsterdam*, XXII, 215-226.

Edinger, T. 1948. Evolution of the horse brain. *Mem. Geol. Soc. Amer.*, xxv, 1-177.

Gregory, W. K. 1936. On the meaning and limits of irreversibility of evolution. *Amer. Natur.*, LXX, 517-528.

Hooijer, D. A. 1947. Pleistocene remains of *Panthera tigris* (Linnaeus) subspecies from Wanhsien, Szechwan, China, compared with fossil and recent tigers from other localities. *Amer. Mus. Novit., 1346*, 1-17.

Jepsen, G. L. 1946. Review of *Tempo and Mode in Evolution*, by G. G. Simpson. *American Midland Naturalist, 35*, No. 2, 538-541.

Lull, R. S. 1933. A revision of the Ceratopsia or horned dinosaurs. *Mem. Peabody Museum Nat. Hist.*, III, Pt. 3, 1-175.

Lull, R. S. and N. E. Wright. 1942. Hadrosaurian dinosaurs of North America. *Geol. Soc. Amer., Special Papers No. 40*, 1-242.

Muller, H. J. 1939. Reversibility in evolution considered from the standpoint of genetics. *Biol. Rev. Camb. Philos. Soc.*, XIV, No. 3, 261-280.

du Noüy, L. 1947. *Human Destiny.* 289 pp. New York.

Osborn, H. F. 1929. The titanotheres of ancient Wyoming, Dakota and Nebraska. Vol. 2. *U.S. Geol. Surv. Mon. 55*, 703-953.

——. 1936. *Proboscidea. A monograph of the discovery, evolution, migration and extinction of the mastodonts and elephants of the world.* Vol. I. Amer. Mus. Nat. Hist., 802 pp.

Romer, A. S. 1927. Notes on the Permo-Carboniferous reptile *Dimetrodon. Jour. Geol.*, XXXV, 673-689.

——. 1941. *Man and the Vertebrates.* 405 pp. Chicago.

——. 1942. Cartilage an embryonic adaptation. *Amer. Natur.*, LXXVI, 394-404.

——. 1945. *Vertebrate Paleontology.* 687 pp., Chicago.

——. 1946a. The primitive reptile *Limnoscelis* restudied. *Amer. Jour. Sci.*, CCXLIV, 149-188.

——. 1946b. The early evolution of fishes. *Quart. Rev. Biol.*, XXI, 33-69.

—— and L. I. Price. 1940. Review of the Pelycosauria. *Geol. Soc. Amer., Special Papers No. 28*, 1-538.

Simpson, G. G. 1944. *Tempo and Mode in Evolution.* 237 pp., New York.

Stirton, R. A. 1940. Phylogeny of North American Equidae. *Univ. Calif. Publ. Bull. Dept. Geol. Sci.*, XXV, 165-198.

Watson, D. M. S. 1913. *Batrachiderpeton lineatum* Hancock and Atthey, a coal-measure stegocephalian. *Proc. Zool. Soc. London*, 1913, 949-962.

——. 1919. The structure, evolution and origin of the Amphibia. The "orders" Rachitomi and Stereospondyli. *Phil. Trans. Roy. Soc. London*, (B), CCIX, 1-73.

——. 1926. The evolution and origin of the Amphibia. *Phil. Trans. Roy. Soc. London*, (B) CCXIV, 189-255.

Weidenreich, F. 1946. *Apes, Giants, and Man.* 122 pp., Chicago.

Wood, H. E. 1941. Trends in rhinoceros evolution. *Trans. New York Acad. Sci.*, (2), III, No. 4, 83-96.

Woodward, A. S. 1910. Presidential address. *Rept. Brit. Assoc. Adv. Sci., Winnipeg* (1909), Sect. C, 462-471.

Wright, S. 1934. Polydactylous guinea pigs. Two types respectively heterozygous and homozygous in the same mutant gene. *Jour. Heredity*, XXV, 359-362.

· 8 ·

ON THE EVOLUTION OF THE DIPNOI

BY T. STANLEY WESTOLL[1]

INTRODUCTION

THE Dipnoi have provided, since the time of Dollo (1895), a well-known textbook example of an evolutionary trend; the progressive change in the median fins has been variously interpreted, but it remains a fact. The skull-structure of fossil Dipnoi has been the subject of rather comprehensive studies by Watson and Gill (1923) and by Romer (1936), while Holmgren and Stensiö (1936) have commented extensively on these forms in a general account of fish-skulls.

The post-Paleozoic lung fishes have shown hardly any significant structural change, and are often quoted as good examples of slow-rate evolution, together with the coelacanths. But it is already well-known that the Devonian and Early Carboniferous Dipnoi showed much more rapid evolutionary change. The Middle Devonian *Dipterus* shows many significant resemblances (in body-form, fins, histology of bones and scales, and in the pattern of dermal bones and latero-sensory canals) to the approximately contemporaneous Rhipidistia (the "basal stock" of the Crossopterygii). These resemblances are clearly a common heritage from a common ancestor. The essence of our problem is the rate and mode of the early differentiation of the Dipnoi from this ancestral stock, which involves analysis of early fossil populations. Backward extrapolation, from later forms alone, would suggest that these common ancestors could not have lived later than a period well before the Devonian, but knowledge of the Devonian forms leads to a very different conclusion. Indeed, had *Dipterus* been the earliest known form, it would have been a reasonable deduction that the common ancestor could not have lived before the Middle Devonian (see Fig. 11)! It will be shown that the most probable date is in the Early Devonian.

The fossil Dipnoi allow an unusually clear picture of a tachytelic phase (Simpson, 1944, p. 134) to be drawn, and late and living genera may be a bradytelic group (*ibid.*, p. 133); they thus provide a useful commentary on some modern views on the evolution of major groups.

In this study the writer has been able to use the large and most valuable collections of *Dipterus* from Achanarras, Caithness, made by the late Sir Clive Forster-Cooper, F.R.S. (Forster-Cooper, 1937; Westoll, 1937b,

---

[1] University of Durham, Newcastle, England; formerly of University of Aberdeen, Scotland. Paper submitted December 1, 1947.

Graham-Smith and Westoll, 1937); fairly large material of *Dipterus* from Banniskirk, Caithness, in various museums and in the writer's collection; numerous *Scaumenacia*, including part of the Patten collection at Dartmouth College, Hanover, N.H.; and important Carboniferous material in the Royal Scottish Museum, Edinburgh, and the Hancock Museum, Newcastle-on-Tyne.

A most important new form from the Early Devonian of Germany has recently been discovered by Dr. W. Lehmann of Nahe. It is fully discussed in Lehmann and Westoll (1949), and most grateful thanks are due to Dr. Lehmann for his great generosity in permitting the writer to use excellent photographs of the fossil.

COMPARISON OF DIPNOI WITH RHIPIDISTIA

It is only necessary here to list some of the characters which assure us that Dipnoi either stemmed from the Rhipidistia, or that both groups have an immediate common ancestor. Both are moderately abundant in the Middle Devonian (*Dipnorhynchus, Dipterus*; and *Osteolepis, Thursius, Diplopterax, Glyptolepis*), but very rare in the Early Devonian (*Dipnorhynchus* is the only lungfish, and *Porolepis* the sole rhipidistian). No trace of either group is known from Downtonian or earlier strata.

The most primitive members of both groups have very similar histology of dermal bones and scales, with cosmine; and in both the peculiar markings termed "Westoll-Linien" by Bystrow (1942) may be developed on the cosmine-surfaces, and seem to indicate periodic resorption of cosmine (Westoll, 1936; but see also Bystrow, 1942). The body-form in Middle Devonian types is very similar, and there is the same complement of fins. The paired fins have a very distinct scale-covered muscular lobe, which on direct or indirect evidence had a longitudinally segmented endoskeletal axis with distinct rays borne by each segment. The shoulder-girdles are rather closely similar (Jarvik, 1944b). The latero-sensory system is very similar in general plan, and in particular the jugal line is developed as an enclosed canal. The lateral-line bones of the mandible in these early forms are easily comparable. It is significant that these points of resemblance are in sharp contrast with all other contemporary and earlier fishes.

But it is also true that the Middle Devonian *Dipterus* and *Osteolepis* show remarkable differences: in *Osteolepis* there is a highly characteristic intracranial kinetism between the trabecular and parachordal portions, while in *Dipterus* the cranium is entire and the palatoquadrates are fused with it; the skull-proportions are different; there are large dermal bones forming an integrated pattern in the skull-roof and cheeks of *Osteolepis*, but not in early Dipnoi; the dermal bones of the jaws and palate show rather notable differences, *Dipterus* lacks highly-developed marginal tooth-bearing bones, and also palatines, ectopterygoids, and coronoids; the dentition is characteristically different; the "parasphenoids" of older accounts are remarkably different in shape and extent; the opercular bones differ in detail; and Jarvik (1942) considers that the structure of the nasal capsule is very different in the two groups.

These and other differences are fully considered by the writer elsewhere (Lehmann and Westoll, 1949) and it need only be said here that they offer no insuperable bar to the conception of a very close relationship. Indeed, the very primitive Early and Middle Devonian *Dipnorhynchus* shows indications of a possible division of the endocranium, pterygoid bones almost osteolepid in proportions, a much longer cheek than in *Dipterus*, and parasphenoid bones of somewhat modified osteolepid type. Again, the large dermal bones (e.g. squamosal, "frontal" of authors) in osteolepids are almost certainly secondary developments within the history of that group. And finally the writer has given an analysis (Lehmann and Westoll, 1949) showing that Jarvik's conclusions about the nasal capsule and the snout are open to very serious question, and that the dipnoan structure could be derived immediately from that of primitive Rhipidistia.

We are therefore in a position to delineate in fair detail the structure of a form directly ancestral to the Dipnoi and to at least some Rhipidistia. The body must have been of about the same proportions as in *Dipterus* and *Osteolepis*, with a decidedly heterocercal tail; two dorsal fins, both short-based and with concentrated endoskeletons; paired fins with well-marked muscular scale-covered lobes fringed with fin rays, and not so elongated as in *Dipterus*; and scales covered (at least at intervals of time, in well-grown individuals) with cosmine, and either rhombic or rounded-rhombic in shape. The skull must have been sheathed with exoskeletal dermal bones, cosmine-bearing like the scales and forming a mosaic in which only certain "series" of elements retained a marked individuality from one specimen to another. These more constant series were associated with enclosed latero-sensory canals and the circumorbital and opercular regions. The endoskeletal cranium was, at least in juvenile forms, ossified in separate sphenethmoid and otico-occipital portions, the former floored by the parasphenoid (s.s.), the latter by paired parotic plates. There is not sufficient evidence to determine whether intracranial kinetism was developed, or whether the dermal bones of the skull-roof showed a marked division, as in osteolepids, but both are distinctly possible. Other points will be noted in discussions below.

GEOLOGICAL DISTRIBUTION OF GENERA

Unfortunately only a small number of genera of fossil Dipnoi is known in detail sufficient for general comparisons. In order of geological age, and omitting for the moment some specialized forms, they are: *Dipnorhynchus* (late Early Devonian, from the Hunsrückschiefer, marine Upper Siegenian or possibly Lower Emsian [Coblenzian] strata of Germany; Middle Devonian, marine limestones of Taemas, New South Wales, and probably also from Buchan, Victoria—both probably Eifelian); *Dipterus* (Middle Old Red Sandstone, also rarely in marine Middle Devonian, all material used in this paper probably of Givetian age; also doubtfully from Upper Devonian strata); *Pentlandia* (upper part of Middle Old Red Sandstone, probably Late Givetian age); *Scaumenacia* (lower part of Upper Old Red Sandstone, probably Frasnian age); *Phaneropleuron* (Upper Old Red Sandstone, Famennian age); *Uronemus* (the type species, *U. lobatus*, is from the Burdiehouse Limestone of Scotland, in the Oil-shale group of the Calciferous Sandstone series, of Late Dinantian age; *U. splendens* is from the Loanhead No. 2 Ironstone of Midlothian, in the Limestone Coal Group of the Carboniferous Limestone series, which falls within the D3 zone of the British Early Carboniferous, of very Late Dinantian or Early Namurian age); *Sagenodus* (from the Late Dinantian and Westphalian of Scotland, and the Westphalian of England and Europe; found also in the Pennsylvanian and in the Wichita of America); *Ctenodus*, including "*Prosagenodus*," Romer and Smith, 1934 (from the Late Dinantian of Scotland and the Late Mississippian [Chester] of Illinois; and from the later Carboniferous of Europe [rare in America], and possibly also from the Early Permian); *Ceratodus* (mostly very fragmentary remains in Triassic and later rocks); and the three living genera, *Epiceratodus* (*Neoceratodus* auctt.), *Protopterus* and *Lepidosiren*. These genera are what might be termed "normal" Dipnoi. Certain other genera are very obviously specialized. *Rhynchodipterus* (Säve-Söderbergh, 1937) and *Fleurantia* (Graham-Smith and Westoll, 1937) have elongated narrow snouts, and both are from strata of Late Devonian age. Dipnoan forms with elongated snouts are reported from rocks of very Late Devonian age in Greenland (e.g. Säve-Söderbergh, 1934). Finally, *Conchopoma*, from the Early Permian (Lebach group) of Germany, is a peculiar form with remarkably modified dentition and palatal structure; it may be noted here that *Uronemus* has also a modified dentition, though not so "aberrant" as that of *Conchopoma*.

Very many records of fossil Dipnoi, especially from post-Palaeozic strata, are based on isolated upper or lower tooth-plates; a broad comparative study would be necessary to determine their usefulness in stratigraphical and general palaeontological studies. The present is not intended as a revision of fossil Dipnoi, either morphological or stratigraphical.

EVOLUTION OF SKULL

The earliest fossil Dipnoi have a more or less ossified endocranium with a very large number (about 100) of dermal plates covering the outside of the head, together with tooth-bearing bones of the palate and mandible, "parasphenoid" elements and opercular bones. In the living genera the number of separate bones is greatly reduced, e.g. in the skull-roof, from 35-40 in early forms to about 10 in *Epiceratodus* and about 6 in *Protopterus* and *Lepidosiren*. Moreover, in early forms the dermal bones were superficial, but in general closely related to the endocranium. In *Epiceratodus* the bones lie in general much deeper, and the large median posterior bone is partly separated from the cartilaginous endocranium by muscles; and in *Protopterus* and *Lepidosiren* the posterior median bone is very deep, closely applied to the endocranium, while the paired so-called "frontals" have long posterior processes well separated from the endocranium. In these respects the Dipnoi present many similarities to other groups of teleostome fishes; the conditions in primitive Dipnoi are very like those in primitive Rhipidistia (except that these have some large dermal bones developed) and Actinopterygii (in which the skull-pattern is still more stable, consisting of a relatively small number of large bones). There is some reason to suppose that early Dipnoi may retain a condition which is in many respects primitive to all bony teleostomes.

The terminology of the dermal bones of Dipnoi has given rise to great difficulties. Some authors, such as Watson and Goodrich (cf. Watson and Day, 1916; Watson, 1926; Watson and Gill, 1923; Goodrich, 1925, 1930), have attempted directly to apply normal tetrapod terms to the bones of the dipnoan skull, and have, as is well known, reached very different conclusions; for instance, the bones termed frontal, parietal and supraoccipital by Goodrich are termed nasal, frontal and parietal by Watson. These differences are of some interest, since Watson's interpretation places the bones at about the correct rostro-caudal relationships to certain other structures if the comparison be made with bony fishes (the "orthodox" nomenclature), while Goodrich's interpretation agrees on the whole with the rostro-caudal extent of the similarly-named bones in tetrapods. It is now known that tetrapod names have been incorrectly applied to fishes (cf. Westoll, 1943a, for review). But we shall see later that no single element among those just discussed is correctly identified by either author in *Dipterus*, for example. The true homologues of nasals, frontals and parietals of Rhipidistia, or of frontals, parietals and post-parietals (dermo-supraoccipitals) of tetrapods, is to be sought in bones traversed by latero-sensory canals, lying lateral to the bones so named by Watson and Goodrich respectively in Devonian Dipnoi.

Another attempt to apply a more or less consistent terminology to dipnoan skull-bones is due to Stensiö and his school (especially in Holmgren and Stensiö, 1936). The assumption is made (as usual with Stensiö's school) that large bones in one form, which cover an area occupied by several bones in another, are due to fusion; this leads to what has aptly been termed "scissors-and-paste" homologies. Comparison of the figures of Holmgren and Stensiö (1936) with material used in this work shows that those workers made substantial errors in the courses of the latero-sensory canals and were not successful in identifying corresponding bones even in different material of the same or closely similar genera, or in making what seem to be obvious correlations with dermal bones in either osteolepids or tetrapods. Their work will not be referred to in what follows, but evidence bearing on their methods of homology will be discussed.

Because of these various confusions Forster-Cooper (1937) introduced a system of letters and numbers to distinguish the dermal bones of *Dipterus*, based on a single well-preserved skull (Forster-Cooper, 1937, Pl. IV, Fig. 7; see Fig. 2c). This system was adopted, with certain modifications, by the writer (Westoll, 1937b, 1943a; Graham-Smith and Westoll, 1937). The modifications were necessitated by the discovery that some of the bones (those lettered D, E, F, O and P) are extremely inconstant and are sometimes replaced by many more elements, and that the bones lettered Y and L, which are lateral-line elements, are rather frequently represented by two separate bones, which have been termed Y_1 and Y_2, and L_1 and L_2. Two adjacent latero-sensory bones are quite frequently fused, so the condition in Forster-Cooper's original was a normal variation from type. In the same way, some of the circumorbital bones, numbered 1-7 by Forster-Cooper, are probably composed of two fused elements; there were probably nine or ten elements in the series. Other bones of the cheek etc. were also given index-numbers. It is the writer's experience that the indices used here can be applied directly and with no ambiguity to all primitive Dipnoi, and that their homologues may be recognized with little difficulty in osteolepiform Rhipidistia. However, there is some evidence that *Dipterus* has lost a few elements present as separate bones in earlier forms (*Dipnorhynchus*), and for such the terminology is modified (bones J_1-J_3 and B_1-B_2 of *Dipnorhynchus*).

Romer (1936) has also applied a simple code-system to the dermal bones of the dipnoan skull. He recognizes a median series, which he letters "A" (A_0, A_1, A_2 from back to front), a medial paired series "B" (B_1-B_4 etc.), a more lateral paired series "C" (C_1-C_5, with at least five extra elements in *Dipnorhynchus*), and a still more lateral series "D" of supra-orbital and cheek elements. A spurious order was thus introduced among the dipnoan skull-bones; further knowledge of the latero-sensory canals shows, for example, that "B_1-B_2-C_4-C_{5-10}" form one true series in *Dipno-*

rhynchus, where Romer's B_3 and B_4 and C_1-C_3 are of entirely different nature from the B and C elements just named. Furthermore, "C_1" in Devonian forms ($=Y_1$ of this paper) is not homologous with "C_1" of later forms ($=H$ of this paper). The Forster-Cooper notation is therefore used throughout this paper.

Unfortunately little of critical value is known about the endocranium of fossil forms; it is only ossified at all completely in some Devonian species, and even there only in favorably preserved material—an interesting circumstance, paralleled in many other groups, which suggests the possibility that endoskeletal bone is selectively destroyed during maceration and decomposition of the corpse. There is, however, no doubt that at least the otico-occipital part of the endocranium in *Dipterus* was in essentials very much like the corresponding region in *Epiceratodus*, and there is no certain evidence that *Dipterus* had a marked division between the otico-occipital and sphenethmoid parts of the endocranium. But, as shown elsewhere, *Dipnorhynchus* may have had such a division. In view of the almost complete lack of information concerning the endocranium of fossil Dipnoi, this account will be restricted to a discussion of the dermal bones.

Dipterus

(Figures 1-4)

It is most convenient to discuss this genus here and afterward return to earlier forms. The generic name was published (Sedgwick and Murchison, 1828, p. 143) for fishes from the quarry of Banniskirk, Caithness (Middle Old Red Sandstone). Four species were named: *D. brachypygopterus*, *D. macropygopterus*, *D. valenciennesi* and *D. macrolepidotus*; the last now the genotype of the osteolepid *Thursius*, and the other three are regarded as synonymous and the species has generally been known, since the time of Pander (1858) as *Dipterus valenciennesi*, in spite of the priority of *D. brachypygopterus* S. & M. Later, Agassiz described *Polyphractus platycephalus* from the Thurso flagstones, and this has long been referred to *Dipterus*, the most obvious difference being the cosmine-coating and "snout" of the *platycephalus*-type. These forms have also, for more than 60 years, been referred to *D. valenciennesi*. Recently (Westoll, 1936; Forster-Cooper, 1937) it was shown that the cosmine may be present or absent in the same species, which confirmed this recognition of a single species (with exception of *Dipterus macropterus* Traq., the genotype of *Pentlandia*). But the writer now finds a notably different pattern of skull-roof bones in the Banniskirk from that of all other known material in Caithness, though the body and fins show little or no significant differences, and each set may include individuals with or without cosmine. The name *D. valenciennesi* should therefore be abandoned. Fortunately it is possible to use *D. brachypygopterus* S. & M. (which has line-priority over *D. valenciennesi*) for the Banniskirk material, and *D. platycephalus* for the form found in the Thurso flagstones. The best-known and most extensive material is of the latter type, from Achanarras.

1. *D. platycephalus.* A large material is available from Achanarras, especially in the valuable collections made by Sir Clive Forster-Cooper, to whom the writer is greatly indebted. The nature of the bone-pattern will be clear from Figures 1-3. The hard tissues of the "lips" are found only in specimens with well-developed cosmine (e.g. holotype of *Polyphractus platycephalus,* and similar material from Achanarras). In this tissue in the snout the supraorbital canal of each side makes a characteristic curve, and passes back into normal dermal canal-bones. The preparation of this canal in the snout-tissue is not easy; its walls are frequently extremely indefinite. But there appears to be no "anterior commissure" (cf. Goodrich, 1930, Fig. 722) where the paired canals lie closest together, and the writer has seen no evidence of any "rostral commissure" (Goodrich, 1930) or of the ethmoidal commissure linking the anterior ends of the infraorbital canals. It is probable that the rostral and anterior commissures of Goodrich's figure of *Epiceratodus* are "new" primary tubule anastomoses, and not primitive; they show variation in different individuals of *Epiceratodus* and are not present in early growth-stages.

From the snout, the supraorbital canal traverses a series of small often nearly square bones, namely, Q, N, M, L_2, L_1, K; it usually passes back to end in bone J (J_1) and is continued only by the anterior pit-line of the head. In K it gives off the primary tubule which anastomoses in X with one from the infraorbital canal. Within this longitudinal series there is frequently a bone which occupies the normal territory of two elements; thus L_1 and L_2 in Forster-Cooper's "standard" specimen (Fig. 2c) were represented by one element. Ontogenetical studies on living bony fishes such as *Amia* show that true fusion of adjacent bone rudiments developed along a latero-sensory canal is a normal feature of the development of large bones. It is here accepted that fusion of this type occurs in *Dipterus* (see discussion below).

The main lateral line enters the skull-roof in bone H, and anastomoses in that bone with the occipital cross-commissure. The main canal continues forward through bones Y_1, Y_2 and X, in which it turns laterally to enter bone 4 and becomes the infraorbital canal. This traverses bones 4, 5, 6, 7, 1A, 1B, 1C (bone 5 may just possibly be double). The infraorbital canal enters the lateral portion of the peculiar bony tissue of the ethmoidal region, but its precise forward continuation is uncertain; no ethmoidal commissure appears to be developed.

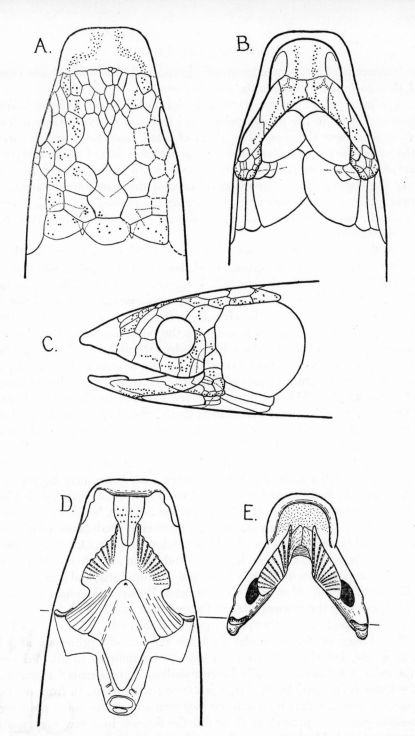

Figure 1. Dipterus platycephalus Ag. Reconstruction of skull in A, dorsal; B, ventral; C, lateral; D, palatal views; E, occlusal view of mandible. From Westoll, in Graham-Smith and Westoll, 1937, modified by addition of hypophysial foramen and oral sensory-line. For identification of bones, see Figures 10C and 3D. The external dermal bones from a single well-preserved specimen without cosmine from Achanarras (Univ. Mus. Zool. Camb.), snout, "ossified" lower lip, palate and prearticulars from Thurso Flagstone material.

The occipital cross-commissure swings forward from bone H into bone I, then backward again into the median bone A.

The jugal canal anastomoses with the infraorbital canal in bone 5, and passes down into the preopercular canal in bones 8 and 9. Only a few specimens show the succeeding chain of small canal-bones which carry the rest of the preopercular canal and the posterior part of the mandibular canal; the best material shows six or seven small bones between bone 9 and the angular. The other external bones of the mandible are angular, post-splenial, and pre-splenial, all carrying the mandibular canal. There is also, in these three bones, an enclosed canal apparently representing the "oralo-mandibular line."

All these latero-sensory canal bones are extremely constant in their development, with the exception noted above that adjacent members may "fuse." This fusion extends even to $X + K$, members of two different series. There are other bones which are also extremely constant: bones 2 and 3 above the orbit, bone B (the characteristic dipnoan median bone), the paired bones C, and the main bones of the opercular folds. But the remaining regions of the head are filled in by extremely variable elements. Thus between the supraorbital canal series, and in front of bone B, there is usually but not always a pair of bones (CC), and also a number of other elements which include the bones D, E and F of Forster-Cooper's original "key" specimen. In various specimens these bones in front of B number from 6 to 20 or perhaps even more. They include quite typical anamestic bones (cf. Westoll, 1936, p. 166), but the bones C are nearly always present. Small variable anamestic bones may also be present between bones 2-3 and the series L_1-Q; up to seven such bones may be present on either side in different individuals, two to four being most usual. The region covering the quadrate-articular region has also, besides the latero-sensory canal-bones already discussed, a number of small bones which are rarely well preserved but are clearly somewhat variable. One (rarely two or three) is wedged between bones 8-9 and 5-6 in all individuals, and is clearly comparable with the quadratojugal of Rhipidistia, and is numbered "10" in the figures. About three others occur between the chain of small bones, carrying the preopercular and mandibular canals, and the angular, but this region is nearly always very greatly disturbed.

The bones of the opercular fold are only rarely preserved at all completely, but the arrangement seems to be uniform in all. A large opercular is followed ventrally by two shallow "subopercular" elements; the lower is followed by the large posterior paired gular. In front of the posterior paired gulars is an anterior pair, and an anterior and a posterior median gular are present as shown in the figures. In a few very well-preserved individuals two small paired scale-like elements overlie the lateral parts of the anterior and posterior paired gulars.

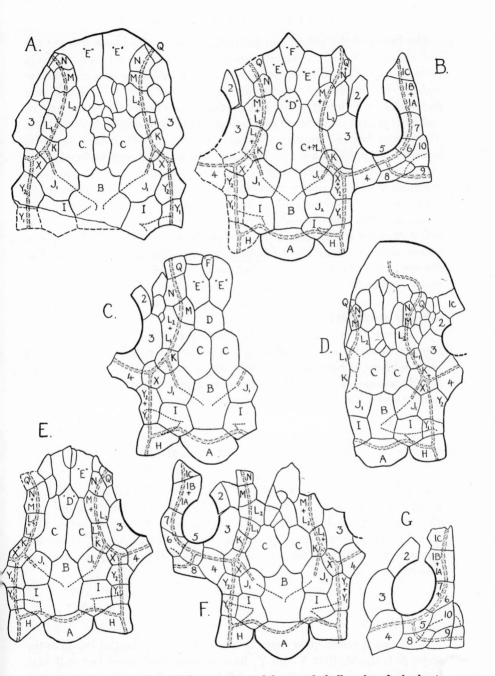

Figure 2. Dipterus platycephalus Ag. Dermal bones of skull-roof and cheek. A, from Thurso Flagstones (Roy. Scot. Mus.); B-G from Achanarras (all originally in Forster-Cooper collection, Univ. Mus. Zool. Cambridge). Latero-sensory canals in part restored from distribution of pores and local or partial collapse of their thin roofs. C is the original of Forster-Cooper's index-lettering system; B shows presence of bone J_2, and A shows series of bones dividing C-C.

The bones of the palate and internal surface of the lower jaw are not well shown in any of the Achanarras material, but they are well shown in material from Thurso which has a very similar cranial pattern and must at present be considered conspecific. The writer has seen insufficient material for a thorough study of variation. The vomers are rather narrow and bear sparse denticles. The pterygoids are of familiar dipnoan type. The dental battery consists of some ten rows of rather high denticles arranged in typical fan-shape; each row consists of almost separate teeth, and there are frequently slight irregularities in the pattern. The parasphenoid is a broad almost rhomboidal element, with a small hypophysial canal near its anterior end; it has no trace of the highly-developed posterior "stalk" which underlies the anterior vertebrae of later forms, and it does not reach back to the level of the radix aortae. As shown elsewhere, this bone may be of compound origin. The only dermal bone of the internal surface of the mandible is the prearticular, with its "toothplate" similar in structure to that of the pterygoid.

We are now in a position to analyze some of the differences shown by different individuals.

A. FUSION OF LATERAL-LINE ELEMENTS. As noted above, "fusion" of adjacent latero-sensory canal elements is fairly frequent; hardly a skull exists without at least one case easily interpreted in this fashion on either side. In a series of skulls, 21 sets of bones (right or left side) of the skull-roofing series were completely preserved. Fusions as follows were noted:

$$Y_1+Y_2\text{---}4 \qquad\qquad L_1+L_2\text{---}3$$
$$Y_2+X\text{---}3 \qquad\qquad L_2+M\text{---}13$$
$$X+K\text{---}6 \qquad\qquad M+N\text{---}2$$
$$K+L_1\text{---}10 \qquad\qquad N+Q\text{---}4$$

In this rather limited sample, as in all other available material, no single case of three fused elements could be detected (except in one very abnormal individual, Fig. 3E). If two is the normal limit of fusion, then $K + L_1$ clearly cuts out any possibility of $X + K$ or $L_1 + L_2$. If the frequency of fusion between any one bone and either neighbor be considered, we get:

$$Y_1\text{---}4 \qquad\qquad K\text{---}16 \qquad\qquad M\text{---}15$$
$$Y_2\text{---}7 \qquad\qquad L_1\text{---}13 \qquad\qquad N\text{---}6$$
$$X\text{---}9 \qquad\qquad L_2\text{---}16 \qquad\qquad Q\text{---}4$$

From this it seems clear that the main region of potential fusion is the series $K\text{-}L_1\text{-}L_2\text{-}M$, that X and Y_2 have a somewhat lower but still high fusion potential, and that Y_1, N and Q have a still lower fusion potential. These figures will be significant in discussing later forms.

In the circumorbital series only a few specimens are suitably preserved, and there is some doubt concerning element 5, which *may* normally

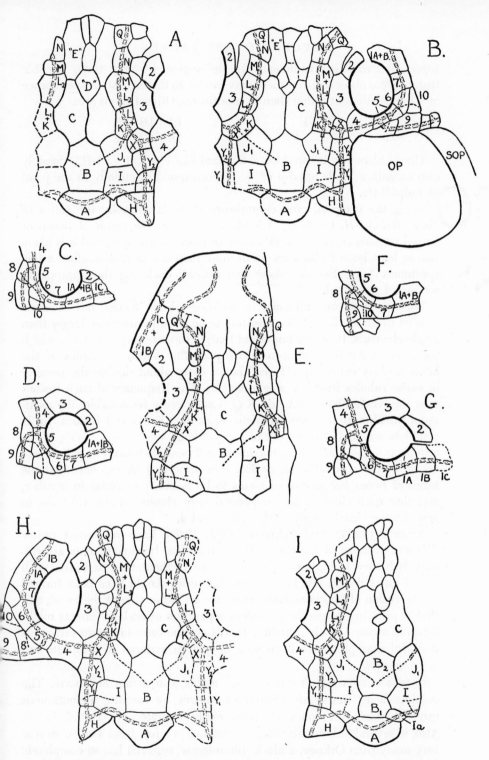

Figure 3. Dipterus platycephalus Ag. Dermal bones of skull-roof and cheek. E, from Thurso Flagstones, Thurso East Shore (Univ. Mus. Zool. Camb.); all others from Achanarras (A, C, D, G-I, from Univ. Mus. Zool. Camb.; B, in Zoology Dept., Univ. Coll. London, P. 146; F, in Brit. Mus. Nat. Hist., P. 17643). Note interesting conditions in B (anterior pit-line, right side!), E (multiple anomalies), I (B_1 and B_2, also small separate extrascapular on right).

represent two fused rudiments. In the region 4-6 only three possible fusions were observed, and these may be due to the inconstant appearance of a bone-rudiment rather than to true fusion. Other fusions are:

$$6+7\text{---}1 \qquad\qquad 1A+1B\text{---}8$$
$$7+1A\text{---}1 \qquad\qquad 1B+1C\text{---}2$$

The tendency is to produce a lacrimal-like element ($1A$-$1C$, possibly also including 7); bones 5-6 ($? + 7$) correspond essentially to the jugal of Rhipidistia.

Along the occipital cross-commissure there is normally the series of bones H-I-A-I-H. Of these, A is almost certainly the result of fusion of paired rudiments, each related to one or more neuromasts, and it is likely that at least bone I also arose from more than one rudiment, since a few specimens (e.g., Fig. 31) show two ossicles enclosing the appropriate section of the canal.

There is never any difficulty in deciding where "fusion" has occurred at least in the skull-roof; the resulting bone is quite distinctly larger than single elements. It is very important that, in those few specimens in which the bones have been dissected to expose the dendritic tubules of the latero-sensory canals, the "fused" bones carry about double the number of major tubules found in single ossicles. The frequency of such fusions over the whole series Y_1-X and K-Q is sufficiently remarkable; the maximum possible in any one complete series of 9 bones is 4 fusions. In 21 complete series, 45 fusions out of a possible 84 were noted (54%); in the sequence K-L_1-L_2-M, with a maximum of 2 possible fusions in pairs, there are 26 out of a possible 42, or 62%. It is important also to note that the series of bones just discussed seems to be basically constant in number, and that each element has in general very closely similar relations to neighboring "fixed" bones—I, J, C, 2-3, and 4.

Nielsen (1936) and Pehrson (1922, 1940) have supported rather different versions of the theory that lateral-line bone-rudiments are frequently binary. It might be expected, on such a theoretical basis, that each lateral-line bone of, say, the supraorbital series should have been formed by the fusion of two bone-rudiments, one on either side of the canal, and that in primitive forms the persistent separation of such rudiments might be quite a common abnormality. This is not the case; only two extremely doubtful examples have been seen in a large material of *Dipterus* and *Scaumenacia*.

B. FUSION BETWEEN "LATERAL-LINE" BONES AND OTHER ELEMENTS. The cosmine layer frequently obliterates sutures by forming a continuous external "skin" over bones which are really separate (cf. Westoll, 1936). Also, in several individuals from Achanarras, in a few from Thurso, and in very many from Orkney, a black "bituminous" material has so completely impregnated the dermal bones that the pattern of sutures may be entirely obliterated. Such material has been entirely neglected in this section, which is based entirely on Achanarras material without cosmine.

In view of the sweeping and almost indiscriminate "fusions" accepted by Stensiö, Säve-Söderbergh, and others of their school in any comparisons of different fossil fishes and early Tetrapoda, and of the clear demonstration just given of the "fusion potential" of adjacent lateral-line elements, numerous clear cases of fusion between lateral-line elements and other neighboring dermal bones might be expected. In fact, no single example of fusion between bone 3 and L_2, L_1, K or X was ever seen in several dozen favorably preserved specimens; only one possible (and doubtful) case of fusion between C and any member of the supraorbital canal series (L_1) (see Fig. 2B) and none between X, Y_2, or Y_1 and J or I (except perhaps in a single specimen (Fig. 3E) with multiple "anomalies"— an irregular *single* C bone, left J absent and replaced by extensions of B, Y_2 and X—which appears to have suffered injury during development). These are the only regions in which a clear-cut evidence of such fusion would be seen, and the evidence is overwhelmingly against fusions between lateral-line ossicles and adjoining "general" dermal bones. More anteriorly, with no fixed points for guidance, the lateral-line bones show small differences in shape and width in different specimens. Such differences are present also in the more stable posterior region, and offer absolutely no grounds for the supposition that the slightly larger elements in some individuals have developed as a result of fusion with neighboring bones.

C. THE ANAMESTIC BONES OF THE FRONT OF THE SKULL-ROOF. The term "anamestic" was introduced by the writer (1936, p. 166) to describe dermal bones which appear merely to fill in a space between more frequently occurring bones; in different individuals of the same species they may differ greatly in number and individual shape. In *Dipterus* from Achanarras the space between the supraorbital canal-bones and CC is filled by from 4 to about 20 bones which seem to be typically anamestic, and up to seven similar elements occur between bones L_1-Q and 2-3. A poorly-known series of about 4 occurs behind the angular and below bones 6-7. The median series has been analyzed by superposing tracings made to comparable scale. No definite common pattern can be made out; the superposed suture-tracings make, in the aggregate, a complex network of approximately even distribution of lines. The writer takes this as evidence of haphazard distribution of the rudimentary growth-centers from which these bones developed. It follows that no single element of such a group can properly be homologized with one in another animal, so that their appearance was probably not under any strict genetical and developmental control. This contrasts clearly with the great uniformity of the lateral-line canal-bones and such elements as B, 2, 3, and the opercular bones. Bones C are rather constant in this material, but show more variation than the last-named, and in Banniskirk material they may be absent.

D. "ABNORMALITIES" IN DERMAL BONES OF SKULL-ROOF. A small number of specimens, otherwise clearly of *platycephalus* type, show certain other differences from the norm. Some of these are doubtless due to accidents during development; one specimen, for instance, has no bone J on the left side (its space being occupied by extensions from B, Y_2 and $X + K$), and a single C element of curious shape suggests an early fusion of paired rudiments (Fig. 3E). Abnormalities in the posterior part of the skull-roof of some specimens, which might otherwise have passed with a cursory note, are interesting in comparison with *Dipnorhynchus*. Three specimens have been seen in which bone B is "replaced" by two median elements (Fig. 3I) and three others in which a large bone-plate (J_2) is intercalated between I and J_1, so that I is largely squeezed out of the skull-roof (Fig. 2B). In some six others a small median bone is enclosed between C-C (Fig. 3I), in one a similar element reaches B (Fig. 2A) and in two others it meets anteriorly the posterior members of the anterior anamestic series which normally wedge between the anterior ends of C-C. This is the position of the pineal foramen in *Dipnorhynchus*.

E. ABNORMALITIES IN LATERO-SENSORY SYSTEM. *Dipterus* shows a clear-cut difference between the latero-sensory canals (large, enclosed in bone) and surface grooves for lines of pit-organs (pit-lines). Though information on some parts of the system of enclosed canals (in the mandible!) is not complete, it may be said at once that these canals show no abnormalities in the material studied. Though the pit-line grooves show a general similarity of arrangement throughout, they show several abnormalities. The supraorbital canal passes back through L_1 and K (in which it normally gives off the primary-tube anastomosis with the canal in bone X) and curves medially into bone J_1, in which it ends in a dendritic cluster of tubules. Across the radiation center of J_1 towards that of B is the groove for the anterior pit-line, which is to be regarded as a "degenerate" continuation of the supraorbital line. In one specimen only, the posterior branch of the canal towards J_1 is very short and confined to K; in it the anterior pit-line traverses K, J_1, and B. The middle pit-line normally runs from the center of Y_1, across that of I, and (very rarely) continues towards the center of B. The posterior pit-line runs from near the radiation-center of I towards that of H. On B, the hind ends of the anterior pit-line do not usually meet, but bend outward again. Forster-Cooper (1937, Fig. 5) shows diagrammatically some variations he has observed in this region; the most important concern the apparent duplication of certain lines. Some of these instances are not due to pit-lines but to the breakdown of the "roof" of thin tubules from the enclosed canals (his Fig. 5A, B, C in particular). True duplication may occur, but rather rarely. Much more remarkable is the clear evidence that certain pit-lines may have widely different courses without any modification in the pattern of bones. Thus the anterior pit-line has been seen to bend from J_1 over Y_2 to Y_1 or back onto I, or into the suture between I and Y_1 (cf. Fig. 3B). In all these cases there is no confusion through duplication, and we have the clearest evidence of "capture" of a pit-line by other bones in such cases. Similarly the middle pit-line has been seen in one specimen to run nearly parallel with the posterior pit-line from I over H, and then to turn sharply forward to Y_1.

The pit-line of the cheek may curve over bones 8 and 10, or 8, 5, and 10, or 8, 5, 6, and 10 in different individuals, and no doubt its ventral continuation would show similar differences if adequately known. The importance of such observations will be obvious in a later section; meantime it is clear that the pit-lines just discussed can play no part in the determination of the pattern of dermal bones.

2. *Dipterus brachypygopterus*, S & M. (Fig. 4). This form is at present known only from Banniskirk, from a horizon probably (unless powerful faulting intervenes) distinctly above that of Achanarras, some 2 miles away. There are interesting problems involved here. The Achanarras type recurs above the probable horizon of Banniskirk, and it is possible that something very like the Achanarras type (*D. platycephalus*) occurs very rarely at Banniskirk. One such individual was figured by Pander (1858, Pl. 1, Fig. 2). The Banniskirk material seems to form, therefore, an enclave (in the time-sense) in a continuous *platycephalus* faunal range.

Unfortunately the material available for study is neither so plentiful nor so well preserved as that from Achanarras, but a number of remarkable differences are plainly obvious. The Banniskirk material is mostly distinctly smaller than the Achanarras *Dipterus*. As in the smaller Achanarras individuals, the "*platycephalus*" snout-structures and extensive development of cosmine are rare, but fragmentary remains of the former and occasional specimens with some partly resorbed cosmine (cf. Smith Woodward, 1891, Fig. 38, p. 239) have been recovered.

The only significant differences between the two forms concern the dermal bones of the skull-roof. They may be summed up quite briefly:

a. the median bone B extends much farther forward than in the Achanarras material;

b. the paired bones C-C are (with the possible exception figured by Pander) very much smaller and are generally absent;

c. the series of lateral-line bones from L_2-Q tends to be distinctly broader than in the Achanarras material; and

d. partly in relation to (*c*) above, the anterior anamestic bones occupy
a much smaller area and tend to be fewer but perhaps individually
larger.

Otherwise the dermal bones are arranged in a very closely similar
manner. The precise shape and size of bone *B* varies very greatly, and
even in the small material available a few remarkable anomalies have
been noted. In one specimen (Fig. 4D) there are no separate J_1 elements,
whose territory is occupied by lateral "wings" of bone *B*. Whether this
is due to fusion or to simple invasion of territory cannot be directly
determined. But in all specimens the conditions may be understood as a
result of a single process—the ontogenetic failure, or delayed appearance,
of bones in the region enclosed by *B*, J_1, and the supraorbital canal-
bones (*K-Q*). This area has here been largely filled by expansions of *B*
and L_1-*Q*, but to a varying degree. In a few individuals there may be no
anterior anamestic bones, or only a very few; but in a few at the other

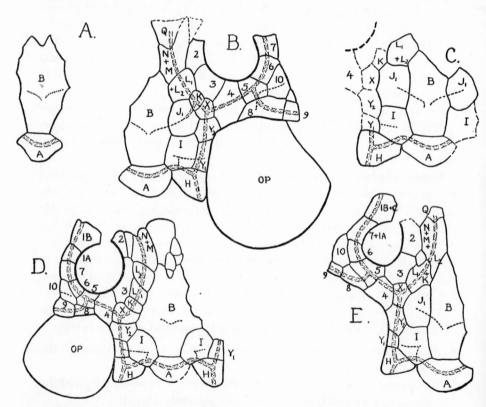

Figure 4. Dipterus brachypygopterus, S and M. Dermal bones of skull-roof and
cheeks. All from Banniskirk Quarry, Caithness. A, D, in Yorkshire Museum, York; B, in
Oxford Univ. Mus.; C, E, in Inverness Mus., Nos. 54 and 124 respectively.

extreme the conditions may not be very dissimilar from those in $D.$ *platycephalus.* Perhaps the abnormal individual with no separate J_1 is due to an extension of the same process.

Since the whole assemblage shows this characteristic aspect it seems that the implied differences in development compared with Achanarras individuals were governed by factors controlling osteogenesis. If a special genotype were responsible, it appears to have had almost complete penetrance in the Banniskirk population, but very varying expressivity, and (in so far as the precise pattern of dermal bones is concerned) a very varying specificity. These points are worth making since the Banniskirk population represents a blind alley in dipnoan evolution, and what is apparently the parent type persisted long after. It is reasonable to suppose that we are dealing with an isolated population, derived from an ancestral *"platycephalus"* type, but which probably became extinct. It is always possible that the genotype was not notably different in the two forms, and that the phenotypic differences may be due to environmental factors affecting osteogenesis. It is with these considerations in mind that the writer previously hesitated to regard the Banniskirk material as a separate species.

Dipnorhynchus

(Figure 5)

Hills (1933, 1941, 1943) has provided excellent accounts of a single magnificently preserved skull-roof from the Middle Devonian Murrumbidgee Limestones of Taemas, N.S.W., originally described as (?) *Ganorhynchus sussmilchi* R. Eth. fil. and made the type of the new genus *Dipnorhynchus* by Jaekel (1927). These limestones, on the evidence of invertebrate fossils, are regarded as of Couvinian age. From the Buchan Limestones of Buchan, Victoria, probably of about the same age, a fine mandible has been described by Hills (1935); it belongs in all probability to the same or a closely related species.

Recently W. M. Lehmann has obtained a remarkable dipnoan skull from the Early Devonian (Late Siegenian?) Hunsrückschiefer of the Rhineland. This should be referred to the same genus, but is unquestionably more primitive.

D. sussmilchi (Fig. 5, A-D). The first description by Hills (1933) has been used, among other writers, by Romer (1936) and Westoll (1943a) in comparative accounts, but the new information provided by Hills (1941, see also 1943) somewhat alters our conception of the structure. The dermal bones have a good coating of cosmine, with typical "Westoll-Linien" (Bystrow, 1942), and there is a snout and "lower lip" of *D. platycephalus* or *Ganorhynchus* type. The skull-roof has, compared with *Dipterus*, a shorter preorbital region and a longer, broader postorbital region.

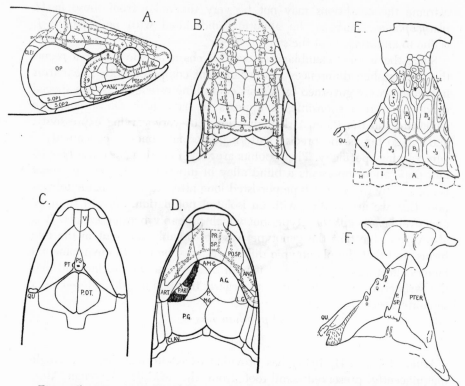

Figure 5. A-D, *Dipnorhynchus sussmilchi* (Eth. fil.). Reconstruction based on material described by Hills (see text). Opercular series, cheek-bones and infraorbital bones conjectural, palate hypothetical. A, lateral; B, dorsal; C, palatal; D, ventral view.

E-F, *Dipnorhynchus* sp., from German Hunsrückschiefer. Distortion due to slaty cleavage rectified. E, skull-roof; F, palate. From photographs generously supplied by Dr. W. Lehmann. (See page 142 for correction to E.)

The most important more primitive features are the presence of a "pineal" foramen and the nature of the supraorbital latero-sensory canal, which continues far back as an enclosed canal instead of degenerating to form the anterior pit-line, and does not anastomose with the infraorbital canal. The bones Y_1 and Y_2 are large, and lateral to Y_2 there is on one side a separate element, probably a supraspiracular or prespiracular plate. Bones X and 4 seem to be fused on both sides. Bones 2 and 3 are easily identified and in the supraorbital canal there is no difficulty in recognizing the homologues of Q, N, M, L_2, L_1 and K; L_2, L_1, and K appear to be fused on the right side. Slight differences in the contacts of 3-4-X with L_1-K as compared with *Dipterus* are apparently due to the relatively more anterior position of the orbit in *Dipnorhynchus*, so that $(4 + X)$ is slightly forwardly displaced and 3 is shortened. Behind K the writer formerly recognized two bones (J_1 and J_2) carrying the supra-orbital canal and lying in front of the series H-I-A, but Hill's new description makes it clear that there are three such bones—J_1, J_2, and J_3. In *Dipterus* there is normally only one *J* bone, and the loss of J_2 and J_3 may reasonably be associated with the loss of osteogenic stimulus when the posterior end of the supraorbital canal "degenerated." This loss has allowed bone *I* to wedge firmly into the skull, a feature providing a firm anchorage for the dermal shoulder-girdle. Unfortunately only a fragment of bone *I* is present, on the right side, in *Dipnorhynchus sussmilchi*.

Between the supraorbital canal-series there are about 9 or 10 bones. The most posterior (B_1) is almost certainly not a member of the extra-scapular series. It is followed anteriorly by B_2, which gives some indication of having been formed by the fusion of two elements, and at first suggests comparison with C-C of *Dipterus*. However, the bone reaches anteriorly to the level of the line through the centers of *K*, or slightly behind it, and does not reach the line through the centers of $(4 + X)$. It therefore covers the same part of the skull-roof as the anterior part of *B* of *Dipterus*, and is entirely behind the region of C-C; it may be compared directly with B_2 of certain individuals of *Dipterus*. In front of B_2 is a group of small irregular bones; the pineal foramen is enclosed between the two most posterior. The irregular shape of these bones suggests either fusion of separate rudiments or anamestic origin. C-C in *Dipterus* lie between L_2-L_1-*K* on each side. This is precisely the position of the posterior three elements (one on left, two on right) which surround and lie closest to the pineal foramen. The more anterior elements fade out under the continuous cosmine of the snout-region. Romer (1936) thought that this anterior shield was in the "process of breaking up into a host of small elements." This overlooks the effects of the cosmine in obliterating sutures, but there is another point which makes any interpretation of this region as a mosaic of bones very dubious. In *Dipterus* this region is not occupied by separate bones, and in the various Devonian forms like *Ganorhynchus* the snout and anterior part of the mandible are found entirely separate from the rest of the skull, suggesting a different nature and histology. It is true that the ancestors of Dipnoi may have had numerous lateral-line and other bones in this region, but the most detailed histological and other investigations of the snout will be necessary before its structure in *Dipnorhynchus* can be assured.

In Figure 5, A-D is given a suggested reconstruction of *Dipnorhynchus*. The various fusions of the lateral-line bones are resolved, and from the shape of the lateral margins of the skull-roof the bones of the cheek, sub-orbital region, and opercular apparatus have been freely restored. Since Y_1 and Y_2 appear to be the homologues of the bones normally termed supratemporal and intertemporal in Rhipidistia, the approximate position of the proximal articulations of the hyomandibular can be fixed. The operculum must lie behind this, which fixes approximately the back of the cheek-bones. The mandible is taken from the Buchan specimen, and fits very well. Compared with *Dipterus* and Rhipidistia (*Osteolepis* or *Eusthenopteron*) the conditions in *Dipnorhynchus* are almost exactly intermediate; the cheek in *Dipterus* has been much shortened and the operculum is moved forward, while in Rhipidistia the cheek is greatly elongated and the operculum lies far back. As already indicated by Hills (1943), such a revised version of *Dipnorhynchus* is extremely close to the hypothetical common ancestor of Dipnoi and Rhipidistia figured by the writer (1943a). The palate (Fig. 5c) shows again a hypothetical condition intermediate between those of *Dipterus* and Rhipidistia, with separate parotic plates.

On all counts, therefore, *D. sussmilchi* is a very primitive form, showing the clearest indications of not very distant relationship to Rhipidistia.

Dipnorhynchus lehmanni, sp. nov. The skull from the Hunsrückschiefer will be fully described elsewhere (Lehmann and Westoll, 1949). It is clearly related to, but specifically distinct from, *D. sussmilchi*, and I take pleasure in naming the new species *Dipnorhynchus lehmanni*. This remarkable discovery confirms and extends the deductions made from *D. sussmilchi* (cf. Lehmann and Westoll, 1949). The specimen shows the usual distortion of specimens preserved in cleaved slates, and this has been partly corrected by simple graphical methods. In the skull-roof the median line is obvious and several originally transverse lines can be plotted with some accuracy. The resulting figure (Fig. 5, E-F) may be slightly too compressed either laterally or antero-posteriorly, but the morphological relationships are clear. Y_1 and Y_2 are as in the right side of *D. sussmilchi*; there was probably a prespiracular plate as in that form. In the left supraorbital canal, series J_3 is very large, J_2 small; J_1 and K appear to be fused, as are L_1 and L_2. On the right side J_2, J_1, and K appear to be fused. B_1 is small, but B_2 is represented by a pair of large bones (cf. conditions in *D. sussmilchi*). In front of B_2-B_2 is a series of some 20 (at least) anamestic bones; a pineal opening is present between two posterior members of this series. The dermal bones have a thick cosmine-layer with "Westoll-Linien" and there is a poorly preserved cosmine-covered snout. No pit-line grooves are visible.

The reconstruction in Figure 5E, though correct where drawn in full lines, is inaccurate in the region of bone A. X-ray photographs show that bone B is pointed posteriorly, and that no bone A is present, bones I being large elements meeting in the mid-line. The same may be true of *D. sussmilchi*. This is not a fundamental difference in pattern, since the extrascapular series was derived from a series of paired rudiments, and bone A of other early Dipnoi undoubtedly arose by fusion. In *Dipno-*

rhynchus these elements arising in this position fused with bone *I*. Comparable differences may be noted among Actinopterygii, e.g. between primitive palaeoniscoids (cf. *D. lehmanni*) and the Permian *Paramblypterus* (cf. *Dipterus*). *Acipenser* also has a median extrascapular formed by fusion of paired rudiments.

The palate is quite remarkable. The ventral aspect of the snout is thoroughly dipnoan, and the pterygoids are not unlike those of *Dipterus*, except that there is no well-marked lateral process at the back of the tooth-plate. The teeth are not well preserved, but seem to have been arranged in rather crude radiating rows. The most remarkable feature is the parasphenoid, which is rhipidistian-like; the basisphenoid seems to have had basipterygoid processes rather like those of Rhipidistia. If any posterior parasphenoids were developed, they must have been separate parotic plates. There is no ossification present in the otico-occipital part of the brain-case, which suggests that such may have been removable after death, and invites comparison with the brain-case of Rhipidistia.

These features are exactly comparable with the reconstruction of *D. sussmilchi*, which was made on theoretical grounds before the German specimen came to my notice. *D. lehmanni* confirms in a remarkable way the truly primitive and almost annectant character of the genus and greatly strengthens the theoretical considerations behind an earlier synoptic figure (Westoll, 1943a, Fig. 7) and the attempted reconstruction of *Dipnorhynchus* (Fig. 5 A-D).

Pentlandia

Though specimens of *Pentlandia macroptera* showing the characteristic elongated dorsal fin are not uncommon, good cranial material is scarce. So far as known, it closely resembles that of *Dipterus platycephalus*. The main difference is that the individual bones tend to be more "square-cut" than in *Dipterus*. Bones *CC* are well developed, and the more anterior anamestic bones appear to be few in number and large. Bones *H*, *I*, and *A* are as in *Dipterus*. The supraorbital latero-sensory canal probably enters bone J_1, since the anterior pit-line groove starts on that bone.

Scaumenacia

(Figure 6)

A considerable material of this genus has been used in this study. Some was collected in the years 1934 and 1937 by Dr. Graham-Smith and the writer, and much was obtained from Dartmouth College, the Museum of Comparative Zoology at Harvard, and the British Museum (Natural History). The writer is especially indebted to Professor A. S. Romer, who most generously made available the material he had brought together and relinquished a most interesting study.

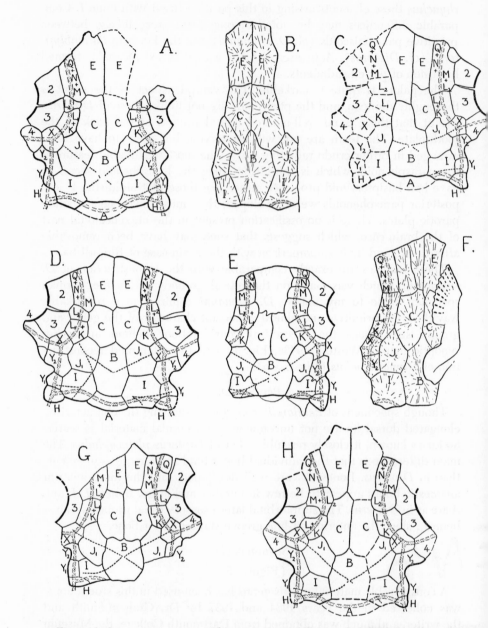

Figure 6. Scaumenacia curta, Whiteaves. Dermal bones of skull-roof. A, C, coll. Graham-Smith; B, F, sketches of B.M.N.H., P. 7073 and P. 6786; D, Park Museum, Providence, R.I., No. E.2853; E, A.M.N.H., 7656; G-H, Patten Coll., Dartmouth College.

The dermal bones of the skull are extremely similar to those of *Dipterus platycephalus* in general features. The circumorbital and cheek-regions are extremely similar, and the opercular bones are almost identical.

The bones carrying the occipital cross-commissure (H, I, and A) are present as in *Dipterus*, but H is a much smaller, rounded bone, set in a deep notch formed by Y_1 and I. Bone A is much less frequently present than in *Dipterus* and is apparently thinner and less heavily ossified. H and A are widely separated, unlike the conditions in *Dipterus*. These are developments carried further in later Dipnoi.

Bones Y_1, Y_2, X and 4, 3, and 2 are almost exactly as in *Dipterus*, but there is a most characteristic deep notch between Y_1 and Y_2 occupied by the antero-dorsal corner of the operculum. In front of this, in one or two specimens (Fig. 6D), is a separate prespiracular bone; in most this is replaced by an extension of Y_2, and these conditions may be compared directly with those in the two sides of the *Dipnorhynchus sussmilchi* skull. The supraorbital canal series (K-L_1-L_2-M-N-Q) is almost precisely as in *Dipterus*, and the individual bones have exactly the same relations to the bones 4, 3, and 2. Fusions are much more extensive than in *Dipterus*; it is not unusual to find three elements fused, and two specimens show apparently four elements fused. Out of 20 complete sides, the following fusions were noted:

Y_1+Y_2——0	$K+L_1+L_2$——4
Y_2+X——0	L_1+L_2+M——2
$X+K$——2	L_2+M+N——3
$K+L_1$——14	$M+N+Q$——8
L_1+L_2——3	Y_1+Y_2+X+K——0
L_2+M——1	$Y_2+X+K+L_1$——0
$M+N$——3	$X+K+L_1+L_2$——0
$N+Q$——4	$K+L_1+L_2+M$——0
Y_1+Y_2+X——0	L_1+L_2+M+N——0
Y_2+X+K——0	$L_2+M+N+Q$——2
$X+K+L_1$——0	

The frequencies of fusions between neighboring elements are as follows:

Y_1—Y_2——0	L_1+L_2——9
Y_2—X——0	L_2+M——8
X—K——2	$M+N$——16
K—L_1——18	$N+Q$——14

There seem therefore to be two regions of high fusion-potential, K-L_1-L_2 and M-Q. The fusion-potential of each individual bone is as follows:

Y_1:0	K:20	M:19
Y_2:0	L_1:23	N:20
X:2	L_2:15	Q:14

The main differences from *Dipterus* are the almost complete absence of fusion-potential behind *K* and the great increase in front of *M*.

Bone *B* is constantly present, and normally extends as far forward as a line through the centers of *X-X*, though its median process may extend further. It is thus no larger than in *D. platycephalus*. In front of *B* there is normally a large pair of bones (*C-C*), in front of which another large pair of bones (*E-E*)[2] frequently completes the skull-roof. This contrast with *Dipterus* is remarkable. Out of 18 specimens which show this region well, bones *E-E* are present without modifications in 12; in two, a single median bone is present (Fig. 6E); in two (Fig. 6F), additional bones are present (three in all in one, four in the other); and in two the bones *E-E* are present but modified by the loss of *C* on one side (Fig. 6c). Bones *C* are also normally present without modification; out of 25 specimens, 20 are "normal," 2 have bone *C* missing on one side and replaced by extensions from *B* and *E* (Fig. 6c), and 3 have a narrow bone wedged between J_1, K-L_1, *C* and *B* (Fig. 6B), or a prong from bone *B* occupying the same territory. Jaekel's "*Canadiptarus*" (*sic*, 1927, Fig. 62) shows apparently multiple anomalies in a *Scaumenacia*.

The circumorbital bones are much as in *Dipterus*. Bone 4 meets 5 and 8 below, 6 occupies the postero-ventral part of the orbit. Next anteriorly is a long element which does not normally meet bone 2; it may, however, be fused with the most posterior of the succeeding three elements, of which the first two meet bone 2 above, and the most anterior lies in front of that bone. Pending the study of more extensive collections, these are provisionally identified as the homologues of bones 7, 1A, 1B and 1C of *Dipterus*.

The jugal-preopercular-mandibular canal is carried by a series of bones arranged almost as in *Dipterus* (cf. Westoll, 1937a, Fig. 3b). Bones 8 and 9 are easily recognized, but are squeezed into an even narrower space than in *Dipterus*, suggesting still further forward movement of the operculum. The chain of small bones carrying the canal down to the angulo-post-splenial comprises only four or five other elements in the available material, against six or seven in *Dipterus*, but this may be due, at least in part, to fusion of neighboring elements. The anamestic bones in this region may be reduced in number, but bone 10 is generally present. In the mandible a single element occupies the territory of the angular and post-splenial of *Dipterus*; it will be termed angulo-postsplenial. The presplenial is normal. As in *Dipterus*, there appear to be two latero-sensory canals in the angulo-postsplenial section.

[2] Forster-Cooper's original key-specimen from Achanarras seems to have been chosen deliberately because of its resemblance to later Dipnoi; the index letters *D*, *E*, and *F* are used here, though the bones so lettered may not always be strictly homologous.

The opercular region is composed of precisely the same bones as in *Dipterus*.

The bones of the roof of the mouth and inner face of the mandible call for little comment. The pterygoids are, on the whole, very similar to those of *Dipterus*; each bears about 10 rows of compressed high teeth which meet or almost meet their neighbors so that each row is almost like a saw-edged ridge. The parasphenoid is considerably more "advanced" than that of *Dipterus*, having a long posterior process. The vomers are narrow bones with quite sharp teeth. The prearticulars are closely comparable with those of *Dipterus*, but their tooth-rows are like those on the pterygoids, and number 8 or 9. In several specimens up to four small strips of bone bearing slender conical teeth are found in the debris of the anterior part of the head. They may represent marginal teeth and are conceivably derived from an ancestral type with maxillaries, "premaxillaries," and dentaries. On the other hand, no sign of such teeth has been noted in *Dipterus*, and they may be secondary developments.

The latero-sensory system shows a few differences from conditions in *Dipterus*. The supraorbital canal never, in my material, extends into bone J_1. The remnants of this prolongation, and the anterior end of the anterior pit-line, have been "pirated" by bone X, from which the pit-line groove runs over J_1 towards the center of B, where it is frequently hooked outwards. The middle pit-line runs normally from Y_1 over I towards the center of B, the posterior pit-line from H to I, sometimes also continued onto B. Abnormalities in the courses of these grooves are not infrequent; the most remarkable is the case of a middle pit-line which runs from Y_1 to the center of I, bends forwards to the junction of I, J_1, and B, and then to the center of J_1 (Fig. 6D). The pit-line of the cheek is rarely well preserved, but usually seems to run over the canal-bones 8-9-etc., not swinging forward onto 5, 6, and 10 as is frequently the case in *Dipterus*.

Phaneropleuron

(Figure 7)

Though a large number of specimens of *P. andersoni* from the type-locality of Dura Den exists in museums, really well-preserved heads are extremely rare. Hence only a cursory description of the conditions in this most interesting form is possible. But with small exceptions, the structure is very close to that of *Scaumenacia*. Bones H, Y_1, Y_2, I, J_1, and B are almost identical in the two genera, except that Y_1 and Y_2 are on the whole narrower, and Y_2 is deeply notched for the reception of the antero-dorsal corner of the operculum. Bone A is very rarely preserved, and was possibly absent. In front of J_1 and B, between the supraorbital canal series, the "normal" condition is the presence of two pairs of large bones (C-C,

E-E) filling the entire space, but in several individuals the anterior pair is replaced by a single bone, and in at least one fossil a single pair of long bones occupies the entire area (Fig. 7E).

The circumorbital series is rarely preserved, which makes the interpretation of the supraorbital-canal series more difficult. In addition, the latero-sensory canals are often not easy to follow. Bone *X* is almost invariably separate from *K*, but considerable fusion has always taken place between more anterior members of the series *K-Q*. No details can yet be given. While it is clear that the other bones of the skull are essentially as in *Scaumenacia*, a systematic account of variations is impossible. This is unfortunate since *Dipnorhynchus-Dipterus-Scaumenacia-Phaneropleuron* would afford a most valuable morphological series.

The pit-line grooves of the skull-roof are essentially as in *Scaumenacia*; the anterior pit-line may start from *K*, or (much more rarely) from *X*, as in that genus.

Before proceeding with a review of the later "normal" genera, it is as well here to consider *Rhynchodipterus* and *Fleurantia*, two Late Devonian genera with long narrow snouts. Some remarkable forms with long and

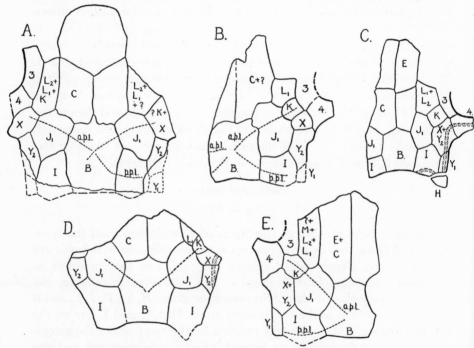

Figure 7. Phaneropleuron andersoni, Hux. Sketches to show skull-roof structure. A, Manchester Mus., L 10867; B, C, St. Andrew's Univ. Mus.; D, E, Roy. Scot. Mus., both on 1895.147.12.

broad snouts have been found in the Late Devonian of Greenland. Details of their skull-structure are awaited with great interest.

The head of *Rhynchodipterus* (Säve-Söderbergh, 1937) is unfortunately not very well preserved, and the type specimen (in Elgin Museum) has had paint-lines placed along what Säve-Söderbergh took to be sutures. These are not always reliable, and the paint obscures the structure. *Rhynchodipterus* will be omitted from this account.

Fleurantia

This genus was rather fully described by Graham-Smith and Westoll (1937), and essentially the same bone-terminology was used as in this paper. The structure of the circumorbital region and posterior part of the skull-roof is precisely comparable with that of *Scaumenacia*; the only correction the writer would make concerns the bones labelled 7, 1, 1a and 1b in 1937. Of these, "1" is the element here called 1A, and "1a," which is large, is probably $1B + 1C$; "1b" would therefore be a still more anterior element, 1D (cf. discussion of bone R below).

In the skull-roof, in front of B and J and between the supraorbital-canal series, is normally a pair of bones C, reaching forward to about the level of the back of bone M, but in one specimen there are two such bones on one side. These C bones are succeeded by a strong median element F (growth-center very anterior) in all specimens where this region is known (three new specimens have been discovered since 1937).

The supraorbital canal series begins posteriorly with a long element which covers precisely the territory of K, L_1, and L_2 in *Dipterus* or *Scaumenacia*, and evidence for its compound origin has already been discussed in 1937. The next bone is precisely similar in its relationships to M of *Dipterus* and *Scaumenacia*, and this is succeeded by N, Q, and R, the latter not found in at least the vast majority of earlier forms. This more anterior ossification along the supraorbital canal may be compared with the presence of 1D on the infraorbital canal.

The bones carrying the sensory canal from bone 8 to the angulo-post-splenial are not preserved, but were probably present somewhat as in *Scaumenacia*. In the mandible a long angulo-postsplenial is present, with a short splenial.

The bones of the palate represent a simple modification of the conditions in *Scaumenacia* and *Dipterus*. The bones named "dermopalatines(?)" in 1937 are the vomers, and should be placed in front of the pterygoids, in contact along the middle line. The nature of the peculiar modified teeth has been discussed by Bystrow (1945); the writer is in substantial agreement with his conclusions. The parasphenoid has a long posterior stalk.

The arrangement and distribution of the latero-sensory canals and pit-lines is as in *Scaumenacia*. Bone *A* is absent in all known specimens; it may have failed to ossify. A development of considerable interest is the presence of an important tubule from the occipital commissure which leaves the center of bone *I* and runs towards the center of *B*. A similar development has been noted in *Scaumenacia*.

Sagenodus

(Figure 8A, A')

Remains of *Sagenodus* are common in the Coal-Measures of Europe and the Pennsylvanian of America, and are found also in beds probably of Early Permian age. *Sagenodus quinquecostatus*, from the latest Dinantian or Early Namurian of Loanhead, Scotland, is a typical *Sagenodus* in cranial structure. The new genus *Prosagenodus*, instituted for "*Ctenodus interruptus* Barkas" (in the sense of Traquair, 1890) by Romer and Smith (1934), is really a "pro-*Ctenodus*," with no sign whatever of the typical *Sagenodus* skull-modification.

The skull-pattern in the species of *Sagenodus* is astonishingly stable. The early S. *quinquecostatus*, various Westphalian species from Britain, Late Carboniferous material from Europe and America (Romer and Smith, 1934), and Early Permian remains alike show a most characteristic structure, which has been carefully described by Watson and Gill (1923) and Romer and Smith (1934). The material described by the latter workers is incomplete and they reversed the dorsal and ventral surfaces of the skull roofing bones, while the former do not describe the latero-sensory system and, in the writer's opinion, have misinterpreted the circumorbital region. In view of the great similarity in structure throughout, it has been thought sufficient merely to modify the figure of Watson and Gill (1923, Fig. 1) in the circumorbital region, and to insert the courses of the latero-sensory canals and pit-line grooves (Fig. 8A). Important variations in structure are so rare that it is sufficient here to give them a single composite figure (Fig. 8A').

Certain bones can be recognized at once by comparison with *Scaumenacia* or *Dipterus*, e.g. 2, 3, 4, $(X + Y_2)$, Y_1, H, I, B, J_1. In the vast majority of cases, X and Y_2 are fused, but they are separate in two individuals seen by the writer. In front of X, J, and B is a large bone carrying the supraorbital canal, which seems without much doubt to represent $K + L_1 + L_2 + M$. In one specimen, K is separate on one side. In front of this large bone there is usually a somewhat smaller element, $N + Q$, which is represented by two bones in some specimens. Q represents the normal anterior limit of ossification along the supraorbital canal in earlier forms, but here it is followed by a series of small bones along the in-turned section of the canal. These, which are somewhat irregular and

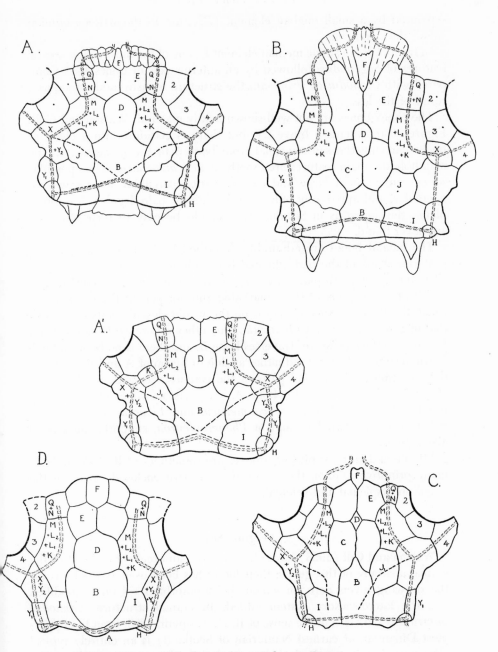

Figure 8. Dermal bones of skull-roof of Late Paleozoic Dipnoi.

A, A′, *Sagenodus*; A′ assembles certain abnormalities; separate bone *K*, bones *X* and Y_2 sometimes separate. B, *Ctenodus*. A and B based on figures by Watson and Gill (1923), modified in circumorbital region and with latero-sensory canals added.

C. *Uronemus splendens* (Tr.); D, *Conchopoma gadiforme*. Both original.

separated by a small median element (F?), are in the writer's opinion "new" developments.

In front of B is a single median element D, one of the most characteristic features of *Sagenodus*, followed by an anterior pair of bones E-E. Compared with *Ctenodus* or *Uronemus* the structure is easily understood as a result of the loss of C-C.

The cheek-bones are not well-shown in any material; Watson and Gill's Figure 20 represents a brave try, but there is certainly also a chain of bones carrying the sensory-canal from bone 5 to the mandible. In the mandible the main features are exactly as in *Scaumenacia*. The opercular series consists of a large and characteristic operculum, a narrow subopercular, and apparently only a small anterior paired gular. Any other plates, developed as in *Scaumenacia*, should be easy to recognize, and are never found.

The palatal bones are admirably described by Watson and Gill. The posterior shank of the parasphenoid is even longer in proportion than in *Fleurantia*. The tooth-plates are very familiar and require no comment.

With the exception of the remarkable anterior part of the supraorbital canal, the latero-sensory system is on the whole closely comparable with that of *Scaumenacia* and *Fleurantia*. One other difference is noteworthy: the "occipital commissure" traverses bone B, and there is no bone A. Such a structure may be regarded either as due to fusion of A and B, or to the degeneration of the medial parts of the commissure, with resulting loss of osteogenic stimulation for bone A, and anastomosis of other primary tubules, as foreshadowed in *Scaumenacia* and *Fleurantia*. The known structure of the two last, and of *Phaneropleuron*, supports the second alternative.

Middle and anterior pit-line grooves are sometimes well marked. As in many primitive Dipnoi, there appear to be two enclosed canals in the angulo-postsplenial and splenial.

Ctenodus

(Figure 8B)

Watson and Gill (1923) have already given an excellent account of the cranial anatomy of this genus; their figure has been used as the basis for the drawing given here, in which the supraorbital region is modified and the latero-sensory system added. In cranial structure "*Ctenodus interruptus* Barkas" (in the sense of R. H. Traquair, 1890, from the uppermost Dinantian or earliest Namurian of Scotland) is an entirely typical *Ctenodus*, but its tooth-plates are more like those of "normal" earlier forms and have not the characteristic appearance of later *Ctenodus* material. Romer and Smith proposed the new genus *Prosagenodus* for this form, but it is probably a very primitive *Ctenodus*.

Ctenodus shows many resemblances to *Scaumenacia* and *Phaneropleuron* on the one hand, and to *Sagenodus* on the other (Fig. 8ʙ). The occipital commissure traverses H (a very small bone), I, and B as in *Sagenodus* (see discussion above); A is absent. Y_1 and Y_2 are normally separate, and J_1 is typically developed. X is a separate small bone in all available material, and bones 2, 3, and 4 are normal. Along the supraorbital canal, a large posterior bone $(L_2 + L_1 + K)$ is sometimes followed by a small separate M, but all four are not infrequently fused. Still more anterior elements are not well preserved; the figure shows the conditions in the only specimens which show this region well. More anteriorly the peculiar "prenasal fan" described by Watson and Gill is at present not susceptible to detailed study; the inward flexure of the supraorbital canals must have crossed this region, and some evidence suggests that they pierced some of the bones of the "fan."

The more median elements of the skull-roof are very like those of average *Scaumenacia* or *Phaneropleuron*, except that two median elements D and F (the "interfrontal" and "internasal" of Watson and Gill) are constantly present.

As in *Sagenodus*, we have in *Ctenodus* a genus with at least a few species in which the cranial pattern, contrary to conditions in earlier forms, is strikingly stable. Abnormalities are rare; one specimen has J_1 missing on the right side, and its territory is occupied by extensions from $(L_2 + L_1 + K)$, Y_2, and I.

The latero-sensory canals are exactly as in those individuals of *Sagenodus* which have separate X-bones. No pit-line grooves have been observed; the dermal bones appear to have been deeper-lying than in earlier forms.

Remains of the cheek, etc., are not preserved in intelligible form. The structure of the palate and mandible are essentially as in *Sagenodus*, with only minor differences. The tooth-plates are familiar and need no comment.

Uronemus

(Figure 8c)

The genotype, *U. lobatus* Traq., from the Late Dinantian Burdiehouse Limestone of Scotland, lacks adequate cranial remains in all known specimens. *U. splendens* Traq., from strata of somewhat later age, is perhaps doubtfully congeneric, but the poor body-remains are at least fairly closely comparable with those of the smaller *U. lobatus*.

The skull of *U. splendens* has been described by Watson and Gill (1923), and the writer has seen considerable material. It is notable for the range of variation in the shape of the skull-roof as a whole; the breadth/length ratio at extremes may be 15-20 per cent different from the mean.

The skull-roof structure is closely comparable with that of *Ctenodus*, except that X and Y_2 are apparently always fused. Along the supraorbital canal, a large bone represents $K + L_1 + L_2 + M$ and a smaller anterior element is $N + Q$. Cheek-bones are not adequately preserved. The only "abnormality" is in the specimen figured by Watson and Gill (1923, Fig. 30A), in which the anterior pair of bones *E-E* is represented by a single median bone.

The structure of palate and lower jaw has been discussed in part by Watson and Gill. No complete description is required here, but it may be noted that the parasphenoid has a very long posterior shaft, that the pterygoid dentition is curiously reduced to one row (or possibly two closely adjacent rows) of compressed conical teeth along the margins of the pterygoids, and a series of small denticles aranged in rows internal to these, that the vomers are much like those of *Phaneropleuron* or *Scaumenacia*, and that the teeth of the prearticular consist of two closely adjacent rows of compressed conical teeth along the dorsal margin and a few small denticles on the lingual surface. This is clearly a greatly-modified dentition, adapted for sectorial action. Small narrow "marginal" tooth-plates occur, as in *Scaumenacia* and *Phaneropleuron*.

The latero-sensory system presents few points of interest. The canals are deeply enclosed in the dermal bones, and the occipital commissure traverses bone *B*. The groove for the anterior pit-line is sometimes present, and in one specimen shows marked differences from the "normal" course over the centers of $(X + Y_2)$, J_1, and B.

Conchopoma

(Figure 8D)

This remarkable genus, well known from the Early Permian Lebach Shales, has a most remarkably modified dentition; the parasphenoid expansion is covered with denticles, and this type of bone (*Peplorhina* of Cope) is known from the Late Carboniferous of Linton, Ohio. The only useful cranial material is that from Lebach, described by Watson and Gill (1923) and by Weitzel (1926). The writer has also seen useful material in the British Museum (Natural History), but only three or four good specimens form the basis of the present account. Better collections would probably necessitate the consideration of various "abnormalities."

The structure of the skull-roof is shown in Figure 8D. There is a clear resemblance in pattern to *Sagenodus*, particularly in the bones between the supraorbital canals. Also X and Y_2 are fused, as in *Sagenodus*, a very large element $(M + L_2 + L_1 + K)$ is found associated with the posterior part of the supraorbital canal, and it is possible that this canal turns medially from $(Q + N)$ into the element lying immediately antero-ventral, as in the anterior series of *Sagenodus*.

However, *Conchopoma* shows some quite obvious differences from *Sagenodus*; bone J_1 is always absent and is replaced by extensions from I, $(Y_1 + Y_2)$, and $(M + L_2 + L_1 + K)$; and Y_1 is frequently fused to $(Y_2 + X)$. These are "progressive" changes in the group, but it is rather remarkable to find that bone H is not deeply wedged into the skull-roof, and that the occipital commissure runs behind bone B, probably in a separate bone A. These are "primitive" characters which have been lost in typical *Sagenodus*, *Ctenodus* and *Uronemus*.

The latero-sensory canals are embedded in the thin bones, forming ridges on the inner surfaces. Only faint traces of pit-line grooves have been seen.

The bones of the cheek are badly preserved in all the available material.

The parasphenoid is a remarkable bone; a moderately long posterior "stalk" bears a very large anterior expansion, which is covered anteriorly with closely-set rounded denticles. The pterygoids, which are unusually narrow, are provided anteriorly with a similar dentition. In the mandible, Watson and Gill figure a (possibly incomplete) prearticular with a granulation of teeth which presumably engaged those of the pterygoid; and Weitzel indicates that the parasphenoid was opposed by an unpaired lower tooth-plate ("Zungenbein"?), unknown in other fossil Dipnoi.

Ceratodus

(Figure 9A)

We have now unfortunately almost completely exhausted the useful fossil material. A partial skull from the marine Wengen shales (Norian, Middle Triassic) of the Austrian Alps, was described under the name *Ceratodus sturii* by F. Teller (1891). What little is known in detail is most remarkable. The dermal bones of the skull appear to have been deeply set in the skin, so that the latero-sensory canals merely formed grooves on the outer surfaces of the bone. Teller's figures show two median bones, which he equates with the two large median elements of *Epiceratodus*. These are flanked by a large paired element, bearing the supraorbital canal groove ("C" of Teller's figures) and a posterior paired element ("D" of Teller). The orbital margin is very imperfect, and it is impossible to decide whether bones 2 and 3 were present. The posterior median bone is undoubtedly bone B of the present account (see Fig. 9A). It has spread laterally into the area normally occupied in earlier forms by J_1 and I. The anterior median element is too far back to be identified as the homologue of F, the large anterior element of *Epiceratodus*; it is much more like D of *Sagenodus*. Teller's element "C" is clearly

$(M+)$ $L_2 + L_1 + K$ of Late Palaeozoic genera. His "D" is probably $Y_1 + Y_2$; his Plate IV gives some evidence of the presence of a process from this bone lying outside the quadrate, and there is probably a separate bone X. The main differences in pattern between *C. sturii* and *Epiceratodus* are the continued importance of D in the former and the invasion of the territory of J_1 by bone B in the former and $M + L_2 + L_1 + K$ in the latter. These are not perhaps very important differences. It is possible to draw limited conclusions from Teller's account—that in this Triassic form the number of skull-roof bones are reduced and appear to have lost their primarily superficial position in the dermis, and that in some ways (loss of J, etc.) it resembles *Epiceratodus*; it may form a link between *Sagenodus* and *Epiceratodus*.

The few other Triassic Dipnoi which have been described from any material other than scattered scales and loose dental plates (e.g. *Gosfordia truncata*, Woodward, 1890; *Ceratodus formosus*, Wade, 1935) agree in showing very thin dermal bones. In Wade's species there is even some evidence that a secondary growth of scales had begun to extend forward over the head-bones. The teeth of *Ceratodus* are obviously quite closely similar to those of *Epiceratodus forsteri*. A very useful discussion of the *Ceratodus* problem is given by Stromer (1938).

It is possible to point to the ancestral forms of only one of the three living genera. *Ceratodus* is at present merely a form-genus based on tooth-plates, but it certainly includes the ancestry of the living *Epice-*

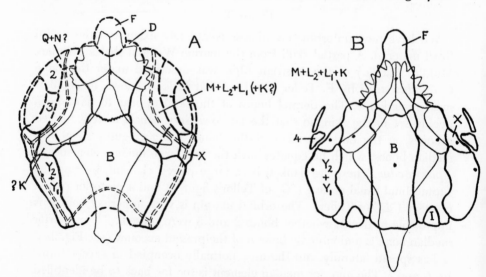

Figure 9. Skull-structure of A, *Ceratodus sturii* Teller, and B, *Epiceratodus forsteri.* A is an interpretation of Teller's figures (1891); B is based on Goodrich's figure (1930), modified after specimens.

ratodus (cf. Stromer, 1938 and references therein), which had emerged in Late Cretaceous times. The familiar tooth-plates of *Ceratodus* have 4 (rarely 5) tooth-ridges in the mandibular plate, 5 (rarely 6) on the pterygoid. Each ridge is normally without much sign of separate denticles in the adult, though occasionally such traces can be seen. Romer and Smith (1934) note correctly that certain Late Palaeozoic tooth-plates, with tooth-ridges showing no sign of separate denticles, differ from the normal *Sagenodus-Ctenodus* tooth-plates; they erect the new genus *Protoceratodus* for a Pennsylvanian pterygoid tooth-plate from Illinois, and refer to the same genus material from the Cleveland Shale of Ohio (Early Mississippian or latest Devonian) and the "Permian" of Texas. Unfortunately the evidence of the very numerous isolated teeth, from Devonian to Recent, requires a very great deal of careful sifting. It seems at present premature to accept fully this "protoceratodont" lineage of Romer and Smith, and it is perhaps most reasonable at present to suppose that the Carboniferous or Permian ancestors of *Ceratodus* were closely related to a *Sagenodus*-like form. For a résumé of other views, see Stromer (1938).

The modern *Lepidosiren* and *Protopterus* have even more remarkably modified skull-structure and tooth-plates than *Epiceratodus*; the dentition is modified to a purely sectorial type. The peculiar Carboniferous and earliest Permian *Gnathorhiza* from North America occurs also in the Coal-Measures of Northumberland. As pointed out by Romer and Smith (1934) it strongly recalls some of the features of *Lepidosiren*, and may perhaps be an ancestor of the latter. At such a distance in time, this can be no more than a suggestion, and Stromer (1938) thinks that *Protopterus* may have descended from a *Ceratodus*-group and produced *Lepidosiren* as a derivative.

Epiceratodus

(Figure 9B)

The dermal bones of the skull are markedly different from the primitive Devonian condition. They are few in number, separated from the epidermis by considerable thicknesses of tissue, including separate scales in the posterior part of the head(!), and in the adult bear no very close relation to the latero-sensory canals. The precise pattern of dermal bones varies somewhat. There is always a posterior (B) and an anterior median bone (F) in the skull-roof, flanked by a long pair of bones extending back from above the orbit to cover the region of the auditory capsules ($M + L_2 + L_1 + K$). These in turn are flanked by a large posterior bone ($Y_1 + Y_2$) which covers the lateral part of the otic region and sends down a sheath outside the otic process of the quadrate, and a small anterior element (X) which lies above and behind the orbit. Quite frequently (perhaps always in complete skulls) an additional pair of bones (I) is present at the posterior margin of the skull (figured by Huxley; Kisselewa, 1929, etc.). The precise interpretation of these bones would not have been easy without embryological evidence; G. D. Oury has allowed the writer to quote some of his results. In the first place, at total length of say 50 mm., the sensory organs are well developed and in places folded under the general level of the skin, and dermal bone forms are in fairly close relationship to some of these infolded sections. The anastomosis of the occipital commissure with the main lateral-line lies behind the dermal bones, and on the commissure is an extrascapular corresponding clearly to I. The medial parts of the commissure appear to be ill developed. The posterior median bone B apparently develops from a center well in front of the commissure. Bone $(Y_1 + Y_2)$ is recognized by its relation to the forward continuation of the main lateral line and to the end of the middle pit-line. The identification of X is quite clear; this is the region of the anastomosis of supraorbital and infraorbital canals, and the anterolateral end of the anterior pit-line is slightly medial to the developing bone. In some individuals X may have fused with $Y_2 + Y_1$. The large bones flanking B are related to a section of the supraorbital canal lying just behind the middle of the orbit, a section which may include four well-developed neuromasts. We may therefore regard this bone as equivalent to the $(L_2 + L_1 + K)$ or $(M + L_2 + L_1 + K)$, elements so characteristic of post-Devonian Dipnoi. The anterior median element can hardly be directly comparable with the next median bone (D) in front of B in *Sagenodus, Ctenodus, Uronemus,* and *Conchopoma.* It lies, at early development-stages, far in front of the orbits and in the region near or just behind the place where the supraorbital canals swing close together. Oury thinks the bone may actually be related to the lateral-line, in which case it may be derived from such apparent "neomorphs" as those in front of and between Q-Q in *Sagenodus*, but it is perhaps more likely to be a hyperdevelopment of the most anterior median bone F so constantly seen in such genera as *Sagenodus, Ctenodus, Uronemus,* and *Conchopoma.* On this basis certain abnormalities can easily be understood, e.g. in Kisselewa's (1929) Figure 1 a bone is intercalated between B and the anterior element, which occupies some part of the area filled by $C, D,$ and E in Late Palaeozoic forms.

The circumorbital region shows, immediately ventro-lateral to X, a postorbital bone (4), succeeded by a somewhat variable and ill-developed series along the infraorbital canal (cf. 5-6-7-1 etc. of *Dipterus*). The jugal canal is carried by a separate bone (cf. 8 of *Dipterus*) which lies outside the quadrate-process of $(Y_1 + Y_2)$ and is followed by a variable chain of small bones which ultimately convey the mandibular canal to the region of the angulo-postsplenial (cf. Westoll, 1937a, Fig. 3c). The bones of the palate and mandible call for no special comment; they are extremely like those of *Sagenodus*, for example. It may, however, be noted that marginal teeth appear in development near the front of Meckel's cartilage, and may develop a small bony plate. No separate trace of either bone or teeth persists in the adult; they may have been resorbed and lost (which is quite possible) or absorbed into the presplenials.

Comparing *Epiceratodus* with *Sagenodus* or *Ctenodus* the following changes are obvious: the bones 2 and 3 above the orbit are lost; bones $(N + Q)$, according to all published figures, are lost, but the writer has seen probable remains of this element in one skull; bone J_1 is completely absent, its territory is invaded entirely by $(? M +)L_2 + L_1 + K$, a moderately frequent type of "abnormality" in the Carboniferous genera (cf. also *Conchopoma* and *Ceratodus sturii*); and the paired elements CC, EE and the median element D have normally been lost. There is no evidence from the developmental study of fusion of numerous non-lateral line elements. The evolutionary process apparently has in general been the result of invasion of territory from more precocious centers of ossification rather than widespread fusion.

Lepidosiren and *Protopterus* afford an even more remarkable picture. Bones B and $(Y_2 + Y_1)$ are very deeply embedded, and meet one another (cf. *Ceratodus sturii*). The bone corresponding to $(? M +) L_2 + L_1 + K$ remains largely superficial, except over the orbit, and forms a pair of remarkable spines in the prepared skull. Otherwise the structure compares with that of *Epiceratodus*. Many of the interesting points discussed by Dollo (1895) show that *Lepidosiren* is the most modified of Dipnoi (cf. also Stromer, 1938).

It is now possible to review some of the main features in the evolution of the skull in Dipnoi. The evidence of Devonian forms shows very clearly that the early Dipnoi were very closely related to the contemporaneous Rhipidistia (Fig. 10, A-E). All the known early Rhipidistia differ from early Dipnoi in having numerous bones in the snout, well-developed marginal tooth-bearing bones (dentary, maxillary, "premaxillary"), and an intermediate arcade of tooth-bearing bones (palatine, ectopterygoid, coronoids). There are also some differences in the opercular series. But the most remarkable differences are to be found in the existence of large bones in Rhipidistia, such as those currently termed in "orthodox" texts the parietal, frontal, and squamosal (= postparietal, parietal, and squamosal respectively of primitive Tetrapoda, see Fig. 10, D-F). The evidence of living bony fishes as *Amia* suggests that such bones as the "frontal" in that fish originate as a series of separate rudiments, each related to a section of the supraorbital latero-sensory canal carrying (in general) a single neuromast. Early Dipnoi have, quite clearly, a series of lateral-line bones which seem to have been related each to a neuromast, or to a short section of infolded canal carrying a neuromast. In these early forms more or less random fusions of two or three adjacent bones is frequent, but later members have a few stable larger fusions, such as the $(L_2 + L_1 + K)$ or $(M + L_2 + L_1 + K)$ or Carboniferous, Permian, and later genera. These larger bones seem to develop at the expense of anamestic bones. Their importance is foreshadowed by the fusion-potential of separate bones in *Dipterus*. Another interesting feature in the evolution of the skull-pattern of Dipnoi is the fate of bones related to a "degenerating" section of a latero-sensory canal, i.e. one being replaced by a pit-line. The best possible example is the series K-J_1-J_2-J_3 of early Dipnoi (*Dipnorhynchus*). By the time we get to *Dipterus* (Fig. 10, B-C), the section of the canal in J_2 and J_3 has degenerated, and the pit-line has normally been "captured" by B. At the same time J_3 has entirely disappeared as a separate bone, and J_2 is very rarely present, their territory being occupied by bone I. In view of the above analysis, it is quite unlikely that J_2 and J_3 have "fused" with I, though bone I has no doubt invaded territory in which the fundamental physico-chemical changes necessary for osteogenesis had proceeded some distance.

On comparing *Dipnorhynchus* with primitive osteolepids (Fig. 10, B, D-E), certain homologies are at once clear. $H + I$ and A of the former are the lateral and median extrascapulars of the latter.[3] Y_1, Y_2, and X are in every important way homologous with the so-called "supratemporal," "intertemporal," and "dermosphenotic" of osteolepids, i.e. with the tabular, supratemporal, and intertemporal respectively of early tetrapods. Bone 4 and the postorbital of osteolepids and early tetrapods are homologous; bones 2 and 3 are respectively the pre- and post-frontals of tetrapods and their equivalents in osteolepids (cf. Graham-Smith and Westoll, 1937; Westoll, 1943a). In primitive osteolepids the supraorbital canal anastomoses with the infraorbital in bone X (as in moderately advanced Dipnoi). In a few individuals a small back-turned sprig of the canal has been observed in the osteolepid "frontal" (= tetrapod parietal), but in most the anterior pit-line extends back over the "frontal" and may occasionally pass onto the "parietal" or even onto the "intertemporal." The "frontals" normally extend almost to the suture between 2 and 3; they correspond to $(L_2 + L_1 + K)$ of Dipnoi, and probably also include the equivalent of J_1. The anterior limit may vary even on the two sides of one specimen, so that we may get $(M + L_2 + L_1 + K + J_1 \,?)$ on one side and $(L_2 + L_1 + K + J_1 \,?)$ on the other. The parietal of primitive tetrapods corresponds rather to the latter condition. Between these osteolepid "frontals" is the pineal foramen, often surrounded by a circlet of small bones; comparison with *Dipnorhynchus* is thus far-reaching (Fig. 10, B, D-E). The elements $(M \,?)$, N, Q of Dipnoi represent only those most posterior elements of the "nasal series" of osteolepids, which may be

[3] See above, pp. 142-143.

equated roughly with the frontals of early Tetrapoda. Between these bones in osteolepids is a series of anamestic bones; these tend to be numerous and irregular in earlier forms, and fewer, larger and less variable in later forms (cf. Westoll, 1936; Jarvik, 1944a), a decided parallel to their nature in Dipnoi. .

We are left with a most critical region, the so-called "parietals" of osteolepids. The normal condition in all later osteolepids is a pair of long bones, meeting the "supratemporal" and "intertemporal" laterally, receiving the medial parts of the middle pit-lines and the posterior pit-line grooves, and overlying the medial parts of the otic cavities. The commonest "abnormality" in primitive osteolepids is the presence of two pairs of "parietals," approximately opposed respectively to the "supratemporal" and "intertemporal," and in such cases it is the former which normally carries the pit-line grooves and overlies part of the otic cavity. In a number of specimens of the Middle Devonian *Thursius, Diplopterax,* and *Osteolepis* the "parietals," divided in this way, are partly separated by median or irregular bones. These again may represent relics of an ancestral condition.

Comparing these structures with *Dipnorhynchus,* where Y_1, Y_2, and X are quite firmly established as homologous with the osteolepid "supratemporal," "intertemporal," and "dermosphenotic," it is clear that the two parts of the "parietal" of osteolepids may be equated with J_2 and J_3, and that the greater development of "median" bones in the Dipnoi is a measure of the broadening of the skull and brain-cavity. The position of the otic cavities can be fixed in *Dipterus,* where they occur under Y_1 and I, with slight extensions under Y_2 and J_1, and not at all under B. The corresponding region in *Dipnorhynchus* would be covered essentially by Y_1 and J_3.

It is not necessary here to go into further details of the skull-roof of osteolepids, but it is now fairly clear that, with all the original supraorbital-canal bones from Q and J_3 accounted for in primitive members of both groups, the ancestral structure worked out by the writer (1943a, Fig. 7) is very reasonable, even though at that time the structure of *Dipnorhynchus* was not well known, and the probable incorporation of J_1 in the "frontal" of osteolepids was not appreciated (cf. Fig. 10). The retention of J_2 and J_3 (usually replaced by the single "parietal") in osteolepids after the loss of the osteogenic stimulus of the supraorbital canal structures, may be paralleled by the retention of J_1 in numerous Carboniferous Dipnoi and the clear evidence that bone-patterns, primarily conditioned in early fishes by the presence of the latero-sensory system, can be traced into such forms as modern Dipnoi (see above) and Tetrapoda, where the bones subserve new functions. In Dipnoi the median bone B was no doubt of growing importance (protecting brain during development),

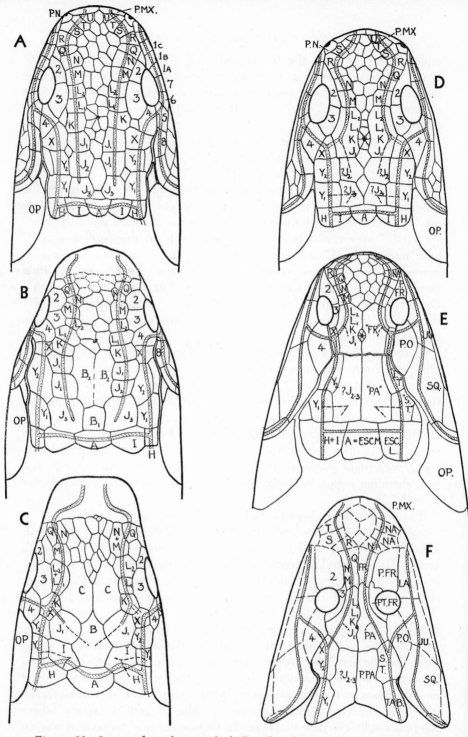

Figure 10. Suggested evolution of skull-roofing bones of Dipnoi, osteolepid Rhipidistia and primitive Tetrapoda from a common ancestral type, A, B, *Dipnorhynchus*; C, *Dipterus*; D, hypothetical pre-osteolepid; E, based on *Diplopterax*; F, *Elpistostege*. In E and F the bone-names commonly used in osteolepids and early tetrapods are indicated on the right side—*P.MX*, premaxillary; *NA*, nasal; *FR*, frontal; *PA*, parietal; *P.FR*, pre-frontal; *PT.FR*, post-frontal; *I.T*, intertemporal; *S.T*, supratemporal; *TAB*, tabular; *E.SC.M* and *E.SC.L*, median and lateral extrascapulars; *LA*, lacrimal; *JU*, jugal; *P.O*, postorbital; *SQ*, squamosal; *OP*, opercular. Modified from Westoll, 1943.

and bone *I* gives support to the shoulder-girdle, so that its wedging into the skull-roof in later forms than *Dipnorhynchus*, replacing J_3 and probably J_2, is structurally advantageous. In the osteolepids, where the "parietals" were probably important in protecting the roof of the brain, their retention was structurally advantageous. In the "reptiliomorph" pattern of early tetrapod skull-roofs their homologues (postparietals) are much shortened, as though the true parietals had grown backwards more vigorously in those forms.

It is now proposed to investigate the rate of evolution of important characters in the Dipnoi, starting from an ancestral skull-type (cf. Westoll, 1943a; Fig. 7A; and Fig. 10A of this paper). In various properties a sequence of evolutionary changes can be determined, and in 17 of these a more or less graded series of steps, from the presumed ancestral condition to that of living forms, has been worked out and a grading is given to each genus according to the degree of "primitiveness" shown by each character; high marks indicate primitive conditions. Many other features (including some stressed by Dollo, 1895) cannot be studied in fossil forms.

I. *Skull-proportions.*

  5. Ancestral type; otic region moderately long, narrow.
  4. Otic region becomes broader.
  3. Posterior shortening of otic region begins (cf. *Dipno. sussmilchi*).
  2. Further shortening of posterior part, reduction of otic cavities (*Dipterus*).
  1. Further shortening, bones *H-I* much compressed.
  0. Conditions of *Ceratodus*, etc.

Here it may be noted as a significant fact that nearly all primitive fishes (e.g. Arctolepida (Dolichothoraci) among placoderms, *Cheirolepis*, etc. among actinopterygians, osteolepids and primitive Tetrapoda in the lines leading to higher vertebrates, and *Dipnorhynchus* in Dipnoi) have very elongated otic regions, with presumably large otic structures and large brain-nuclei supplying important latero-sensory systems. The change of proportions in later members may be due in part to rapid loss of the relative importance of the acoustico-lateralis system.

II. *Size of cheek.*

  4. Ancestral conditions; cheek long, but not so long as in most osteolepids, which have diverged in the opposite way to Dipnoi.
  3. Cheek somewhat shorter, as probably in *Dipnorhynchus*.
  2. Cheek shortened, as in *Dipterus*.
  1. Cheek further shortened, as in *Scaumenacia*.
  0. Cheek as in *Epiceratodus*.

This series of changes is bound up, *inter alia*, with the attitude of the quadrate, which must have been nearly vertical in *Dipnorhynchus*, somewhat forwardly directed in *Dipterus*, and very forwardly directed in *Scaumenacia* and *Epiceratodus*, starting in each case from the otic process.

III. *Nature of bone-tissue in snout.*

    5. Ancestral conditions; probably nearly as in osteolepids.

    4.) Loss of marginal elements, gradual replacement by special tissue
    3.) developed only after considerable growth.

    2. Cosmine-covered "snout" liable to resorption (*Dipterus*).

    1. Only traces of snout-ossification.

    0. No ossification in snout.

IV. *Nature of dermal bones.*

    6. Bones thick, superficial, cosmine present, sensory-canals in lower parts of bones, pit-line grooves deep where present.

    5. As in 6, but cosmine largely absent.

    4. As in 5, but pit-line grooves shallow.

    3. Bones thinner, pit-line grooves absent because bones lie deeper in skin.

    2. Bones thinner, deeper in skin, still enclosing sensory canals.

    1. Bones lying deeper, sensory canals in grooves or gutters on upper surface.

    0. Many dermal bones in adult separated from sensory canals; bones lie deep, may be covered by scales, etc.

V. *Degree of ossification of endocranium.*

    3. Heavy ossification, at least in some individuals.

    2. Moderate ossification, at least in some individuals.

    1. Slight ossification, at least in some individuals.

    0. Only very slight or no ossification.

This is not an easy character to work with, since individuals of the same species and the same size from one locality may show notable differences in apparent degree of ossification, presumably because of differences in maceration of tissues.

VI. *Division of cranium.*

    It is presumed that the ancestral type had an endocranium ossified in more than one piece, a sphenethmoid region (trabecular) and a separate element derived from the parachordals, with (or possibly without) incorporation of otic capsules.

    5. Complete division.

    4. Division probably partly retained.

    3-1. Fusion at earlier stages of growth.

    0. Completely fused even in late embryonic stages.

VII. *Nature of parasphenoid.*

This is bound up with the last.

5. "Parasphenoid" in 3 separate bones; parasphenoidal rostrum, paired parotic plates; foramen for hypophysial duct present.
4. Incipient fusion or suture between 3 bones.
3. Three elements fused; no posterior "stalk"; foramen present.
2. Posterior "stalk" short, foramen lost.
1. Posterior "stalk" of medium size.
0. Posterior "stalk" long.

VIII. *"Pineal" foramen.*

3. Foramen well-developed.
2. Foramen occasionally present, or indicated by macula.
1. Epiphysial fontanelle in adult endocranium, roofed by bone.
0. Adult with strong cartilaginous and dermal-bone roof in this region.

IX. *Nature of supraorbital latero-sensory canal.*

As in all primitive fishes, early members of this group have no anastomosis between the supraorbital and infraorbital canals.

4. Conditions primitive; enclosed canal extends back to J_3, anterior pit-line possibly not developed or very short.
3. Anastomosis present; enclosed canal extends back into J_3, anterior pit-line short.
2. Enclosed canal extends back only into J_2, anterior pit-line longer.
1. Enclosed canal extends only into J_1, anterior pit-line still longer.
0. Canal very short or absent behind anastomosis entering X or confined to K; pit-line groove begins on X or K.

X. *Fate of J_1-J_3 bones.*

This is consequent upon IX, but the effect shows a time-lag.

3. Bones J_1-J_3 all present.
2. Bone J_3 absent
1. Bones J_3 and J_2 absent ⎱ Bone I wedged into skull-roof.
0. Bones J_3, J_2, and J_1 absent ⎰

XI. *Degree of fusion of bones along supraorbital canal.*

4. Irregular, more or less random fusions.
3. Tendency for fusions to be in twos, especially in some parts of canal.
2. Still stronger tendency to fusion, rarely in threes or fours in specific sections.
1. Three or four elements (K to M) generally fuse, but numerous irregularities.
0. Three or four elements (K-L_2 or K-M) always fuse.

XII. *Temporal bones.*

    3. Y_1, Y_2, and X all separate or randomly fused, separate supra-spiracular or perspiracular plate.

    2. Y_1, Y_2, and X all separate or randomly fused, Y_2 extended in place of supraspiracular or prespiracular plate.

    1. $X + Y_2$ normally fused, Y_1 separate.

    0. $X + Y_2 + Y_1$ normally or frequently fused.

XIII. *Presence or absence of bones 2 and 3.*

    2. Both bones present, well-developed.

    1. Development possibly irregular, one or both absent.

    0. Both bones absent.

XIV. *Nature of anamestic series and B, between supraorbital canals.*

    5. B_1 small, B_2 paired and perhaps irregular; more anterior elements small and highly variable.

    4. B_1 small, B_2 single, more anterior elements small and highly variable.

    3. Usually only one *B*-bone, but two in some specimens; more anterior elements usually includes large *C*-bones (but even these may be irregular), and a large number of small and highly variable bones.

    2. Single *B*-bone normal, large; more anterior elements nearly always include large *C*-bones, and a small number of other large plates.

    1. *B* single, large; very settled pattern of general dermal bones replaces anamestic mosaic (some or all of *C, D, E, F*).

    0. *B* single, large; bone *F* large, other elements of this series small or absent.

XV. *Fusion of mandibular elements.*

    2. Pre-splenial, post-splenial and angular separate.

    1. Fusion of post-splenial and angular in some individuals.

    0. Post-splenial and angular normally fused.

XVI. *Opercular series.*

    5. Fully developed, possibly intermediate between the *Dipterus* and *Osteolepis* types.

    4. Fully developed, *Dipterus* type.

    3. Posterior paired gulars reduced.

    2. Median gulars reduced, posterior paired gulars and lateral gulars lost.

    1. Opercular and subopercular slightly reduced.

    0. Opercular and subopercular greatly reduced.

XVII. *Dentition.*

  5. Marginal tooth-bones, palatines, ectopterygoids and coronoids probably present.
  4. Those bones probably absent; increasing importance of teeth on pterygoids and prearticulars.
  3. Numerous separate teeth in many rows on pterygoids and pre-articulars.
  2. Teeth in each row compressed and confluent at base.
  1. Teeth forming saw-like ridges.
  0. Teeth forming smooth ridges.

Table 1 indicates the rating of the important genera, which are arranged in stratigraphical order.

These "total" figures are clearly in several cases not precise, but the writer believes that the inaccuracies will prove small with further knowledge. They have been plotted against geological time in Figure 11. The time-scale used is the current radioactivity scale (based on Holmes, 1947). Considerable interpolation is necessary, but the general picture is sufficiently remarkable, and only minor modifications could be made in any case by manipulating the time-scale. Other comments are reserved until the body and fins have been discussed.

EVOLUTION OF POST-CRANIAL CHARACTERS

Here will be considered the evolution of scales, fins, and axial skeleton. It would be interesting to consider also the body-form as a whole (cf. Dollo, 1895), but the material of most of the fossil genera does not allow accurate comparative studies. Much unpublished material is incorporated in the tabular matter. The characters are numbered consecutively with those concerning the skull.

XVIII. *Nature of scales.*

  The scales in such fairly early types as *Dipterus* are more or less rounded in shape, but there is a possibility that they may have been more or less "rhombic" in ancestral forms. The early forms have thick scales covered with cosmine, which may show prominent "Westoll-Linien." For some time the history of the scales is parallel to that of the head-bones, but the scales remain relatively very superficial.
  7. Scales thick, bony, with strong cosmine, possibly not "cycloid" in shape.
  6. Scales thick, bony, cosmine well-developed, shape "cycloid."
  5. As (6) but cosmine not well-developed.
  4. As (5) but cosmine quite absent.
  3. Scales fairly thick, bony, ornamented surface in exposed region.

TABLE 1

GENUS	"CHARACTERS" CONSIDERED																	TOTAL
	I	II	III	IV	V	VI	VII	VIII	IX	X	XI	XII	XIII	XIV	XV	XVI	XVII	I–XVII
Presumed ancestor	5	4	5	6	3	5?	5	3	4	3	4	3	2	5	2	5	5	69
Dipnorh. lehmanni	4±	3–4?	3–4?	6	3–2	4	5	3	4	3	4	3–2	2	5	2	5–4	4?	61–65
Dipnorh. sussmilchi	3	3	8±	6	2?	3?	5?	3	4	3	4	3–2	2	5–4	2	5–4	4?	57–60
Dipterus	2	2	2	6	2	1?	3	1–2	1–2	1–2	3–2	2	3	4	2	4	4–3	39–43
Pentlandia	2	2?	1½	5+	1	1–0	2–3	1	1	1	3–2	2	2	4	2	4	3?	34–37
Scaumenacia	2	1	½	5—	1	1–0	2	1	0	1	2–1	2	2	4	1?	4	2	27–29
Fleurantia*	2—	1	0	5—	1–0	0?	1—	1?	0	1	0	2	2	4?	1–0	4?	3?	23–25
Phaneropleuron	1½	1	0	4½	1–0	1–0?	1½	0?	0	1–0	2–1	2	2	1½	0	4?	2	21–24
Ctenodus	1	0	0	3	1–0	0?	½	0?	0	1–0	1–0	2?	1	1½	0	3	2–1	18½–17½
Uronemus*	1	½?	0	3–4	1–0	0?	½—	0?	0	1–0	0	1	1	1½	0	3	?	12–15
Sagenodus	1	0	0	4	1–0	0?	½—	0?	0	1–0	1–0	1	1	1½	0	3	2–1	18½–17½
Conchopoma*	1½	0?	0	3	1–0	0?	½—	0?	0	0	0	1–0	1	1	0	3?	?	11–13
Ceratodus	0	0	0	1–2	1–0	0	0	0	0	0	0	1–0	1–0	1	0	1?	0	3–7
Epiceratodus	0	0	0	0	1–0	0	0	0	0	0	0	1–0	1–0	0	0	0	0	0–2
Protopterus	0	0	0	0	0	0	0	0	0	0	0	0?	0	0	0	0	0	0
Lepidosiren	0	0	0	0	0	0	0	0	0	0	0	0?	0	0	0	0	0	0

* Indicates specialized forms.

2. Scales moderately thin, bony, smooth surface.

1. Scales thin, bony(?), with markedly reticular structure.

0. Scales thin, little or no bone, reticular structure.

To anyone familiar with dipnoan fossils these categories require no comment.

XIX. *Median fins.*

The remarkable "degenerative" evolution of the median fins of Dipnoi has been stressed by Dollo (1895) and frequently quoted since that time. It is most convenient here to consider four separate changes:

a. Change in nature of tail.

3. Tail very heterocercal.

2. Tail moderately heterocercal

1. Tail slightly heterocercal

0. Tail secondarily diphycercal (gephyrocercal).

b. Size and importance of anterior dorsal fin, D_1.

4. D_1 short-based, strong.

3. D_1 with longer base, strong.

2. D_1 somewhat long-based, flabby.

1. D_1 long and low.

0. D_1 incorporated in D_2 (posterior dorsal).

c. Nature of D_2.

4. D_2 short-based, strong.

3. D_2 with somewhat elongated base.

2. D_2 moderately elongated.

1. D_2 very elongated, but not yet confluent with epichordal lobe of tail.

0. D_2 very elongated, confluent with epichordal lobe of tail.

d. Nature of anal fin.

2. Anal short-based, well separated from tail.

1. Anal very close to tail.

0. Anal confluent with hypochordal lobe of tail, no separate anal basal skeleton.

XX. *Nature of paired fins.*

Here there are two progressive changes, the change from a relatively short stout muscular lobe to a very long slender lobe (which may even lose its fin-rays and all but the axis of the endoskeletal structures), and an interesting change in the position of the pectoral fins. In early forms the pectorals are carried low down on the flank, and were probably oriented in a similar manner to that of the rhipidistian pectoral fin (cf. Westoll, 1943b). In the living genera the pectorals are borne high up on the flanks and have apparently become rotated in the process, so that the preaxial margin is uppermost when the fin is pressed back along the flank. No evidence bearing on this change of attitude of the fin as such is yet available from the vast majority of fossil forms.

a. Size of muscular lobes.

    3. Paired fins rather stout, short and muscular.

    2. Paired fins moderately elongated, covered with scales and bearing fin-rays.

    1. Paired fins very elongated, with scales and fin-rays.

    0. Paired fins extremely elongated, no fin-rays.

b. Position of pectoral fins.

    3. Pectorals very low, as in Rhipidistia.

    2. Pectorals low, a little above the old position.

    1. Pectorals arise some way up flanks.

    0. Pectorals arise very high up flanks.

XXI. *Nature of axial skeleton.*

Here again we have two sets of factors: firstly, degree of ossification (a factor very difficult to judge in early forms), and secondly the nature of the neural and haemal arches and spines, fin-radials, etc. The second point was discussed in outline by Graham-Smith and Westoll (1937).

a. Degree of ossification.

    2. Heavily ossified, at least in some individuals.

    1. Lightly ossified.

    0. Not ossified.

b. Arrangement of axial and fin skeletal elements.

    3. Neural and haemal spines continuous with their arches; median fins with two rows of radials.

    2. Anterior neural spines separate from neural arches.

    1. More posterior neural spines, and anterior haemal spines, separate from their arches.

    0. Neural and haemal spines separate from their arches; various complexities as in *Epiceratodus*.

As with "characters" I-XVII, these ratings for each genus are set out in Table 2.

The figures for *Ctenodus* and *Sagenodus* are mere estimates for most characters, but the known material is quite consistent with the ratings given, and distinctly higher ratings are quite excluded. So far as *Dipnorhynchus* is concerned, we may be quite sure that the total rating cannot be lower than in *Dipterus*. A provisional rating of 28-31 may confidently

TABLE 2

GENUS	XVIII	"CHARACTERS" CONSIDERED								TOTAL XVIII-XXI	GRAND TOTAL I-XXI
		XIX				XX		XXI			
	7	a	b	c	d	a	b	a	b	31	100
Presumed ancestor	7	3	4	4	2	3	3	2	3	31	100
Dipnorh. lehmanni	—	—	—	—	—	—	—	—	—	(ca. 28-31)	89-96
Dipnorh. sussmilchi	—	—	—	—	—	—	—	—	—	(ca. 28-31)	85-91
Dipterus	6	3	3	3	2	2½	3	2	3	27½	66½-70½
Pentlandia	6-5	2½	2½	2	2	2	3	2	3	24-25	58-62
Scaumenacia	4-3	2	1	1	2–	2–	3	2	3	18½-19½	45½-48½
Fleurantia*	3	3-2	3	2	2	2–	3-2	2	3	21-23	44-48
Phaneropleuron	3-2	1	0	1–	1	2–	2	1	3?	12½-13½	33½-37½
Ctenodus	1	0?	0?	0?	0?	1?	1?	1	?	ca. 6 (est.)	19½-24½
Uronemus*	2-1	½	0	0?	0?	1	2–	1	?	ca. 7-8 (est.)	19-23
Sagenodus	1	0?	0?	0	0?	1?	1?	1	?	ca. 6 (est.)	18½-23½
Conchopoma*	1-	0	0	0	0	1	1	1	2	6	17-19
Ceratodus	1-	0	0	½	0	1	1–	1	1	5	8-12
Epiceratodus	0	0	0	0	0	1	0	0	0	1	1-3
Protopterus	0	0	0	0	0	0	0	0	0	0	0
Lepidosiren	0	0	0	0	0	0	0	0	0	0	0

* Indicates specialized forms.

be assigned to *Dipnorhynchus*. If body-form be considered, *Lepidosiren* is the most "degenerate" living lungfish.

These figures, and the "grand total" figures, are again plotted against geological age in Figure 11. The character of the curve which best fits the points is clearly similar to that obtained from cranial characters.

RATES OF EVOLUTION IN DIPNOI

If the graphs and tables set out above can be trusted they provide an interesting picture of the changing rate of evolution of the group as a whole. From the graphs, tables and discussions it seems quite clear that

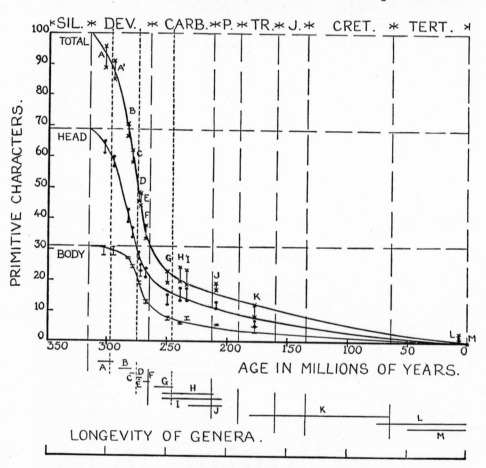

Figure 11. Graph showing rate of loss of characters of the ancestral type during evolution of Dipnoi, and the approximate time range of the main genera. A, A', *Dipnorhynchus*; B, *Dipterus*; C, *Pentlandia*; D, *Scaumenacia*; E, *Fleurantia*; F, *Phaneropleuron*; G, *Uronemus*; H, *Ctenodus*; I, *Sagenodus*; J, *Conchopoma*; K, *Ceratodus*; L, *Epiceratodus*; M, *Protopterus* (and *Lepidosiren*).

the Dipnoi diverged from the common ancestral stock shared with Rhipidistia not significantly earlier than the beginning of Devonian times. Apart from the Early Devonian members, the Dipnoi form a group with a rapid rate of change in the Middle and Late Devonian, which falls off very markedly with the passage of time. Indeed, the curve for post-Early Devonian times resembles an exponential curve. It must now be inquired how far this appearance is significant.

The time-scale is based on the recent work of Holmes (1947). His two scales, A and B, differ mainly in two respects: in scale A the Devonian is considered to end some 20 million years earlier, and the Cretaceous to end some 10 million years earlier, than in scale B; the intervening periods are shifted more or less bodily. The duration of the Devonian is taken as 43 million years on scale A and 58 million years on scale B. Although Holmes favors scale B, it is thought preferable here to use average figures for the time elapsed since the end of any given period; the end of the Ordovician is accepted as 350 million years ago in both scales. Only a rough estimate of the relative lengths of the Early (= Gedinnian-Coblenzian), Middle (= Eifelian + Givetian) and Late Devonian (= Frasnian + Famennian) is possible. Revision here would somewhat, though not gravely, alter the nature of the early part of the curve.

It is obvious that the twenty-one factors used above are not by any means of equal value. Some are of considerable importance no matter what may be one's views on the degree of weighting to be accepted— such are, for example, factors I, II, III, IV, VI, VII, IX and X, XI, XIV, XVI, XVII, XVIII, XIX and XX. A rather crude and admittedly subjective relative weighting has been given to a few of the various "characters" in the figure representing ancestral conditions. No doubt another worker would alter the weighting adopted here, and the writer is conscious of having undervalued some. But it is probably significant that the great majority of the characters, taken individually, also show a sharp drop in the rating during Devonian times; the main exceptions are IV, XII, XIII, XV, XVI and XXI, all of which show slow changes, or changes late in geological time, while XVII and XX show a slower fall than some others. Of these, XII and XV show very few "stages"; XIII and XVI appear to concern quite late degenerative features. XX is very difficult to assess, and XXI represents factors of at least two kinds. IV is also complex; the first part of the change (6-4 or 6-3) takes place rather quickly, and the change from grade 3 to grade 0 is a highly distinctive end-stage, in which the dermal bones of the skull-roof have come to have new relationships to the musculature; this second phase is effectively distinct from the first.

It would therefore appear that, with any reasonable weighting of the various characters considered and any reasonable division of the allowance for each into stages, a very similar overall picture would be obtained.

The subjective nature of many of the figures used here is fully appreciated, but this is a difficulty inherent in the material.

The three curves of Figure 11 all seem to show a distinctly lower gradient in early times. It is unfortunate that the material of *Dipnorhynchus* is so rare that an accurate analysis of its nature cannot be made. The rating of *D. lehmanni* for cranial characters is taken as 61-65 (out of 69), but it could easily be somewhat higher, and if this form is indeed very close to the immediate ancestor of Dipnoi the maximum possible rating would be rather below 69. Hence this early part of the curve is more doubtful than the remainder, though the obviously close comparison possible between *D. lehmanni* and *D. sussmilchi*, with their separation in geological time, points to a decided fall in the gradient of the curve hereabouts. This initial part of the curve is therefore accepted, though with reservations about its accuracy.

A perusal of the tables given above seems to show slight differences in the rate of incidence of many of the changes so characteristic of the Devonian forms. Thus characters I, II, III, V, VI, VIII, IX, X and XIV, all concerning the skull, have completed far the greater part of their total change before the Late Devonian, while the post-cranial characters were then at about their maximum rate of change. It seems likely, therefore, that the great modifications of the dipnoan skull were well under way before the characteristic fin-changes, etc., had really begun. Changes in body and fin structures in Dipnoi certainly imply loss of rapid locomotory abilities and assumption of ripple-movement swimming. We may now consider how far such changes may be related to changes of dietary and other habits. It is a well-worn theory that relates the increasingly sluggish locomotion of Dipnoi to their adoption of a triturating rather than a slashing or sharply biting dentition, and the writer unhesitatingly supports it. It is now possible to state rather definitely that the changes in dentition probably pre-dated the changes in body and fins.

It is furthermore very clear that several changes in the skull of Dipnoi can be shown to be direct correlatives of changes in the dentition. It seems to the writer entirely reasonable to suppose that the immediate ancestors of Dipnoi had, besides well-developed pterygoids and prearticulars, tooth-bearing bones comparable with ectopterygoids, palatines, and coronoids, and possibly also marginal tooth-bearing bones. The teeth may quite safely be assumed to have included well-developed conical teeth as well as shagreen-like smaller teeth; Bystrow (1942) gives a clear comparison of the tooth histology in the two groups. The jaw suspension probably included a strong basal, a well-defined ethmoid, a poorly-developed ascending, and an extensive but not very intimate otic connection, with the cranium; and the jaw musculature arose mainly from the palato-quadrate and its related dermal bones and passed back obliquely to be inserted near the *pars articularis* of the mandible. Such a musculature would allow the wide gape and rapid snapping of the jaws suitable for seizing moving prey.

But the assumption of a triturating dentition clearly requires a different organization, and the typical holostylic suspensorium is an easily understandable corollary. The conditions in *D. lehmanni* strongly suggest that the characteristic dipnoan dentition was well developed before the pterygoid bone showed very great changes. Again we may with good reason suppose the change of habits to have been reflected first in the teeth and associated bones. Quick closure of the jaws is now not advantageous, but a better mechanical advantage of the jaw musculature is very definitely so. The following changes may reasonably be related to this factor: bracing of whole cranium by fusion of anterior and posterior sections and development of dipnoan parasphenoid; fusion of otic process with cranium; more anterior insertion of adductor muscles in the mandible; more vertical and direct pull of adductor muscles, whose origins spread on the lateral wall of the cranium; in consequence of the necessary increase in power of these muscles, increase in cross-sectional area. As direct correlatives of these changes, note: the shortening of the cheek-region; forward movement of opercular bones; broadening of otic section of skull-roof, probably correlated in turn with the increasing importance of the median bones (B_2 and B). It is possible that the rostro-caudal shortening of the otic region in the adults (i.e. the area covered by X-Y_1, and by J_1-J_3) is partly correlated with the same changes in jaw musculature, but a similar progressive drastic shortening of the otic region is noticeable in quite a number of early groups of vertebrates (e.g. Arthrodira, the Rhipidistia and early Tetrapoda, and the early palaeoniscoids), and it seems very probable that this may be associated with the loss of a very highly-developed lateral-line system, with its necessarily large lateralis part of the acoustico-lateralis tracts in the hindbrain.

The other noticeable features of the otic section of the skull-roof—the development of the anastomosis between the supra- and infraorbital sensory canals, the subsequent degeneration of the posterior end of the supraorbital canal, and the partial and eventually complete loss of (J_1-J_3)—are interrelated but have no apparent connection (except in the shortening of the *J*-series) with the changes in dentition, jaw musculature, etc. Here again we have an interesting comparison with other groups of fishes. Osteolepids have already arrived at stages corresponding to IX.1 by Middle Devonian times, though still at X.3. But several Middle and Late Devonian derivatives of the osteolepids (e.g. holoptychiids, coelacanths) have attained stages corresponding to X.1, perhaps even X.0, by Middle and Late Devonian times. In the Palaeoniscoidea the pattern of dermal bones is at first sight very different from that in Dipnoi, but it may be said that conditions corresponding to IX.4 and X.3 persist in most members of the group until Triassic times or even later, though changes parallel to the dipnoan IX.4→0 occur even in some Carboniferous forms (Westoll, 1944), and the parietals (corresponding essentially to J_2 and J_3) are lost in a number of "advanced" or specialized Actinopterygii.

In passing, many other evolving characters of the skull in Dipnoi are paralleled in other groups: IV, VI, and VII are shown by osteolepids→ Tetrapoda, and by many Actinopterygii; VIII is shown in holoptychiids, coelacanths, late osteolepids, and various Tetrapoda, and also by Actinopterygii; XI is clearly shown in an advanced stage by early Actinopterygii, though even living types give developmental evidence of the process, and it is well advanced in osteolepids (so-called "frontals" = parietals of early Tetrapoda), and a similar process almost certainly affected the so-called "nasals" of osteolepids in the production of the frontals and nasals during the transformation to Tetrapoda (cf. Westoll, 1943). It is the other group of characters, most characteristic of Dipnoi (I, II, III, VI, VII, XVII, and probably XIV), which appears in the main to be correlated directly with change in dietary habits.

Of the post-cranial characters, XVIII follows IV to a considerable degree, but the thinning of the scales is more rapid than that of skull-bones, and the end-stages are different. The loss of the layer of cosmine is strictly paralleled among the Rhipidistia and their tetrapod derivatives, and the corresponding dentine-tissue in the scales of Actinopterygii is also progressively lost. The other characters are clearly associated with changes in locomotory habits. They, too, show very rapid change during the Devonian; but *Dipterus*, in which the cranial characters have already changed considerably from the ancestral pattern, has only changed relatively little in post-cranial characters, so that at least in temporal succession the changes in body form seem to follow those of the skull.

It is of the greatest significance that the Dipnoi as a whole occupy so narrowly-defined an evolutionary track. The side branches so far known are few and involve very little difference in overall rating from contemporary forms where such are known. We may note the long- and narrow-snouted *Fleurantia* and *Rhynchodipterus* with somewhat more "archaic" body-shape and median fins than their contemporaries, *Uronemus* with its modified but recognizably dipnoan dentition, and *Conchopoma* with its distinctly aberrant dentition. Moreover, such forms are known at present only from Late Devonian and later times, *after* the period of most rapid changes in cranial structure.

There can be little doubt that Dipnoi have come to occupy an ecological zone quite different from that of their ancestors, and that they have done so by what must be allowed to be a relatively very rapid evolutionary shift. We are, in fact, dealing with an example of mega-evolution (Simpson, 1944, p. 105), involving the mode termed quantum evolution by the same author (1944, pp. 198-199, 206-217). The result has been the differentiation of an order (Dipnoi) which could certainly be divided into "families," though these would necessarily be somewhat arbitrarily defined. For the moment it will be convenient to disregard family divisions; the "families" recognized in text-books are of doubtful value.

The remarkably stimulating pioneering discussion of mega-evolution and quantum evolution provided by Simpson (1944) was necessarily largely inductive in nature, and it is of great interest to see how far the present example conforms to his conclusions. In the first place the early evolution of the group appears to have been moderately slow (*Dipnorhynchus*), and in this range the fossil material is extremely scarce. There succeeded a phase of relatively very rapid change (*Dipterus* to *Phaneropleuron*), marked by considerable variability in skull-pattern in any given population, and with considerable fossil populations known from several horizons. The next phase includes the segregation of a number of Carboniferous-Permian genera, each of very much more closely defined skull pattern, and many (if not all) with a markedly longer range in geological time. The last phase is one in which generic differentiation is possibly questionable and certainly slow; the Triassic *Ceratodus*, on a conservative view, could be held congeneric with the living Australian lungfish, and it is possible that the *Lepidosiren-Gnathorhiza* resemblance is truly indicative of direct descent. In these living forms some details are very variable (e.g. some head-bones, latero-sensory canals).

As genera are currently defined in Dipnoi, the overall rate of generic evolution in the group is not extremely high. We may reckon perhaps ten "genera" (possibly as few as 8, possibly as many as *ca.* 12-15) in the history of any of the three living genera from Early Devonian times, or something of the order of 1 genus to about 30 (20-40) million years on the average. Even in the most rapid part of the whole history, during the Devonian period, no more than about 5 genera are recognized in the main track, and this over a period of some 25-30 million years (estimated), or 1 genus per 5-6 million years. This last figure is closely similar to that given for horses (1 in 5-6 million yrs.), but there can be no real comparison here, since if Dipnoi were known as well as horses we may be sure that very much finer generic divisions would be recognized. But the Dipnoi as a whole have evolved in slow-motion, which allows us to see the process more clearly.

The rapid period of dipnoan evolution in the Middle and Late Devonian is clearly of the type called tachytelic by Simpson (1944, p. 134); later a period of modest differentiation of phyletic type produced a number of side branches not radically different from the "main line" forms, and a few late genera which became so completely rutted in the evolutionary track as to be apparently bradytelic. In earlier Devonian times the rate of change was probably not so striking as in the Middle Devonian, at any rate there is apparently not a catastrophically "explosive" beginning, but a period of accelerating change (*Dipnorhynchus* stage).

At least in so far as characters of the dermal skull are concerned, the early (essentially Devonian) forms show high variability, and the Carboniferous and Permian genera are each very rigidly defined, while the living genera show a rather high degree of variation in dermal bones and laterosensory system, of a kind more haphazard than in early forms.

These observations allow rather detailed commentary on some of the conclusions (many of them quite tentative) reached by Simpson. We may first note his discussion (1944, pp. 105-124) of major systematic discontinuities of record. It remains true that there is still a distinct gap between the earliest known Dipnoi and Rhipidistia, and it seems certain that each has diverged from the common ancestral structure. The really early Dipnoi (pre-Givetian) are very rare indeed, and further knowledge of them is likely to be sporadic and fortuitous. Simpson's discussion (*op. cit.*, pp. 109-114) based on fossil mammals is not altogether acceptable in the present study, or in the cases of the origin of coelacanths and of early Tetrapoda, which the writer has also studied. Simpson's point No. 1 (p. 109), that "missing forms . . . were, as a rule, small animals compared with their best-known contemporaries and with their descendants," is not likely to be true in any of these three cases. *Dipnorhynchus* is decidedly large, so is an extremely primitive coelacanth now being studied by the writer, and so is *Elpistostege* (Westoll, 1938, 1943a). His point No. 2 is supported by all three groups, and so are Nos. 3 and 4, except that really early forms ancestral to Dipnoi and at least some Rhipidistia are not certainly known. The Dipnoi allow a rather clear estimation of the time taken to develop well-marked dipnoan characters. It is clear that it was not an immeasurably brief time; the earliest fairly completely known genus (*Dipterus*) had probably at least ten and possibly as much as thirty million years of specifically dipnoan ancestry. With regard to his point No. 6 (p. 112) it is as least tempting to correlate the rise of the Dipnoi with the results of earth-movements of the periods usually termed "Acadian" and "Caledonian." Comment on Simpson's point No. 7, with which the writer is in general agreement, will be held over until the whole complex of Rhipidistia, coelacanths, Dipnoi, and various early Tetrapoda has been subjected to analysis.

From the formal point of view of population genetics, Simpson's explanation of such discontinuities (*op. cit.*, pp. 115-124) is not immediately satisfying if applied to Dipnoi, though it seems possible to harmonize the results. It is obvious however that there has been no very large scale saltation in the sense of Goldschmidt (1940). The very scarce remains of pre-Givetian Dipnoi suggest but by no means prove that these transitional forms were few in number. But these forms very probably evolved less quickly than the relatively well-known Middle-Late Devonian members, which, according to Simpson's analysis, would be expected to represent small populations subjected to very strong selection pressure. At any one time such populations would be expected to show exceptionally low variability (see Simpson, 1944, p. 40), but such Devonian forms as *Dipterus* and *Scaumenacia* are represented by extremely numerous remains from individual horizons and in some ways (dermal skull-patterns) show conspicuously high variability. The latter point may be of small significance, since the rest of the organism shows far less variability, and perhaps selection-pressure was far from strong in its effects on skull-patterns in detail. But it does appear that definite evolutionary trends affect skull-patterns of later forms (e.g. large $K + L_1 + L_2 + ? M$ elements), and this point deserves attention by other workers. The large fossil populations of *Dipterus, Scaumenacia, Phaneropleuron,* etc. known from single localities, are at first sight surprising, since these forms were probably evolving rapidly. But there can be little doubt that all these Middle and Late Devonian genera lived in rigorous conditions, probably in each case with strong seasonal or other cyclic changes. In such conditions the population-size may fluctuate widely, and thus the effective breeding-population over a period of time may have been quite small, in spite of local and temporary shoals of fishes (as at Dura Den!). The discussion by Simpson (1944, p. 69) is very suggestive on this point. It seems probable that conditions in the Old Red Sandstone cuvettes would favor isolation of small remnants during hard times, and it is tempting to regard the peculiar cranial pattern of the Banniskirk population of *Dipterus* (above, p. 139) as due to descent from such a small "cyclic-relict" population in which a modified genotype became important. This population may have been annihilated with the next onset of hard times.

It is thus possible to fit only part of what is known of the evolution of Dipnoi, and that only with reservations, to Simpson's analysis of the processes and results of mega-evolution.

Turning now to rates of evolution, it is important to try to decide whether any of the later Dipnoi have become truly bradytelic. It is not possible to give more than crude estimates of the duration of each genus of Dipnoi, and there are unfortunately very few genera concerned. Analysis on the lines of Simpson's discussion of pelecypods and land carnivores (1944, pp. 20-29, 126-143) strongly suggests that the curve for survivorship of extinct genera is of the same type as in Simpson's examples, while the longevity of living genera indicates that *Epiceratodus* is almost certainly, and *Protopterus* may be, bradytelic. If *Gnathorhiza* is really closely connected with the ancestry of *Protopterus* and *Lepidosiren*, both these genera are possibly bradytelic. The section of the record from *Dipterus* to *Phaneropleuron* is essentially tachytelic. So far, Simpson's terminology and definitions are accepted; but the data on Dipnoi provide a much less complex overall picture than the Carnivora or Pelecypoda and suggest that bradytely in this particular case is not strictly separable from the later phases of increasingly slow horotelic evolution. The statistical picture in the Pelecypoda, which led Simpson (1944, p. 133) to define bradytelic evolutionary rates and bradytelic "phyla," could result from the summation of a large series of evolutionary patterns like that shown by Dipnoi, the "curves" beginning at different times and having different "lengths." The longevity of a "genus" is clearly, to a first approximation, inversely proportional to the rate of evolution (Fig. 11), and if that rate falls almost to nothing, as it does in late Dipnoi, we have the requirements for a "bradytelic" genus. The writer can see no convincing reason for defining bradytely on any other grounds than very slow horotely.

It is reasonable to regard very early Dipnoi as "inadaptive" in the sense that they had lost "the equilibrium of [their] ancestors or collaterals," but they were undoubtedly, as events were to show, "preadaptive" in being able to realize new functions in a different environment. With reservations concerning the terminology, the Dipnoi compare well with the pattern of three phases of Simpson's quantum evolution (1944, p. 207), with a second rapidly-changing "preadaptive" phase grading into a final "adaptive" phase.[4] There is no doubt that by this quantum evolution the Dipnoi have actually entered a new zone of the adaptive grid.

It is significant that modern Dipnoi live in fresh water, often with widely fluctuating conditions. From at least Middle Old Red Sandstone times the group seems to have been adapted to generally similar conditions. Adaptation to such a range of conditions implies wide tolerances, and the survival of the group is obviously a measure of its thoroughgoing nature. It is true that all the known specimens of *Dipnorhynchus* come from marine deposits; it is probable that the Hunsrückschiefer were laid down quite near land and *D. lehmanni* might have been carried out from rivers, but little can be deduced about the conditions of formation of the Buchan and Murrumbidgee marine limestones of Australia. It remains an open question whether the immediate pre-Dipnoi were marine or not.

Another important point concerns Simpson's comments (1944, p. 141) on the large breeding populations to be expected in bradytelic "phyla." The writer knows of no evidence concerning any of the living genera of lungfishes which would support the existence of really large effective

---

[4] In the writer's experience the terms *inadaptive*, *preadaptive*, and *postadaptive* have often proved semantic blanks in discussions, since their connotations are heavily subjective.

breeding populations. This again appears to be a case where current generalizations from population genetics do not give a very good fit to the data. To anyone familiar with the rich Old Red Sandstone fish beds, it must be very highly probable that lungfish populations then (at a time of tachytelic evolution) were larger than those of the present day.

Nearly all modern discussions on evolution involve genetics (especially population genetics) and the comparative anatomy on which most of systematics and paleontology are founded, but there is a large and habitually neglected "middle term," namely *Entwicklungsmechanik* in its broader modern meaning. Analysis of methods of change in genotype can properly benefit analysis of temporal successions of phenotypes, and vice-versa, only when there is an adequate corpus of information about the way in which a new genotype modifies the phenotype and its ontogeny. It is proposed very briefly to indicate some lines of thought which the writer has found fruitful. It is assumed that individual development is an epigenesis regulated by a complex sequence of organizer-controlled processes which in various ways determine the fate of tissues hitherto labile. These are the essentials of Waddington's lively synthesis (1935, 1939, Chap. VI). In "normal" individuals of any species the succession and mutual relations of organizers (the "epigenotype") are recognizably similar. Genetical changes of the type most suitable for laboratory experiments normally affect only relatively late-stage or peripheral members of the organizer systems, though quite ordinary single-locus mutations may have remarkable effects on the appearance of the phenotype, indicating great interference with the earlier more fundamental organizers. The vast majority of all such "deep-level" modifications of the epigenotype are not very viable, but they illustrate the important principle, too frequently overlooked in discussions on large-scale evolutionary changes, that changes in epigenotype and phenotype do not depend simply upon the total accumulation of mutation. The writer explicitly does not imply support for the cruder "saltation" hypotheses by these remarks. But it seems obvious that the epigenotype of, say, *Phaneropleuron* was quite markedly different in many ways from that of the hypothetical Early Devonian pre-Dipnoan. All that is suggested is that this total change did not necessarily proceed by myriad minimal modifications of the epigenotype, but that from time to time genetic mutation may have resulted directly (by interference with time of action, by suppression, or by chemical or physical modification of evocators) in changes at a "deep" level in the epigenotype such that considerable possibilities of new combinations of more peripheral epigenetic effects became possible. The primary effect might very occasionally be selectively advantageous, and could then result in a rapid offset from the parent population, since there would then be a new field for genetic recombinations to "explore." Of course it is not suggested that a natural order such as the Dipnoi arose simply as the result of one or two such lucky breaks! But it seems a possibility worth bearing in mind that during a "quantum evolution" the epigenotype in a substantial part of a whole population may be in a sensitive condition, peculiarly liable to changes of the type just outlined. These brief speculative considerations lead the writer to suspect that "quantum evolution" may occur at many levels; with relatively small shift it may result in some forms of speciation, while with a considerable offset, undoubtedly composite and resulting from the integration of smaller changes, the differentiation of a group like Dipnoi can be understood. This possibility is now, with the development of the "population cage" for *Drosophila* by l'Héritier and Teissier (see also references in Wright and Dobzhansky, 1946; Dobzhansky, 1947), open to experimental investigation at intraspecific levels. The history of Dipnoi is not only a "quantum evolution"; it is a quantum evolution on a large (ordinal) scale, in which habitat and conditions of sedimentation have allowed a moderately good record of the early transitional stages to be preserved, in contrast to the known history of terrestrial animals.

REFERENCES

de Beer, G. R. 1937. *The Development of the Vertebrate Skull*. Oxford Univ. Press.
de Beer, G. R., and J. A. Moy-Thomas. 1934. On the Skull of Holocephali. *Phil. Trans. Roy. Soc. Lond.*, B. 224, 287-312.
Bystrow, A. P. 1942. Deckknochen und Zähne der *Osteolepis* und *Dipterus*. *Acta Zool.*, 23, 263-289.
——. 1944. On the dentition of *Fleurantia denticulata*. *C. R.* (*Doklady*) *Acad. Sci. U.S.S.R.* 44, 31-32.
Dobzhansky, Th. 1947. Adaptive changes induced by Natural Selection in wild populations of *Drosophila*. *Evolution*, 1, 1-16.
Dollo, L. 1895. Sur la phylogenie des Dipneustes. *Bull. Soc. Belge Géol.*, 9, 79-128, 6 Pls.
Forster-Cooper, C. 1937. The Middle Devonian Fish Fauna of Achanarras. *Trans. Roy. Soc. Edinb.*, 59, 223-239, 8 Pls.
Goodrich, E. S. 1925. On the Cranial Roofing Bones in the Dipnoi. *Jour. Linn. Soc. Lond., Zool.*, 36, 79-86.
——. 1930. *Studies on the Structure and Development of Vertebrates*. Macmillan, London.
Graham-Smith, W., and T. S. Westoll. 1937. On a new Long-headed Dipnoan Fish from the Upper Devonian of Scaumenac Bay, P.Q., Canada. *Trans. Roy. Soc. Edinb.*, 59, 241-256, 2 Pls.
Hills, E. S. 1933. On a Primitive Dipnoan from the Middle Devonian Rocks of New South Wales. *Ann. Mag. Nat. Hist.*, ser. 10, 11, 634-643, 1 Pl.
——. 1935. Records and Descriptions of some Australian Devonian Fishes. *Proc. Roy. Soc. Victoria*, 48 (N.S.), 161-171, 1 Pl.
——. 1941. The Cranial Roof of *Dipnorhynchus sussmilchi* (Eth. fil.) *Records Austral. Mus.*, 21, 45-55, 1 Pl.
——. 1943. The Ancestry of the Choanichthyes. *Austral. Journ. Sci.*, 6, 21-23.
Holmes, A. 1947. The Construction of a Geological Time-Scale. *Trans. Geol. Soc. Glasgow*, 21, 117-152.

Holmgren, N., and E. A. Stensiö. 1936. Kranium und Visceralskelett der Acranier, Cyclostomen und Fische. In *Handbuch d. vergl. Anat.*, edited by Bolk, Göppert, Kallius, and Lubosch, Bd. 4.

Jaekel, O. 1927. Der Kopf der Wirbeltiere. *Zeitsch. gesamte Anat., Ergebn. d. Anat. u. Entw. Gesch.*, 27, 815-974.

Jarvik, E. 1942. On the Structure of the Snout of Crossopterygians and Lower Gnathostomes in General. *Zool. Bidrag*, Uppsala, 21, 235-675, 17 Pls.

——. 1944a. On the Dermal Bones, Sensory Canals and Pit-lines of the Skull in *Eusthenopteron foordi* Whiteaves, with some remarks on *E. säve-söderberghi* Jarvik. *K. Svensk. Vet. Akad. Handl.* 3 ser., Bd. 21, No. 3.

——. 1944b. On the Exoskeletal Shoulder-Girdle of Teleostomian Fishes, with special reference to *Eusthenopteron foordi* Whiteaves. *K. Svensk. Vet. Akad. Handl.* 3 ser., Bd. 21, No. 7.

Kesteven, H. L. 1931. Contributions to the Cranial Osteology of Fishes. No. VII. The Skull of *Neoceratodus forsteri*: a Study in Phylogeny. *Rec. Austral. Mus.*, 18, 236-265.

Kisselewa, Z. N. 1929. Zur vergleichend-anatomischen Kenntniss des Skelettes der Dipnoi (Russian with German summary). *Mem. Zool. Sci. Inst.*, Moscow, 3, 1-45.

Lehmann, W., and T. S. Westoll. 1949. A primitive Dipnoan fish from the Lower Devonian of Germany. (M.S.)

Nielsen, E. 1936. Some few preliminary Remarks on Triassic Fishes from East Greenland. *Medd. om Grönland*, 112, No. 3.

Pander, C. H. 1858. *Ueber die Ctenodipterinen des Devonischen Systems*. St. Petersburg, 64 pp., 9 Pls.

Pehrson, T. 1922. Some points in the cranial development of Teleostomian Fishes. *Acta Zool.*, 3, 1-63.

——. 1940. The development of dermal bones in the skull of *Amia calva*. *Acta. Zool.*, 21, 1-50.

Romer, A. S. 1936. The Dipnoan Cranial Roof. *Amer. Jour. Sci.*, 5th ser., 32, 241-256.

——. 1937. The braincase of the Carboniferous Crossopterygian *Megalichthys nitidus*. *Bull. Mus. Comp. Zoöl.*, Harvard, 82, 1-73.

——. and H. J. Smith. 1934. American Carboniferous Dipnoans. *Jour. Geol.*, 42, 700-719.

Säve-Söderbergh, G. 1937. On *Rhynchodipterus elginensis*, n.g., n.sp., representing a new group of dipnoan-like Choanata from the Upper Devonian of East Greenland and Scotland. *Ark. Zool.*, 29B, 1-8.

——. 1934. Further Contributions to the Devonian Stratigraphy of East Greenland. *Medd. om Grönland*, 96, No. 2, esp. p. 24.

Sedgwick, A., and R. I. Murchison. 1828. On the Structure and Relations of the Deposits contained between the Primary Rocks and the Oolitic Series in the North of Scotland. *Trans. Geol. Soc. London*, ser. 2, 3, 125-160 (esp. p. 143), Pls. 13-17.

Sewertzoff, A. N. 1902. Zur Entwickelungsgeschichte des *Ceratodus Forsteri*. *Anat. Anz.*, 21, 593-608.

Simpson, G. G. 1944. *Tempo and Mode in Evolution*. Columbia Univ. Press, New York.

Stromer, E. 1938. Der Wüstenfisch *Ceratodus* Ag. 1838 und seine meso- und känozoischen Verwandten. *N. Jahrb. Min. Geol. Pal.*, Beil-Bd. Abt. B, 80, 248-263.

Teller, F. 1891. Ueber den Schädel eines fossilen Dipnoers, *Ceratodus Sturii*, nov. spec., etc. *Abh. K. K. Geol. Reichsanst.*, 15, Heft 3, 1-39, 4 Pls.

Traquair, R. H. 1890. Notice of new and little-known Fish Remains from the Blackband Ironstone of Borough Lee, near Edinburgh. *Geol. Mag.*, Dec. 3, 7, esp. p. 249.

Waddington, C. H. 1935. *How Animals Develop*. George Allen & Unwin, London.

——. 1939. *An Introduction to Modern Genetics*. George Allen & Unwin, London.

Wade, R. T. 1935. *The Triassic Fishes of Brookvale, New South Wales*. British Museum (Natural History), London.

Watson, D. M. S. 1926. The Evolution and Origin of the Amphibia. *Phil. Trans. Roy. Soc. Lond., 214B,* 189-257.

——. and H. Day. 1916. Notes on some Palaeozoic Fishes. *Manchester Memoirs, 60,* 1-48, 3 Pls.

——. and E. S. Gill. 1923. The Structure of Certain Palaeozoic Dipnoi. *Jour. Linn. Soc., Zool., 25,* 163-216.

Weitzel, K. 1926. *Conchopoma gadiforme* Kner, ein Lungenfisch aus dem Rotliegenden. *Abh. Senck. Naturforsch. Ges., 40,* 159-178, 6 Pls.

Westoll, T. S. 1936. On the Structures of the Dermal Ethmoid Shield of *Osteolepis. Geol. Mag., 73,* 157-171, 2 Pls.

——. 1937a. On the cheek-bones in teleostome fishes. *Jour. Anat.,* London, *71,* 362-382.

——. 1937b. The Old Red Sandstone Fishes of the North of Scotland, particularly of Orkney and Shetland. *Proc. Geol. Assoc.,* London, *48,* 13-45.

——. 1943a. The Origin of the Tetrapods. *Biol. Rev., 18,* 78-98.

——. 1943b. The Origin of the primitive Tetrapod limb. *Proc. Roy. Soc. Lond.,* B, *131,* 373-393.

——. 1944. The Haplolepidae, a new Family of Late Carboniferous Bony Fishes. A Study in Taxonomy and Evolution. *Bull. Amer. Mus. Nat. Hist., 83,* 1-121, 10 Pls.

Woodward, A. S. 1890. The Fossil Fishes of the Hawkesbury Series at Gosford. *Mem. Geol. Surv. New South Wales,* Sydney: Palaeontology, No. 4.

——. 1891. *Catalogue of Fossil Fishes in the British Museum (Natural History).* Part II, London, 1891.

Wright, S., and Th. Dobzhansky. 1946. Genetics of Natural Populations. XII. Experimental reproduction of some of the changes caused by natural selection in certain populations of *Drosophila pseudo-obscura. Genetics, 31,* 125-156.

· 9 ·

EVOLUTIONARY RATES AND TRENDS
IN RHINOCEROSES

BY HORACE ELMER WOOD, II[1]

THE rhinoceroses are not merely one more example of an evolutionary case history. Like the horses, they belong to the order Perissodactyla; but, having a sharply contrasted phylogenetic development, they can counterbalance the frequent tendency to overgeneralize from the horse record.

The general impression that horses evolved far more rapidly than rhinoceroses is broadly true, yet there are many exceptions and qualifications to this summary statement. Rates of rhinoceros evolution may be conveniently measured in "horse-units," using the familiar main horse line as the standard of comparison. The plural form, rates, is used advisedly, since different lines of rhinoceroses evolved at very different rates. Different parts of the body—the skull, teeth and feet, in particular—have also evolved at very different rates in any given line, in contrast with the roughly parallel evolutionary rates of horse teeth and feet. Except for the head and feet, the skeleton remained very stable. For example, the white rhinoceros of Africa and the Pleistocene woolly rhinoceros of Eurasia reached a stage comparable to Pliocene horses in crown height of the cheek teeth; in weight distribution their tridactyl feet are most comparable with Oligocene horses. The Indian and Javan rhinoceroses still barely survive, in the Oriental Region; comparative anatomy and paleontology indicate that of the two the Javan rhinoceros is much less modified from their Pliocene common ancestry. Compared with horses, their teeth and feet have reached only Miocene stages.

The extraordinary elasmotherine rhinoceroses can be traced from the Pleistocene back to the Late Miocene, and, less certainly, farther back into the more generalized aceratheres of the Late Oligocene. While always remaining rhinoceroses, they out-horsed the horses in developing high-crowned cheek teeth with crenellated enamel buried in cement to form an efficient grinding mill. From the Late Miocene until their extinction before the end of the Pleistocene, the elasmothere cheek teeth evolved in the same direction as, but definitely farther than, the horses evolved from the Middle Miocene to the present. Over the same time, their feet elongated slightly, with some emphasis on the middle digit, thus also

---

[1] Professor of Biology, The Newark Colleges of Rutgers University.

paralleling the horses, but making only the progress made by the horses from Early to Middle Miocene.

The baluchitheres were by a wide margin the largest of all land mammals. By the time of their extinction in the Early Miocene they had developed gigantism farther, and I believe more rapidly, than any other mammalian line, during the Oligocene epoch. Their legs had elongated and their feet had emphasized the middle toe rather more than the contemporaneous Early Miocene horses. Their teeth, at the same time, compare more nearly with latest Eocene than with any Oligocene horse teeth in molarization of the premolars and in the retention of low crowns; in comparison with other rhinos their teeth represent an Early Oligocene stage.

In the same way, tapir evolutionary achievement can be summarized as follows: from the Early Eocene to the present day, tapir cheek teeth have made roughly the progress that horses made by the Early Oligocene; in size and skull, tapirs compare best with Miocene horses; during all this time, their feet have remained in an Eocene stage, compared with perissodactyls in general, or with horses in particular.

If Goldschmidt had kept to his saltatory concept of "macroevolution" as a possible occasional *deus ex machina*, it would be impossible to disprove it by paleontological evidence; but for its universalized form such refutatory evidence is readily available. There are many such evolutionary series as the European dicerorhine rhinoceroses, where one closely-knit species succeeds another from a primitive Late Oligocene form to the highly specialized woolly rhinoceros of the Pleistocene. The curves of variation of the populations of some succeeding levels overlap, but the total amount of evolutionary change from beginning to end is more than "macroevolutionary" by Goldschmidt's standard. There is, however, no single level at which his postulated evolutionary jump could have occurred. The familiar horse series from *Mesohippus* to *Equus* covers an even longer time, produced a greater morphological change, and shows still more closely-knit successive populations.

So far as evolutionary trends are concerned, the rhinoceroses are perhaps more instructive than the horses, since they show as diverse trends as the messenger who jumped on his horse and galloped off in all directions. They have run to larger size than the horses, and have specialized in brawn rather than brain, but even in brain they show some progress, although at a slower rate than their rivals. Their well-publicized stupidity is only relative; even a pretty stupid rhinoceros is more intelligent than a brilliant alligator. Both horses and rhinoceroses developed distinct browsing and grazing trends; in the horses, the grazers predominated and alone survive to the present. Both types occur in living and fossil rhinoceroses. The browsers, the predominant type, had low (or, at most, medium) crowned teeth, represented by the living Sumatran and black rhinoceroses and most fossil forms. The white rhinoceros, the only living grazing form, has high crowned teeth. *Elasmotherium,* presumably a grazer, surpassed any horse in height of crown, being rivalled only by a few rodents. A few lines of rhinoceroses have even gone in for speed: *Diceratherium* and *Hyracodon,* or, as the extreme form, *Triplopus,* with its gazelle-like figure. The development of bulk has been much more typical, with the elasmotheres and the baluchitheres as the most striking examples. A semiaquatic fluviatile habitat like that of the hippos has been adopted twice independently, in the amynodonts and in *Teleoceras*; the former developed hippo-like canine tusks, and the latter, a more extreme barrel-like torso than the hippo.

The rhinoceros horn, which may be described as a high cone of appressed fibers (like hair without follicles), is unique in the animal kingdom. Besides this original invention, rhinoceroses have shown their individuality in the number and placement of their horns. The following patterns occur: a single median horn on the nasals, as in the Indian and Javan rhinoceroses, or on the frontals as in *Elasmotherium,* or on both, in a file, as in the Sumatran rhinoceros, the woolly rhinoceros, and the African rhinoceroses, or paired horns on the nasals as in *Diceratherium.* Most of these fashions evolved more than once from the diversified primitive stock of hornless rhinoceroses.

It is customary, though not very accurate, to cite the horses as a prime example of monophyletic evolution. The rhinoceroses have the opposite extreme, a "bushy" family tree, with no definite main stem but all side-branches, as illustrated either by the thirteen or so "main" lines of rhinoceros evolution (whether they are assigned family, subfamily, or supergeneric rank), or by the equally bushy development of the relatively primitive subfamily Caenopinae in both hemispheres.

One of the most striking convergences in parallel evolution (if the mathematicians will condone the solecism) is that between the woolly rhinoceros and the living white rhinoceros of Africa. The resemblance, especially in skull and teeth, is so close that it long seemed incontrovertible that they were extremely closely related. This now appears not to be the case. The white rhinoceros seems to be derived, with its relatively primitive cousin, the more abundant black rhinoceros, from a different Miocene-Pliocene ancestry, whereas the woolly rhinoceros is descended from a long known line of dicerorhine rhinoceroses related to the living Sumatran rhinoceros.

In the past, paleontologists have been among the worst offenders in offering orthogenetic interpretations of what appear to be more or less straight-line sequences. The rhinoceroses furnish a striking illustration of this type of phylogeny together with the evidence to act as antidote for this interpretation. The accompanying table shows the distribution in time and space of all known American amynodonts. No actual intergradation has yet been established in this sequence except between *Amynodon advenus* and *A. intermedius,* where there is either stratigraphic or morphologic intergradation, according to one's concept of species in paleontology. If species are defined strictly by their morphology,

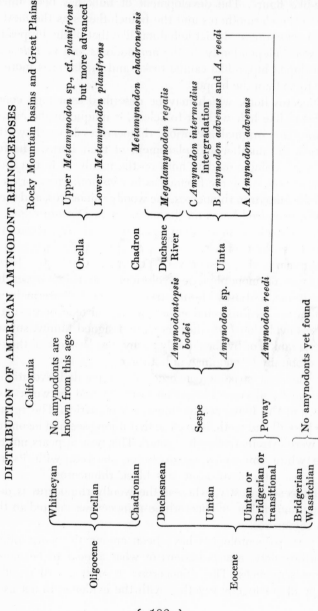

one specimen of A. *intermedius* is known from Uinta B and several members of A. *advenus* have been collected from a quarry in Uinta C. On the other hand, if species are defined partly in terms of their geologic levels and (purely theoretical[2]) opportunities to interbreed, then the two species can be separated stratigraphically but overlap somewhat in structure. There is a virtually unitary succession of progressively more specialized types at each ascending geologic level. Except for the occurrence of *Amynodon reedi* (the most primitive species) in Uinta B as well as in the probably earlier Poway conglomerate of California, and the somewhat aberrant Californian *Amynodontopsis*, this series is a made-to-order example of so-called orthogenetic evolution. I know no other authentic case so devoid of side lines in which an "internal perfecting principle" seems so clearly to drive the organism through the predestined stages of racial youth, maturity, and old age to the inevitable doom of racial senescence and extinction. Such a plausibly mystical interpretation of the American amynodonts is rendered slightly ludicrous when the Mongolian amynodonts are examined; preliminary study shows that they include forms closely related to the American stock, by direct migration, as well as a group of autochthonous forms, diverging in multiple directions, in typical rhinoceros fashion. If the "orthogenetic" evolution of the North American amynodonts is attributed to some kind of purely internal control, it is difficult to see why this control should have disappeared at what was later to become the International Date Line.

Some amynodont evolutionary trends are remarkable illustrations of "relative growth." The progressive atrophy of the incisors and premolars contrasts sharply with the hypertrophy of the canines and molars. The molars seem to suffer plastic deformation; the lower molars are pulled out antero-posteriorly, with some shear, and pinched in transversely, and the buccal sides of the upper molars become progressively more hypsodont than their lingual sides, as if trying to grow over them in an arc. Altogether this is a remarkable evolutionary development, toward which the South American astrapotheres converge remarkably, as the only really similar combination. In all lines of amynodonts the skull tends toward achondroplasia. In both America (*Amynodontopsis*) and in Mongolia a wedge-shaped front of the skull evolved.

---

[2] Obviously, it is pure fiction that individuals from, say, the top and bottom of Uinta B belonged to a single interbreeding population, whereas those from the top of B and the bottom of C belonged to different populations.

· 10 ·

EVOLUTIONARY TRENDS IN THE ANGIOSPERMS

BY RALPH W. CHANEY[1]

WITH the exception of the flower, all of the organs used in the classification of land plants had appeared before the close of the Paleozoic era, some two hundred million years ago. Since that time the fossil record shows many new characters developing in stems, roots, leaves, and cones, all of which may be of value in classification; but few of these characters have progressed along recognizable trends suggesting lineal descent. Most of the structures which provide a basis for establishing plant phylogenies had reached the culmination of their evolutionary development before Cretaceous time and the appearance of flowering plants. Only a brief mention of these older trends is within the province of this discussion.

The most ancient land plants, assignable to the Psilopsida and Lycopsida, or to a position intermediate between these major groups, appear in many parts of the world in rocks of latest Silurian and older Devonian age. Their stems show the most primitive structure, the protostele, with a narrow strand of conducting tissue at the center. One of the most typical Paleozoic genera of the lycopsids, *Lepidodendron*, may have a protostelic stem, but an advanced type is more characteristic, a siphonostele with an interior cylinder of pith. Development of a cortical shell or periderm for support in the stems of these older trees is followed by growth of secondary wood. In earlier and smaller forms this was centripetal, but the Middle Devonian stems of *Callixylon* show a centrifugal growth like that of modern trees.

The first roots appear in the lepidodendrids, where elongate basal extensions of the trunk known as rhizomorphs served both for root attachment and as support for the trunks of *Lepidodendron* and *Sigillaria*. These tall trees disappeared before the close of the Paleozoic era and were followed by *Pleuromeia*, a smaller genus of the Triassic; the base of its trunk shows short tuber-shaped lobes from whose surface branch numerous rootlets. A third stage has recently been described, represented by *Nathorstiana* of the Cretaceous; this much smaller form has greatly reduced rhizophomorphs. Finally in the living herbaceous genus, *Isoetes*, the rhizophomorphs are short and thick, with many lateral roots.

The oldest leaf occurs on *Baragwanathia*, a small plant from the Late

[1] Professor of Paleontology, University of California, and Research Associate, Carnegie Institution of Washington.

Silurian of Australia; while this simple scale-shaped enation shows a vascular connection with the stele, it appears not to have led to higher types of leaves. In the fern-like psilopsid, *Protopteridium*, and in one of the oldest seed ferns, *Eospermatopteris* from the Late Devonian, lateral branchlets divide in a single plane to form a blade-like expansion. With further lateral growth, a leaf-blade of the fern type appears both in the Filicineae and the Pteridospermae of the Carboniferous. The dichotomously branching vascular strands of the original branch become the veins of the leaf, which are dichotomous in primitive ferns and seed ferns. Gradually a more efficient vascular circulation results from the cross-connection of these parallel nerves to form a coarse network. This type of leaf first appears in the Middle Carboniferous and becomes abundant in such Mesozoic ferns as *Clathropteris* and *Lonchopteris*; it is still further developed in the leaves of the Angiospermae. Increasing effectiveness shown in the structures of leaf, stem, and root seems clearly related to the trend toward larger size among land plants in their competition for sunlight.

The evolution of reproductive structures in land plants, from the simple terminal sporangium of *Rhynia* to the cone of the Abietineae has been so well elaborated that we need not review it here. Of particular interest are the recent studies of Florin (1) on the cones of the Cordaitales and Voltziales, which suggest an evolutionary trend from this Permo-Triassic order to the Mesozoic and modern conifers.

The Record of the Angiosperms

The flower appears rather suddenly in the record of the Cretaceous period, in rocks laid down one hundred million years ago. In these and later deposits it is supplemented by the remains of stems and leaves, which resemble those of angiosperms and further establish the existence of this class during later geologic time. In the classification and resultant phylogenies of angiosperms, living and fossil, such conservative organs as stems and leaves are little used. The structure of the flower provides the principal basis for recognition of relationships and evolutionary trends. The rarity of fossil flowers and fruits in which internal details of structure have been preserved presents a serious problem to the paleobotanist who seeks to study the history of the group along the lines followed by botanists. As a result studies of fossil angiosperms have emphasized their distribution in time and space, and the building of phylogenies has been left largely to students of modern plants. In spite of this incompleteness of the record, it seems desirable to summarize the available data which bear upon the origin and evolution of flowering plants.

Although fragmentary and doubtful remains of angiosperms have been discovered in rocks of Jurassic and Triassic age,[2] the first reliable record of their occurrence is in rocks of Early Cretaceous age from Greenland. Before the end of the Early Cretaceous, they were beginning to appear in eastern North America, western Europe, and southern Siberia, but they were neither abundant nor widely distributed until Late Cretaceous time. Whether Greenland is the actual area of origin or whether flowering plants became established there after migration from the south is difficult to demonstrate. The known record favors a northern origin; but our meager knowledge of past life in the tropics, due in some degree to the rapid disintegration there of sediments exposed at the surface, imposes an element of caution. Wherever their source, the oldest *known* angiosperms are in no sense to be considered the *oldest* angiosperms. The Kome flora of Greenland includes such diverse families as the Magnoliaceae, Menispermaceae, Lauraceae, Platanaceae, and Moraceae. With the exception of the first two, these families are placed at a relatively high level in most phylogenies of dicotyledons; even the two simpler families are wholly unrelated. Some of the fossils suggest an extended pre-Cretaceous history. Leaves of *Platanus* show no recognizable distinctions from those on living trees.[3] Wood from the Early Cretaceous of England, referred to the genus *Woburnia*, exhibits no characters by which it may be separated from stems of existing members of the tropical family Dipterocarpaceae. If, as is commonly supposed, the environment of the first angiosperms was in the uplands, no satisfactory record of their remains may ever be found, for deposition and preservation of plant fossils are limited largely to lowland basins of sedimentary accumulation.

Many leaf prints from the Greenland and other Cretaceous floras may be said to represent somewhat blurred copies of their existing equivalents. While they resemble the leaves of families to which they have been assigned, most of them are properly referable to form genera rather than to genera now in existence. The Dakota flora from the area east of the Rockies includes numerous plants of this type, and even the latest Cretaceous plants from the Laramie of this region show marked differences from modern genera to which they have been assigned, according to Dorf, who has been working with them in recent years (2). There have been, as indicated by these leaves, some recognizable changes in many families and genera, but only rarely may a developmental trend be noted.

[2] (1) A leaf resembling that of a dicotyledon from the Rhaetic of Greenland (Harris); (2) an ash-like seed from the Rhaetic of Argentina (Wieland); (3) a leaf resembling *Populus* from the Jurassic of England (Seward); (4) *Propalmophyllum* from the Jurassic of France (Lignier); (5) wood resembling that of the Lauraceae from the Early Cretaceous of Madagascar (Fliche); (6) leaves *Ficophyllum*, *Proteaephyllum*, *Rogersia*, from the Early Cretaceous of the eastern United States (Fontaine).

[3] Fruits essentially like those of living species occur in the Late Cretaceous of Europe.

The best example of such a trend is found in the oak-like leaves of the Fagaceae in rocks ranging in age from Cretaceous through Tertiary, and is expressed in changes in size, shape, and marginal characters. Leaves from the Early Cretaceous of Virginia and Wyoming have been referred to the form genus *Quercophyllum*. While not all of them appear to be fagaceous, there is at least one species, *Q. chinkapinense* Ward, which may be an ancestral oak. It is small, ovate in shape, with an entire margin except for small teeth near the apex. Another form genus, *Dryophyllum*,[4] is wide-ranging from Late Cretaceous to Eocene, although many of its later species appear indistinguishable from true oaks (*Quercus*). D. *gracile* Debey, from the Late Cretaceous (Ripley) of Tennessee, is of medium size, with secondary nerves terminating in short marginal teeth, a typical oak character. Two species of *Dryophyllum* from the Laramie of Wyoming and Colorado have larger leaves with similar nervation and margin characters.

The oldest reference to *Quercus* is in the Late Cretaceous (Patoot) of Greenland. These leaves are of relatively small size, with entire margins or short teeth. Several species with teeth large enough to be considered shallow lobes have been referred to *Quercus*, though there is some doubt about their relationships. Late Cretaceous leaves of *Quercus* are recorded from the eastern United States and the Rocky Mountain region, most of them of larger size than those above mentioned. Three types of margin are represented. The widely distributed *Q. morrisoniana* Lesquereux has entire margins, and in general appearance is suggestive of the modern *Q. transmontana* Trelease, *Q. scherzeri* Trelease, and other evergreen oaks of low latitudes in the Americas and Asia. A second type has shallow pointed teeth, as in *Q. primordialis* Lesquereux from the Dakota sandstone of Nebraska, resembling the smaller species of *Dryophyllum* above mentioned, as well as numerous living species of *Quercus, Castanopsis,* and *Lithocarpus* from middle to lower latitudes in North America and Asia; this type may represent the oldest record of the subgenus *Erythrobalanus*, or black oaks. Finally there are species from Alaska (*Q. pseudomarioni* Hollick) and Utah (*Q. antiqua* Newberry) which have shallow rounded teeth almost large enough to be considered lobes; these appear referable to the subgenus *Leucobalanus*, or white oaks. In spite of the close resemblance of many of these leaves to modern oaks, the discovery of acorns in rocks of Cretaceous age must be expected to precede any final conclusion that the genus *Quercus* was represented in the forests of that time.

Quercus groenlandica Heer from the Eocene of Spitzbergen, Greenland,

---

[4] While this genus was established to include other members of the Fagaceae, most of the species assigned to it resemble *Quercus* more closely than other living genera of the family.

and Alaska is represented by large leaves with shallow rounded lobes; they resemble the leaves of *Q. prinus* Linne and other chestnut oaks from the eastern United States and Asia. Similar species with more deeply and simply-lobed leaves suddenly became common during the Miocene and have been abundant members of the temperate forests of North America ever since, with a few living in Eurasia. Leaves with rounded-compound lobes of large size and great depth also made their first appearance in the Miocene of Oregon. These leaves are larger than older leucobalanoids and resemble those of numerous species of temperate white oaks living mostly in eastern North America; none of the living white oaks of Eurasia have compoundly-lobed leaves. In the Miocene of Oregon there also appear suddenly abundant black oaks with deep lobes, both simple and compound. Erythrobalanoids of this type are confined to North America, in fossil as well as living floras. A probable ancestor of the Miocene black oaks is *Q. xalapensis* MacGinitie from the Eocene of California, whose leaf margins are coarsely spinose-dentate.

In western North America, and doubtless in other parts of the continent where the record is largely missing, lobed oaks made up a conspicuous part of Miocene and Pliocene floras. More than any other Tertiary plants they provide a striking illustration of gradual speciation during geologic time, with suggestions both of divergence and of convergence into a mesh-like pattern of development. Recent discussion with Babcock and Stebbins has indicated that the high variability of leaf form in *Quercus* is consistent with the genetic make-up of modern members of the genus. Like most widespread living plants, the oaks are heterogenic, including great numbers of biotypes which may be grouped into more or less distinct ecotypes. Ready interpollination by wind has tended to accentuate their heterozygosity, and great genetic variability is the result. The wide range of leaf form within living species and the marked intergradations between species otherwise distinct find a close parallel in the white oaks and black oaks of the Tertiary. Ultimately we may anticipate the extinction of many living species and the more restricted distribution of their survivors. The more nearly homogenic oaks of the future should present fewer problems of classification than must now be met by the botanist and paleobotanist.

The beginnings of such local extinction and restriction may be seen in the later Tertiary history of the western United States, where oaks with large lobed leaves are now much fewer in number than on the eastern side of the continent. During the Pliocene epoch, which was characterized by reduced and more seasonally restricted precipitation than in the Miocene and earlier epochs, the white oaks were greatly reduced in size and abundance. The modern *Q. douglasii* H. & A., a small-leafed species restricted to dry slopes and valleys in California, may be considered to represent the culmination of this trend; in the eastern United States, where summer-wet climate like that of the Oregon Miocene has continued, the living white oaks have more fully maintained their Miocene leaf characters. A tendency toward smaller size and thicker texture may be noted for the black oaks as early as Middle Eocene time, when *Q. distincta* Lesquereux, an ancestor of the coast live oak, *Q. agrifolia* Nee, appeared in west central California. The Pliocene black oaks of western America are predominantly small-leafed, with shallow lobes and thick texture suggesting an evergreen habit. One of them, *Q. wizlizenoides* Axelrod, has a modern descendant, *Q. wizlizenii* A. De-Candolle, the interior live oak, which hybridizes with the common California black oak, *Q. kelloggii* Newberry, to produce *Q. morehus* Kellogg, a species restricted in distribution and numbers. Occurrence in the Mio-Pliocene Remington Hill flora of central California (3) of the Tertiary equivalents of both these parent species, as well as of a third fossil species, *Q. remingtoni* Condit, having leaves like the hybrid, suggests that hybridization similar to that in the modern oaks may have been taking place several millions of years ago on the western slopes of the Sierra Nevada. *Q. remingtoni* is not to be considered the direct ancestor of the living *Q. morehus*, but merely a Tertiary manifestation of a tendency to hybridize similar to that among surviving black oaks in California.

Other western live oaks, representing the Tertiary equivalents of species referred to the subgenus *Protobalanus*, appear to have had their center of development in the cool dry Sierra Madrean region of northern Mexico. Trelease (4) has suggested that *Protobalanus* represents the ancestral stock of *Quercus*, an idea for which there is paleontological support in the presence of small entire-leafed or shallow-serrate leafed oaks in the Cretaceous of high latitudes. Oak leaves of this type may be found at most horizons of the Tertiary in western America. During the Pliocene, when the climate in the northern hemisphere was becoming cooler and more arid, partly as a result of topographic changes, these small-leafed evergreen oaks spread out widely in the western United States as the most typical genus of the Madro-Tertiary Flora. From that time to the present they have been associated with the small-leafed species of white and black oaks above mentioned, in woodland and chaparral formations of the West.

The developmental trends of leaves of *Quercus* from Cretaceous time down to the present may be summarized as follows:

1. The oldest oak leaves are for the most part of small size and generalized form and may be tentatively included in the primitive subgenus *Protobalanus*. Before the close of the Cretaceous, differentiation may be

noted into the subgenus *Leucobalanus* or white oaks, and possibly into the subgenus *Erythrobalanus* or black oaks.

2. There has been an increase in size and in numbers of species of the white oaks and black oaks, suddenly reaching its culmination in the Miocene. In eastern North America their Miocene size and species representation has been maintained. In the west the size of these broadleafed deciduous oaks was reduced, as was their number of species, during the Pliocene. The prevalence of semi-arid climate over much of the western interior since the Pliocene seems directly related to the smaller size and fewer species of surviving oaks, as compared with their eastern occurrence in a continuing summer-wet climate. As is the case with most other leaves of the tropics, fossil and modern species from warm humid environments are characterized by larger leaves than those of most temperate species.

3. From the round-toothed white oaks of the Late Cretaceous, there developed species with shallow simple-lobed leaves in the Eocene, and much deeper and larger lobes, both simple and compound, by Early Miocene time. Both shallow and deep-lobed species of the subgenus *Leucobalanus* have survived in temperate and subtropical forests, although species with deep-lobed leaves are more characteristic of temperate latitudes, largely in the western hemisphere.

4. From the sharp-toothed black oaks of the Eocene and possibly the Late Cretaceous there developed species with deeply simple- and compound-lobed leaves by Early Miocene time. Living members of the subgenus *Erythrobalanus* are confined to the western hemisphere, with most of the deep-lobed species characteristic of temperate latitudes.

5. A reversal in the trend toward increasing size may be noted in western North America among certain white and black oaks of the Pliocene. Species with small non-lobed or shallow-lobed coriaceous leaves reached their maximum abundance at this time and have continued down to the present, commonly in association with members of the primitive subgenus *Protobalanus*, and largely in semi-arid regions.

6. As Trelease has pointed out, there is "a long existing foliage plasticity" in the genus *Quercus*, which extended from Cretaceous to Miocene time and was doubtless accentuated by free-hybridizing so characteristic of wind-pollinated trees. The greater expansion of lobed oaks in North America than in Eurasia, both today and in the past, seems related to modifying geographic factors. One of these may have been the elimination of migration routes, both over the Bering Sea and Greenland land bridges, before the expanded development of lobed oaks during the Miocene epoch. Subsequently there have been both topographic and climatic barriers to migration of these oaks from North America to

Eurasia. Another geographic factor involving competition is discussed by Stebbins in Chapter 12 of this volume.

Turning now to the evidence of evolutionary trends afforded by reproductive structures, the relative scarcity of available material in the fossil record has been a serious handicap. To be of great value, the fruits, seeds, and flowers of most angiosperms must show relatively complete surface details and/or their original internal structure. Such fossils are rarely found, and have been adequately studied only in floras from the Tertiary of Europe, most notably in the flora of the London Clay from the Early Eocene of England (5). Even here Reid reports there is little evidence of developmental trends. Certain fruits which are clearly referable to the walnut family, Juglandaceae, are of doubtful relationship to living genera, according to Reid and Chandler. The details of form and structure of the seeds suggest relationship both to *Juglans* and *Carya*, and in certain respects show differences from both these modern genera. As a result, they have been placed in the form genus *Juglandicarya*. Since neither *Juglans* nor *Carya* are recorded from these beds, and since the seeds seem to be somewhat simpler in form than those of living members of the family, these Eocene species of *Juglandicarya* may be considered as possibly ancestral to both *Juglans* and *Carya*. Leaves referred to the form genus *Juglandites* and to the botanical genus *Juglans* have been reported from the Cretaceous of North America, and *Juglans* is widely represented by leaves in Eocene deposits. Walnut-like fruits have been reported from two Eocene floras in North America, the Brandon lignite of Vermont, and the Clarno formation of Oregon, but study of these specimens has not progressed to a point where they can be said fully to establish the record of *Juglans* in the Eocene. *Carya* has been recorded from both the Cretaceous and Eocene of North America, but only on the basis of leaves. From the evidence at hand it may be questioned whether the foliage referred to *Juglans* and *Carya* provides conclusive evidence of the presence of these genera in rocks as old as Eocene, during which time the intermediate and possibly ancestral genus *Juglandicarya* was living in England. It seems more probable that the modern genera of the Juglandaceae may have become differentiated subsequently. Records of other genera, based largely upon leaf fossils, may also be subject to correction, for with discovery of their well-preserved fruits additional evidence of intermediate forms may be forthcoming. Our common assumption that most modern genera of the angiosperms were fully differentiated during Cretaceous and Early Tertiary time must be checked by the evidence of their fruiting structures as well as of their leaves.

Study of the monocotyledon *Stratiotes* by Chandler (6) has provided the most completely consecutive history of any genus yet published. A series of seven species in chronological order, ranging without considerable stratigraphic break from Late Eocene to Recent, shows seeds of this aquatic plant ranging from short and broad to long and narrow. Pronounced ornamentation of the testa in older species has largely disappeared in many of the Pleistocene specimens, and seeds of the living monotypic plant are perfectly smooth.

Similarly detailed study of fruiting structures of grasses has been made by Elias (7), although the time limits of his series are considerably less. This occurrence of hollow silicified husks of grass seeds in continental deposits of Miocene and Pliocene age east of the Rocky Mountains provides critical information regarding the development of prairie vegetation at a time when the history of plains mammals is especially complete and significant. The later Tertiary members of the tribe *Stipeae*, including the Tertiary genus *Stipidium*, show a close resemblance to the modern genus *Stipa*. Elias states, ". . . they have essentially the same hull, with typically constructed and overlapping lemma and palea, with a long callus at the base and a joint at the summit of the hull. Even the ornamentation of the hull is the same and consists of tubercles, cusps, and hairs. In the course of evolution of this type of hull in the late Tertiary no innovation of any kind developed. . . . The evolutionary trends observable in the hull of the fossil and living *Stipeae* consist of change of its size and differential changes in the hull and its parts and minor modifications of these parts. Some of the parts underwent reduction or complete suppression. On the whole, therefore, the evolution of the hull of *Stipeae* and probably of the whole plant, from the early Miocene to our time, may be characterized as differentiation (Guppy) or down-grade process in which reduction plays a conspicuous part. However, this process includes also developments of orthogenetic progressive type, such as increase in size of the hull, which is noticeable in some phyletic branches of *Stipidium* and *Berriochloa*, a modification of the lemma and palea for better protection of the grain, probable elaboration of the awn for better dispersal of the seeds, and other apparent progressive adaptations." Numerous abrupt changes are noted by Elias in the grass floras of the High Plains, resulting, he believes, not from extinction of earlier forms but from migration "into more suitable environments in connection with apparent change of climatic conditions." Several species show a progressive increase in size which reached its culmination in Middle Pliocene time, and none of the living equivalents here have seeds of equal size.

This development of grasses, associated with increasing areas of grasslands at the expense of forests, came at the same time that the oaks of Oregon and California were changing from forest to woodland and chaparral types, in response to a major climatic trend. Just how far such changes in vegetation, both in its floristic aspects and in the details of the structures involved, are the product of migrations, or to what extent they represent modifications in structure of indigenous plants resulting from spontaneous mutations, it is not now possible to determine. The answers to such questions are antecedent to any estimates of rate of evolution, since if migration is the only factor in a changing assemblage of plants, speed of movement rather than rate of evolution is to be measured by the floral sequence from age to age.[5]

A final example of an evolutionary trend among angiosperms may be noted in the stem of *Eopuntia*, an Eocene cactus from Utah (8). The flattened stems of this fossil show evidence of a siphonostele like that of the most primitive Cactaceae, rather than the specialized dictyostele which characterizes *Opuntia* and other advanced types of modern cacti. Details in shape and structure of the fruits of *Eopuntia* also suggest relationship to some of the less specialized living members of the Cactaceae. We have here an opuntioid which in its outward form closely resembles modern *Opuntia* but whose internal structures place it in ancestral relationship. Discovery of fossil cacti in rocks younger than the Eocene may be expected to add other intermediate stages in the development of this now highly specialized family.

Summary

Although the structures which contribute most significantly to our knowledge of the phylogeny of angiosperms are not commonly well-preserved in the fossil record, there are available sufficient materials to suggest the general pattern of evolution since the Cretaceous period. The genus *Quercus* is represented by an abundance of leaves which show a trend toward increasing size and lobation to the middle of the Tertiary period. Judging from these foliar organs there has been little if any evolution among the oaks since the Miocene epoch, some thirty million years ago. Study of the acorns of *Quercus*, if and when they are available as well-preserved fossils, may indicate a degree of post-Miocene speciation not reflected by the leaf and fruit impressions now at hand. Fruits of the Juglandaceae from the London Clay indicate that the walnut (*Juglans*) and hickory (*Carya*) were not generically differentiated during the Eocene, although their leaves have been recognized as distinct in floras of that age. Clearly we may expect earlier development and stabilization in some organs of a plant than in others. It will be necessary to study more than the leaves of *Quercus* and other dicotyledonous genera before we shall reach a satisfactory understanding of their phylogenies.

Fossil fruits of such monocotyledons as *Stratiotes* and the grasses show recognizable trends in size and surface markings during the Cenozoic. To

---

[5] On the other hand, Babcock suggests that speed of migration in *Crepis* is directly dependent on adaptive structures for wind transport. Reduction in size of seed in relation to the pappus is shown in more advanced types, and appears to have aided rapid Plio-Pleistocene evolution.

an extent not now measurable, major changes in climate appear to stand in causal relationship to the more marked stages of floral evolution. Mountain making and variations in the solar constant appear to have been responsible for increasing diversity of environment in western North America during Pliocene time. Restriction of forests, as shown by the reduction or extinction of many forest types and by the smaller and thicker leaves of later Tertiary oaks mentioned above, seems to have been accompanied by a marked expansion of grasslands, by increased speciation of the grasses, and by their development of larger fruits.

To facilitate the gathering and interpretation of critical information regarding the angiosperms, the following suggestions may be made for future studies:

1. Consideration of taxonomic rather than regional or stratigraphic units of vegetation will place increased emphasis on the phylogeny of well-represented families and genera. Observations will then accumulate, showing relationships of plants now distinct, permitting estimates of the rates of change, and ultimately leading to greater understanding of evolutionary processes.

2. There is need for more collecting and study of fruits and seeds showing structures useful in establishing plant relationships. In North America the Brandon lignite of Vermont, the Clarno tuffs of the John Day Basin, and numerous Pleistocene deposits along the Pacific Coast give promise of supplying valuable information regarding plant trends and relationships through later geologic time.

3. The sudden appearance of the angiosperms in rocks of Cretaceous age can be accurately interpreted only after exploration of older Mesozoic rocks, particularly in upland deposits, and at low as well as middle and high latitudes. If a comprehensive search fails to produce a record of the ancestors of Early Cretaceous angiosperms, the case for their rapid evolution in Middle Mesozoic time will be greatly strengthened; but it seems highly probable that older sediments will reveal their presence.

4. Collection and detailed study of carbonaceous films associated with leaf impressions, along the lines followed by Florin with fossil and by Foster with modern leaves, may disclose trends in structure which will permit a wider use of foliar organs in the building of plant phylogenies.

5. Emphasis on studies like those made by Bailey on the wood and leaves of the Winteraceae, if adequate fossil material can be found, may be expected to confirm his conclusions regarding this primitive family, and to extend its relationships to other ancient families of the angiosperms.

REFERENCES

1. Florin, R. 1944. Die Coniferen des Obercarbons und des Unteren Perms, Part 7. *Palaeontographica*, Band 85, Abt. B, Heft 1-8, pp. 457-654.
2. Dorf, E. 1942. Upper Cretaceous Floras of the Rocky Mt. Region. *Carnegie Inst. Wash. Pub. 508*, pp. 1-168, Pl. 1-19, 1-17.
3. Condit, C. 1944. Pliocene Floras of California, *Carnegie Inst. Wash. Pub. 553*, No. 2, Remington Hill Flora, pp. 43-46, Pl. 5-8.
4. Trelease, W. 1924. The American Oaks. *Nat. Acad. Sci. Vol. 20*, pp. 1-255, Pl. 1-419.
5. Reid, E. M., and M. E. J. Chandler. 1933. *London Clay Flora*. Brit. Mus. (Nat. Hist.), pp. 1-561, Pl. 1-33.
6. Chandler, M. E. J. 1923. Geological History of the Genus *Stratiotes*. *Quart. Jour. Geol. Soc. Vol. 79*, pp. 117-138, Pl. 5-8.
7. Elias, M. K. 1942. Tertiary Prairie Grasses and other Herbs from the High Plains. *Geol. Soc. Am. Spec. Papers No. 41*, pp. 1-176, Pl. 1-17.
8. Chaney, R. W. 1944. Fossil Cactus from the Eocene of Utah. *Am. Jour. Bot. Vol. 31*, pp. 507-528, Pl. 1-5.

PART IV

EVOLUTIONARY RATES

· 11 ·

RATES OF EVOLUTION IN ANIMALS

BY GEORGE GAYLORD SIMPSON[1]

MUCH has been said and written about rates of evolution in animals. Most of these studies have, however, been so cursory and unsystematic that our resulting knowledge of this subject is diffuse and inadequate. The present need seems to be not so much the compilation of data, although that is needed too, as the development of methodology in this field and more extensive but more precise definition of its problems. The study now of methods and problems, in the light of what has been done, should promote the more systematic and useful future gathering of data, and this in turn should advance us more rapidly toward the solution of these problems.

This is the point of view and purpose of the present summary. It would be foolish to hope that an adequate methodology in so large a field could be supplied in one paper or by one student, or that all outstanding problems could be listed, not to say discussed. It is perhaps too grandiloquent even to mention these pressing general needs in connection with an attempt to exemplify rather than to supply them. Among the many different sorts of rates of evolution, some that may prove to be most useful are first designated and defined. Some methods of measurement, integration, comparison, and interpretation are then mentioned. Finally a few examples are given of broader evolutionary problems on which rates of evolution have a crucial bearing.

DEFINITIONS OF RATES OF EVOLUTION

The expression "rate of evolution" has so many possible meanings as to be almost meaningless without further qualification. Study of the scattered literature of the subject soon shows that different authors have in mind quite different things when they write about rates of evolution. Clarity demands more careful definition and specification.

Evolution is, to begin with, studied under several different aspects of which three are most pertinent here. Evolution may be considered as change in genetic composition of populations, as morphologic change in ancestral-descendent lines, or as taxonomic progression and diversification within a line or complex of larger taxonomic scope. There are thus genetic,

---

[1] American Museum of Natural History, and Columbia University.

morphologic, and taxonomic rates of evolution.[2] These are closely inter-related, but each has its special data, methods of study, and theoretical implications.

GENETIC RATES. Genetic rates of evolution underlie most other rates and are more basic than most, but their direct study is so limited in scope that little will be said regarding them here. The ideal would be to obtain measured changes in total genetic make-up in numerous different organisms over periods of time comparable to those usually involved in the origin of species in nature. This ideal is not attainable at present and there is no real prospect that it can ever be closely approached. Short range fluctuations of particular genes or gene arrangements are being studied successfully in both natural and laboratory populations (e.g. Dobzhansky, 1943). Rates of dispersion of particular mutants have also been studied (e.g. Dobzhansky and Wright, 1943). This work clearly has an important bearing on the study of rates of evolution, especially by the provision of interpretive and explanatory principles. It seems unlikely, however, that it will directly provide examples or measurements of evolutionary rates of a scope applicable to specific or even subspecific evolution in the history of animal life.

Another genetic approach is by comparison of the genetic make-up of two or more living populations and by estimation of the time involved in their differentiation (see e.g. Mayr, Stebbins, and Simpson, 1945). This problem is even more complex and its study has not so far been strikingly successful. Genetic analysis and comparison of the groups involved is necessarily very incomplete, and it is virtually if not completely impossible unless they are all closely related. Even with a few selected genes or gene arrangements study can only exceptionally rise beyond and seldom can rise to the specific level. It is also difficult to determine the time of divergence of the groups in question, and when this can be done with even rough accuracy it is usually on a morphological or taxonomic basis. The study of genetic rates of evolution in such cases, if possible at all, is thus secondary to determination of morphologic and taxonomic rates. In spite of these numerous and serious difficulties, this approach may nevertheless be most promising for genetic rates.

MORPHOLOGIC RATES. Morphologic rates of evolution are more readily determinable and are far less limited, in some cases virtually unlimited, as to time because they can be determined from fossils. I have discussed and exemplified such rates at some length elsewhere (Simpson, 1944) and therefore will only summarize them here. The morphologic change studied may be in a single character (e.g. length of skull), in a complex of characters (e.g. the dentition as a whole), or in the whole organism. In

[2] There are also ecologic and other sorts of rates. This list is obviously not exhaustive.

practice, however, a primary morphologic approach to the evolution of the whole organism involves too many separate characters for ready analysis and combination, and the more practical study of this broader aspect of evolutionary rate is by taxonomic methods. Morphologic rates, in the strictest sense, are most profitably studied in terms of single characters.

Morphologic changes can be converted to rates by relating them to the passage of time or to simultaneous changes in other characters or other groups of organisms. In many respects the most interesting and enlightening of evolutionary rates are those of morphologic change per unit of absolute time, e.g. the increase in mean molar size (ectoloph length) in early Tertiary horses.[3] There are several possible ways of measuring the morphologic change in such rates, notably by absolute dimensions, by percentage change, or by standard deviations. However this be measured, the rate of morphological change per absolute time comes so immediately to mind that some paleontologists, particularly, seem to think of it as *the* rate of evolution, but much valuable information would be lost if our attention here were directed only to absolute rates in unit characters.

Knowledge of absolute geochronology is so imperfect that such rates are always rough approximations and can only rarely at present be usefully determined for geologically short periods of time. A method frequently applicable to shorter sequences is that of rate of morphologic change per unit thickness of deposited strata. This method also has numerous shortcomings, but it does yield objective numerical values, which are, within limits, comparable with each other even if not directly comparable with absolute time rates. Rate of morphologic change on the sequential geologic scale, e.g. rate per epoch or per period, is frequently mentioned but lends itself only to verbal expression and has the serious disadvantage that it cannot be expressed, as a rate, numerically except in a very arbitrary way.

Relative rates of morphologic change do not involve any measurement or estimate of elapsed time. In view of our present inability to supply accurate time measurements, this is a great advantage. The elimination of the time factor gives such rates quite different interpretive values and limitations than time rates. Speaking of a rate that does not involve time seems anomalous at first glance, but it can readily be seen that such rates do have considerable significance for evolutionary studies. There are two principal useful sorts of relative morphologic rates. Degree of change in one character may be measured relative to the simultaneous change in another character within the same organisms. This is the now familiar

[3] This proceeded at the rate of about 0.1 to 0.2 mm. per million years. The change in less than 5,000,000 to 10,000,000 years was practically imperceptible under the usual sampling conditions, even though the whole history shows that this rate was an essential factor in horse evolution.

relative growth or allometric concept applied phylogenetically rather than ontogenetically (see, *inter alia,* Huxley, 1932; Robb, 1935). Or, degree of change in a character in a given group of organisms may be measured relative to simultaneous change in the same character in a different group of organisms (see, e.g. an example in Simpson, 1937). Thus these rates determine whether one character is evolving faster than another in a given phylum or whether the same character is evolving faster in one phylum than in another. Quantitative estimates of the relative rates may also be obtained. These are clearly significant facts about the animals concerned, even though they do not tell us just how fast the character is evolving in absolute terms.

TAXONOMIC RATES. Taxonomic rates are concerned with the rate of origin of new taxonomic categories at any level, from subspecies to kingdom (although in practice there seems little point in applying this concept to levels above orders or, at most, classes). The taxonomic categories are almost always recognized and defined on a morphologic basis and are in the best modern practice, at least, assumed to have a genetic basis and made to correspond as nearly as possible with genetic groupings. The use of taxonomic rates may thus be viewed as a device for indirect study of genetic and morphologic rates in terms of the whole organism, rates not amenable to direct study by methods now available. This makes the taxonomic rates in many respects the most interesting of all, and more attention has been given to them than to other sorts of evolutionary rates here discussed.

Taxonomic rates of evolution are also of several possible sorts, each different in method and implications. The two most important of these sorts may be qualified as phyletic taxonomic rates and as rates of taxonomic diversification.[4] A phyletic taxonomic rate concerns the length of time involved in the origin of a new taxonomic unit, such as a species or a genus, from an ancestral unit, or the length of time over which such a unit persists without evolving to the extent recognized as requiring classification under a different name. Such rates are hardly simple in themselves and they may be measured and expressed in various different ways. Thus the average number of genera per million years in the ancestry of the horse (approximately .15)[5] is a phyletic taxonomic rate and the origin of a distinct Scottish subspecies of deer (*Cervus elaphus scoticus*) in the last 7,500 years (*fide* Zeuner, 1946a) is also a phyletic taxonomic rate. Such rates are usually and most usefully given in terms of the absolute

---

[4] Examples of both are common in recent literature on evolutionary rates, but they are seldom clearly distinguished and I have not found terms less clumsy than those here proposed. This terminology is not satisfactory, but with the accompanying definitions it will suffice for clarity here.

[5] See Simpson, 1944. I now use somewhat larger figures for the lengths of the Tertiary epochs.

time scale. In some cases they may, however, be related to the geologic time sequence or given in terms relative to other contemporaneous phyla.

Rates of taxonomic diversification are concerned with the increase or decrease in numbers of taxonomic units included within a higher category. These, too, may be given in terms of absolute time, for instance if a family had three genera in the earliest Pliocene (taken as roughly 12,000,000 years ago) and now has eleven, its diversification rate might be said to be 2/3 genera per million years.[6] For these rates, however, the data are also frequently arranged according to the relative geologic time scale, and the numbers of known taxonomic units in the various geologic periods or epochs are used to demonstrate changes in rate of diversification.

In summary, the following main sorts of evolutionary rates have been defined (others exist but are not considered here):

I. Genetic rates (subdivisions not listed)
II. Morphologic rates (for unit characters and character complexes)
   A. Temporal morphologic rates
      1. Absolute (per unit of time in years)
      2. Correlative (per thickness of strata, etc.)
      3. Sequential (per epoch, etc.)
   B. Relative morphologic rates
      1. Intra-group (between different characters of the same organisms)
      2. Inter-group (between the same characters in different organisms)
III. Taxonomic rates
   A. Phyletic taxonomic rates (by duration of units)
   B. Rates of taxonomic diversification (by numbers of units)

MEASUREMENT AND INTERPRETATION OF TEMPORAL MORPHOLOGIC RATES

The basic concept of rates in general is essentially quantitative and, as with any other quantitative concept, evolutionary rates should be studied as far as possible in numerical terms. In the present state of knowledge numerical expressions of temporal rates are seldom more than rough approximations, but even these are better than vague verbal expressions that a rate is fast or slow, or faster or slower than another. Approximate numerical data also lend themselves to legitimate manipulations that are far more revealing than any non-numerical treatment.

Absolute geochronology is one essential numerical basis for absolute temporal rates. The present state of knowledge has been discussed by

---

[6] For various reasons, some of which will appear later, this is a very crude example. Proper evaluation of the taxonomic diversification would involve considerably more complex study and statement, but this will here serve to illustrate the general sort of rate under discussion.

Knopf in this volume and by Zeuner (especially 1946a, with many references to older studies). Accuracy is slight, but involves the right order of magnitude, at least; and the rates calculated on the basis of a consistent scale, even though it be inaccurate, are sufficiently comparable for most purposes. Use of a correlative of time, of which the most practical is thickness of strata, may permit better or complete numerical accuracy, although still inaccurate in absolute time, because the correlation of thickness of strata with elapsed time is not perfect.[7]

It has often been questioned whether rates of evolution on a scale of time in years may not be spurious and whether the natural unit would not be the generation. At first sight this would appear logical and proper, but I do not believe that it can be maintained in practice. The only way of determining a rate per generation, for any sufficiently long span to be of much use, is first to obtain a rate per year (or other absolute temporal unit) and then to apply the appropriate factor for mean length of generations. It then remains to be demonstrated empirically whether, in fact, rates per generation are more nearly comparable with each other, or, from another point of view, whether the length of the generations does really have a significant influence on the (absolute temporal) rate of evolution. This is one of many fields in which we badly need more concrete data. It may be rather surprising that the preliminary and inadequate studies that have so far been made suggest that length of generations does not have a strong or, at least, a consistent influence on rate of evolution (Zeuner, 1931, 1946a; Simpson, 1944). If this is confirmed, the absolute temporal rate, which is in any case the primary datum, will properly continue to be the main object of study rather than the rate per generation. The two rates have, however, somewhat different implications and it is probable that both should be considered in many cases.

There are several different ways in which the morphologic change involved in these rates may be measured. Simplest and most obvious is the change in units of raw measurement, e.g. in millimeters for a linear dimension, in cubic centimeters for a volume, or in degrees for an angle. These have the drawback that the comparability of rates of change may and probably does, as a rule, depend on the absolute dimensions involved. That is, a change of 0.1 mm. in a linear variate with mean value about 1 mm. may correspond, in evolutionary significance, with a change of 1 mm. in a variate with mean value about 10 mm. In such a case the rate of change may be given in terms of percentage increase rather than absolute increase, or, what amounts to the same thing and may be more convenient mathematically, rates may be studied and compared in terms of the logarithms of the dimensions involved.

[7] It is conceivable that we may in a few cases be able to calculate absolutely accurate temporal rates, for instance within the varved Eocene Green River shales.

A third suggestion[8] is to measure rates of this sort in standard deviations. For instance, if a population has a standard deviation of 0.5 mm. for a given variate and if this variate is evolving at the rate of 0.2 per million years, the rate may be given as 0.4 standard deviations per million years, or 2.5 million years per standard deviation. Such a rate reveals how rapidly the actual population overlap in variation is being reduced, and in this way it has considerable interest and significance. The standard deviation rate may also give some insight into the rate at which the population variation is being utilized by the evolutionary process of shifting the mean by selection of variates on one side or the other of that mean. On the other hand, the standard deviation rate cannot be considered an acceptable substitute for a rate of change in the mean itself. The same significant amount of change in the mean would appear to be a lower rate in a more variable than in a less variable population, if expressed in standard deviations. The comparison involved here would be valid only if the coefficient of variation were the same in all groups compared, and in such a case the more general expression of a percentage or logarithmic rate would be simpler and preferable.

Transformation of the basic morphologic data (mean differences in absolute form, in percentages, in logarithms, or in standard deviations) and temporal data (years, stratigraphic thicknesses, etc.) into rates can be done graphically by plotting the morphologic data on one scale (preferably the ordinate) and time, or its correlative, on the other. A percentage or logarithmic rate can be plotted directly from the absolute dimensions by the use of arithlog quadrate paper. The graphic procedure is always a useful preliminary and is sometimes adequate, without further operations, for presentation and interpretation of the data. A line may then be drawn to represent the trend, and the slope of this line is the rate of evolution of the particular character entered. The rate is constant if the line is straight and variable if it curves. The fitting of such a line and determination of its slope at appropriate points can be made exceedingly complicated but fortunately only simple methods are necessary, or justified, for most studies of evolutionary rates. Simple inspection usually shows sufficiently well whether use of a straight line is justified, that is, whether the rate has been approximately constant. Such a line can readily be fitted by well-known rough methods or, if the data are sufficiently good and numerous, by the also well-known method of least squares, explained in all textbooks of statistics.

When the data definitely suggest a curve, i.e. when the rate in question has varied significantly, this also can usually be determined by inspection

---

[8] Made by J. B. S. Haldane in open discussion at the Princeton Conference on Genetics, Paleontology, and Evolution and afterwards also discussed privately with Th. Dobzhansky. See *Evolution, 3,* 51-56.

and a sufficiently good curve sketched in freehand, if desired.[9] If numerical values of the rate are desired, these can be supplied as adequate approximations by treating successive appropriately short segments of the curve as if they were straight lines.

The interpretation of such data, on the descriptive level, at least, seems too obvious to require elaboration. Relatively few morphologic sequences have, in fact, been presented in this way. (For some examples, see Simpson, 1944.) Further accumulation of such graphic and numerical records should provide a wealth of information on comparative rates of various single characters (differences in slope of their separate trend lines), on acceleration (inflexion of the curve upward) and deceleration (inflexion downward), etc., as a source for more theoretical study.

MEASUREMENT AND INTERPRETATION OF RELATIVE MORPHOLOGIC RATES

The treatment of relative rates of evolution of different characters in the same organism is an application to phylogeny of techniques originally developed for the study of relative growth in ontogeny. Graphic treatment is similar to that for temporal rates except that a second morphologic character, rather than time, is plotted on the abscissa. These, too, frequently give straight lines. As a special case, the "allometric equation" $y = bx^k$ has frequently been found applicable when the graph is a curve.[10] The fitting of this curve is fairly simple and is adequately explained in Huxley, 1932, Simpson and Roe, 1939, and elsewhere. The applicability of this formula implies that change in size of the variates involved was geometric (that is, they tended to increase or diminish by a percentage of their former size, rather than by a fixed arithmetic amount) and that these geometric rates of change had a constant ratio (k of the equation). A straight line implies that the ratio of arithmetic rates was constant.

The existence of such a constant relationship between rates of evolution of two different characters is an important empirical conclusion when it can be established. It suggests, although it cannot rigidly prove, that these characters are not evolving independently but that they are cor-

[9] The point is open to debate, and decision depends on the use to be made of the curve, but in many cases it is doubtful whether the empirical fitting of a mathematical curve is justified, regardless of the labor involved, if no definite biological meaning can be given to the constants and variables of the corresponding equation.

[10] It may also be applicable when the graph is a straight line, but in that case an equation of the form $y = a + bx$ may be preferable. Fitting of the allometric curve to a graph of relative rates does not necessarily incur the objection made against some other types of curve-fitting in a previous note, because a definite biological meaning can be assigned to the variables y and x and the constants b and k. There is, however, some dispute as to the logical status of the equation, and it has been misapplied. See discussion, with references to other papers on this subject, in Kavanagh and Richards, 1942; Richards and Kavanagh, 1945; and Reeve and Huxley, 1945.

related or determined by some common factor. It is somewhat speculative but is, at least, a plausible inference that the common factor is genetic (see, e.g., Robb, 1935, criticized by Reeve and Murray, 1942; Hersh, 1934; Simpson, 1944). It may then be concluded that although proportions of the different parts of an organism may change (as they will if k is greater or less than 1 in the allometry formula), the underlying genetic determinant may remain unchanged (as reflected in the constancy of k), so that in fact there has been no mutation in this factor. Similarly, if the relationship is not the same in allied lines (k is different) or in one line at different times (the trend is divisible into two or more sections each fitted well enough by $y = bx^k$ but with different values of k), the segregation of a mutant in this genetic growth factor may have occurred (compare Phleger, 1940; Gray, 1946).

As with many other lines of study of evolutionary rates, so little work of this sort has yet been done that its possibilities can hardly be estimated. It seems, however, to be exceptionally promising because it is one of the few approaches that may make possible inferences regarding definite genetic factors in evolution on the basis of morphologic paleontologic observations.[11]

The method has further interest because it is a step toward the desirable and elusive goal of measuring rates of evolution of form or shape, rather than only of dimensions. From this point of view, observed changes in relative growth rates (e.g. systematic changes of k with time in the formula $y = bx^k$) may be of even greater interest than a constant rate relationship. A necessary next step is to bring the relative rates of change in two or more different dimensions, which may define or measure a shape, into relationship with time, thus progressing to the measurement of temporal rates of evolution of shape. Approaches to this difficult problem on an ontogenetic basis have been sketched out by Medawar (e.g. 1945) and by Richards and Kavanagh (e.g. 1945), in part as a development of the method of transformed coördinates proposed by D'Arcy Thompson (e.g. 1942, following original publication in 1917). These later students have not applied their techniques to phylogenetic data, and although the original method of D'Arcy Thompson has been so applied, it yields no direct information concerning rates of evolution. Here is an

[11] It is noted, however, that the existence of an approximately constant relationship between the evolutionary rates of two characters does not necessarily and invariably indicate that both are governed by one constant genetic factor. This inference may not be justified unless some further developmental basis for the relationship can be inferred or demonstrated—unless, for instance, it can be shown that the ontogenetic rates of the two characters are similarly related. This is not because "ontogeny repeats phylogeny" but because the inheritance of ontogenetic patterns is phylogeny. In a sense, it is more nearly correct to say in such cases that phylogeny repeats ontogeny.

important field for future work by paleontologists, one so new that it is impossible to judge even how promising it may be.

In the study of relative evolutionary rates of the same character in different lines of descent, the logical and biological concepts of relative growth do not apply. It would be entirely possible in such cases to plot and study the rate in one line in terms of the progression in the other, in a way analogous to relative growth, but the inferences to be drawn would not be those of relative growth, and interpretation might be difficult and confusing. As far as I know, this method has never been used. It might be worth while to explore its possibilities, but it seems likely that plotting the two separate lines against the same time scale, rather than one against the other, will continue to be the more useful method. This method has been employed repeatedly and found enlightening. The time scale may be absolute or may be the relative or sequential geologic scale. In the latter case, no numerical value for either rate can properly be calculated, but the relationship between the two rates is nevertheless made clear. (There are examples in Gregory, 1937.) The numerical value of the slope of either line is meaningless, but differences in slope between the two for any one time interval correctly indicate and are proportional to differences in their evolutionary rates.

MEASUREMENT AND INTERPRETATION OF PHYLETIC TAXONOMIC RATES

Taxonomic data for study of evolutionary rates have two special weaknesses for which due allowance must always be made. The first is involved in the long-emphasized incompleteness of the paleontological record. We seldom know the full duration of, say, a genus; and it is probably even more seldom that we know, for example, all the species of a given genus at any given time in the past. Many groups of animals are so poorly known as fossils that their taxonomic rates of evolution cannot usefully be studied by any direct paleontological method, but many groups are now well enough known to make such study possible.

The second important weakness of taxonomic data is inherent in their subjective nature. One man's species is another man's genus. The rate of evolution in taxonomic terms would appear much more rapid if based on the work of the latter, a splitter, than if based on the work of the former, a lumper. Among rather closely related animals, within an order, for instance, it is nevertheless usually possible to gather taxonomic data based on reasonably uniform criteria and therefore permitting sufficiently reliable comparisons of evolutionary rates. For very diverse groups this may be impossible and the comparisons may have little objective value. A related difficulty is the great difference in complexity and in available taxonomic characters among different groups. *Lingula* shells, for instance, are simple objects with few characters to distinguish one from another, while mammal skeletons are exceedingly complicated objects distinguishable from each other by thousands of determinable characters. A slight morphologic change from one species to another in *Lingula* might conceivably be equivalent, in underlying genetic and evolutionary significance, to a generic or even to a familial or higher change in mammals. This factor may be, I think probably is, one reason for the evidently faster rates of evolution in mammals and other "higher" more complicated organisms than in molluscs and other "lower" simpler organisms. This does not alter the fact that the taxonomic rates do average higher in mammals than in molluscs, but it should be kept in mind when we think of the evolutionary significance of this fact.

Among many possible approaches to the study of phyletic taxonomic rates, three have been most generally employed, all involving the duration of one or more comparable taxonomic entities. The first and perhaps most obvious of these involves the age of taxonomic units now existing. The Tertiary epochs were originally defined by Lyell (1833) on the basis of the percentage of living species occurring at the various horizons. The particular figures given by Lyell are, of course, no longer valid in terms of modern taxonomy and the method is now in disrepute as a means of stratigraphic correlation and subdivision, but it is still a useful and actively used source of data on evolution. A good recent example is given by Umbgrove (1946) for reef corals and molluscs in the East Indies, plotting percentage of living forms against the absolute time scale. Both curves show a sharp upturn in Middle to Late Miocene,[12] indicating an increased radiation of new species at that time. There is undoubtedly a relationship between this observation and evolutionary rate, but the relationship is probably not as simple as it might appear on the face of the data. On one hand, such an increase might and probably does indicate accelerated diversification, but not necessarily phyletic progression, while on the other hand it might indicate decrease, rather than increase, in phyletic rates. That is, if in the Late Miocene phyletic evolution of corals became markedly slower, then this factor alone would result in an increase in the number of coral species destined to survive into the recent and the upturn of the curve would represent a deceleration of evolution and not an acceleration as might seem more probable at first sight.

The same sort of data may be more directly related to evolutionary rates by conversion into survivorship tables and curves and into age composition tables and graphs for the recent fauna, as I have elsewhere illustrated (Simpson, 1944). It is assumed that there is some sort of inverse relationship between mean survivorship or mean present age of a group and its average rate of evolution, that is, the longer an average species, genus,

---

[12] Also in the Pleistocene, but this is interpreted as an artifact of the data.

or other taxonomic unit survives as such, the slower it is evolving. (As will be remarked later, data based on extinct groups show that this relationship as observed in surviving forms is subject to certain interesting complications.)

Many other more scattered observations on the time required for the evolution of one taxonomic group from another of the same rank have been based on the recent fauna. Besides the direct paleontological approach, estimates may usefully be based on insular forms or others the separation of which from a main parental stock can be approximately dated. Without attempting to cite or discuss the widely dispersed literature, reference is made to representative examples given by Huxley (1942) and by Zeuner (1946a, b). As would be expected, the periods of time involved at any given taxonomic level vary enormously, and as far as I know the data of this particular sort are not yet numerous enough or have not yet been sufficiently systematized to warrant many generalizations. There is evidence that subspecies or, at least, clearly differentiated local races may evolve in less than a century but commonly require 10,000 years or so for their evolution, and may evolve for as much as 500,000 years without rising to the specific level. The evolution of a species, fully distinct genetically and morphologically, seems usually to require 50,000 years or more in nature and even in groups with fairly rapid average evolutionary rates, such as mammals, some living species are about 1,000,000 years old. As shown by grouped survivorship data of the sort mentioned previously, some living invertebrate species are much older than this and in a few cases seem to be as much as 30,000,000 years old.

One generalization that is already reasonably clear from the available information but that seems to merit more intensive study is that phyletic taxonomic rates of evolution vary inversely with the inclusiveness of the taxonomic category involved. Subspecies evolve more rapidly than species in the same group, species more rapidly than genera, and so on. This perhaps appears obvious, but it has an important bearing on evolutionary theory because it does not seem (to me) to be consistent with the view that species, genera, or higher categories normally arise by single "systemic mutations." Accumulation and evaluation of more quantitative data on, say, the relative survivorship of species and genera within given groups would also permit a more systematic approach to the now rather arbitrary definition of these various categories.

Study of evolutionary rates based on living groups has the defects that we do not know that living forms are representative in this respect (indeed for some groups we may be quite sure that they are not) and also that duration for these groups is really indeterminate (we have no very good idea how much longer they will endure before evolving into something else or becoming extinct). The two other principal methods of attack on problems of phyletic taxonomic rates to be discussed here avoid these difficulties because they are based on groups that are now extinct and that have therefore complete and (theoretically) determinate durations.

The most accurate available data on such evolutionary rates are provided by the members (excluding the first and the last) of known continuous ancestral and descendant phyla. In such cases the duration is determinable within the limits of the geochronological scale and it represents, so to speak, the full potential life span of the unit in question because this is not curtailed by extinction. The usefulness of the method is, however, limited by the fact that relatively few long lines of this sort are sufficiently well known and that still fewer have as yet been studied from just this point of view. The figure of about 0.15 genera per million years in the direct ancestry of the horse has been cited above as an example. Figures given in this form are directly proportional to the average phyletic taxonomic rate of evolution for the time span concerned, while figures directly derived from the observed duration, e.g. 6½ millions years per genus, are inversely proportional to that rate.

The final method to be discussed in this section is that of compilation of known durations for all known extinct taxonomic units within a given group. This, also, has some fairly serious disadvantages. It lumps together units that evolved into something else and those that became extinct, although the duration of the latter must, on an average, be shorter for any given rate of evolution. It also necessarily ignores the fact that for the many groups of unknown ancestry, unknown descendants, or both, the actual duration must average longer than the known duration. Both these factors tend to make the figures of record for duration shorter than the real duration. If, however, the data are carefully gathered and systematized for reasonably large numbers of taxonomic units, it is probable that this bias will be more or less uniform throughout, so that it will not seriously affect the form of the distribution of durations and so that comparisons of durations for different groups will still be valid.

Of the various ways in which data of this sort can be assembled and presented for the study of evolutionary rates, two seem to me particularly useful and I have exemplified and discussed both of these elsewhere (Simpson, 1944). One is to transform the data into survivorship tables and graphs and the other is to transform them into evolutionary rate distributions on the postulate that evolutionary rate is inversely proportional to survivorship. In the work cited I have demonstrated that for some groups (e.g. Carnivora) survivorship based in this way on extinct genera is similar to that based on living genera, while in others (e.g. Pelecypoda) it is quite different. It was possible in this example to demonstrate that the difference is mainly if not solely due to the fact that there are living pelecypod genera that are virtually immortal, that have greatly exceeded any life expectancy that could be derived from survivorship in their extinct relatives.

MEASUREMENT AND INTERPRETATION OF RATES OF
TAXONOMIC DIVERSIFICATION

Basic data for study of taxonomic diversification are the numbers of taxonomic units within some larger taxonomic category known or first appearing at stated times. A great many data of this sort have been gathered and paleontological publications contain numerous examples, varying from precise tabulations in great detail for various groups to the common, generalized phylogenetic charts with the relative abundances of the various phyla suggested by the widths of the lines representing them. In view of this abundance of material and its frequent emphasis in the literature, it is surprising to find relatively little really careful analysis of such data or consideration, above an elementary level, of its significance for the study of rates or other evolutionary problems. For instance the phenomena involved are analogous, at least, to those of population growth, a subject that has been elaborately investigated and for which some unusually elegant and enlightening special techniques have been developed.[13] It seems probable that more extensive application of these or similar techniques to paleontological data would give interesting and important results. What has been done has recently been emphasized and partially summarized by Zeuner (1946 a, b) in a way especially pertinent here because he stresses the temporal aspect and hence the bearing of these observations on evolutionary rates.

The general weaknesses of taxonomic data for rate studies, already mentioned, are very evident in this field. Our knowledge of numbers of smaller taxonomic categories, particularly, is certainly very incomplete for any given group at any time in geological history, and, what is worse, our knowledge is very uneven at different times. Before the data become reliably meaningful they must be scrutinized more carefully than has been usual in past studies, to be sure that each time-entry represents reasonably intense sampling of the faunas of that time and, especially, that the successive entries represent samplings approximately equal in intensity. The interpretation of these data in terms of evolutionary rates is a complicated problem and also seems to call for considerably more careful study than has yet been given to it.

Zeuner (1946b) gives interpretations based on a theoretical model in which the time-frequency curve, as he terms it, is the result of a rate of splitting and a rate of extinction. The rate of splitting is postulated as

[13] See, for example, the relatively simple introduction to this subject in Pearl, 1941.

geometric (doubling the frequency of taxonomic units in a given period of time), while the rate of extinction is arithmetic (a given number of units becoming extinct in a given period). Aside from the question whether rate of extinction should not also be considered geometric, it seems to me that this model is too simple to be really enlightening as to the evolutionary rate phenomena of the time-frequency curve, and that even on this over-simplified level it is somewhat unreal.

The time-frequency curve, supposing that the data are adequate and representative, must be the resultant of at least four, not two, factors of quite different evolutionary significance. Among, say, the genera of a family between two different times:

(*a*) some may persist unchanged (on the generic level),

(*b*) some may persist but sufficiently changed to be classified as new genera at the later time,

(*c*) some may split into two or more genera one of which may, for purposes of analysis, be considered as representing the unchanged (*a*) or changed (*b*) ancestry while the others are new lines arising by splitting, and

(*d*) some may become extinct without issue.

Factors *a* and *b* do not change the frequency between any two successive times (although their own numbers do change), while *c* increases and *d* decreases the frequency. The total frequencies compared are for Time 1, $a + b + d$ and for Time 2, $a + b + c$ and the net change in frequency is $c - d$. The number of new species at Time 2, also commonly graphed (by Zeuner among others) is $b + c$. Factors *a* and *b* are mainly affected by the phyletic rate of evolution, not by a rate of splitting or of taxonomic diversification, but the relationship is not simple and linear. A time will come when most or all of the genera concerned have evolved into new genera (*a* has reached a minimum and *b* a maximum) and thereafter this phyletic evolution may continue at the same rate or may radically increase or decrease without having any further effect on the numerical value of *a* or *b*. Elimination of *a* and *b* from the time-frequencies would eliminate the effect of phyletic evolutionary rates and give a result determined solely by splitting and extinction, as in Zeuner's model. This is not, however, actually done in the examples given by Zeuner or in others known to me and perhaps cannot usefully be accomplished on any large scale because of the difficulty of distinguishing *b* and *c*, units that are merely the ancestral units transformed and those that are additional to the ancestral units.

Factor *c* is determined by the rate of splitting or the rate of taxonomic diversification, and it would provide an adequate measure of that rate but, as just noted, it is not distinguished in the usual data and is difficult to distinguish adequately. Total extinction as read from the data is generally taken as $b + d$ at Time 1, that is, all the genera (or other units) known at that time and not encountered at Time 2 or thereafter, and this is the only extinction figure readily noted from the usual data, but in fact only d involves true extinction or can give a determinate extinction rate. Even if $(b + d)$/time be defined and understood as an extinction rate, it may become indeterminate or meaningless because of the fact that more than one linear change of genus (or other unit) may occur between Time 1 and Time 2.

These complexities are real and highly pertinent, but they do not deprive even the oversimplified time-frequency or new-unit curves of all value. They do necessitate cautious and in some respects modified interpretation of these curves. Aside from the previous caution as to representative sampling, the period interval used should evidently be no greater than the time involved in the rise of an average genus (or whatever taxonomic unit is under study) within the group in question. The various interpretive principles cannot be exemplified or studied in any detail in this general summary, but the following points are noted (assuming that the data are properly representative):

1. A rise in the time-frequency curve indicates an increased rate of taxonomic diversification. It does not, however, reliably indicate the duration or continuity of this higher rate and may, for instance, combine two episodes of "explosive evolution" separated by an interval of low rate.

2. A continued high level in the time-frequency curve does not indicate a continued high rate of taxonomic diversification and is likely to be accompanied by an underlying *decrease* in this rate.

3. The rate of taxonomic diversification may increase significantly without causing a rise in the time-frequency curve.

4. A rise in the new-unit curve above an average level (maintained by phyletic evolution) may and probably usually does represent increase in rate of taxonomic diversification but may be caused wholly by increased taxonomic phyletic rate.

Some Special Problems and Implications of Evolutionary Rates

This summary has been mainly devoted to the definition and methodology of evolutionary rate studies. Little space can be devoted to the broader theoretical implications of such studies, but the discussion would be incomplete without brief mention of some of these, given as suggestive examples rather than as a review of the field. The examples are purposely chosen among those most open to discussion or perhaps to controversy.

Evolutionary Rate Distributions. This topic was discussed at some length in Simpson (1944) but necessarily only in a preliminary and somewhat speculative way because of the paucity of data available or analyzed for this purpose. I then found what seemed to be a characteristic sort of taxonomic rate distribution among extinct genera of widely different groups of animals. The actual rates in each group cover a wide range and the mean value is very different in different groups, but the distribution pattern of these rates (strongly leptokurtic and negatively skewed) is coherent and is similar in shape for different groups. Being based on extinct forms only, with determinate and complete spans, this distribution is assumed to represent a normal sort of evolutionary metabolism, so to speak, for the groups in question, and I have called it the horotelic distribution. Similar distributions based on living forms would be essentially the same if rates of evolution of living forms were comparable to those of their more ancient relatives. This is true in some cases but in others there are strong discrepancies which are explicable, after further analysis, by the hypothesis that there are in such groups more or less numerous surviving lines with average rates of evolution and with a distribution of rates unlike those of the horotelic distribution of the group. It is therefore inferred that the evolutionary rates of these particular lines form a distribution of relatively slow rates, distinct from the previously established horotelic distribution, and called bradytelic.[14] Less direct evidence further suggests that at certain periods in their history, almost always poorly recorded paleontologically, most major groups have evolved at rates above any shown in their horotelic distributions. It is inferred from this that there is still a third type of rate distribution, effective only during certain crucial relatively short evolutionary episodes, which is designated as tachytelic. These are merely working hypotheses at present, but they seem to systematize some otherwise irregular and inconsistent results of rate study and may merit more extensive study and application to larger bodies of data.

EVOLUTIONARY RATES AND LAMARCKISM. It has often been suggested, for instance by Wood Jones (1943),[15] that the inheritance of acquired char-

[14] This hypothesis seems to have been misunderstood by some readers of my earlier discussion, who have assumed that any particularly slow rate is bradytelic as defined by me. There are both slow and fast rates within the horotelic distribution, and the slower rates are not, *ipso facto*, bradytelic. The hypothesis, whether or not it stands up under further investigation, is that certain rates belong to a different rate distribution entirely, one with lower range and mean, although it may possibly be found sometimes to overlap the horotelic distribution for the same group. Bradytelic rates as a whole are slower than horotelic, but a relatively fast bradytelic rate might conceivably be faster than a relatively slow horotelic rate. All groups have horotelic rates, by definition, but the fact that some rates in the horotelic distribution are relatively slow does not mean that the group also has bradytelic rates. The evidence is that some groups of animals have no bradytelic lines. Space is lacking here for further elaboration, but this comment may clarify these admittedly rather difficult concepts.

[15] It may appear to an audience which is probably overwhelmingly non-Lamarckian that I am belaboring a dead horse in selecting their bearing on neo-Lamarckism as one example of the deeper theoretical implications of evolutionary rates. Wood Jones's

acters, although not detectable in the brief span of experimentation, may yet occur in the long periods of natural evolution. Rate studies might be adduced in support of this view and, indeed, Zeuner (1946a) has mentioned this possibility in a somewhat noncommittal but still generally favorable way. The morphologic rate observable in many phyla is so slow that it certainly could not be observed in contemporaneous groups, as exemplified by the average change in diameter of early equid molars, not more than 0.2 mm. per million years during a time when differences of 3.0 mm. or more occurred within single populations. Similarly, it is probable that taxonomic rates in such lines are seldom faster than approximately 500,000 years per species. How, ask the adherents of Lamarckism, can one maintain in the face of these figures that the failure to demonstrate inheritance of acquired characters in the laboratory has any bearing on its possibility in evolution at the rates observed in nature?

The possibility merits discussion, surely, but I may say that to me this is only a begging of the question or an echo of the pious ejaculation that "with God all things are possible," with Father Time raised to the rank of deity. These considerations do not really demonstrate even a possibility, and demonstration of a possibility would hardly establish a theory. Nor is the failure of experimental verification the only objection to the hypothesis of the inheritance of acquired characters. Equally important are the failure to discover or even to postulate an acceptable mechanism, the failure of neo-Lamarckism to provide a general explanation of the phenomena of adaptation on which it is based, and the failure to adduce examples for which there are not other demonstrated or probable alternative explanations (see, e.g., Huxley, 1942, but candor compels me to admit that in a few cases the alternatives are not completely satisfactory).

Probably the most cogent argument for neo-Lamarckism is that it could explain the rise of adaptive characters through incipient stages when their selective value appears to be or is asserted to be too small to be effective. In this respect the argument based on the general slowness of evolutionary rates and the enormously different time scales of natural as opposed to experimental evolution seems to rebound sharply against neo-Lamarckism. Any selective value, no matter how small, could become effective if it

---

clever little book resuscitates the issue, if it could ever be called moribund. That the issue is not truly dead is also attested by a number of paleontologists, one of whom could recently say that, "To them [the geneticists] the idea that external conditions can so influence an organism that in course of time their effect becomes heritable is almost absurd; to me it is axiomatic." (Hopwood, 1945.) Indeed there are students in most other fields of biology who incline to a favorable, even if not wholly enthusiastic, attitude toward the possible inheritance of acquired characters. Until the Utopian day when the processes of evolution are all really well understood, we cannot afford to close our minds conclusively to any factors that might conceivably prove to be at the root of the many mysteries still remaining.

operated (in suitable populations) for a sufficiently long time. The power of stronger selection to change the genetic composition of groups can quite readily be demonstrated in the laboratory, while the power of acquired characters, large or small, to do so (except through a secondary selective process) cannot be or, at least, has not been demonstrated. Surely with two processes that might conceivably produce the same result given the vast periods of time actually involved in evolutionary rates, theoretical choice should fall on the process that is known to be real and not on the other.

Nor, finally, can it reasonably be argued that time alone can make effective a process that produces no effect whatever in a shorter period and therefore is completely undetectable in the study of living populations in nature or in the laboratory. Ten million times zero is still zero. Caullery has suggested, most recently in his excellent short history of biology (Caullery, 1942), that the natural laws of today may not rigorously apply throughout the vast stretches of past geological time. I do not believe that there is any real evidence for this (Caullery mentions it only as an interesting possibility), and even such tentative rejection of the principle of uniformity would, in the absence of strong evidence, quite needlessly undermine the whole foundations of the study of evolution. Passing mention may also be made of the suggestion (e.g. by Jordan, 1936) that the physical principles of indeterminism and discontinuity might accord with the reality of such a biological factor as the inheritance of acquired characters, but might make its manifestations so rare that they might not occur at all in circumstances available for observation. The rejection of this wholly unacceptable idea is perhaps sufficiently justified by merely pointing out that a process responsible for the universal and continuous adaptation of the whole organic realm throughout geologic time cannot be manifested only by statistically rare events. What seems to me a more rational relating of indeterminism and discontinuity to heredity is given, for example, by Schrödinger (1945) and is more consistent with Darwinian than with Lamarckian evolution.

EVOLUTIONARY RATES, SELECTION, AND QUANTUM EVOLUTION. If it be granted, as I think it must, that natural selection is an effective factor in most of our examples of phyletic evolution, the conclusion to be drawn from the rates of phyletic evolution, so slow in terms of human observation and experiment, is that the selective forces involved are indeed very small. If, for instance, it had been *very* advantageous for an early equid to be larger than its fellows, *Epihippus* might well have achieved the size of *Equus*.

Such considerations, among others, strongly suggest that the steadily but rather slowly evolving lines which constitute a majority of those for which there are good suites of paleontological materials had already achieved a good adaptive status at the beginning of their continuously recorded history. Then any selective pressures on them were slight and arose or increased only as small and gradual changes occurred in the population and its environment, and phyletic evolution was correspondingly slow and gradual. We observe, moreover, that a more marked shift in adaptive status, as from browsing to grazing in horses, is accompanied by a definite and measurable increase in the rate of evolution of the organs concerned, and, to me at least, it seems rather obvious that this is a response to increased selective pressure.

The origin of such lines and of higher taxonomic categories in general usually involves a pronounced change in adaptive type from that of the ancestry. On a larger or smaller scale it involves a transformation, in the sense of Gregory (e.g. 1936), rather than simple phyletic progression, or, especially at higher levels, what Sewertzoff (1931) has called "aromorphosis," a change in organization that increases the energy or life activity of the organisms.[16] A balance of evidence of several different sorts suggests that these changes usually occur much more rapidly than the subsequent phyletic evolution of the same groups. In terms of rate distributions, they are tachytelic as opposed to horotelic. The increased rate of evolution takes place in a period during which the group is not in adaptive equilibrium but is in a relatively unstable transition from one (usually slowly shifting) equilibrium to another, a transition for which I have proposed the term evolutionary quantum step. It is evident that selection pressure would be unusually great during such a step, and the independent conclusion that the evolutionary rate is then also high is another item in the considerable body of evidence that, on the whole, evolutionary rates tend to vary with selection pressure. Undoubtedly there are other important contributing factors, such as size of population, but it seems likely that selection is the most important single determinant of evolutionary rates.

EVOLUTIONARY RATES AND EARTH HISTORY. The thought that, as Barrell (1917) put it, the "forces which make for evolution work intermittently, not continuously," is not applicable to the usual instances of phyletic progression, demonstrably continuous in many cases, but it finds support in other rate phenomena and has often been stressed in studies of historical geology. Quantum evolution, as briefly defined above, is clearly an intermittent process, and so are the episodes of marked increase in rates

[16] I am not quite satisfied that this is an adequate or accurate statement of what is increased by, say, such "aromorphs" as the vertebrate jaws. They may not especially increase the energy or metabolism of the individuals that first attain them. Yet some, at least, may increase the total flow of energy in the organic world as a whole, and so accord with the interesting suggestion of Lotka (1945). These more remote and rather philosophical problems are too complex for discussion here, and less highly theoretical interpretation of the phenomenon merely as a shift in adaptive type is here preferred.

of diversification, which may occur with such relative rapidity as to merit the term "explosive evolution" and which are normally followed by a sharp decrease in diversification rates. It is probable that markedly new sorts of animals usually (always?) arise by the first of these intermittent processes and that their rise is often (usually?—apparently not always) more or less closely followed by an episode resulting from the second sort of intermittent process.[17]

It has long been asserted that the distribution of such intermittent events in geologic time is not random but that they tend to recur rhythmically, constituting a sort of "pulse of life" (Lull, 1918). The physical history of the earth is also characterized by intermittent events and these, too, are believed to be rhythmic (see, among many others, Schuchert and Levene, 1927; Umbgrove, 1942), an idea so appealing to the scientific sense of order as to become almost obsessional at times (as it perhaps rather nearly was with Grabau, e.g. 1940). The thought is inescapable that the two rhythms may be related or identical. It has become one of the commonplaces of historical geology to claim that the intermittent tectonic episodes of earth history coincide with the intermittent rate episodes in evolutionary history. Unqualified statements to this effect are usual in the textbooks (e.g. Schuchert and Dunbar, 1933: "Great crustal disturbances thus bring on critical conditions for most types of life and lead to a period of accelerated evolutionary change. . . .").

It seems so obvious that this *should* be so that we may be too much inclined to take it for granted that it *is* so. In spite of voluminous discussion and repeated dogmatic assertion, there is a paucity of carefully gathered and objectively evaluated evidence. As far as I know no one has tabulated all the now available material on the dates of markedly accelerated evolution of both sorts, and determined whether these are objectively rhythmical and do coincide with established earth rhythms. Probably they will be found to do so, at least in part, but surely it would be worth while to restudy this question with an open mind. I suspect that a great number of exceptions and complications will be found and that the generalization is neither so universal nor so simple as is now often superficially taken for granted.

There are, in the data already at hand, ample reasons for such suspicion. In considering any given major episode in the history of life, it is always possible to find a tectonic episode that occurred in the neighborhood of that time and to assume a relationship that may not really have existed and

[17] Many writers seem to assume that the two episodes are simultaneous or identical, a general intensification of evolutionary rate rather than increases in two different sorts of rate, phyletic rates and rates of diversification. I think the two sorts of intensified evolution are distinct and separable. They may well be essentially simultaneous in some cases, but in other instances they occur at different times.

that certainly cannot be demonstrated without evidence of closer coincidence and without evidence from enough different episodes to rule out pure chance. There is, for instance, always some supposed "earth pulsation" within about 50,000,000 years, at most, of the appearance of a new major group of animals, and in many cases the coincidence of the two is no more nearly demonstrated than this.[18]

There is, moreover, considerable evidence that critical episodes in different groups of organisms commonly do not tend to occur at the same time. As a very generalized example it is well known that the Paleozoic, Mesozoic, and Cenozoic, broadly characterized by faunal types, are not coextensive with broad paleophytic, mesophytic, and cenophytic floral types.

Of course I do not mean by these remarks to deny any connection between evolutionary rates and earth history, but only to suggest that we do not know nearly enough about this connection and that part of what we think we know is probably wrong. The physical environment of the earth has certainly undergone both repeated and continuous changes, and animal evolution must certainly have been influenced by these changes, whether or not the influence was reflected in simultaneous rhythms of evolutionary acceleration and tectonic cycles.

The most obvious relationship and perhaps the only one that should now be accepted as well-established is primarily distributional. The sudden influx of varied mammals into the known fossil collecting areas at the beginning of the Paleocene and again, for different groups of mammals, around the Paleocene-Eocene boundary, for instance, is evidently a matter of suddenly expanded distribution and not of evolution in situ. It seems almost certain that this expansion had some physical cause or concomitant. It is not clear that this cause had any particular relationship to the *origin* of the groups that expanded at those times or had any *direct* influence on evolutionary rates. The great expansion in distribution, with invasion of vast and varied areas new to the animals involved, must considerably have increased their rates of diversification for a time, and hence the physical cause may be said to have had a secondary influence on this particular sort of evolutionary rate.

---

[18] As an example, the nine evolutionary events entered by Umbgrove (1942) on his carefully prepared and enlightening table of "the pulse of the earth" presumably were selected to show the postulated influence of this "pulse" on evolution. Yet only two of these items come near to coinciding with an episode of mountain building, of basin formation, or of abnormal climate, and the others follow the next preceding episode by variable spans of 15,000,000 to 30,000,000 years (Umbgrove's dating). In fact the distribution of the evolutionary items seems to be random with respect to the physical episodes, and on the face of it, if this chart indicates anything (in this particular respect), it indicates that there is no connection.

REFERENCES

Barrell, J. 1917. Rhythms and the measurements of geologic time. *Bull. Geol. Soc. Amer.*, *28*, 745-904.

Caullery, M. 1942. *Les étapes de la biologie.* Paris.

Dobzhansky, Th. 1943. Genetics of natural populations. IX. Temporal changes in the composition of populations of *Drosophila pseudoobscura*. *Genetics*, *28*, 162-186.

Dobzhansky, Th., and S. Wright. 1943. Genetics of natural populations. X. Dispersion rates in *Drosophila pseudoobscura*. *Genetics*, *28*, 304-340.

Grabau, A. W. 1940. *The Rhythm of the Ages.* Peking.

Gray, S. W. 1946. Relative growth in a phylogenetic series and in an ontogenetic series of one of its members. *Amer. Jour. Sci.*, *244*, 792-807.

Gregory, W. K. 1936. The transformation of organic designs. *Biol. Rev.*, *11*, 311-344.

——. 1937. Supra-specific variation in nature and in classification; a few examples from mammalian paleontology. *Amer. Nat.*, *71*, 268-276.

Hersh, A. H. 1934. Evolutionary relative growth in the titanotheres. *Amer. Nat.*, *68*, 537-561.

Hopwood, A. T. 1945. The living mollusc, II. How it works. *Proc. Malac. Soc. London*, *26*, 111-130.

Huxley, J. S. 1932. *Problems of Relative Growth.* London.

——. *Evolution, the Modern Synthesis.* New York and London.

Jordan, P. 1936. *Anschauliche Quantentheorie.* Berlin.

Kavanagh, A. J., and O. W. Richards. 1942. Mathematical analysis of the relative growth of organisms. *Proc. Rochester Acad. Sci.*, *8*, 150-174.

Lotka, A. J. 1945. The Law of Evolution as a Maximal Principle. *Human Biol.*, *17* (3), 167-194.

Lull, R. S. 1918. The pulse of life. In, *The Evolution of the Earth and Its Inhabitants*, by Lull and others. New Haven.

Lyell, C. 1833. *Principles of Geology.* Vol. 3. London.

Mayr, E., G. L. Stebbins, and G. G. Simpson. 1945. Symposium on age of the distribution pattern of the gene arrangements in *Drosophila pseudoobscura*. *Lloydia*, *8*, 69-108.

Medawar, P. B. 1945. Size, shape, and age. *Essays on Growth and Form*, pp. 157-187. Oxford.

Pearl, R. 1941. *Introduction to Medical Biometry and Statistics.* 3rd ed. Philadelphia and London.

Phleger, F. B. 1940. Relative growth and vertebrate phylogeny. *Amer. Jour. Sci.*, *238*, 643-662.

Reeve, E. C. R., and J. S. Huxley. 1945. Some problems in the study of allometric growth. *Essays on Growth and Form*, pp. 121-156. Oxford.

Reeve, E. C. R., and P. D. F. Murray. 1942. Evolution in the horse's skull. *Nature*, *150*, 402-403.

Richards, O. W., and A. J. Kavanagh. 1945. The analysis of growing form. *Essays on Growth and Form*, pp. 188-230. Oxford.

Robb, R. C. 1935. A study of mutations in evolution. Part 1: Evolution in the equine skull. *Jour. Genetics*, *31*, 39-46.

Schrödinger, E. 1945. *What is Life?* Cambridge and New York.

Schuchert, C., and C. O. Dunbar. 1933. *A Textbook of Geology.* Part 2: Historical geology. 3d ed. New York.

Schuchert, C., and C. M. Levene. 1927. *The Earth and Its Rhythms.* New York.

Sewertzoff, A. N. 1931. *Morphologische Gesetzmässigkeiten der Evolution.* Jena.

Simpson, G. G. 1937. Super-specific variation in nature from the viewpoint of paleontology. *Amer. Nat.*, *71*, 236-267.

——. 1944. *Tempo and Mode in Evolution.* New York.

Simpson, G. G., and A. Roe. 1939. *Quantitative Zoology.* New York.

Thompson, D'A. W. 1942. *On Growth and Form.* A new edition (first edition, 1917). Cambridge.

Umbgrove, J. H. F. 1942. *The Pulse of the Earth.* The Hague.
——. 1946. Evolution of reef corals in East Indies since Miocene time. *Bull. Amer. Assoc. Petrol. Geol., 30,* 23-31.
Wood Jones, F. 1943. *Habit and Heritage.* London.
Zeuner, F. E. 1931. Die Insektenfauna des Böttinger Marmors. *Fortschr. Geol. Palaeont.,* (9) 28.
——. 1946a. *Dating the Past, an Introduction to Geochronology.* London.
——. 1946b. Time and the biologist. *Discovery, 7,* 242-249, 256.

· 12 ·

RATES OF EVOLUTION IN PLANTS

BY G. LEDYARD STEBBINS, JR.[1]

IN the plant kingdom the fossil record provides much less evidence on rates of evolution than it does in animals, largely because of the more fragmentary nature of this record. Although plant remains are abundant in many deposits, these fossils usually consist of single organs, like leaves, stems, fruits, and seeds, which often fail to provide completely the diagnostic characters needed for classification and for comparison with modern forms. Furthermore, the fossil record of plants is much more highly selective than that of animals. The plants most easily preserved are woody species which grow in lowland forests, chiefly near large rivers or lakes which are the usual sites of deposition. Plants of uplands, and particularly of savanna, steppe, or desert areas rarely enter the fossil record. In paleobotany, therefore, the absence of a species from the fossil record means little, and parts of plants which differ widely from existing ones are hard to connect with their modern descendants or relatives.

Nevertheless, recent intensive work on fossil plants (see Chaney, in this volume) has provided us with much valuable evidence on the composition of pre-existing floras, and two main conclusions can be drawn from this evidence. In the first place, most of the genera of woody plants have existed for a long time, at least since the early part of the Tertiary period, and many species have changed relatively little since the middle or latter part of this period, that is since the Miocene or Early Pliocene epoch. Secondly, the past distribution of many of these genera and species was very different from the present one, and in particular the temperate regions have suffered a large amount of extinction of woody types. In other words, the woody plants which form the bulk of the more recent fossil records have evolved very slowly during most of the time over which abundant fossil remains have been deposited and at the time when they were evolving more rapidly they left few recognizable remains. Rates of evolution in the plants which preceded the angiosperms are hard to estimate because most of these plants are so different from modern forms that their relationships are obscure.

In order to determine whether evolutionary rates were any different in herbaceous species from those in woody ones, I shall summarize the evidence from the three best fossil records of such species known to me.

[1] Division of Genetics, Hilgard Hall, University of California.

The first is the excellent series of seeds described by Reid and Reid (1915) from the Pliocene deposits of northwestern Europe. As their illustrations show, many of these seeds can be compared directly with those of modern species now living in the mountains of China, and thus represent species which have become extinct in part of their range but remain unchanged in another part. Other seeds were identified to the genus but did not seem to resemble any living species, while a small percentage were unidentifiable as to genus or even to family. It is, of course, possible that these seeds belong to some as yet unrecognized modern species, and there is no way of saying how many of them, instead of becoming extinct, gave rise instead to divergent modern European species of their genera. Nevertheless, the proportion of unidentifiable seeds as compared with those resembling modern species should provide a rough estimate of the amount of evolution which has taken place in western Europe since the Pliocene. In particular, the fact that these floras contain seeds of herbaceous and woody species in about equal proportions should provide a basis for comparing the rate of evolution in the two types. The results of such a comparison, compiled from Reid and Reid's (1915) data on the Early Pliocene Reuverian flora, are given in Table 1.

TABLE 1

Comparison between rate of extinction in woody and herbaceous species of the Early Pliocene Reuverian flora.

	Woody		*Herbaceous*	
	no. spp.	per cent	no. spp.	per cent
Fossil seeds referred to modern species, either European or exotic	25	27	31	25
Fossils referred to modern genus, but not species	56	59	70	57
Fossils not identified	13	14	22	18
Total	94		123	

From these figures it seems likely that the herbs associated with the forest existing in western Europe in Early Pliocene time have not evolved any more rapidly than the woody species of this flora.

The second example, which comprises only a single genus, but which gives the most complete sequence known for any herbaceous plant, is the series of seeds of the genus *Stratiotes* from Europe described by Chandler (1923). The oldest seeds in this series, of Eocene age, are small, broad, and heavily sculptured, while those of younger strata are progressively longer, narrower, and smoother, until in the uppermost Pliocene there occur seeds which are indistinguishable from the modern European S. *aloides*. During the Tertiary period there was undoubtedly extensive evolution in this genus and perhaps its relatives, but its significance is hard to estimate. *Stratiotes* is today a monotypic genus of the small, exclusively aquatic family Hydrocharitaceae, and according to the synopsis in Engler and Prantl, *Die natürlichen Pflanzenfamilien*, occupies a rather isolated position in that family. The seeds of its other modern genera have not been studied and are not available among the collections of specimens in the larger herbaria. There is no way of deciding, therefore, whether the recorded changes in the seeds are on the species level, or whether the Eocene seeds belonged to plants of a different genus. Furthermore, it is not even possible to infer what types of changes were taking place in the rest of the plant and whether the Early Tertiary species grew under similar or different conditions from the modern one. *Stratiotes*, therefore, represents an isolated case of undoubted progressive evolution of which the causes and significance are obscure.

The third and most significant series is that of the grass seeds of the tribe Stipeae described by Elias (1942). This shows a clear progression from the beginning of the record in the Early Miocene epoch to its end in the Middle Pliocene. The fruits found in all of the earlier deposits are different from any known in modern species of Stipeae, but many of those of the mid-Pliocene beds resemble modern species of the genus *Piptochaetium*, subg. *Podopogon*, nearly all of which are now confined to South America. The history of the Stipeae on the North American Great Plains since the middle of the Pliocene epoch has been mainly one of extinction. Instead of fifteen to twenty species as in the Pliocene, there are now only four related to the group found in the fossil series. And these four modern species, *Stipa comata* Trin., *S. spartea* Trin., *S. neomexicana* (Thurb.) Scribn., and *Oryzopsis hymenoides* (Roem. and Schult.) Ricker are all polyploids with respectively 46, 46, 44, and 48 chromosomes, and probably allopolyploids, while the close South American relatives of the Pliocene Stipeae are diploids with 22. The evidence therefore suggests that progressive evolution in the Stipeae of the Great Plains continued from the middle or early part of the Tertiary period until some time in the Pliocene epoch, and then ceased, to be replaced by extinction, hybridization, and polyploidy. Moreover, Elias has noted the fact that the only seeds of woody plants found in these deposits, those of the genus *Celtis*, are identical with seeds of the modern *C. reticulata*, still existing in the same area. In the Great Plains, therefore, the herbaceous species seem to have evolved with some rapidity, while the woody ones, like the trees and shrubs of the forest belts, may have remained relatively static.

As has been noted elsewhere (Stebbins, 1945, 1947), indirect evidence from present distribution patterns can give a clue to the age of species, particularly when these patterns are correlated with those of the woody species with which they are now associated. They indicate that most of the herbs now growing in the surviving parts of the formerly widespread Arcto-Tertiary forests have either failed to evolve at all or have produced only minor specific differences since the middle or early part of the Tertiary period. In other words, the prevailing evidence indicates that the herbaceous plants in the great forest belts of the temperate zone have evolved just as slowly as the woody ones.

This may be much less true of the herbs of tropical forests, particularly the epiphytes. In this group, represented chiefly by the Orchidaceae and Bromeliaceae, there are many genera and tribes, very rich in species, which are confined to one continent or even a single relatively circumscribed area, and often clusters of related species grow in the same or adjacent regions.

Distributional evidence from some of the plants inhabiting drier habitats in the temperate zone suggests that they may have evolved much more rapidly in Recent geological time. This is particularly true of the annuals found in such areas as California and the Mediterranean region. These often form large genera, containing clusters of related species which occupy localities near together but nevertheless geographically and ecologically distinct. One of the best examples is the tribe Madinae, of the family Compositae, in which species relationships and speciation processes have been fully analyzed in the largely unpublished work of Clausen, Keck, and Hiesey (1941). In this tribe there are many examples of closely related species which occupy localities near together but nevertheless geographically and ecologically distinct, and are separated from each other by imperfectly developed isolating mechanisms. For instance, the three species *Layia Jonesii*, *L. Munzii*, and *L. leucopappa* occupy small areas in three valleys of south central California. These localities are fifty to sixty miles apart and have rather different climatic and ecological conditions. The habitats may have been still more different during the Pleistocene, and were inundated by the sea shortly before that time; thus they are new. These three species of *Layia* surely sprang from a common ancestor, and at present the genetic isolating mechanisms separating them are incomplete, since F_1 hybrids are about 25 to 30 per cent fertile as to seed setting. They are species in the state of becoming. A similar group of two similar species consists of *Layia chrysanthemoides* and *L. Fremontii* of north central California; these also have probably descended recently from a common ancestor and are just barely distinct species. The two groups mentioned are separated from each other by about two hundred miles and have a somewhat more remote common ancestor. The genetic barrier between them is rather well developed. A species somewhat more distantly related morphologically and genetically is *L. platyglossa*; its wider range overlaps those of both of the previously mentioned groups. Similar patterns indicating species actively evolving have been found by Clausen, Keck, and Hiesey in other genera of Madinae (Clausen, 1947), and undoubtedly exist in most of the large groups of annual species in California. In the Mediterranean region the annual species of *Crepis* have very similar distributional and genetic patterns and likewise are probably in an active state of evolution (Babcock, 1947).

But the active evolution in these regions is not confined to the annuals or even to the herbs. In the perennial species of *Delphinium* which occur in the same parts of California, evidence has been obtained for the recent origin of at least one species, *D. gypsophilum* Ewan, from hybridization between two others (Lewis and Epling, 1946), and other species which occur in habitats which have been changing rapidly in Late Tertiary and Pleistocene time are likewise probably recent. In the genus *Brodiaea* and its relatives, a group of bulbous perennials, there are several "species," particularly *Triteleia laxa*, *T. ixioides*, and *T. peduncularis*, in which several different chromosome numbers, both euploid and aneuploid, have been counted. These probably consist of a number of species recently evolved or still evolving, and the conclusion of Burbanck (1944), that they are in an active state of evolution, is fully justified. The same is probably true of the other large Californian genera of Liliaceae, such as *Allium* and *Calochortus*. Among woody plants the genus *Ceanothus* contains many plastic species and local endemics which are certainly in an active state of evolution (McMinn, 1942). The same is true of *Arctostaphylos* in some regions, although in parts of California, especially in the Sierra Nevada, its species appear to be relatively stable. On the other hand, the dominant trees of the California savanna area are species of *Quercus* and *Pinus* which have changed little or not at all since the Miocene epoch.

The following generalizations can be made from the data outlined above. In the first place, the larger, dominant woody plants of all modern floras, whether temperate or tropical, forest or savanna, are relatively ancient and have been evolving very slowly since the early part of the Tertiary period. On the other hand, the rate of evolution in shrubs and herbs has differed widely from one region to another. In the great temperate forest belts, particularly in those regions not influenced by the Pleistocene glaciation, the shrubs and herbs have evolved little if any faster than the trees. Very little is known about the history of the herbaceous vegetation in the tropics, but some evidence suggests that in the rain forests at least the epiphytes and parasites have been evolving relatively rapidly in recent times. In savanna and probably desert as well as alpine areas the smaller plants, both woody and herbaceous, have been in a more or less active state of evolution, and this has been particularly true in regions like the southwestern United States, which have undergone great orographic and climatic changes. There is a rough correlation between shortness of generation and speed of evolution, but this is by no means absolute, as is evidenced by the comparatively rapid evolution in such slowly growing plants as the California manzanitas (*Arctostaphylos*). The difference between the relative stability of the trees and the plasticity of the shrubs and herbs is due to other factors than the smaller number of generations in the former plants.

Furthermore, the lower rate of evolution in trees does not seem to be the result of a lower mutation rate. The species of forest trees are rich in genetic variability and present some of the best examples of polytypic species in the plant kingdom. Furthermore, horticulturists have been able to select from many species of conifers a great array of different genetic types, many of which appear like recessive mutants. This is true even in the big tree, *Sequoiadendron giganteum*, one of the most ancient and conservative of living species. According to J. T. Buchholz (oral communication) many horticultural varieties have been selected from this species in the comparatively short time that it has been known.

A second set of factors which might be conceived as reducing the rate of evolution, namely inbreeding, homozygosity, and consequent loss of genetic variability, likewise are not operating in these woody plants. Most of them have floral structures well adapted to cross pollination; and progeny tests, whenever they have been made, indicate that they are highly heterozygous. The highest degree of panmixy in the plant kingdom is almost certainly among the widespread and dominant tree species of temperate forests. On the other hand, inbreeding and homozygosity are particularly common among the rapidly evolving annuals of savanna and other dry areas.

The conclusion that these internal factors are not the ones which govern slow evolution, or bradytely, agrees with that of Simpson (1944, p. 137). Simpson's further conclusion, that bradytelic groups should have large populations, is in general true of plants, although a number of exceptions exist. The presence of large populations, however, does not of itself produce bradytely, since many of the rapidly evolving annual species have equally large populations. Simpson's next conclusion, that groups are not primitive but specialized and advanced when they become bradytelic, is likewise true of plants. The anatomical studies of the past twenty years have established without question the fact that the flowers and inflorescences of the oaks, poplars, hickories, and other groups formerly placed in the order Amentiferae are highly specialized structures. And the vegetative parts of these plants, such as their wood, their winter buds, and their deciduous leaves, are equally specialized. And the modern conifers, although they are relatively primitive as regards their gymnospermous condition, are nevertheless highly specialized in most of their vegetative and reproductive characteristics (Florin, 1944). Even such archaic types as the cycads and Gnetales are in their vegetative characteristics among the most specialized plants known. In their morphological and anatomical condition these gymnosperms correspond in every way to such animals as the lingulids, limulids, sphenodonts, and crocodiles. We can paraphrase for them Simpson's remark (1944, p. 139): they are primitive in the recent flora, because they have been passed in the evolutionary race, not because they had an initial handicap.

Furthermore, Simpson's conclusion that most of the bradytelic groups formerly had high rates of evolution is fully borne out by the fossil evidence on these plant groups. Most of the modern families of woody angiosperms appear suddenly in the middle of the Cretaceous period, and evidence for an earlier existence of the flowering plants is very scanty. While this is doubtless due partly to the imperfections of the fossil record, nevertheless the evolution of families and genera of woody angiosperms must have been much more rapid during the early part of the Cretaceous period than at any time since. And the profound differences between Cretaceous and Early Tertiary floras of the same climatic zones which have been brought out by Chaney in this volume show that some of this evolution continued into the latter period. In fact, the relative evolutionary stagnation in the woody angiosperm flora is chiefly a feature of the last thirty million years. The recent studies of conifer evolution by Florin (1944) have shown that these plants underwent extensive evolution from the Carboniferous to the Jurassic period, but have since then been relatively static.

The complete agreement with Simpson's conclusions in all points yet mentioned indicates that, like him, we botanists should look for the principal factors governing rates of evolution in the organism-environment relationship (Simpson, 1944, p. 140); and here again we find that the situation in most woody plants closely corresponds to that described for bradytelic animals. Their specialized characteristics are all highly adaptive. This is evident from the fact that the angiospermous trees of the temperate zone are among the best examples in the plant kingdom of convergent evolution. Such families as the Fagaceae and Juglandaceae, or the Salicaceae and Betulaceae, have developed very similar adaptations from entirely different origins. The broadness of this adaptation is evident from the wide distribution of most species of trees in the temperate zone, and the still wider distribution of the genera. They are less sensitive to differences in soil conditions and other edaphic factors than are most herbaceous species. They are governed principally by climatic factors, and since they can often tolerate extreme annual or cyclic fluctuations in climate they can become adapted to certain of the major alterations during geological epochs with less change in their genetic composition than can the more particularly adapted herbs. We can again quote Simpson's remark: they "are so well adapted to a particular, continuously available environment that almost any mutation occurring in them must be disadvantageous."

In the herbaceous types we should again expect that the differences between the relatively static and the rapidly evolving floras can be sought in the organism-environment relationship, and this is undoubtedly true for the herbs associated with the temperate forests. These are highly adapted to an environment which is made and governed for them by the trees under which they grow. As long as the forest is present, conditions within it are constant, and when the trees are destroyed, the herbaceous forest flora becomes extinct. This is partly because these herbs have evolved certain definite specializations of vegetative habit. Most of them produce thickened rhizomes, corms, or bulbs, and many of them have a very specialized growth rhythm, like that of *Trillium,* in which leaf and flower formation, including meiosis and the partial maturation of the pollen, is completed underground in the buds during the fall proceeding their emergence. These plants are so highly adapted to their own environment that almost any new mutations are disadvantageous, and they are so specialized that when the environment changes they become extinct rather than evolving.

Turning to the epiphytes and parasitic flowering plants of the tropical rain forests, we again find a high specialization to a constant climatic and edaphic environment, so that in vegetative characteristics we should expect to find evolved a standardized constant pattern of adaptation. This is exactly the case. In the epiphytic orchids, species, genera, and even tribes are remarkably similar in habit. They are also relatively constant in the characteristics of fruit and seed. Their remarkable diversity and extensive evolution is in the structure of the flower, which obviously represents a series of adaptations to cross pollination by insects. In this factor we see the principal difference between the floor of the temperate forests and the upper stories of the rain forest in the tropics. The former is poor, the latter very rich in species of insects; and many of these insect groups may still be actively evolving new species and genera. So while the secular environment of the rain forest epiphytes is remarkably constant, their biological environment has been and may still be undergoing considerable changes, which continually call forth new adaptive evolution in their flowers. The epiphytic bromeliads are much less rich in species than the orchids, but they include at least as many different types of vegetative habit. But since related species of the rain forest habitat are usually very similar in habit and fruits, differing mainly in characteristics of the flowers, the selection pressures producing these species have probably been similar to those acting in the orchids. In the parasitic mistletoes (Loranthaceae) of the tropics, seed dispersal as well as cross pollination is effected by insects. This family is remarkably diversified and shows evidence of active evolution in Recent times in the form of clusters of related species inhabiting the same or adjacent areas.

In short, the epiphytic and parasitic herbs of tropical jungles appear to be in an active state of evolution, or at least have been so in the not so distant past. This evolution has consisted principally in the elaboration of mechanisms for pollination and seed dispersal. Thus the evolutionary significance of these groups, already recognized by Darwin, will be among the greatest in the plant kingdom if we can obtain a more complete picture of their ecology and cytogenetics. They deserve careful study by modern methods.

In the herbs of savanna and other dry areas, as well as in the arctic-alpine vegetation, rapid evolution has been associated with the great climatic changes which have taken place in these regions since the middle of the Tertiary period. It has chiefly consisted of the perfection of various adaptations to life under these conditions, but has been greatly aided and diversified by the alternate isolation and reunion of populations which have resulted from the climatic changes. But not all groups of herbs and shrubs subjected to these conditions have evolved equally rapidly. The two major factors which have brought about this unequal response to the same climatic and edaphic changes have been on the one hand the length of generation and on the other the presence or potential development of adaptations to dry conditions. Rapidly developing plants, either annuals or perennials which could become annuals with relatively little genetic change, have been consistently favored and stimulated to rapid evolution. Among plants with slower growth and long life cycles, xerophytes or potential xerophytes have evolved extensively, and meso-phytes have been relatively static. It is no accident that the modern genera richest in local, endemic, recently evolved species should be such types as *Eriogonum, Lupinus, Astragalus, Euphorbia, Salvia, Crepis, Senecio, Stipa, Eragrostis, Andropogon,* and *Allium,* all of which have marked adaptations for life under dry conditions. And it is also according to expectation that primarily mesophytic genera like *Aquilegia, Ranunculus, Saxifraga, Rumex, Viola, Pedicularis, Campanula, Carex,* and *Juncus* should be represented in the drier areas by relatively few but usually common and widespread species, and that they should possess distribution patterns suggestive of recent active evolution in montane and alpine regions.

We can therefore suggest that when the environment is changing, plants preadapted or potentially preadapted in the direction of the change will evolve rapidly and become rich in genera and species, while groups in which the primary adaptive norm is in the direction of the conditions that are disappearing will remain relatively static and will decrease in numbers. This may explain the two examples given above of differential rates of evolution between groups inhabiting the same territory during the same period. In the North American Great Plains during the Miocene and Pliocene epochs the climate was gradually becoming drier. Under these conditions the genus *Celtis*, which is essentially a mesophyte, remained static, but the Stipeae, whose seeds are admirably adapted to dry conditions, progressed rapidly. In California during the Pliocene and Pleistocene epochs the genus *Quercus* evolved little or not at all while *Arctostaphylos* and *Ceanothus*, both of which are woody and have generations as long as or at least not much shorter than those in the oaks, evolved much more rapidly. This might be explained by the fact that the acorns of the oaks are short lived and need a certain amount of moisture continuously for germination, while the seeds and seedlings of *Arctostaphylos* and many species of *Ceanothus* tend to be much more drought resistant. Hence a much greater diversity of genetic types can become established in the two latter genera than in the former, giving the species populations greater opportunities for "exploring" new adaptive peaks. The same is very likely true of such xerophytic woody genera as *Atriplex, Acacia, Eucalyptus*, and *Artemisia*, all of which have been actively evolving in geologically recent times.

One factor of the organism-environment relationship is of particular significance when we compare the rates of evolution in plants with those in animals, as well as in comparisons between the higher and lower plants. This is the relation between the evolving population and the other types of organisms surrounding it or, as Shmalgausen (1946, p. 353) has expressed it, the position of the organism in the hierarchy of nutrition. The lowest position in this hierarchy is occupied by small organisms which have no defense against aggressors except rapidity of reproduction. Since in these organisms elimination is largely non-selective, they will tend to have the slowest rates of evolution. The largest proportion of such organisms is in the fauna and flora of plankton, and Shmalgausen has given several examples of extreme evolutionary conservatism in plankton organisms. Entirely in accord with this hypothesis is the fact that the most primitive of nuclear organisms, the euglenoids and volvocales, are plankton organisms. Similar small defenceless organisms are the bacteria and fungi, and there is every reason to believe that the non-parasitic members of these groups have been relatively conservative in their evolution.

The next lowest position in the hierarchy of nutrition is occupied by those organisms with purely passive forms of protection. All sedentary organisms, but particularly those with heavy armor, are in this category, which includes almost the entire plant kingdom. This, according to Shmalgausen, is the reason for the fact that plants have in general evolved more slowly than animals, particularly vertebrates. It is in the latter group that we find most of the organisms in the two highest positions of the hierarchy of nutrition, namely those that escape from agressors by their activity, and those that are themselves predators, competing with each other for their food.

Since nearly all plants are placed by this scheme in the same category, differential rates of evolution within the plant kingdom can only be explained if the concepts of Shmalgausen are amplified, and two facts about plants suggest how this amplification can be made. In the first place, different groups of plants differ widely in the extent of their demands on the environment. We can therefore postulate that evolution will be slowest in those organisms which demand relatively little of their environment, and progressively more rapid as the minimum requirements for existence become greater and greater. In particular, small plants make fewer demands on their environment than large ones. They require less mineral nutrition and often less light, while their problems of support and conduction are less. We should therefore expect a positive correlation between plant size and rate of evolutionary specialization in vegetative characteristics, a tendency which Watson (in this volume) has emphasized in vertebrate animals. This agrees with the fact that the most primitive and probably slowest in evolution of plant groups are the blue-green algae, green algae, certain fungi, and lichens. The modern representatives of the most primitive groups of vascular plants, which are certainly bradytelic lines, are all smaller than their extinct Paleozoic relatives. Such plants are *Psilotum, Lycopodium, Equisetum,* and *Botrychium.* The annual species of seed plants might be considered exceptions to this rule, but in these plants evolution of vegetative characteristics has lagged behind that of the reproductive structures, and such evolution as occurred in leaves and stems has been chiefly simplification rather than elaboration of parts. Furthermore, aquatic plants have their demands more easily fulfilled than those of dry land, hence we should expect slower evolution in water than on land. This is in general true, as far as can be judged, of higher as well as lower plants.

A second and more important amplification of Shmalgausen's concepts is based on the fact that in the sedentary plants problems connected with reproduction and dispersal are far more important than those involved in maintenance. The primary differences between plant groups at nearly every level—phyla, classes, orders, families, and genera—are in the reproductive organs. The selective value of these differences lies in the ecology of their reproduction. We can therefore recognize in plants a hierarchy of reproduction containing three levels comparable to the four established by

Shmalgausen for the hierarchy of nutrition. The lowest is that in which success in reproduction depends entirely on numbers. In respect to fertilization, this stage is represented by plants which make use of passive agents like wind and water and therefore produce huge numbers of male gametes or gametophytes. As regards the other critical stage of plant reproduction, namely dissemination of seeds, spores, or other propagules, the lowest stage is represented in plants which again rely on wind or water for this process, and in addition possess no protective devices either for these propagules or for the young plants derived from them, but merely produce huge numbers of seeds or spores. The second level in the scale of reproduction is that in which passive protection of propagules is emphasized. To this level belong all plants with tough resistant seeds or spores. In addition we might classify here plants which because of the extreme longevity and resistance to disease or other enemies of the mature individual, or because of efficient vegetative reproduction, have relatively little need for reproduction by the sexual method. The highest level is represented by plants which make active use of other organisms, particularly animals, for either fertilization, dissemination of propagules, or both.

In this reproductive scale the lowest position among land plants is occupied by homosporous types, in which successful dissemination of propagules depends entirely on the great numbers released and on the passive agency of the wind. Here we find the bradytelic genera of vascular plants mentioned above (*Psilotum, Botrychium,* etc.). Among seed plants the conifers, which early developed efficient methods of wind dispersal for both pollen and seeds, have been the most successful of the bradytelic lines. Even in the angiosperms the evolution of floral parts which produce large numbers of either pollen grains or seeds has been followed by slow evolution in these structures. The stamens have in general shown less evolutionary progress than other parts of the flower, and they have been particularly constant in wind-pollinated groups like the grasses and sedges. Many-seeded capsules show much less evolutionary differentiation in the groups in which they occur than do achenes, nuts, or other few-seeded types of fruits.

The middle position in the reproductive scale is occupied by the more advanced thallophytes with oögamy and resistant resting spores, and by a considerable proportion of seed plants, while in the highest position are the angiosperms which are cross-pollinated by insects and have fruits adapted to dispersal by animals. In the latter a high selective value is placed on devices for attracting animals or for promoting the transport of pollen and seeds. Since diversity among animals is much greater than among climatic and edaphic conditions, many more adaptive gene combinations are possible in plants which rely on animals for their vital reproductive functions. We should expect, therefore, to find the most rapid evolutionary rates and the greatest diversity of adaptive devices in plants which are either insect pollinated, or have methods of seed dispersal by animals, or both. This explains to a large extent the evolutionary diversity and plasticity of such families as the Leguminosae, Malvaceae, Labiatae, Compositae, Gramineae, and Orchidaceae. It explains also the fact that this diversity has affected principally or entirely the organs involved in the dispersal by animals. Thus in the Orchidaceae and Asclepiadaceae pollination is by insects but seed dispersal by wind, hence the perianth is very diverse and specialized but the capsule uniform and relatively un-specialized. In the Gramineae, on the other hand, pollination is by wind but seed dispersal usually by animals. In grasses, therefore, the floral structures connected with anthesis, namely the palea, lodicules, and anthers, are very constant, and the great diversity and evolutionary specialization is found in the floral and inflorescence structures connected with seed dispersal.

The present discussion can be summarized in the form of the following hypothesis. Rates of evolution are determined primarily by the relation between the evolving population and its environment, and secondarily by forces inherent in the population itself. If all of the selective environmental forces acting on the population are constant, evolution will slow down until it stops at a level which represents the attainment in the population as a whole of the set of gene combinations which gives it the best adaptation to the environment that is possible on the basis of its fundamental structure and mode of life. This evolutionary stability is a stable equilibrium, in which new mutations and gene combinations are constantly entering into the population and are being removed from it by selection.

If the environment changes, the rate of evolutionary alteration of morphological and physiological characteristics in response to this change will depend on a number of factors, of which the principal ones are:

1. The amount of genetic variability in the population in terms of heterozygosity of individuals and genetic differences between actually or potentially interbreeding races.

2. The structure of the population, whether large or small, and whether continuous and panmictic or subdivided into partly isolated subpopulations (Wright, this volume).

3. The nature of the adaptation of the population to its environment, whether generalized or specialized, and whether typical or extreme in relation to the adaptive norm for the group to which the population belongs. The more general is the initial adaptation, and the less it depends on structures that are divergent or aberrant in relation to the characteristics of the group to which the population belongs, the greater are the evolutionary possibilities.

4. The ease or difficulty, determined by the number and extent of the genetic changes needed, of adaptation in the direction of the changing environment. If the environmental change produces a new series of unoccupied ecological niches, then that group of organisms which possesses characteristics most nearly adapting them to those conditions will expand and become diversified in these unsaturated environments.

5. The position of the organism in the hierarchy of nutrition; the higher the position the more rapid and extensive the evolutionary change.

6. The position of the organism in the hierarchy of reproductive adaptations.

7. The intrinsic mutation rate.

The various points of this hypothesis can be tested on a variety of organisms, both plant and animal, by both observation and experimentation, as well as by gathering significant data from available literature. If they are correct, then an intimate study of any group of organisms in relation to these points should enable us to determine their evolutionary possibilities and to accelerate greatly their rate of evolution, provided that the group can be handled experimentally. As Haldane has stated elsewhere in this volume, the eventual control of evolution by man is not an impossible goal.

REFERENCES

Babcock, E. B. 1947. *The Genus Crepis.* University of California Publ. Bot., *21* and *22,* 1030 pp.

Burbanck, M. P. 1944. Cytological and taxonomic studies in the genus Brodiaea. II. *Bot. Gaz., 105,* 339-345.

Chandler, M. E. J. 1923. The geological history of the genus Stratiotes: An account of the evolutionary changes which have occurred within the genus during Tertiary and Quaternary times. *Quart. Jour. Geol. Soc. London, 79,* 117-138.

Clausen, J., D. D. Keck, and W. M. Hiesey. 1941. Experimental Taxonomy. *Carnegie Inst. Wash. Yearbook* No. 40, 160-170.

——. 1947. Heredity of Geographically and Ecologically isolated races. *Am. Nat., 81,* 114-133.

Elias, M. K. 1942. Tertiary prairie grasses and other herbs from the high plains. *Spec. Papers Geol. Soc. Amer.,* No. 41. 176 pp.

Florin, R. 1944. Die Koniferen des Oberkarbons und des unteren Perms, Vol. 7. *Paleontographica, 85(B),* 457-654.

Lewis, H., and C. Epling. 1946. Formation of a diploid species of Delphinium by hybridization. *Am. Jour. Bot., 33,* 21s-22s.

McMinn, H. E. 1942. A systematic study of the genus Ceanothus. In *Ceanothus,* publ. Santa Barbara Botanic Garden, pp. 131-279.

Reid, C., and E. M. Reid. 1915. *The Pliocene floras of the Dutch-Prussian border.* Mededeel. van de Rijksopsporing van Delftstoffen, No. 6. 178 pp.

Shmalgausen, I. I. 1946. *Faktory Evoliutsii.* Moscow, 397 pp.

Simpson, G. G. 1944. *Tempo and Mode in Evolution.* 237 pp. New York, Columbia University Press.

Stebbins, G. L., Jr. 1945. Evidence for abnormally slow rates of evolution, with particular reference to the higher plants and the genus Drosophila. *Lloydia, 8,* 84-102.

——. 1947. Evidence on rates of evolution from the distribution of existing and fossil plant species. *Ecological Monographs, 17,* 149-158.

· 13 ·

RATES OF EVOLUTION IN TAENIODONTS

BY BRYAN PATTERSON[1]

THE Taeniodonta are an order of mammals confined to North America and known to have ranged in time from the earliest Paleocene to the later Eocene, a span of approximately 33 million years. Once strongly suspected of close relationships with the Edentata, they are now regarded as an isolated group, probably derived from unknown Cretaceous insectivores. The order includes but one family, the Stylinodontidae, divided into two subfamilies, the Stylinodontinae and the Conoryctinae. Stylinodontines occur in all of the major divisions, or provincial ages, of the Paleocene— Puercan, Torrejonian and Tiffanian[2]—and in the Wasatchian, Bridgerian, and Uintan, which together constitute the greater part of the American continental Eocene, as currently recognized. Conoryctines, except for one poorly preserved fragment from an Early Tiffanian horizon, are confined to the Puercan and Torrejonian.

Five genera are included in the Stylinodontinae: *Wortmania* of the Puercan, *Psittacotherium* of the Torrejonian, *Lampadophorus* of the Tiffanian, *Ectoganus* of the Early and Middle Wasatchian, and *Stylinodon* of the Late Wasatchian to Uintan. Fragmentary evidence (Gazin, 1941) indicates that a form intermediate between *Wortmania* and *Psittacotherium* occurs in the Dragon, Early Torrejonian, local fauna. *Stylinodon* is found in deposits of three successive provincial ages; it is quite possible that more than one genus may be distinguished in the future within this time span, but the specimens now known are, for the most part, not directly comparable and are really inadequate to prove even a specific difference between the earliest and the latest representatives.

These genera appear to form a direct phyletic series. Indeed, Wortman, an earlier student of the group, enthusiastically claimed that they constitute "... as complete and perfect a phylum as has ever been deciphered within the whole range of paleontology." This was a somewhat sweeping

---

[1] Curator of Fossil Mammals, Chicago Natural History Museum.

[2] The standard work on the North American continental Tertiary (Wood et al., 1941) recognizes two additional Paleocene provincial ages: the Dragonian (post-Puercan and pre-Torrejonian), and the Clarkforkian (post-Tiffanian). Further study of the "Dragonian" by Gazin (1941) has demonstrated, however, that there are two local faunas of this supposed age; one, the Wagonroad, slightly later than the typical Puerco; the other, the Dragon proper, somewhat earlier than the typical Torrejon. Analysis of the post-Torrejonian Paleocene faunas fails to demonstrate a clear-cut division that would warrant recognition of more than one provincial age. For these reasons, Dragonian and Clarkforkian are not used here.

statement, considering what was even then known of the horse sequence, but it was by no means completely unjustified. Although poorly documented in comparison with such records as those of the horses, titanotheres, camels, and proboscideans, stylinodontine history nevertheless does provide the longest and most complete direct phylogeny that dates from the beginning of the Age of Mammals. The evolutionary trends in the group, particularly as expressed in the dentition, may be interpreted and indeed seem explicable only in terms of rather recent and, for the most part, entirely independent work carried out by several geneticists, anatomists, and paleontologists. The very paucity of the documentary evidence is in itself interesting, as it suggests, however tentatively, that in this group the sizes of successive populations were at most medium rather than large. Any information bearing on the rates of evolution in such populations is a desideratum in paleontology. That the record of these populations should demonstrate part of a series of quantum steps in evolution is a fortunate circumstance that considerably enhances the interest attached to it.

The three known genera of the Conoryctinae—*Onychodectes* of the Puercan and *Conoryctella* of the earlier and *Conoryctes* of the later Torrejonian—also appear to form a direct ancestral series. Their less spectacular evolution provides an interesting and instructive contrast to that of their more remarkable relatives.

In order to provide an adequate background for the discussion that follows, it will first be necessary to present some description of the trends observed. This has been summarized from a more extended account of these animals that will be published elsewhere (Patterson, in press).

I am indebted to Mr. D. Dwight Davis for access to a manuscript of his paper that appears in this volume, and to him and to Mr. Robert F. Inger for critical comments. The figures are by Mr. John Conrad Hansen, based in part on preliminary sketches by me.

EVOLUTIONARY TRENDS IN THE STYLINODONTINAE

Dentition

Reference to Figures 1 and 2 will reveal that knowledge of the dentition is not complete. The upper teeth are somewhat better known than the lower; the cusps of the cheek teeth of *Wortmania* are unfortunately not fully revealed by the specimens so far discovered; certain teeth are unknown in this form, in *Lampadophorus*, and in *Stylinodon*, and no unworn crown of the latter has yet come to light. Nevertheless, the broad outlines of the trends followed are quite clear, and there is an amount of information available on details that might not readily be apparent to one unaccustomed to dealing with paleontological evidence.

Wortmania differed from the conoryctine genera in two conspicuous dental features: the number of incisors had been reduced to one on each side above and below, and the canines were markedly larger. These are diagnostic characters for the subfamily, which was thus distinguished, although not by any means fully differentiated, at the time of first appearance in the record. Another diagnostic character, the structure of the claws, was almost fully expressed (see p. 254). The canines, in addition to being absolutely larger, were relatively larger in comparison with the other teeth, and the same is true of the incisors.[3] They showed some indications of a posterior buttress and were completely invested by enamel,

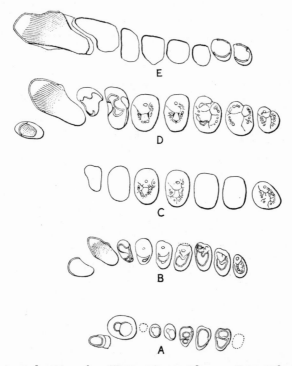

Figure 1. Left upper dentition of A, *Wortmania otariidens*; B, *Psittacotherium multifragum*; C, *Lampadophorus expectatus*; D, *Ectoganus gliriformis*; and E, *Stylinodon* sp. × 1/2. Outlines represent alveoli. C and E from single specimens in Chicago Natural History Museum; A, B and D composite drawings from specimens in the American Museum of Natural History and the United States National Museum. In B and D, worn canines and incisors have been combined with unworn cheek teeth in order to bring out the more important characteristics of each; such a combination would not have occurred in nature.

[3] Owing to the small number and fragmentary condition of the known specimens, it is impossible to obtain adequate quantitative data in support of statements such as this. They are of necessity based on observation, but every effort has been made to keep them as objective as possible.

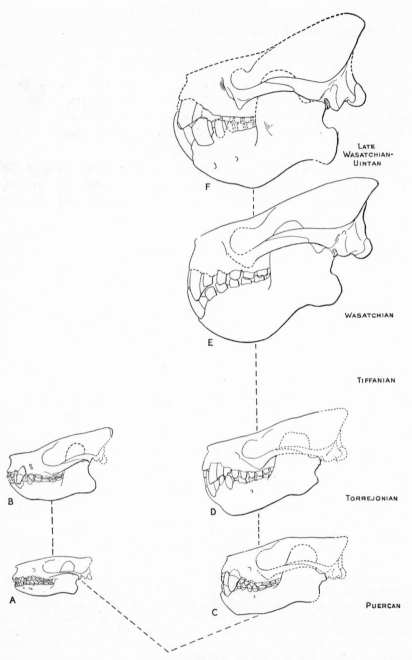

LATE
WASATCHIAN-
UINTAN

WASATCHIAN

TIFFANIAN

TORREJONIAN

PUERCAN

Figure 2. Skulls of A, *Onychodectes tisonensis*; B, *Conoryctes comma*; C, *Wortmania*;
D, *Psittacotherium*; E, *Ectoganus*; and F, *Stylinodon*, × 1/5. *Lampadophorus* is too poorly known
for inclusion. A and B slightly modified from Matthew; C-F composite drawings based upon
specimens in the American Museum of Natural History, Chicago Natural History Museum,
United States National Museum, and Yale Peabody Museum of Natural History. The dashed
lines indicate phylogeny.

although this was thin on their posterior faces and rapidly worn off.[4] Crown structure in the molars is unfortunately not fully known; rather well worn specimens show that there was a large internal cusp (protocone) and suggest that a small postero-external cusp (metacone) was present in addition to the larger antero-external one (paracone). A cingulum ran from the protocone around the external part of the tooth. M^{1-2} (M^3 is unknown) were three-rooted; the roots were very long and well separated, the internal being stouter and rather longer than the two external. The enamel extended a little farther up over the internal root than over the external ones. From this last character it may be inferred that the upper molars resembled those of the conoryctines, although to a lesser degree, in having the inner portion of each crown somewhat higher than the outer. Such an arrangement indicates an outrolling of the tooth in the course of eruption and abrasion; this or the reverse, inrolling, are not uncommon phenomena among the Mammalia. The opposing lower teeth tend to roll in an opposite direction, although the action is usually by no means as strikingly apparent. Inheritance of this character by *Wortmania* was of significance in the later evolution of the group, as will appear. The premolars were essentially bicuspid, the inner cusps, and also each tooth as a whole, progressively increasing in size posteriorly. All the lower and the first two upper premolars were single rooted; the lower appear to have been implanted transversely.

The subsequent history of the canines in the subfamily is remarkable. *Psittacotherium* shows a great advance over *Wortmania* in the structure of these teeth, being indeed closer in this respect to the terminal members of the series than to its predecessor. The enamel was limited to the anterior half of the tooth, which, because of the presence of this resistant substance, was at a higher level than the posterior flat, enamel-free portion, the equivalent of the incipient buttress in *Wortmania*. The canines thus became in effect double-action tools, the anterior portions capable of cutting and the posterior of grinding, a combination that long ago attracted Cope's attention (1884, pp. 190-195), and to which there is, to the best of my knowledge, no exact parallel among the rest of the Mammalia. In comparison with *Wortmania*, these teeth were enormously lengthened, the base of the root of the upper carried, in young animals, back to a point medial to the orbit and that of the lower well down into the symphysis of the mandible; the enamel extended over more than half of their lengths. Although not of fully persistent growth, they, or rather the enamel bands they bore, were evidently long enough to have maintained the peculiar shapes of the occlusal surfaces until well on in their bearers' lives. Persistent growth of the canines, including the enamel bands, appears to have

---

[4] Of the three specimens of this tooth known to me, one, an upper, shows the complete investment.

been attained before the stage represented by *Lampadophorus* of the Tiffanian. About the only change in crown pattern that occurred from Torrejonian to Uintan was a progressive narrowing of the posterior portion and apparently a slight relative increase in total size.

The premaxillary bone seems to have been peculiarly liable to post-mortem breakage in this group; at any rate the tooth-bearing part of it is hardly ever preserved. In consequence, the history of the upper incisors is rather poorly known. Such clues as are available indicate a close parallel to that of the canines, namely confinement of the enamel to the anterior faces and great increase in length by Torrejonian, succeeded by attainment of the rootless condition by Early Wasatchian if not Tiffanian. The muzzle in all stylinodontines was wide, the canines were set widely apart and the upper incisors were separated from them and perhaps from each other as well. The lower incisors followed a rather different course and one difficult to interpret. In *Wortmania* and *Psittacotherium*, they were comparable in size with their fellows of the upper series, whereas in *Ectoganus* and *Stylinodon*, they were reduced in size, apparently had no persistent enamel, were displaced posteriorly to a position medial to the posterior portions of the canines, and abraded during life in a curiously rounded way. Yet they appear to have been rootless.

As stated above, the crown structure of unworn molars is not known in *Wortmania*. *Psittacotherium* had short wide teeth in the upper series, consisting of a large paracone, a much smaller metacone, and a large protocone. The latter was connected to the bases of the external cusps by low ridges, remnants of the cingulum seen in *Wortmania*, that exhibited a tendency toward the development of small cuspules on their rims. The first of the series (M^1) appears to have been the peak tooth, certain characters, e.g. size of the metacone, decreasing posteriorly from it. The lower molars consisted of two parallel, transversely aligned crests formed from four cusps—the antero-external and -internal (proto- and metaconid) and the postero-external and -internal (hypo- and entoconid). The ridges connecting these cusps also show a tendency to develop cuspules. These structural details were largely confined to the tips of the crowns, becoming obscured by only a moderate amount of wear. The roots were coalesced to a considerable extent. The enamel extended, in the form of an incipient band, farther upward on the internal than on the external faces of the upper molars, and farther downward on the external than on the internal faces of the lowers.

The ensuing history of the molars is not completely known, although its main features are clear enough. The crowns of the upper teeth became longer antero-posteriorly relative to their widths. Advances in crown complication took place, but remained limited to the superficial part of the crown. The metacones became enlarged, a postero-internal cusp (the hypocone) came into existence,[5] the transverse ridges moved apart, the central valley enlarged in consequence and there was a very considerable further development of cuspules, not only on the rims of the lophs but also on the slopes of the cones. Less information is available on the lower molars; about all that can be said concerning their crown structure is that in the development of cuspules they fully kept pace with the upper molars. The roots of both uppers and lowers underwent a very considerable amount of change. Those of *Lampadophorus* were longer than those of *Psittacotherium* and almost entirely coalesced, the relation of tooth to alveolus being that of a peg to its socket. Those of *Ectoganus*, in turn, were completely coalesced and longer still, unworn teeth being approximately as deep as in the succeeding *Stylinodon*. This terminal member of the series had rootless cheek teeth, the change from the rooted to the rootless condition clearly having taken place within Wasatchian time. A comparable amount of change occurred in the distribution of enamel. *Lampadophorus* differed only slightly from *Psittacotherium*; the bands of enamel on the internal faces of the upper and the external of the lower extended a little farther, and in one species two prongs at the bases of the enamel on the opposite faces represented the beginnings of a second band. *Psittacotherium* was evidently still in the outrolling (upper) and inrolling (lower) stages of molar eruption and abrasion, and, indeed, appears to have increased this tendency beyond the stage seen in *Wortmania*. In *Ectoganus*, the first band extended well toward the extremities of the roots, the second, spearheaded in its advance by prongs such as those seen in *Lampadophorus*, for a somewhat shorter distance. No trace of rolling eruption persisted, this earlier trend being completely reversed. Enamel on the anterior and posterior faces did not lengthen. At a certain stage of wear, therefore, these teeth are almost identical in pattern with those of *Stylinodon* (cf. Figs. 1E, 3E), in which both bands were of persistent growth. As already stated, no unworn tooth of *Stylinodon* is known. There can be little doubt, however, that the crown in the molars was originally entirely invested by enamel. The continuously growing molars of *Stylinodon* convey, at first glance, the impression of a considerable difference between this form and its immediate predecessor. Actually, however, an advance as great, if not greater, in development of enamel bands took place between *Lampadophorus* and *Ectoganus* than between the latter and *Stylinodon* (Fig. 3). When a series of quantitative steps leads to a qualitative change, attention is very likely to be focused on the latter rather than upon the stages in the former.

Starting from the rather simple conditions seen in *Wortmania*, the premolars evolved in different directions, the history of the first and second

---

[5] This cusp may have been present in rudimentary form in *Psittacotherium*, but known specimens are too worn for certainty on this point.

contrasting quite sharply with that of the third and fourth. In the first two the crown pattern remained simple, never consisting of more than two cusps—the external paracone and paraconid and the internal protocone and metaconid.[6] In P^1 and P_1, the external cusp was elongated antero-posteriorly to form an external ridge that became progressively longer in succeeding genera. P^2, in at least one specimen of *Psittacotherium*, had a posterior ridge connecting the protocone to the base of the paracone and bearing one or more cuspules. This tendency appears to have been eliminated in later forms; there is no trace of it in *Ectoganus*. The roots so far as can be determined from the evidence, were never divided. In *Psittacotherium* and possibly in *Lampadophorus* the root of the first was shorter than that of the second, and also those of the third and fourth, but by the stage represented by *Ectoganus* it had become longer than that of any of the other cheek teeth. P^2 and P_2 (later P^1 and P_1) were longer rooted than P^{3-4} and P_{3-4}, and these in turn were longer rooted than the molars. The enamel, even in *Psittacotherium*, extended much farther up on the external sides of P^1 and P_1 than on the internal sides, where this

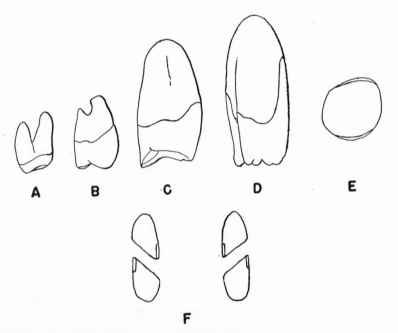

Figure 3. Posterior left upper cheek teeth of A, *Wortmania*; B, *Psittacotherium*; C, *Lampado-phorus*; and D, *Ectoganus*. E, crown view of upper molar of *Ectoganus* after the tooth has been worn beyond the complete enamel investment (cf. *Stylinodon*, Fig. 1, E). × 1/1. F, hypothetical illustration of interlocking chisel edges that would have resulted from unequal growth of external and internal enamel bands on the molars.

[6] The homology of this cusp is not quite clear.

{ 250 }

substance did not become involved in the increasing hypsodonty of the tooth as a whole and was therefore rapidly abraded away. The combination of these trends culminated, in *Stylinodon*, in first premolars that were essentially thin, antero-posteriorly elongated, cutting edges molded around the canines and complementary in function to them. P^2 and P_2 did not elongate antero-posteriorly and the enamel on the internal sides was considerably more extensive. Nevertheless, if we may judge from one specimen of *Stylinodon*, the internal enamel of this latest member of the group did not participate in the complete hypsodonty of the tooth but became worn off during life. The evolutionary history of the external and internal enamel bands of P^{1-2} was thus very different from that of the molars.

The third and fourth premolars had a history that rather closely resembled that of the molars. Progressive changes in root structure, external and internal enamel bands and increasing length were almost exactly comparable. Changes in crown structure were also comparable, up to a point. P^{3-4} of *Psittacotherium* resembled the molars in the possession of ridges connecting the protocone to the anterior and posterior sides of the base of the paracone, and differed from them in the absence of metacones and in the lesser development of cuspules on the ridges. The corresponding teeth of *Lampadophorus* possessed small metacones and numerous cuspules on the ridges, being essentially comparable therefore to the molars of *Psittacotherium*. No advance was registered between *Lampadophorus* and *Ectoganus*, P^{3-4} in the two agreeing almost cusp for cusp and groove for groove. This is a striking example of evolutionary stagnation, especially in view of the fact that the molars of *Ectoganus* (and, very probably, *Lampadophorus* to a somewhat lesser degree) had well developed metacones and separate hypocones. Unworn crowns are unfortunately unknown in *Stylinodon*. The lower teeth followed a similar course. The posterior portion, or talonid, was incipiently developed on P_4 in *Psittacotherium*; cuspules have not been observed, although no entirely unworn teeth are known. The talonid of *Lampadophorus* was almost as large as that of the molars on P_3 as well as on P_4; both it and the trigonid bore cuspules, but an entoconid was not developed to any extent. *Ectoganus* was practically indistinguishable from its predecessor as far as the crowns of these teeth were concerned.

There was a decided change in the size gradient of the cheek teeth. In *Wortmania*, M^{1-2} and M_{1-2} appear to have been the peak teeth, the sizes of the others diminishing away from them. The peak shifted anteriorly in the succeeding genera, until, in *Stylinodon*, there was an antero-posterior gradient away from P^1 and P_1. Cement on the cheek teeth first appeared definitely in *Lampadophorus*[7] and was well developed in the later forms.

---

[7] There is a trace of it on a specimen of *Psittacotherium*.

It was deposited mainly on the enamel-free anterior and posterior sides of the cheek teeth and to a lesser extent on the canines and incisors.

Skull

The skull is imperfectly known in all the genera here discussed. Available specimens are, with one exception, incomplete, and are often badly crushed. The figures given here (Figure 2) are restorations, each based on more than one individual, with allowance made for distortion. It is to be hoped that they are not too wide of the mark. Knowledge of the mandible is in a more satisfactory state, as may be seen.

Wortmania had a skull that was still of a rather primitive stamp, but which nevertheless clearly foreshadowed, especially in the short face and massive jaw, the profound changes that took place in its descendants. In succeeding forms the face became even shorter, not by an overall reduction, but rather through a continued shortening of the premaxillaries. The zygomatic arches were rounded and relatively heavy by the *Psittacotherium* stage, and appear to have maintained a fairly constant relationship to total skull size thereafter. The occiput is unfortunately unknown in earlier genera. In the later, it was very high, triangular, and extremely broad at the base, the width in *Stylinodon* being equal to about three-fourths of the total skull length. What is known of the cranial roof in earlier forms suggests that there was a progressive increase in height and width of the occiput within the phylum. Increasing height of the occiput, of course, progressed hand in hand with larger and larger temporal fossae, more prominent sagittal crests, stouter coronoid processes of the mandibles, and greater areas for origin and insertion of the temporal muscles. It will be noted from Figure 2 that there was an apparent decrease, or rather failure to increase proportionately, in the sizes of the orbits. This may possibly have been associated with increase of the canines, which pushed back between and partly above them.

In the mandibles the symphysis became progressively more massive, deepening and lengthening to accommodate the increasing canines, and the coronoid processes became longer antero-posteriorly, stouter and more vertical with respect to the horizontal ramus. One curious feature that persisted throughout the evolutionary history from *Psittacotherium* on was the presence of a conspicuous pit that extended forward into the posterior part of the symphysis at the level of the posterior premolars. This pit underwent an increase in depth *pari passu* with the increase in length of the symphysis. It may be interpreted as indicating the place of origin of the genioglossus muscle of the tongue, evidently a highly important organ in this group. The pit maintained its original position on the symphysis, the bone growing back beyond it. The condyle was wide and moderately convex, the articular surface extending over to face posteriorly as well as dorsally in all forms. The glenoid cavity was correspondingly wide, almost flat, and with only a bare indication of a post-glenoid process. The whole permitted a wide gape and some lateral movement, but very little antero-posterior movement. The latter must have been limited, in any case, by the closely interlocking canines, the former facilitated by the gaps between canines and incisors. The angle increased progressively in size.

Post-cranial Skeleton

Exceedingly little is known of the history of most parts of the post-cranial skeleton. Fragments included in one specimen usually represent different parts from those included in another, or are so crushed as to prevent profitable comparison. As a result, knowledge is really limited to the anterior extremity and especially to the fore foot. The manus is partially known in *Psittacotherium* and *Stylinodon* (Fig. 4, B and C). A considerable amount of change took place between the two. The lunar widened distally to rest upon the entire proximal surface of the enlarged magnum. The centrale was displaced medially and certainly reduced, if not eliminated entirely. The third metacarpal no longer rested partly upon the fourth and had lost its contacts with the unciform and trapezoid.[8] Judging from the size of the facet on the unciform, the fifth metacarpal became greatly reduced in size, and this was very probably true of the

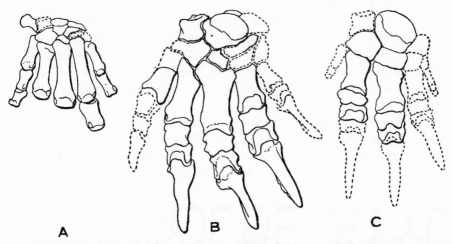

A   **B**   **C**

Figure 4. Right manus of A, *Onychodectes tisonensis*, × 3/4; B, *Psittacotherium multifragum*, × 1/2; and C, *Stylinodon mirus*, × 1/5. A and B from Matthew (B slightly modified), C from specimen in Yale Peabody Museum of Natural History.

[8] So far as can be seen in the only known specimen of the manus of *Stylinodon*, now mounted in a plaster block.

first also. Reduction of the lateral and medial digits in *Onychodectes* (Fig. 4A) suggests that this was a trend inherited from the common ancestry of both phyla. The fifth metatarsal of *Stylinodon* was similarly reduced, to judge from the facet on the cuboid. The ungual phalanges were large, laterally compressed claws. The few foot bones of *Wortmania* that have been found fortunately include an ungual. This reveals that in this character, as in the size of the canine, *Wortmania* stood in sharp contrast to *Onychodectes*, in which the unguals were small and pointed. As will be discussed, early acquisition of compressed claws and enlarged canines appears largely to have determined the course of stylinodontine history.

INTERPRETATION OF STYLINODONTINE TRENDS

More than half a century ago, Bateson (1892, 1894) advanced the view that teeth should be regarded as a system rather than as single units. This suggestion received scant attention until Butler commenced a series of studies (1937, 1939a, 1939b, 1941, 1946) that has gone far toward establishing its validity. Butler (1939a) regarded the dentition as a morphogenetic field with an antero-posterior axis, characterized in the Mammalia by regions of incisivation, caninisation, and molarisation. Within each region the characteristic features are most strongly expressed in one area or peak, i.e. one or more teeth, decreasing in degree of expression away from it. The regions may extend, shift, or concentrate their influence in the course of evolution, and may follow independent evolutionary trends. Butler has adduced much observational evidence in support of this view, which is in itself in accord with and was inspired by work carried out by embryologists. Dahlberg (1945) has applied the concept to the human dentition, but thus far no phyletic sequence of considerable duration and reasonable completeness has been interpreted in terms of it. Such an attempt is made here, with results that, to me at least, are most illuminating.

Tooth history in the Stylinodontinae is hardly understandable except as a resultant of the interaction of gene changes that exerted a regional effect upon the developmental field represented by the dentition as a whole. Characters appearing first in the caninisation or in the molarisation region spread through the field, the degrees of their phenotypic expression depending in part upon the structure of the various teeth in the series (which, once established, they in turn affected), in part upon time of appearance in ontogeny, and therefore, in the final analysis, upon selection affecting the processes of growth through action on the end products. The predominant characters manifested in the caninisation region were increase in size, enlargement in the transverse diameter, restriction of enamel to the anterior (external) face and acquisition of persistent growth in which the enamel band was included. Those in the molarisation region were increasing complexity of crown structure, enlargement in the antero-posterior diameter, and rolling eruption, which involved the lengthening of the enamel on the internal (upper) and external (lower) sides of the teeth. The interaction of the two may clearly be observed in the premolars.

Wortmania displayed the contrast between the two regions character-istic of the Mammalia generally. The cheek teeth exhibited the usual gradient in size and complexity of structure to and from the peak molar. Significantly, however, the canines were enlarged relative to the cheek teeth and the incisors were included in this tendency. Thenceforward, the region of incisivation was subordinated to that of caninisation, the upper incisors evolving in harmony with the canines, the lower undergoing re-duction in the later stages of their history.

As already noted, the very rapid advance in the evolution of the canines that took place between the stages represented by *Wortmania* and *Psit-tacotherium* involved the acquisition of all caninisation characters except development of the fully rootless condition. This advance was ac-companied by an extension of the caninisation region posteriorly. The anterior premolars, in particular, were caught up in this and, in *Psittacotherium*, had become much enlarged and widened transversely, thus beginning the reversal of the primitive size gradient in the cheek teeth. Their roots had become longer, particularly those of P^2 and P_2, which exceeded in length the roots of P^{3-4} and P_{3-4}, as these in turn ex-ceeded those of the molars. This last feature may be attributed in part to extension of the caninisation region, specifically as regards the greater length of the premolar as compared to molar roots, but it is probable that increase in gross size of *Psittacotherium* over *Wortmania* also played a part in the process (cf. Simpson, 1944, pp. 86-87). The relatively short roots of P^1 and P_1 may be interpreted as a character associated with a trend in the molarisation region toward reduction of these teeth inherited from the common ancestry of the family as a whole. This trend evidently con-tinued in the Conoryctinae, resulting in the apparent loss of P^1 and the great reduction of P_{1-2} in *Conoryctes* (Matthew, 1937, p. 251), but was halted and then reversed in the Stylinodontinae by extension of the caninisation region. At the stage represented by *Psittacotherium* the re-versal was well under way, but all specializations of the earlier trend had not yet been eliminated. The disposition of enamel on P^1 and P_1, and on P^2 and P_2 to a much lesser extent, had begun to follow the canine pattern of extension of the external band and curtailment of the growth of the internal. The rapidity with which the two anterior premolars were af-fected by the caninisation characters is explicable on the assumption that these teeth were no longer a fully functional part of the molarisation region, and therefore that no profound genetic disturbance was involved in their "transfer" from the one region to the other. The roots of P³-M³ and M₁₋₃ had begun to unite.[9]

The molarisation region was evolving concurrently and extending its influence anteriorly. In *Psittacotherium*, cuspules had begun to appear on the transverse ridges of P³⁻⁴ and, presumably, on the crests of P₃₋₄, and this influence reached fleetingly to the posterior portion of P², as is shown by one individual. The enamel had extended farther up on the teeth, especially on the internal faces of the upper teeth and the external faces of the lower. This resulted in part from further expression of the molarisation character of rolling eruption inherited from the common ancestry with the Conoryctinae. The fact that these incipient enamel bands were actually longer on the posterior premolars than on the molars indicates that their extension was also in part a result of the increase in total length discussed above and of the expansion of the crown into the root, developments that provided an increased area for enamel growth.

The stage represented by *Lampadophorus* is unfortunately poorly known. There is evidence that the caninisation character of continuous growth had been achieved in the canine. Almost all trace of separate roots had been obliterated in the posterior upper premolars. These teeth had become straighter, indicating that selection had brought about reversal of the molarisation character of rolling eruption and initiated the extension of caninisation influence to the molar region. Increase in the total length of these teeth over the stage represented by *Psittacotherium* was little if any greater than could be accounted for on the assumption of association with increase in gross size; evidently caninisation was just beginning to exert an influence in this direction. The molarisation region, to judge from M³, had been affected by a change in growth that resulted in a relative increase of the antero-posterior diameters of the molars. This permitted a greater degree of phenotypic expression of the factor or factors for metacone and for hypocone than was exhibited by the narrower molars of *Psittacotherium*. The posterior premolars strongly suggest that further cone development in the molars was directly associated with the increase in width. These teeth had not been affected by the relative increase in antero-posterior diameter and their metacones and hypocones were rudimentary. In both ratio of antero-posterior to transverse diameter and cone development they were closely comparable to the molars of *Psittacotherium*. The molarisation character of cuspule development continued to extend its influence forward, P³⁻⁴ being almost fully comparable, in this respect, to the molars.

By the *Ectoganus* stage, caninisation influence, now reinforced by

[9] Actually, the crowns appear to have expanded into and obliterated the individuality of the roots (Fig. 3, A and B), possibly following upon concentration and enlargement of the pulp cavity.

acquisition of continuous growth, had extended posteriorly to a conspicuous degree. The roots of P^1 and P_1 had become longer than those of the
other cheek teeth; in fact, a tooth-length gradient decreasing posteriorly
from the canine had become established. The total lengths of all cheek
teeth had increased notably. This was not accompanied by any marked increase in gross size of *Ectoganus* over *Lampadophorus*, and may, therefore, be attributed almost wholly to extension of the regional influence.
The external enamel bands of P^{1-2} and P_{1-2} extended almost to the bases of
the roots. The internal bands of P^1 and P_1 were strictly limited in growth
and were rapidly worn off during life, resulting in teeth that, so far as
enamel distribution was concerned, were decidedly canine-like. These
teeth had increased very considerably in the antero-posterior diameter of
the external border; selection had made great progress over the stage seen
in *Psittacotherium* toward molding them into cutting adjuncts of the
canines. P^2 and P_2 had become the peak teeth in size. In structure they
had remained purely bicuspid, exhibiting no trace of the other cones,
cuspules, and ridges or crests that characterized the teeth posterior to
them. The specimen of *Psittacotherium* referred to above, in which a
posterior transverse ridge and one or more cuspules occurred on P^2,
exemplifies an extension of molarisation influence, or rather its phenotypic
expression, that did not become established.

In the region of molarisation it would appear that relatively little change
in crown pattern had taken place. To judge from a comparison of M^3 in
Lampadophorus and *Ectoganus*, some further accentuation of metacones
and hypocones appears to have occurred. As already noted, no change in
the crown structure of P^{3-4} had taken place between the stages represented
by these two genera. Such stagnation suggests either that the molarisation
character of increase in antero-posterior diameter had been slow to extend
its influence to the replacement dentition (upper milk molars show that
it had affected the posterior deciduous teeth), or that caninisation influence leading to development of a crown that was short in the antero-
posterior diameter and long in the transverse had inhibited such growth.
Unworn posterior premolars of *Stylinodon* should settle the question;
meanwhile, the former alternative appears more probable.

The changes in the distribution of enamel on P^3 and P_3 to M^3 and M_3
that took place between *Lampadophorus* and *Ectoganus* are of great
interest. The earlier molarisation character of rolling eruption had resulted
in a greater development of enamel on the internal faces of the upper
teeth and on the external faces of the lower. When continuing caninisation influence led to further increase in total tooth length and enamel
deposition, these areas had a head start, so to speak, toward the formation
of bands. The enamel on the opposite faces, however, almost at once
began to form bands also. The first traces of these were the prongs met

with in the species of *Lampadophorus* referred to above. By the *Ectoganus* stage these prongs were not far behind the main band in their progress toward the extremity of the root (Fig. 3D). Selection evidently operated to keep the growths of opposite bands from becoming too uneven. Had the internal bands in the upper teeth and the external in the lower seriously outstripped their opposites, the result would have been the formation, with wear, of opposing chisels, whose bevelled edges would have faced externally in the upper teeth and internally in the lowers (Fig. 3F). Such an arrangement would have made lateral chewing, a motion evidently employed to some extent by these animals (see above), mechanically inefficient, thus imposing a handicap upon them.

Before the final stage in the history of the group had been reached, the caninisation character of persistent growth had spread throughout the dentition. A size gradient that decreased posteriorly from the canine had become established, and P^1 and P_1 had been completely transformed in structure and function, bringing them into close harmony with the canines. The entire dentition of *Stylinodon* conveys the impression of being a mere appendage to the dominant canines, and the remnants of molarisation influence—the more or less quadrangular molars and the presence of two enamel bands—appear, in worn teeth, to be insignificant indeed. Such remodeling of a nearly complete series to conform with the functioning of one dominant tooth is without a close parallel among the rest of the Mammalia.

This record of the action and interaction of gene-controlled ontogenetic reactions upon a field provides an interesting illustration of the process of homeosis at work over a long period of time.

It is evident that the canines were a controlling influence in the evolutionary trends that were followed by the skull, as well as by the dentition. The increase in depth and length of the symphysis and in the massiveness of the mandible as a whole were obvious direct adjustments to enlarging canines. Clearly associated, and evolving *pari passu*, were such changes as increase in height and basal width of the occiput and enlargement of the various fossae, crests, and processes. Shortening of the premaxillaries brought the canines, the principal biting teeth, to the front of the mouth. The apparent failure of the orbits to increase in size proportionately has already been alluded to. Progressive development of the pit for the tongue muscles appears to have been associated indirectly with increase in canine size, the symphysis increasing posteriorly around it.

Such evolutionary trends as can be observed in the manus—suppression of the centrale, enlargement of the magnum, readjustment of metacarpal contacts and decrease in size of digit V (and almost surely of digit *I* as well)—may be interpreted as leading to the development of a progressively more efficient digging or tearing foot of the general type seen in the Edentata and Pholidota (Simpson, 1931, pp. 315-319).

COMPARISON OF THE CONORYCTINAE AND STYLINODONTINAE

It is fortunate for the purpose of this study that the order contains two phyla, one that remained by contrast rather generalized and another that became highly specialized. By comparing, in so far as this is possible, the earliest known representatives of each, some idea may be gained of the basic characters in which the two differ. Knowledge of the Puercan *Onychodectes* and *Wortmania* is far from complete but is nevertheless un-usually extensive for such very early Tertiary forms. The following parts are known in both forms: skull, cervical centra, ulna and radius, three bones of the forefoot (the lunar, a second metacarpal, and an ungual), femur, and tibia.

The skull of *Wortmania* differs from that of *Onychodectes* in being heavier and deeper, especially in the mandible; it has a much shorter facial region, with the anterior margins of the orbits over P^{3-4} rather than over M^1, greatly enlarged canines and reduced premaxillae. I^{1-2} and $I_{1,3}$ are lost, the condyles of the mandibles are lower, and the coronoid processes and temporal fossae are much larger. Only in the structure of the cheek teeth, in which there is a lesser development of rolling eruption and in-equality of enamel distribution on external and internal faces, is *Wort-mania* less specialized than its contemporary.

The cervical centra indicate that the neck was short in both forms. The limb bones are relatively much more robust in *Wortmania*, although a fundamental resemblance to *Onychodectes* in structure is quite apparent throughout. Among the foot bones there is almost no difference other than size between the lunar in the two forms. The second metacarpal is relatively much shorter and heavier in *Wortmania* than in *Onychodectes*; and the ungual is very different, being long, high, and laterally compressed instead of small and pointed. In both metacarpal and ungual *Wortmania* displays a close resemblance to *Psittacotherium*.

This array of differences, which is rather impressive in members of phyla that may not have diverged very long prior to the Puercan, appears to be traceable to two fundamental structural developments in the stylin-odontine phylum—transformation of the unguals into claws and modifi-cation of the jaw mechanism, of which the most striking if not the con-trolling feature was the hypertrophy of the canine.

What is known of the evolution of the extremities in the Stylinodontinae reveals a progressive improvement of a digging or tearing type of limb. Effective claws are the basic requirement for such an adaptation. Once a change in this direction from a simple, pointed ungual, such as that of *Onychodectes*, had begun, the associated trends toward greater robustness and shorter metacarpals and intermediate phalanges, already under way in *Wortmania*, would ensue also. The profound effects of continued canine enlargement and jaw modification on skull form in the stylin-odontines subsequent to *Wortmania* have been outlined above. The departures seen in *Wortmania* from the primitive skull form exemplified by *Onychodectes* are readily explicable as early readjustments to this modification. Thus the deepening of the skull, particularly the anterior portion of the mandible, the reduction of the premaxillae, and presumably loss of incisors were associated with increase in size of the canines. Lowering of the condyle permitted a wider gape, thus allowing these teeth a greater freedom of action. Displacement of the orbit anteriorly and the resulting shortening of the face was a resultant of the enlargement of the temporal fossa and coronoid process (both associated with increase in size of the temporal muscle) and of a forward movement of the anterior root of the zygomatic arch (associated with a forward extension of the masseter) which gave a greater mechanical advantage to this muscle, following the progressive anterior concentration of the main biting point and the weight of the mandible. There is strong suggestive evidence that the claw was the earlier of these two basic characters to appear.

Extension of this comparison to *Conoryctes*, the later Torrejonian representative of the Conoryctinae, yields some additional information. Comparison of the skulls of the three forms by means of the Cartesian coordinate method employed by Colbert (1935, p. 191) shows that *Onychodectes* is an almost ideal structural ancestor for both the other forms (Fig. 5), and that there is, indeed, no reason to suppose that it was not on the direct ancestral line leading to *Conoryctes*.[10] There can be little doubt that the stylinodontine phylum originated from forms essentially similar to *Onychodectes* but with somewhat less advanced cheek teeth.

Of even greater interest is the number of features in the skull of *Conoryctes* that are similar in general to those of *Wortmania*, although not carried to such an extreme or expressed in precisely the same manner as in that earlier form. The canines are notably enlarged over the condition seen in *Onychodectes*, the skull (particularly the mandible) is deepened, the orbit shifted anteriorly, at least one incisor lost, the coronoid process and temporal fossa somewhat enlarged, and the anterior root of the zygoma larger and situated farther forward. This is one more illustration of the fact, familiar in paleontological work, that similar phenotypic

[10] The two genera have actually been placed in different subfamilies by some authors (Winge, 1923, pp. 128, 133; Matthew, 1937, p. 236), chiefly, it would seem, because *Onychodectes* is decidedly more primitive. This is not necessarily a valid reason for such separation (cf. footnote 13, p. 264), especially when the populations of the forms involved were not large.

effects often appear independently and often at somewhat different times in phyla that diverged from a common ancestry. In such cases the genotype of the ancestral stock may have been constituted in a way that similar effects were liable to be brought out independently in the descendants; that is, it may have been so limited in its potential phenotypic expression as to render their appearance almost probable.[11] The circumstances leading to independent appearance of such effects need not

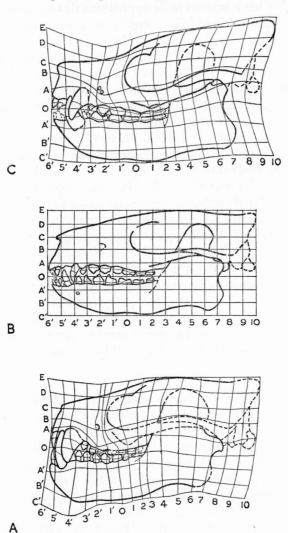

Figure 5. Cartesian coordinate diagram of skulls of A, *Wortmania;* B, *Onychodectes;* and C, *Conoryctes. Wortmania* × 1/2, the others drawn to the same basilar length.

[11] Cf. Blum's remarks at the Symposium as reported by Jepsen and Cooper, p. 9.

necessarily be the same in each phylum. In the present case, it appears likely that in the stylinodontine phylum a new mutation, resulting eventually in a major phenotypic effect elsewhere in the organism, placed a high selective value upon early expression of the cranial features under discussion. This change, I believe, was that leading to the transformation of the unguals. The intimate integration in *Wortmania* and its descendants of the effects of modifications arising from changes in the feet and in the jaw mechanism lends support to the supposition that the latter would have been of immediate selective advantage once a trend toward claws had begun. In the conoryctine phylum there was apparently very little change in the post-cranial skeleton. The few limb bone fragments of *Conoryctes* that have been discovered are not robust like those of *Wortmania* but are, on the contrary, similar in structure, proportions, and size to those of *Onychodectes* (Matthew, 1937, p. 254). Although the feet are unknown, this evidence indicates that the claws had remained simple and pointed. Differences between the skulls of *Conoryctes* and *Wortmania*, especially the unreduced premaxillaries and the posteriorly rather than anteriorly expanded canines of *Conoryctes*, show that the jaw mechanism of the conoryctines was of a rather orthodox type. Expression of the cranial features in these forms appears therefore to have come about in response to a selective advantage conferred upon them by acquisition of a more powerful jaw that, comparatively speaking, evolved more or less alone rather than in close concert with a profound and presumably rapid change in the rest of the organism. Given such conditions, the more gradual and somewhat different nature of the trend is entirely understandable.

There was clearly a profound difference in the tempo of evolution in the two phyla that almost certainly resulted from a difference in the mode, the stylinodontines being the result of a quantum shift.

EVOLUTIONARY RATES

The time that elapsed from the beginning of the earliest Paleocene Puercan to the middle part of the later Eocene Uintan, the known range of the subfamily, may be estimated at approximately 33 million years. This figure has been arrived at by assigning 17 million years to the Paleocene and 20 to the Eocene, and by dividing Eocene time equally among its three divisions, early, mid, and late, two and part of a third of which coincided with the time range of the stylinodontines. Admittedly, it is a crude estimate, but it is in accord with current placement of the only usable Tertiary radioactive date (Knopf, this volume) and with the consensus as to the duration of the Tertiary epochs (Simpson, 1947), the best that we have at the present time. So long as only four absolute dates, only one of them post-Paleozoic, can be tied in to the relative time scale, the study of evolutionary rates will be carried on under a handicap. Attempts to develop additional techniques for measuring absolute time are actively being carried on and their perfection would be one of the greatest benefits that the physical sciences could confer upon the biological. Meanwhile, the data at hand must be discussed in the light of the time estimates available, but it is encouraging to reflect that it may be possible in the not too distant future to reevaluate them in a more precise manner.

Five genera of the Stylinodontinae, regarded as being in a direct ancestral line, are known. As stated at the beginning of this paper, there was almost certainly one additional genus intermediate between *Wortmania* and *Psittacotherium*, and possibly another among the forms now lumped, in default of evidence to the contrary, under *Stylinodon*. Assuming six genera, the average organism rate (time range in years per number of genera in a phyletic series) works out at 5.5 million years per genus, or 0.18 genera per million years; assuming seven, it is 0.21 per million. Adjusting Simpson, 1944, to Simpson, 1947, the organism rate for horses is 0.13. Despite the elements of uncertainty involved, the data indicate that the average organism rate in stylinodontines was faster than in horses. Unfortunately, there are no known mammalian phyletic sequences with the same time range as the stylinodontines with which comparison could be made. A few sequences coincide with parts of this range, but in every case there is some uncertainty as to whether the relationships of the genera involved are truly phyletic. The phenacodontid condylarths of the *Desmatoclaenus*[12]*-Phenacodus* phylum provide an example of these, and one in which the phyletic relationship is rather probable. With three genera and a range from Early Torrejonian to Wasatchian, the average organism rate is 0.18 genera per million years. The rate for the stylinodontines over the same period of time, assuming a genus in the Early Torrejonian Dragon local fauna, is 0.24. Comparisons of the amount of evolutionary change that has taken place in different phyletic sequences, like the basis for estimation of organism rates, involve subjective judgement and can be at best only very rough approximations, but they nevertheless do have a certain usefulness. With due regard to the very different adaptive trends followed, I venture to suggest that the total advance from *Wortmania* to *Stylinodon* was greater than that achieved by the horses in an approximately equivalent span of time, Early

[12] The arctocyonid creodont *Protogonodon* from the Puerco is so similar to *Desmatoclaenus* in dental structure that it could perhaps be regarded as a direct ancestor. To do so would imply that at least three of the condylarth families had an independent origin within the Arctocyonidae or that *Protogonodon* is really a phenacodontid. Either alternative is possible; the matter may be left *sub judice* until there is evidence other than that provided by the dentition upon which to base an opinion.

Eocene to earliest Miocene, and indeed roughly comparable to that achieved by this group in the 60 million years of their history. The advance from *Psittacotherium* to *Ectoganus* was much greater than that from *Desmatoclaenus* to *Phenacodus*. The organism rate was the same, 0.27, in both conoryctines and stylinodontines during the Puercan and Torrejonian, but the amount of evolutionary change in the latter phylum was far greater.

The rate pattern of the dentition shows that evolution of the teeth was by no means regular, but was subject at times to sharp acceleration. The canine is typical of the pattern. Already enlarged relative to the cheek teeth by Early Paleocene, it had not then fully acquired the characteristic double-action tool structure described above. This condition was completely attained by the mid-Paleocene (Fig. 6) and the tooth as a whole was well on the way toward the hypsodont condition. The transition was, geologically speaking, extremely rapid.[13] Thereafter, evolution of the canine proceeded at a slower rate. The posterior cheek teeth show a fairly regular progression in the earlier stages, followed by rapid attainment of increased total length, equalization of enamel bands, and finally complete hypsodonty between the end of Paleocene and the end of Wasatchian time.

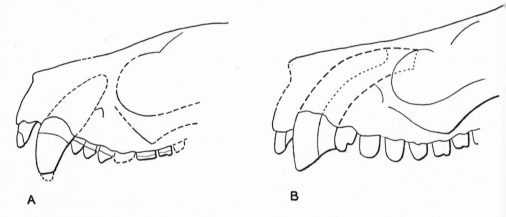

A   B

Figure 6. Demonstration of part of a quantum shift in evolution; the relation of the canine to the facial region in *Wortmania* of the Puercan, A, and in its descendant, *Psittacotherium* of the Torrejonian, B. $\times$ 1/2.

[13] Until quite recently it would have been rather orthodox procedure, on the assumption that there had been insufficient time for so profound a change, to dismiss *Wortmania* from the direct ancestry of *Psittacotherium*, and to suppose that the latter had been derived from some as yet undiscovered Early Paleocene form. Such begging of the question would be entirely unwarranted in this case; there is nothing in the known structure of *Wortmania*, other than its more primitive dentition, and this is not an objection, that conflicts with the beliefs of Wortman (1897) and Matthew (1937) that the genus was on the direct ancestral line leading to *Psittacotherium*.

These two periods of acceleration, separated by ten or more millions of years, appear to have been related events, parts of a chain of quantum steps touched off by the increase in size of the canine and the associated modifications of the jaw mechanism that started this division of the order on the road to the peculiar dental specialization attained by its later members, a trend that was in its turn linked to acquisition of the claws. Enlargement of the canine, accompanied or closely followed by a relative increase in growth of the transverse over the antero-posterior diameter, had led to the evolution of unstable forms by earliest Paleocene time; in other words, a morphological threshold had been reached. *Wortmania,* with its round-oval, relatively short-rooted canine on which enamel growth was strictly limited, was quite certainly ill-suited to the adaptive zone, whatever this may have been,[14] that was so well exploited by its descendants. The incipient posterior buttress on this tooth indicates that the genus was either on or just over the threshold of the zone. Selection at this critical stage must have been intense. Rapid canine abrasion was obviously a major hazard of life in the zone; once the enamel on this tooth had been worn away, the rudiment of the double-action tool would be lost and the animal placed at a disadvantage. Duration of life was probably rather directly dependent upon canine structure, and was perhaps shorter than in earlier forms, in which the canine was not yet as all-important a structure. Under such conditions, any mutations that resulted in lengthening of the canines and particularly in lengthening of the enamel on the external faces of these teeth would immediately be of very positive advantage to the animals in which they occurred. These would, on the average, live longer and therefore have more offspring, thus speeding the spread of the favorable mutations in the successive populations. Intense selection and rapid spread of favorable modifying mutations would continue until canine structure had reached a state of perfection sufficient to maintain the peculiar crown pattern until well on into breeding age. This condition had clearly been attained by the *Psittacotherium* stage, which thus more or less marked the end of this quantum step in the shift. That evolution of the canine was slower thereafter may be interpreted as due to a lessening in the extreme selective value of mutations tending toward its further improvement. As perfection proceeded, the structure of this tooth became a progressively less critical factor in survival. More and more non-progressive and even retrogressive individuals, in regard to the mean for canine at any particular moment in the history of the group, were able

---

[14] I am elsewhere suggesting—speculating is a more honest word—that the stylinodontines were primarily adapted to a diet of hardshelled fruits and nuts, the husks of which were torn off by the claws and the shells cracked by the teeth. Tongue and anterior teeth, particularly the canines, may have functioned in a manner remotely analogous to the action of tongue and beak in the parrots.

to survive and breed for longer periods of time, thereby slowing down (although not stopping) the spread of genetic changes favorable to further progress of the tooth. This is an example, and one possible explanation, of the self-limiting nature of tachytelic evolution.

The second period of acceleration appears, as outlined above, to have coincided with a second period of instability. The first period of instability appears on the evidence to have been rather directly organismal-environmental: the stylinodontines at or about the *Wortmania* stage had to acquire certain modifications of the canine further fitting them for occupation of the new adaptive zone. The second was primarily intra-organismal: a maladjustment resulting from evolutionary trends in the dentition that were earlier harmonious and later conflicting raised a barrier to continued and fuller exploitation of that zone. It has been pointed out that caninisation and molarisation regions evolved more or less independently during the earlier history of the group. While the canine was in process of acquiring its characteristic structure and the anterior premolars were becoming increasingly influenced by it, the molars, due to the conservative factors of heredity (Simpson, 1944, p. 154) and of selection, could and did evolve further along lines inherited from the common ancestry of the group. However, by the time (Late Paleocene) that the definitive canine had been acquired, this trend had not resulted in molars of anywhere near sufficient length to keep pace in wear with this ever-growing tooth.[15] For more orthodox mammals, in which there is a division of function between the various regions of the dentition, such a condition would have been relatively unimportant. For the stylinodontines, in which evolution was bringing about a dentition that functioned more nearly as a unit, it was of considerable importance. As a result, duration of life in these forms probably became once again to an extent dependent upon a portion of the dentition, this time upon the molars and posterior premolars. A second period of intense selection therefore set in, during which those individuals with progressively longer molars and more nearly equalized enamel bands were able, on the average, to survive and breed longer, precisely as were their ancestors with progressively longer canines. This second phase lasted about as long as the first, approximately 5 to 6 million years, according to the crude present estimates. The factors for part at least of the rapid transformation undergone by the posterior cheek teeth were already present in the morphogenetic field, but did not earlier become established phenotypically in this region. The factors may have achieved phenotypic expression in some individuals during the earlier

[15] That they did keep pace before complete hypsodonty of the canine was attained is almost diagrammatically shown by an old individual of *Psittacotherium* in the American Museum of Natural History (Matthew, 1937, Figure 62, p. 258). Here, enamel of canine and cheek teeth were coming to an end almost simultaneously.

stages, but these may have been selected against because the change in the cheek teeth did not then outweigh a possible disadvantage of the genetic alteration to the rest of the organism. So long as the old specializations, long since "set" genetically, were not disadvantageous, there was no selective advantage in disturbing the balance. As soon as such disturbance became positively advantageous, changes tending to bring out these cryptic factors were at once favored by selection. The most likely mutations capable of bringing this about would seem to have been those governing an earlier appearance in ontogeny of the factors concerned. Whatever the process, the result was the elimination, transformation, or reduction in importance of characters once typical of the molarisation region. The complicated crown pattern, with its ephemeral existence in the latest forms, is a conspicuous character that became reduced in importance; it suggests one possible explanation of non-adaptive characters in organisms, namely that these may once have been highly adaptive and then later rendered almost or quite functionless as a result of readjustments following upon a conflict in trends.

The rate of evolution of the fore foot, while unfortunately not at all well revealed by the available evidence, was clearly different from that of the dentition. Acquisition of the claws, which appears to have preceded and to have set the stage for the dental and cranial changes (p. 262), was presumably rapid. Subsequent evolution of the extremities appears to have gone on at a relatively sedate pace. The great change in canine structure from Puercan to Torrejonian, at least, was evidently unaccompanied by any changes of corresponding magnitude in the manus, those that are observed being of a relatively slight nature. Changes of some magnitude did occur between Torrejonian and Bridgerian (Fig. 4, B and C); but whether these took place steadily (as was probable) or at an uneven rate cannot be stated, owing to lack of knowledge of the intervening stages. The rate of evolution of the skull in the known stages appears to have been regular; it is probable, however, that acquisition of the jaw modifications associated with initial canine enlargement was rapid, and possible that better specimens susceptible to accurate measurement might reveal another rather rapid advance associated with later canine evolution between Puercan and Torrejonian. Increase in total size continued at an even rate from Puercan to Tiffanian, with little if any change later.

The evolution of the stylinodontines, as interpreted here, is shown diagrammatically in Figure 7. The great similarity of this diagram to Simpson's generalized example of the quantum mode (1944, Fig. 31, p. 198) will at once be apparent. The available evidence on trends and rates in these animals permits a reasonable reconstruction of the sequence of events, at least of the major ones, in the shift that took them from one adaptive zone to another. The starting point was, I believe, the establishment in a population of conoryctines of a mutation that affected the unguals, and possibly the distal portions of the feet as well, resulting in the trend toward the long, laterally compressed, high claws and the shortened intermediate phalanges and metapodials. This mutation and the modifications that arose around it led to transformation of the limbs, especially the anterior, for a digging or tearing function. This trend created a morphologic threshold, at which phenotypic expression of the factors for the enlarged canine and associated jaw mechanism became very positively advantageous. Rapid integration and interaction of the two trends, resulting in forms that by the *Wortmania* stage were decidedly different in structure and adaptation from the ancestral stock, then led to a second morphological threshold, at which the factors that brought about the extraordinary specialization of the already enlarged canine were selected for. Evolution of the canine and extension of caninisation effects to adjacent teeth created yet another threshold, at which reversal of the molarisation trend became advantageous. According to this interpretation, stylinodontine history involved four quantum steps. Three of these were involved in the shift from the old adaptive zone to the new, while the fourth occurred during the phyletic phase of evolution, after the new zone had been occupied.[16] The rate pattern observable in the last two steps,

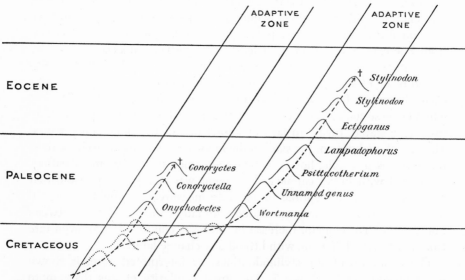

Figure 7. Diagram of the evolution of the Taeniodonta according to the views advanced in this paper. The dashed line indicates phylogeny. The solid and dotted frequency curves represent, respectively, known and inferred stages.

[16] Lest it appear that this distinction between modes is unduly arbitrary, it may be emphasized that the shift had clearly been completed by the *Psittacotherium* stage.

initially rapid and later comparatively slow, was probably the same in all. These animals provide an almost perfect example of a specializing adaptation in which the direction that selection may take is severely restricted (Wright, 1941).

This record strongly suggests that quantum steps are completed gradually and not suddenly. The great change in canine structure between Puercan and Torrejonian, for example, was "rapid" only in the geological sense of that word; 5 million or so years is after all a long stretch of time, probably sufficient for a million if not more generations. There is, furthermore, indirect evidence that the change was more or less uniform during this time. The undescribed genus from the later Dragon (Gazin, 1941) is known from a single upper incisor intermediate in structure between those of *Wortmania* and *Psittacotherium*. Since the upper incisors were incorporated very early in the caninisation region and kept close pace with the canines thereafter, it may be inferred with reasonable assurance that the canines of the Dragon genus were also of intermediate type. The somewhat less radical but still rapid change in molar structure was also achieved by degrees over a similar length of time. The record of another group of fossil mammals, which I believe illustrates the quantum mode, reveals a pattern of rapid but steadily progressive evolution of the basic character. The Mylagaulidae were remarkable rodents of the Middle to Late Tertiary, distinguished by large, extremely complicated and high-crowned P^4 and P_4, remaining cheek teeth much reduced (eliminated in the latest forms), a very broad skull, etc. The basic character appears to have been the structure of P^4 and P_4. McGrew (1941) has shown quite conclusively that they arose from the Aplodontidae, a primitive family represented today by the so-called mountain beaver or sewellel. His data suggest that the time of origin of the mylagaulids was near the end of the Oligocene, and that the ancestral aplodontid was a form close to, if not actually, *Meniscomys*. Evolution thereafter was rapid—four well-marked genera succeed each other during the Miocene—but there is an almost perfect gradation in the structure of P^4 between *Meniscomys* and the terminal members of the descendent family.

The bearing of the evidence just discussed on the possible nature of genetic changes leading to major adaptive changes is mentioned in the concluding section.

The evidence bearing on evolutionary rates in the stylinodontines has now been reviewed. It would appear that they were a rapidly evolving group, not only during the quantum phase but also during the phyletic phase that followed. The work of population geneticists, particularly Wright, Fisher, and Haldane, has demonstrated the all important bearing of population size and structure on evolutionary processes, especially rates. Any suggestion, therefore, that the geologic record of the Taeni-odonta can provide as to the sizes of the successive populations of the group is of interest. Table I shows the number of taeniodont specimens, all single occurrences, compared with the number (in several cases a low estimate) of other contemporaneous mammals in collections. The data are weighted in the direction of taeniodont abundance by several factors. First, the taeniodonts were among the larger mammals of their times and therefore, on the whole, more likely to be preserved and detected than minute forms such as, for example, the apatemyids cited by Simpson (1944, pp. 72-73). Second, they are unorthodox creatures likely to attract the attention of collectors, who would tend to bring in even quite frag-mentary material. Third, the table lists very nearly all taeniodont speci-mens but does not in some instances include all specimens of contempo-raneous forms. Data on numbers of specimens are very rare in the paleontological literature, Simpson's papers being a notable exception. The figures given have been compiled largely from information kindly sup-plied by curators of collections. Not all of those appealed to were able to provide exact numbers or even estimates of specimens in their charge, and several who did respond reported that they had on hand unprepared material not included in their lists. Fourth, not all identifiable fossils encountered in the field are collected. This is less true for the Early Tertiary, where fossils are usually less abundant, than for the later; but, in dealing with the commoner forms of any deposit, collectors do tend to take only the more perfect specimens.

The data show that taeniodonts are rare in formations laid down within their time span. The possibility that the group may have been abundant in areas in which sediments did not accumulate or from which they have subsequently been removed by erosion requires consideration. An interesting case with some bearing on this question is provided by the oreodonts of the genus *Merycoidodon*. Were knowledge of the Oligocene Orellan provincial age restricted to the deposits in the Goshen Hole area of southeastern Wyoming, *Merycoidodon* would be regarded as one of the rarest of mammals (cf. Schlaikjer, 1935, p. 173). How unsound such an inference would be is apparent from the fact that *Merycoidodon* ap-pears to outnumber all other mammals of medium size found in the more extensive and more productive deposits of the same age in nearby south-western South Dakota and northwestern Nebraska. Despite this and other cases, I nevertheless believe that the rarity of taeniodonts in the record reflects a real situation. The example just cited reemphasizes the obvious fact that it is unsafe to base inferences as to rarity or abundance on meager data, but the available evidence on taeniodont occurrences is far from meager. Formations of appropriate Early Tertiary age occur in an irreg-ularly oval area, measuring some 1200 miles from north to south and 450

Numbers of Taeniodonts and of Contemporaneous Mammals in Successive
Paleocene and Eocene Deposits of the Rocky Mountain Region

Provincial ages	Formations and local faunas	Taeniodonts		All mammals	% of taeniodonts to all mammals	
		Conoryctinae	Stylinodontinae		Conoryctinae	Stylinodontinae
Puercan	Nacimiento, N.Mex. (Puerco l.f.)	31	6	1103	2.81	.54
Torrejonian	North Horn, Utah (Dragon l.f.)	4	1	360	1.11	.28
	Nacimiento, N.Mex. (Torrejon l.f.)	15	38	2132	.70	1.78
	Lebo, Montana	3	3	960+	.31	.31
	Polecat Bench, Wyo. (Rock Bench l.f.)	2		900	.22	
Tiffanian	Melville, Montana (inc. Scarritt Quarry)	1		239	.42	
	Melville?, Montana (Bear Creek l.f.)		3	60c.		5.0c.
	San José?, Colorado		1	91		1.10
	(Tiffany l.f.)		(1)	(21)		(4.76)
	DeBeque, Colorado (Plateau Valley l.f.)		14	210		6.66
	Polecat Bench, Wyo. (Silver Coulee l.f.)		3	650		.46
Wasatchian	Willwood and Wind River, Wyoming		20	3138+		.64
	DeBeque, Colorado		4	761		.53
	San José, N.Mex.		19	615+		3.09
Bridgerian	Bridger, Wyoming		3	4027+		.07
Uintan	Uinta, Utah		1	954		.10

Legend of Table I. The plus signs indicate the existence of collections of some size that are not included in the figures for all mammals. The parentheses surrounding the second set of figures for the Tiffany local fauna indicate the surface finds in this deposit; the bulk of the material came from a local pocket believed to be the den of a small carnivore, obviously an unlikely place for the accumulation of taeniodont remains. Formations and local faunas that do not contain taeniodonts are omitted. One or two taeniodont occurrences have not been listed since specimens of other mammals found with them are far too few in number for reliable percentages. For example, taeniodonts formed 16.66% of the few mammals found in the Plateau Valley local fauna during the first season of work in the DeBeque formation. The results of five additional seasons revealed a very different and undoubtedly more correct figure. Available data are insufficient for listing of local faunas in deposits later than Tiffanian in age. Note that deposition of a formation extended in several cases through more than one provincial age.

miles from east to west, in the Rocky Mountain region, slightly west of the center of the North American continent. Not all provincial ages concerned are, to be sure, equally well represented throughout this vast region, the Puercan and Uintan being scantily so. Wasatchian formations and Tiffanian local faunas, however, are widespread within it, while those of the Bridgerian and Torrejonian are somewhat less so. These deposits clearly include animals from a variety of habitats. The various Tiffanian local faunas differ widely among themselves, and the differences are certainly not attributable to age alone. Striking faunal variations due to facies are known, for example, within Wasatchian formations (Van Houten, 1944, 1945); and less obvious ones should become increasingly evident as assemblage collecting is more strictly attended to in these continental sediments.

Taking all factors into consideration, it is, I think, safe to infer from the data that the successive populations of stylinodontines were certainly not large but were at most of medium size (*sensu* Wright) throughout the greater part of the history of the group.[17] This strong probability and the fact of their rapid phyletic evolution from Torrejonian to Late Wasatchian or Bridgerian accord well with Wright's view that populations of intermediate size facilitate rapid evolution. The percentages of stylinodontines to all contemporaneous mammals fluctuate from somewhat over 6 per cent (Plateau Valley Tiffanian local fauna) to small fractions of 1 per cent. Whether this fluctuation is wholly due to random sampling or actually reflects differences in successive population sizes, it is impossible to say. It is tempting to see in the small numbers of Puercan forms an indication of a small population involved in a quantum shift, and in the very few Bridgerian and Uintan specimens a suggestion that small population effects were at work; but to do so would go beyond the evidence. On the other hand, the rarity of *Ectoganus* in the Wasatchian of western Colorado, especially striking in comparison with the relative abundance of this form in northwestern New Mexican deposits of closely comparable age, is very probably real. I have myself had a hand in nearly all the collecting done in Colorado, and a poor eye for a taeniodont is not one of my defects. Possibly, ecological conditions may have been favorable only occasionally in Colorado during Wasatchian time as compared to longer periods in New Mexico. This suggests that populations may have been widespread but at times fragmented and the local groups almost isolated, an important point in connection with Wright's views.

The table indicates that conoryctines, as well as stylinodontines, were rare forms with populations of at most medium size and of similar

[17] It need hardly be emphasized that this discussion merely represents an attempt to obtain some conception of the relative sizes of the populations and not of absolute population numbers, something that would be impossible in paleontology.

structure. If *Onychodectes* was ancestral to *Conoryctes*, as seems probable, evolution in this phylum was rapid, certainly about as rapid as anything that occurred between the successive post-*Psittacotherium* stages of stylinodontine phylogeny. It does not, of course, compare with the amount of change between *Wortmania* and *Psittacotherium*, nor with what must have occurred between an *Onychodectes*-like ancestor and *Wortmania*. This is not surprising, since a quantum shift was not involved in conoryctine phylogeny; smaller populations may facilitiate such shifts but naturally do not insure that they will take place.

Despite the complexity and uncertainty of the subject, the accumulation of data on relative abundance of fossils seems to be worthwhile for paleontology. One additional example of the interest that attaches to such data may be cited. Simpson has given the numbers of horses from various horizons in the collections of the American Museum (1944, Table 14, p. 73). The percentages of horses from the Early, Middle and Late Eocene as compared to all mammals in this collection, is in round numbers, 20,[18] 3, and 4. There was clearly a great and sudden drop in occurrences after Wasatchian time. This drop, unaccompanied by any marked change in the type of deposition of the successive formations or by any great external change in the skeletal structure of the horses themselves, would have been inexplicable a few years ago. It is now known (Edinger, 1948), however, that the horse brain underwent a great evolutionary advance during the Middle and Late Eocene. The rate at which the advance took place could hardly have been attained in very large, continuous, random breeding populations (cf. Wright, 1945), such as the evidence suggests for the Wasatchian horses. The comparative rarity of horses in Bridgerian and Uintan deposits may well be a reflection of this critical time in the evolution of the family.

Concluding Remarks

In view of the great interest in the origin of new major adaptive types, this brief section may be devoted to the bearing on this crucial question of the study just presented. The available evidence, incomplete though it is, does indicate that the starting point of the stylinodontine adaptive type was the establishment of a single, orthodox mutation—that leading to the development of large, laterally compressed claws—of a type that is probably of rather common occurrence in the Mammalia.[19] It even sug-

[18] In the collection from the Wasatchian of Colorado (Chicago Natural History Museum), the percentage of *Hyracotherium* is 38, a considerably higher figure. It may more nearly represent actual abundance in the deposits since the poorer as well as the better specimens were collected.

[19] As may be inferred from the fact that rather similar types of claws were evolved independently at least four times in such a seemingly unlikely group as the ungulates. It will, of course, never be known whether or not homologous genes were involved.

gests, furthermore, that this mutation was the only wholly new major addition to the ancestral genotype throughout the history of the group. Subsequent phenotypic changes, even though profound, appear to have been expressions, variously affected by modifiers at each successive morphologic threshold, of factors already present in the genetic background before the new mutation appeared. This is almost certainly true of the initial enlargement of the canine and the associated modification of the jaw mechanism, and probably true of the subsequent evolution of this complex as well. The unique later specialization of the canine was to a considerable extent a result of the restriction of enamel to an anterior band. A trend toward unequal enamel distribution was characteristic of the molars of all taeniodonts at one stage or another. This suggests that in the common genotype there were numerous similar weak points in the homeostatic system of the dental field that would respond similarly to similar genetic alterations. Thus, once the threshold leading to extreme canine specialization had been reached, selection for localization of enamel in this tooth could operate through the same genetic changes. It would thus appear possible that under favorable circumstances a single new mutation can lead eventually to coordination of an entire genotype in a new and different way.

Davis (this volume) concludes, on the basis of examples discussed in his paper, that origin of a new adaptive type involves an abrupt shift in adaptive direction, and that there is little evidence for an inadaptive phase preceding the shift. Stylinodontine history can best be interpreted in the light of this conclusion. Establishment of the claw mutation must certainly have begun such a shift. Comparison between the two subfamilies of the order, as pointed out on a previous page, suggests that the stylinodontines arose from forms only slightly more primitive than *Onychodectes*, and hence surely in the conoryctine adaptive zone. Similar conoryctines not affected by the claw mutation presumably went on through *Onychodectes* to *Conoryctes*. There is no hint of an inadaptive phase here, although in the absence of direct knowledge the possibility of it cannot of course be ruled out entirely. There is also no hint of one in the case of the aplodontid and mylagaulid rodents referred to above. Davis lists five sub-modes by which new adaptive types may arise. The only one of these that nearly fits the interpretation of stylinodontine history given in this paper is the fourth: "Mutations with conspicuous effects resulting from an alteration of relatively early ontogenetic processes could conceivably produce a new type basically preadapted to a radically different ecological zone." Without ruling out the theoretical possibility of shifts resulting from mutations with immediate and great phenotypic effects, I would be inclined to redefine this sub-mode in the following somewhat different way in order to include cases such as the one under consideration: Given a suitable genotype, establishment of a new mutation ultimately (in extreme cases perhaps immediately) resulting in conspicuous effects may produce a new type basically preadapted to a different ecological zone. Such a mutation need not have an immediate and/or great phenotypic effect; its initial penetrance could be low or medium (cf. Stern, this volume), but once established in a population it would provide the basic adaptation for occupation of a new zone. The stylinodontine claw is, of course, considered to be a case in point. This sub-mode is the only one of the five in which a preadaptive threshold is not involved. The prerequisite for it is a genotype so constituted as to readily permit integration of the new mutation.

As previously stated, there is some suggestion that completion of quantum steps may actually be rather slow, measured in absolute time, however rapid the process may appear to be in geological perspective. Should this prove to be true generally, any group undergoing an adaptive shift toward an already fully occupied zone would usually be placed at a serious competitive disadvantage for a long, rather than for a very short, period. The chances of shifts being carried to completion under such circumstances would be slight indeed. Full exploitation of a zone by a group comparatively low in the scale of evolutionary progress to the exclusion of groups higher in the scale would thus be more readily understandable.

SUMMARY

The single family Stylinodontidae of the order Taeniodonta contains two phyla of subfamily rank, one of which, the Stylinodontinae, was characterized by an unusual combination of adaptive characters. The history of this phylum is believed to provide an example of a quantum shift in evolution.

The dentition of this subfamily, in which canine and molar regions were at first differentiated in the usual manner, became increasingly dominated by a trend toward the evolution of a very peculiar type of canine. The other teeth underwent adjustment to it until finally a dental series without a clear-cut functional division between canines and cheek teeth was attained; in the course of this a trend in the molar region that had been inherited from the ancestral stock was halted and its effects largely obliterated. The trend in the skull was toward great breadth, short facial region, reduced premaxillae, deep and heavy jaw with low condyle, occiput high, temporal fossa and coronoid process large. The extremities were of a digging or tearing type, robust, with well developed claws.

The trends in the stylinodontine dentition are interpreted as the results of interaction of genetic changes affecting this morphogenetic field as a whole, with selection generally favoring those first expressed phenotypically in the caninisation region. Changes in skull form are regarded as adjustments associated with the remarkably modified jaw mechanism, of which the canine is the most striking if not the dominating feature. The trend in the foot led to the evolution of a progressively more efficient digging or tearing organ.

The other phylum, the subfamily Conoryctinae, remained comparatively generalized in structure. A comparison of the earliest known representatives of the two phyla, *Wortmania* and *Onychodectes* of the earliest Paleocene Puercan, reveals that two basic characters determined the course of stylinodontine evolution—the claw and the canine and associated jaw mechanism. The claw is believed to have been the first of these to appear. The stylinodontines probably arose from forms very similar to *Onychodectes*. *Conoryctes*, a later conoryctine, independently acquired certain features of the jaw mechanism that were similar generally, but not precisely, to those of the earlier *Wortmania*. Evidently the genotype of the common ancestral stock was retained relatively intact, with the result that similar phenotypic effects were likely to appear independently in both phyla. Acquisition of claws in the stylinodontine phylum is believed to have placed a high selective value upon early expression of the jaw mechanism characters. The much slower appearance and somewhat different nature of the generally similar characters in the later conoryctines is believed to have resulted from a selective advantage conferred upon these forms by acquisition of a more powerful jaw. What is known of the post-cranial skeleton of *Conoryctes* exhibits almost no advance over that of *Onychodectes*, indicating that skull changes in the phylum did not evolve in concert with a major change in the rest of the organism.

The time that elapsed from the earliest to the latest recorded appearance of the stylinodontines was approximately 33 million years. The average organism rate for the subfamily was faster than that for horses and phenacodontid condylarths. A great amount of evolutionary change took place in the phylum, much greater, for example, than occurred in the Conoryctinae, although the organism rate for the two groups was the same in the Puercan and Torrejonian. The rate pattern of the dentition of the Stylinodontinae shows two periods of sharp acceleration, each period lasting approximately 5 to 6 million years. Canine structure was radically transformed between Puercan and Torrejonian—a major step in the quantum shift undergone by the group—and molar structure was profoundly altered between the end of the Tiffanian and the end of the Wasatchian. The rate of evolution of the foot was different from that of the dentition; following a presumably rapid evolution of claws and associated modifications, acquired by Puercan time, further change was probably rather gradual. Skull modifications appear to have gone on at an even rate, presumably following upon rapid acquisition of the jaw mechanism specializations. Total size increased steadily during the Paleocene and remained more or less constant during the Eocene.

The sequence of events believed to have been involved in the quantum shift undergone by the stylinodontines is outlined; steps in the shift follow attainment of morphologic thresholds. There is some evidence that the step or steps occurring in such shifts are rapid only in the geological sense.

Available data on the numbers of taeniodonts and of all contemporaneous mammals in collections suggests that the successive populations of stylinodontines and conoryctines were of medium size, at most, throughout the history of the order. This is in accord with the rapid evolution undergone by these animals.

A single orthodox mutation resulting in the development of claws is believed to have been the starting point of the new adaptive shift represented by the Stylinodontinae. It is suggested that this mutation may have been the only major new addition to the ancestral genotype, subsequent changes arising largely through the action of modifiers on factors present before it appeared. The possibility would seem to exist that under favorable conditions one mutation can lead eventually to coordination of a genotype in a new and different way.

Stylinodontine history is best interpreted in terms of the view that origin of new adaptive types involves abrupt shifts in adaptive direction and that such shifts are seldom preceded by inadaptive phases. The claw mutation surely initiated a shift of this sort, and there is no clear evidence of the occurrence of an inadaptive phase. A preadaptive threshold is not involved when inception of a new adaptive type is the result of a single mutation. The prerequisite in this sub-mode is a genotype permitting ready integration of the new mutation.

Indication that completion of quantum steps actually may be rather slow in terms of absolute time, if found to be true generally, suggests that groups undergoing an adaptive shift toward a zone already fully occupied would be at a decided competitive disadvantage for a long period of time. Under such conditions, the chances of successful completion of shifts would be few.

REFERENCES

Bateson, W. 1892. On numerical variation in teeth, with a discussion of the conception of homology. *Proc. Zool. Soc. London*, 1892, pp. 102-115, figs. 1-6.

——. 1894. *Materials for the study of variation treated with especial regard to discontinuity in the origin of species.* London: Macmillan & Co., pp. i-xvi, 1-598, figs. 1-209.

Butler, P. M. 1937. Studies of the mammalian dentition. I. The teeth of *Centetes ecaudatus* and its allies. *Proc. Zool. Soc. London, 107* (B), pp. 103-132, figs. 1-28, pls. 1-3.

——. 1939a. Studies of the mammalian dentition. Differentiation of the post-canine dentition. *Ibid.*, *109* (B), pp. 1-36, figs. 1-28.

——. 1939b. The teeth of the Jurassic mammals. *Ibid.*, pp. 329-356, figs. 1-12.

——. 1941. A theory of the evolution of mammalian molar teeth. *Amer. Jour. Sci.*, *239*, pp. 421-450, figs. 1-10.

——. 1946. The evolution of carnassial dentitions in the Mammalia. *Proc. Zool. Soc. London*, *116*, pp. 198-220, figs. 1-13.

Colbert, E. H. 1935. Siwalik mammals in the American Museum of Natural History. *Trans. Amer. Phil. Soc.*, n.s., *26*, pp. i-x, 1-401, figs. 1-198, map.

Cope, E. D. 1884. The Vertebrata of the Tertiary formations of the West. Book 1, *Rept. U.S. Geol. Surv. Terr.*, *3*, pp. i-xxxv, 1-1009, pls. 1-75a.

Dahlberg, A. A. 1945. The changing dentition of man. *Jour. Amer. Dental Assoc.*, *32*, pp. 676-690, figs. 1-7.

Davis, D. D. 1949. Comparative Anatomy and the Evolution of Vertebrates. This volume.

Edinger, T. 1948. Evolution of the horse brain. *Geol. Soc. Amer. Mem.*, *25*, pp. i-x, 1-177, figs. 1-24, pls. 1-4.

Gazin, C. L. 1941. The mammalian faunas of the Paleocene of central Utah, with notes on the geology. *Proc. U.S. Nat. Mus.*, *91*, pp. 1-53, figs. 1-29, pls. 1-3.

Jepsen, G. L., and Cooper, K. W. 1948. *Genetics, Paleontology, and Evolution.* Princeton University Bicentennial Conference, Ser. 2, Conference 3, pp. 1-36, 2 pls. Princeton, N.J.

Knopf, A. 1949. Time in Earth History. This volume.

McGrew, P. O. 1941. The Aplodontoidea. *Geol. Ser. Field Mus. Nat. Hist.*, *9*, pp. 1-30, figs. 1-13.

Matthew, W. D. 1937. Paleocene faunas of the San Juan Basin, New Mexico. *Trans. Amer. Phil. Soc.*, n.s., *30*, pp. i-xviii, 1-510, figs. 1-85, pls. 1-65. A posthumous work edited, with an addendum (pp. 361-367), by Walter Granger, W. K. Gregory, and E. H. Colbert.

Patterson, B. (in press) The extinct mammalian order Taeniodonta. To appear in *Fieldiana: Geology.*

Schlaikjer, E. M. 1935. Contributions to the stratigraphy and paleontology of the Goshen Hole area, Wyoming. IV. New vertebrates and the stratigraphy of the Oligocene and Early Miocene. *Bull. Mus. Comp. Zool.*, *76*, pp. 97-189, figs. 1-13, pls. 1-41.

Simpson, G. G. 1931. *Metacheiromys* and the Edentata. *Bull. Amer. Mus. Nat. Hist.*, *59*, pp. 295-381, figs. 1-23.

——. 1944. *Tempo and Mode in Evolution.* New York, Columbia University Press, pp. i-xviii, 1-237, figs. 1-36.

——. 1947. A continental Tertiary time chart. *Jour. Paleont.*, *21*, pp. 480-483.

Stern, C. 1949. Gene and Character. This volume.

Van Houten, F. B. 1944. Stratigraphy of the Willwood and Tatman formations in northwestern Wyoming. *Bull. Geol. Soc. Amer.*, *55*, pp. 165-210, figs. 1-4, pls. 1-7.

——. 1945. Review of latest Paleocene and Early Eocene mammalian faunas. *Jour. Paleont.*, *19*, pp. 421-461, fig. 1.

Winge, H. 1923. Pattedyr-Slaegter. I: *Monotremata, Marsupalia, Insectivora, Chiroptera, Edentata.* Copenhagen: H. Hagerup, pp. i-viii, 1-360, 1 pl. (An English translation of this and the volume on the rodents, carnivores and primates, prepared by E. Deichmann and G. M. Allen, was published in 1941: The interrelationships of the mammalian genera, 2 vols., Copenhagen: C. A. Reitzel).

Wood, H. E., Chaney, R. W., Clark, J., Colbert, E. H., Jepsen, G. L., Reeside, J. B., Jr., and Stock, C. Nomenclature and Correlation of the North American Continental Tertiary. *Bull. Geol. Soc. Amer.*, *52*, pp. 1-48, chart.

Wortman, J. L. 1897. The Ganodonta and their relationship to the Edentata. *Bull. Amer. Mus. Nat. Hist.*, *9*, pp. 59-110, figs. 1-36.

Wright, S. 1941. The "Age and Area" concept extended. *Ecology*, *22*, pp. 345-347.

——. 1945. Tempo and Mode in Evolution: a critical review. *Ibid.*, *26*, pp. 415-419.

PART V

SPECIATION

· 14 ·

SPECIATION AND SYSTEMATICS

BY ERNST MAYR[1]

It was only rather recently that it was realized what speciation means. Darwin is quite vague on this point; in fact, in his *Origin of Species*, a work which does not contain the word evolution, he seems to consider origin of species as synonymous with evolution. In the last decade of the nineteenth century several authors recognized that evolution comprises several processes. Romanes (1897) calls them appropriately "the transformation of species in time" and "the multiplication of species in space." A number of M. Wagner's followers, as for example Seebohm and Jacobi, also emphasized this point. This clear distinction was unfortunately almost forgotten in the early twentieth century, which is one of the many reasons for the cleavage that existed at that period between geneticists and naturalists. It is now recognized that evolutionary change is possible without multiplication of species, and reciprocally that multiplication of species is sometimes accompanied by rather slight evolutionary changes. This difference is illustrated in Figure 1. If A is, for example, an isolated island, the population on it may change in the course of time from species *a* through species *b* and species *c* into species *d* without ever splitting into more than one species. On the other hand, if a widespread species *a* occurs on the four islands of archipelago B, it may become modified genetically on each island and a whole species swarm may eventually develop through cross colonizations of the islands. Numerous cases of this type of evolution have been found on all archipelagos.

The new species that are produced under the conditions of both A and B are of the same kind, as far as the paleontological record is concerned. But in the case of A the total number of species will stay constant, while only B permits the multiplication of species. It is this multiplication of species which in the current literature is referred to with the term *speciation*.

A consideration of the biological significance of speciation helps in the understanding of the mechanisms that are involved in the multiplication of species. The complex system of discontinuous species that is actually found in the world is not the only thinkable system of organization of living beings. It is quite possible to think of a world in which species do not exist, but are replaced by a single "connubium" of individuals, each

[1] The American Museum of Natural History. Paper submitted: April 1947.

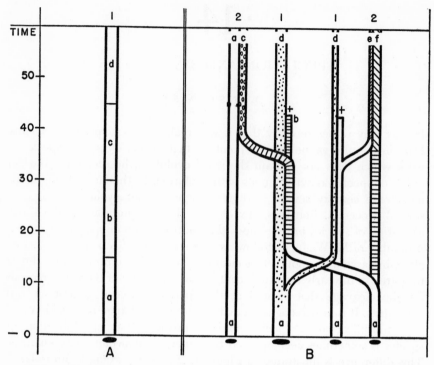

Figure 1. The left part of the diagram represents evolutionary change of a species isolated on island A. The right part illustrates the process of speciation on archipelago B with four islands. The originally monotypic species *a* breaks up into five species through geographical speciation and cross colonization.

one different from every other one, and each one capable of reproducing with those other individuals that are most similar to it. Each individual would then be, so to speak, the center of a concentric series of circles of genetically more and more unlike individuals. What would be the consequences of the continuous, uninterrupted gene flow through such a large system? In each generation certain individuals would have a selective advantage because they have a gene complex that is specially adapted to a particular ecological situation. However, most of these favorable combinations would be broken up through pairing with individuals adapted for a slightly different environment. In this system there is no defense against the destruction of superior gene combinations except abandonment of sexual reproduction. It is obvious that a system that prevents such unrestricted outcrossing is superior. The isolating mechanisms have evolved as a consequence of this situation. They are a protective device of superior gene combinations (and every gene combination that can survive in competition with all the others is *de facto* superior). In order to prevent the destruction of such favorable gene combinations they must be separated by a genetic gap, reenforced by isolating mechanisms, from all other populations with strikingly different gene combinations. These considerations provide the answer for three of the properties of species, their genetically-controlled ecological adaptation, their genetic isolating mechanisms, and the gaps that separate them from each other.

Each species consists then of groups of individuals with more or less similar gene combinations optimally adapted for a given environment. This is the "ecological niche" in which the species fits and where it thrives and is superior to its competitors. The species, or it might be better to say in this context, its gene complex, is less efficient away from this optimum environment. It occurs with lower frequency and it utilizes its environment less efficiently. Finally, at the ecological margin of the environment of a species, it can survive only under specially favorable conditions. This is illustrated diagrammatically in Figure 2.

Species 1 is genetically constructed for maximum efficiency in environmental niche C. Even though it also occurs with lower frequency in niches A, B, D, and E, it is specifically adapted to niche C. It is obvious that the

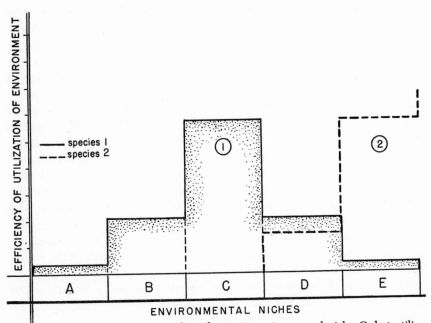

Figure 2. Species 1 finds optimal conditions in environmental niche C, but utilizes niches B and D inefficiently, and A and E very poorly. Species 2 cannot utilize niches A, B, and C at all, but finds optimal conditions in E and F. The absence of competition in niche A will invite the evolution of a species adapted for this niche.

gene complex of species 1 would have to be modified considerably before the previously marginal niche E would become optimal. This is exactly what speciation does—creates gene complexes which find optimal conditions in previously insufficiently or entirely unoccupied ecological niches. The process of speciation leads thus to a continuous increase of the diversity of organic nature, each evolutionary step resulting in an increasingly efficient utilization of the environment. Each new species in turn helps to create new niches. For example, the evolution of flowering plants set the stage for the evolution of many new kinds of insects; the development of this insect fauna was the prerequisite for the evolution of many groups of birds. They, in turn, permitted the evolution of new predators and parasites and so *ad infinitum.*

Speciation is thus an adaptive process toward the most efficient utilization of the environment. An improvement of the environment will create new niches and will favor speciation; an impoverishment will lead to extinction. Seen in this light, speciation is a process of as much concern to the ecologist as it is to the systematist.

THE NATURE OF SPECIES

Speciation is the multiplication of species. The process of speciation cannot be studied until there is some understanding of the nature of species. It is rather hopeless to arrive at a satisfactory species definition, if one wants to include in a single species concept apomicts, hybrid flocks, obligatory hermaphrodites, and asexual organisms. However, it is possible to arrive at a fairly usable species definition for bisexual animals. A study of the population structure and of the attributes of such species shows that the differences between the populations (subspecies) within a single species are often very pronounced. This is strikingly illustrated by certain species of birds of paradise, pheasants, butterflies, and beetles. Forms that were originally described as separate species or even genera have sometimes turned out to be nothing but geographical races of other forms. On the other hand, it has been found in the case of the so-called sibling or cryptic species that differences between perfectly good species can be exceedingly slight (Mayr, 1948). Obviously then, the degree of morphological difference is not an absolute yardstick for determining specific distinctness. Species are recognized not on the basis of the degree of difference but rather on the completeness of separation. "Species are groups of actually or potentially interbreeding natural populations that are reproductively isolated from other such groups." *Sympatric species are always separated from each other by a distinct gap.*

Speciation then is a multiple problem:

(1) How do the gaps between incipient species develop?

(2) How are these gaps maintained?

(3) What genetic processes operate in the separated populations?

There was formerly much disagreement between taxonomists and geneticists concerning the correct answers to these questions. This was largely due on one side to a Lamarckian belief by taxonomists in the directive powers of the environment, and on the other side by an exaggerated emphasis by early geneticists on the evolutionary importance of single individuals and of single mutations.

The fact that speciation in sexual animals is a phenomenon of populations rather than of individuals needs special emphasis. It was the oversight of this fact which caused De Vries to postulate speciation through single mutations and which prompted Bateson to say as recently as 1922 that speciation was still a complete mystery to the geneticist. Bateson looked for the wrong thing when he stated, "The production of an indubitably sterile hybrid from completely fertile parents which have arisen under critical observation from a single common origin is the event for which we wait." Not individuals but populations are the units of evolution and such populations can drift apart decisively through an accumulation of small, often minute, genetic differences. Such *gradual* speciation is the norm while *instantaneous* speciation is the exception.

INSTANTANEOUS SPECIATION

Instantaneous speciation (Mayr, 1942) is understood to mean the production of an individual (or the offspring of a single mating) that is reproductively isolated from the species to which the parents belong. Polyploidy is the only proven mechanism of instantaneous speciation in sexually reproducing organisms. But this phenomenon, common as it is among plants, is of no significance in animals (White, 1945). Wherever it occurs (beetles, isopods, turbellarians, etc.) it seems to be restricted to self-fertilizing hermaphrodites or to parthenogenetically reproducing organisms, but even among those it is rare. The evidence in favor of polyploidy in sexually reproducing animals cited by Lorković (1941) and by Svärdson (1945) is considered by White (1946) as not convincing.

The belief in "hopeful monsters" (e.g. Goldschmidt, 1945; Gunter, 1943) has even less foundation. This thesis neglects the ecological situation as well as the need for isolating mechanisms. Wheeler's fantastic claim of the sudden origin of a new species of Nemertean has been thoroughly refuted by Zimmerman (1943). I shall come back later to the evidence which some paleontologists have interpreted as indicating instantaneous speciation.

GRADUAL SPECIATION

A steadily increasing amount of evidence has accumulated to show that speciation normally is gradual. The origin of a new species of higher animals in a human life span is impossible; in fact, it may require a minimum of about one-half million years, and normally even considerably more than that. Since speciation is such a slow process it has often been claimed that it cannot be ascertained how speciation operates. This is not true, since there is abundant indirect evidence to take the place of direct observation. Such indirect proof is derived from two groups of data, so far as the systematist is concerned:

(1) The study of the gaps between species.

(2) The study of the structure of species.

It was shown by me in a previous publication (Mayr, 1942) that all this evidence indicates that the normal process of gradual speciation is that of geographical speciation. I defined this as follows: "A new species develops if a population, which has become geographically isolated from its parental species, acquires during this period of isolation characters which promote or guarantee reproductive isolation when the external barriers break down." Work by many authors during the past five years has shown that this definition includes a number of ambiguities and omissions that require further discussion. To simplify the following discussion it may be useful at this point to introduce some diagrams (Figure 3).

GEOGRAPHICAL ISOLATION

What exactly does geographical isolation mean? Does it imply that geographically isolated populations are cut off by unsurmountable barriers like oceans or high mountain ranges, or does it merely indicate segregation that is mutual, spatial exclusion without actual separation by barriers?

Before this question can be answered it is necessary to examine the actual conditions under which parts of species are separated from each other. Populations of a species, for example, that live on mountains above 10,000 feet are isolated from each other by all valleys or lowlands descending below this altitude. Is this geographical or is it ecological isolation? Is this isolation any more ecological than if the mountains were sunk into the ocean until the water reached the 10,000-foot level? Grasslands for forest animals, deciduous forests for inhabitants of the coniferous forest, all constitute extrinsic barriers and lead to a reduction of gene flow. The literature is replete with examples of barriers of this nature. This fact makes it quite impossible to distinguish between geographical and ecological barriers (e.g. for element (c) in Fig. 3A).

THE INCOMPLETENESS OF BARRIERS

Isolation between populations of a species is rarely complete. Even where there is apparently an absolute barrier, like an ocean strait, some

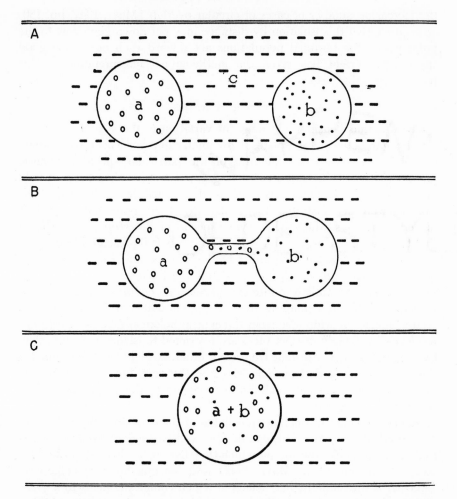

Figure 3. Diagram of various kinds of geographical isolation. A. The two populations *a* and *b* are completely isolated from each other by the unsuitable intervening
area *c*. B. The nature of the intervening area *c* permits a certain amount of dispersal
(gene flow) between populations *a* and *b*. C. Individuals of species *a* and *b* coexist
in random distribution in the same area (sympatrically) without any traces of spatial
isolation.

individuals apparently get carried across the gap at irregular intervals. In
other words there is, as indicated in Figure 3B, only partial isolation; a
certain amount of gene flow continues. The smaller the distances and the
less formidable the barriers, the greater this gene flow. However, even in
the complete absence of barriers there is usually not complete panmixia
within a species but *isolation by distance*. Taxonomists are thoroughly
familiar with subspeciation in the absence of geographical barriers, and

the increasing number of cases of circular overlap (Mayr, 1942, pp. 180-184) prove that this isolation by distance may cut down gene flow to the point where the terminal populations act toward each other like good species. S. Wright has given the mathematical interpretation of this process (Wright, 1943).

INTRINSIC FACTORS

There is thus considerable range of variation in the size of a barrier-forming gap between the isolates. How small can it be? This is determined entirely by the dispersal faculties of the particular species (intrinsic factors). A barrier between two living populations is thus not a strictly mechanical matter, since it is reenforced by intrinsic mechanisms. This can be well demonstrated for birds with their potentially excellent dispersal facilities. Many white-eyes (species of *Zosterops*) have shown that they can cross large water gaps. The genus is represented by various species on many isolated oceanic islands (Ponape and Kusaie in Micronesia, Savaii in Samoa, Fiji, Norfolk and Lord Howe, and the Loyalty Islands). The Australian White-eye (*Zosterops lateralis*) invaded New Zealand in 1856 after jumping an ocean gap of 2000 km. But in a closely related species of white-eye from the central Solomon Islands (*Zosterops rendovae*) strikingly distinct races are restricted to islands not more than two to six kilometers distant from each other. A flight of a few minutes would carry the birds from one island to the next, but intrinsic factors prevent the occurrence of such flights or else make the frequency of their occurrence negligible.

Animals have an instinctive knowledge of their habitat which they are normally loath to leave. This can be observed particularly well in species that are colored like the soil on which they live. It has been described for larks (Niethammer, see Mayr, 1942) and for grasshoppers (Chopard, 1938). It is this same habitat selection which confines animals to a given ecological niche and normally prevents them from leaving it. (Miller, 1942).

Intrinsic factors are also responsible in other ways for preventing the mixing of populations. In migratory birds it happens not infrequently that breeding and non-breeding individuals of the same species coexist at certain seasons in the same region. In New Guinea I saw in the same grove of trees breeding pairs of the native subspecies (*waigiouensis*) of the roller *Eurystomus orientalis*, as well as non-breeding migrant visitors of the Australian subspecies (*pacificus*). Genetically controlled differences in their physiological condition prevent the interbreeding of these two subspecies. In Great Britain also there is no interbreeding between conspecific individuals if one belongs to winter visiting Scandinavian populations and the other to the native resident. The same has been proven abundantly for North American birds where, for example, mixed winter flocks of various subspecies of Juncos, Fox Sparrows, and Rosy Finches are commonplace.

Among the intrinsic mechanisms dispersal facility is the most important. It is different from species to species and it is different in the various stages of the life cycle. The provision for dispersal is one of the basic properties of living matter. Dispersal leads to increased gene recombination and apparently there is selection for an optimum range of dispersal. Too much dispersal leads to too much outcrossing, insufficient dispersal to too narrow inbreeding. As pointed out by many recent geneticists, there is an optimum condition between these two extremes.

Ghilarov (1945) shows that there is a dispersal phase in the life cycle of every species. In the sessile marine organisms (coelenterates, molluscs, crustaceans), for example, it is in the larval stage. In most insects it is in the adult stage. Among birds, in which the adults may have practically no dispersal owing to territoriality and homing faculty, there is considerable scattering of the young. However, this is not random scattering since even the young settle at comparatively short distances from the place of birth, as recent analyses of bird banding records have shown. The limited range of many avian subspecies would otherwise not be intelligible.

There are many ways by which to demonstrate the influence of dispersal on speciation. This is especially evident when related forms with different dispersal facilities are compared. The swimming ducks (*Anas*) in the northern latitudes of the Holarctic have high dispersal rates and a minimum of subspeciation; the geese (*Anser, Branta*) that live in the same latitudes have very limited dispersal and high subspeciation (Mayr, 1942). Speciation on islands also is closely correlated with the dispersal facilities of the respective species.

Dispersal is a complicated phenomenon. It is influenced by homing faculty, by territorialism, by habitat selection, and by the ability to survive in a novel environment. It is different from species to species and in the various phases of the life cycle of a single individual. The complex nature of dispersal is the reason it is so difficult to study gene flow, which is after all nothing but dispersal expressed in terms of the geneticist.

SEGREGATION VERSUS ISOLATION

No two populations of the same species normally coexist at the same locality. Conspecific individuals that are in breeding condition and occur together will interbreed and become thus *de facto* members of the same population. Conversely different populations of a species are spatially segregated. They may meet in a zone of contact and interbreed freely, but their centers of distribution will be different. Such spatially segregated populations are included by most authors under the heading "geographically isolated" but are excluded by others. This has been the cause of much confusion and has been the basis for much of the argument about the possibility of sympatric speciation.

It is still uncertain whether or not spatially segregated populations can develop into full species if they are in complete contact with each other. I have discussed this question on a previous occasion (Mayr, 1942, pp. 188-189). To permit speciation of such populations there must be a bottleneck that seriously impedes gene flow. The cases of the cave fishes described by Pavan (1946) and of the four endemic "species" of fish of Lake Waccamaw (Hubbs and Raney, 1946) are some recently described situations where species may have evolved in geographical segregation without complete isolation.

It would be well worth while to test this possibility experimentally. The natural situation could be simulated by two population cages, each of which is placed in a very different environment but which are joined by a connection that is almost impassable. The unexpectedly large size of the coefficient of selection that has been found in much of the recent research (Dobzhansky, 1947) opens the possibility that natural selection may be stronger than the slight gene inflow across the barrier. The importance of natural selection for the reduction of gene flow is further substantiated by studies of hybrids in zones of overlap of closely related species (e.g. Epling, 1947). It may become necessary to consider this possibility and to define species as follows: "Species are groups of actually or potentially interbreeding natural populations that are either completely reproductively isolated from other such groups or whose genetic differentiation (owing to mutation, selection, etc.) outweighs an actual or potential gene interchange with other such groups." But there are also some serious objections to such an emendation.

THE POLYTYPIC SPECIES AS AN AGGREGATE OF INCIPIENT SPECIES

The concept of geographical speciation is based on the assumption that geographical subdivisions of species are potentially incipient species. The study of speciation thus involves a study of the structure of species. The taxonomist finds that most populations of species are different if proper methods of analysis are employed, but only a small minority are sufficiently distinct to be recognized as subspecies. The most distinct subspecies are usually those that occur along the periphery of the species range; in fact, such peripheral subspecies are frequently so distinct that it is difficult to decide whether to consider them species or subspecies (Mayr, 1948). This difficulty of the taxonomist is of purely practical nature.

Of greater interest is the ecological structure of species. Many authors insist on distinguishing between geographical and ecological races, but the fact remains that geographical races are invariably to a lesser or greater degree also ecological races, in view of the climatic, edaphic, and biotic peculiarities of every district. Conversely, no evidence is available to show that ecological races exist that are not at least microgeographic races.

It becomes evident when one reads the conflicting literature on geographical versus ecological speciation that the disagreement is mainly due to a difference of emphasis. If Speyer (1938) finds that a valley population of a moth hatches on the average one month earlier than the populations on the neighboring hills, one may emphasize either the existing difference and the ecological factors that favored selection for this difference, or one may emphasize the geographical segregation of the two localities which limits gene flow between them. The important fact is that two different populations are involved, each with a locally superior gene combination. Spatial segregation will prevent the destruction of these adaptive gene combinations through gene flow.

Too great an emphasis in the past on the purely taxonomic structure of species has obscured the fact that even the lowest taxonomic category, the subspecies, is composed of numerous genetically distinct populations, each of which is adapted to a local environment. This was proven independently by the geneticists (see Dobzhansky, 1941, for a summary) and by the naturalists. Noll (1934), for example, quotes numerous instances of local bird populations which differ in various physiological and ecological features. Such differences can be sharp and striking if there is a sufficient spatial gap between the populations. The differences are slighter and more gliding if the populations are in complete spatial contact. As a rule the most pronounced ecological differences are found in the populations that are found along the periphery of a species, whether or not they have reached subspecies level.

The response to the local environment in plants is usually even more striking than in animals where it becomes apparent only through genetic and ecological techniques. Botanists therefore often apply a special terminology to the species of the field naturalist and to its locally adapted subdivisions. Turesson (1922) uses *ecospecies* for the "Linnaean species from the ecological point of view." "The term *ecotype* . . . is therefore proposed for the ecological unit, to cover the product arising as a result of the genotypical response of an ecospecies to a particular habitat."

The species then is a compound of locally adapted populations which can be called ecotypes or ecological races. This still leaves the question how these ecological differences evolve and what role these populations play in the evolution of new species. In order to answer these questions it is essential to make a short survey of the speciation process.

THE SPECIATION PROCESS

Speciation in its simplest and most diagrammatic form occurs when a population (or group of populations) becomes completely isolated geographically from the parental population (Figure 3A). The following events take place in the isolated population:

A. Genetic changes owing to mutation, recombination, and random fixation, strongly influenced and directed by selection pressure.

As a consequence of *A.*

B (1) The development of reproductive isolating mechanisms.

(2) Ecological divergence (see Lack, below, pp. 299-308).

(3) Sufficient genetic change to make hybrids between parental and incipient species inferior in competition with either parental population.

The isolated population can spread out into the range of the parental species and thus demonstrate the completion of the process of speciation, as soon as $B(1)$, $B(2)$, and $B(3)$ have reached a certain degree of perfection.

A few words of comment must be said about the definition of isolating mechanisms. It is generally agreed that they have to be divided into two fundamentally different categories: (1) innate reproductive isolating mechanisms, and (2) geographical isolating mechanisms. (A slight transition between these categories, however, is caused by the fact that even the efficiency of geographical barriers is usually reenforced by innate factors.) Geographical isolation, being mainly based on extrinsic barriers, has the important characteristic of reversibility. As has been emphasized especially by botanists (Stebbins, 1945), but is equally true and well-substantiated for animals, geographically isolated populations do not necessarily develop into full species. A number of plant species are found in eastern Asia and eastern North America which have probably been separated for millions of years but are still morphologically indistinguishable. Others (e.g. *Platanus, Catalpa*) show slight differences but are fully fertile. In spite of their complete geographical isolation these forms are not species. Any event in the history of the earth that would eliminate the gap in the distribution would demonstrate this conclusively. Reproductive isolating mechanisms, on the other hand, operate in contrast to geographical barriers only when two populations are in physical contact. Their functioning is thus an essential criterion of species. They have a multifactorial genetic basis which cannot have become perfected without an initial interruption or at least *very* drastic inhibition of gene flow.

If this hypothesis of speciation is correct, it follows that the development of $B(1)$, $B(2)$, and $B(3)$ must occur while the respective populations are still in the stage of incipient species. It must be possible to find evidence for it by comparing geographical races. This is indeed the case.

GEOGRAPHICAL VARIATION OF ISOLATING MECHANISMS. That there is sometimes a great deal of sterility among individuals belonging to different geographical races is well established in the literature (Mayr, 1942, p. 163). In the meantime this has been even better established for certain species of *Drosophila* (for a summary see Mayr, 1948; and Patterson et al., 1947). Moore (1946) made a systematic analysis of developmental disturbances of the F_1 hybrids between various populations of the frog *Rana pipiens*. In hybrids between distant populations there is a retardation in rate of development, and morphological defects are pronounced. Crosses between far-distant populations, like Vermont and southern Florida or Wisconsin and Texas, result in a high degree of hybrid inviability. This type of research is still at its beginning. However, it is already established that in a majority of cases conspicuous differences in mating preference and often also in fertility can be observed between individuals of different populations, particularly if they come from distant localities.

GEOGRAPHICAL VARIATION OF ECOLOGICAL PREFERENCE

Many cases of geographical variation of ecological preference have been described by Studnitz (1935), Stegmann (1935), Bodenheimer (1938), Mayr (1942, pp. 56-57), Huxley (1942, pp. 272, 278), Stresemann (1943), and others. The warbler *Phylloscopus occipitalis* nests on the mainland of Japan on the ground and has a characteristic song and call-note (subspecies *coronatus*). On the island Oshima (Seven Islands) it nests off the ground on bushes and has a strikingly different song (subspecies *ijimae*). In the thrush *Luscinia akahige* the nominate race (*akahige*) lives on the main islands of Japan in the mountains about 1000 meters altitude, while on the Seven Islands (Miyake, Mikura, Hachijo) the subspecies *tanensis* lives at sea level. The nest of *akahige* is on the ground, the nest of *tanensis* in natural cavities in trees one to three meters above the ground (Jahn, 1942).

The fact that in every region the local subspecies of cross-bill (*Loxia curvirostra*) has become adapted in its bill structure to one particularly favored species of conifers is well known (Stresemann, 1934; Kirikov, 1940). In many species different geographical races live at different altitudes. Dwarf races of *Passer montanus*, *P. rutilans*, *Parus major*, *Corvus macrorhynchos*, and *Lanius schach* live in the tropical zone at the foot of the Himalayas and giant races in the Alpine zone (Stresemann, 1943). In the cormorant *Phalacrocorax carbo* the widespread Eurasian race *sinensis* always nests on trees, the Atlantic race *carbo* always on rocks. In the Herring Gull (*Larus argentatus*) the flesh-footed race *argentatus* of Europe always nests on the seacoast. Its eastern neighbor, the yellow-footed *L. a. omissus*, in its western populations, is an inhabitant of the marshy shores of tundra lakes. In north Finland, where both subspecies meet, they retain their ecological characteristics: *omissus* nests in marshes, *argentatus* along the adjacent rocky coasts and on sandy beaches (Stresemann, 1943). This last case illustrates the importance of these acquired ecological differences as isolating mechanisms.

These facts prove abundantly that more or less complete isolating mechanisms as well as ecological differences between subspecies are indeed frequent. Does this mean that the theory of geographical speciation has only limited validity? The answer is apparent from the following discussion.

Geographical speciation is a process that is fully consistent both with the genetic and the taxonomic evidence. Also its operation is abundantly documented by borderline cases. There is universal agreement that the concept of geographical speciation, as developed by the systematists, has greatly clarified our thinking on speciation. With this fact established, the time has now come to ask whether the concept of geographical speciation, as originally presented, was not an oversimplification, and furthermore whether there is not in addition to it a second kind of gradual speciation, variously referred to as ecological or sympatric speciation. This question has never been adequately answered for lack of sufficient data, which is not unexpected since it is only within the past four or five years that the problem has been defined precisely. The available evidence indicates to me that speciation is not always as crudely geographical as sometimes stated, but that, on the other hand, there is no evidence that two entirely different processes of speciation are involved. Rather "geographical" and "ecological" speciation are but two aspects of the same phenomenon.

Sympatric Speciation

The concept of sympatric speciation is very old; in fact, it is a good deal older than that of geographical speciation. It was no doubt the prevailing concept in the latter half of the nineteenth century, Moritz Wagner's efforts notwithstanding. Darwin himself, Weismann (1872), and other leading evolutionists frequently endorsed it rather unequivocally. Even after the importance of isolation began to be realized, sympatric speciation was not abandoned but revived under the label "physiological selection." The muddy thinking of this period is typified by the following quotation: "Suppose that on the same oceanic island the original colony has begun to segregate into secondary groups under the influence of natural selection, sexual selection, physiological selection or any of the other forms of isolation, there will be as many lines of divergent evolution going on at the same time (and here on the same area) as there are forms of isolation affecting the oceanic colony." (Romanes, Part 3, 1897, p. 22.) This is a nearly perfect statement of the concept that species originate sympatrically by segregation of individuals within a single population. The truth is, of course, that a colony on an isolated oceanic island is about the least likely population to break up into several species.

Various forms of sympatric speciation have again been championed in recent years. A detailed analysis of the evidence quoted in favor of this concept is too long for the present discussion and has been published separately (Mayr, 1947). Here I shall content myself with a summary. Reasons listed as proving sympatric speciation:

> The impossibility to conceive that the wonderfully efficient way in which numerous species of a locality utilize their environment could have originated in geographical isolation.
>
> The fact that certain animals may become conditioned to new ecological conditions.
>
> The existence of sympatric species swarms, particularly in fresh water lakes.

Assumptions often made in connection with sympatric speciation:[2]

> New species are founded by aberrant individuals of the parent species.
>
> Species differences are originated by few genes.
>
> Reproductive isolation is by necessity linked with ecological divergence, and vice versa.

Difficulties of the sympatric speciation concept:

> It is difficult to visualize how two balanced well-adapted gene complexes can develop in the same area.
>
> Geographical races are always more or less different in their ecological requirements, and all so-called ecological races are at least microgeographical races.
>
> Incipient cases of sympatric speciation are unknown.

It seems legitimate to conclude from these facts that there is no process of sympatric speciation that differs in principle from spatial speciation. Neither is there any need to postulate it, since all known facts are consistent with geographical (i.e. spatial) speciation. The same ecological differences that are quoted as necessitating the acceptance of the concept of ecological speciation exist between species that are known to have originated in geographical isolation. Various seemingly aberrant phenomena, such as species swarms in lakes, can be interpreted as having resulted from origin of species in spatial isolation.

The process of speciation can thus be summarized as follows:

There is a selective advantage in the multiplication of species since

2 The validity of these three assumptions is considered in Mayr, 1947.

it permits a more efficient utilization of the environment by organisms.

Speciation proceeds through the gradual genetic modification of spatially segregated populations (excepting polyploidy and other aberrant phenomena).

Gene flow between such populations must be greatly reduced with the help of factors of the environment, in order to permit the development of genetically-controlled isolating mechanisms.

OUTLOOK

The findings of the taxonomist on the process of speciation are merely a progress report. Further work will lead to an expansion as well as possibly to a modification of our present concepts. The findings, as they are, carry a different message to the paleontologist, to the geneticist, and to the taxonomist.

PALEONTOLOGIST. The work on living species shows that speciation is a very gradual process and that sudden changes are exceedingly rare. Hence it becomes apparent that the so-called "mutations" in the paleontological record are not genetic events. Rather, as Rensch (1933) and others have pointed out, "mutational" breaks in phylogenetic lineages must be interpreted as biogeographical events (shifts in populations).

The splitting of one population into two seems to be possible only in spatial segregation. However, in the paleontological literature numerous cases are reported of lineages that forked at a single locality in successive strata into two or more species as, for example, the Steinheim snails. It is highly desirable that paleontologists should reinvestigate such cases with the best modern stratigraphic and biometric methods. A confirmation of the older findings would be a powerful endorsement of the hypothesis of sympatric speciation.

GENETICIST. The findings of the systematists pose a number of genetic questions, such as the following:

How great is the number of the genetic differences between species that have recently completed speciation? What is the number of loci involved?

What is the nature of the events that occur during the reorganization of gene complexes in incipient species?

How much gene flow is permissible between diverging incipient species?

Obviously it will be impossible to give a complete answer to these questions, but it seems very desirable that more work be done along these lines.

TAXONOMIST. The process of speciation in ordinary terrestrial bisexual animals is fairly well established. There are, however, large groups of animals of whose speciation nothing is known. This is particularly true of all groups with aberrant reproductive mechanisms. A study of the speciation pattern among animals with temporary or permanent parthenogenesis, self-fertilizing hermaphroditism, and various forms of temporary or permanent asexual reproduction is badly needed. Such studies should first determine whether or not there are well-defined populations within species in these groups, and whether or not some of these populations have the earmarks of incipient species. The subspecies concept has never been consistently employed in any of these groups.

Work along these lines by paleontologists, geneticists, and taxonomists will lead to further advances of our knowledge of the process of speciation.

REFERENCES

Bodenheimer, F. S. 1938. *Problems of Animal Ecology.* Oxford University Press, 183 pp.

Chopard, L. 1938. *La biologie des orthoptères.* Paris, 541 pp.

Darwin, Ch. 1859. *On the Origin of Species by means of Natural Selection, or the Preservation of Favored Races in the Struggle for Life.* John Murray, London.

Dobzhansky, Th. 1941. *Genetics and the Origin of Species.* 2nd rev. ed., Columbia University Press, 446 pp.

——. 1947. Adaptive changes induced by natural selection in wild populations of *Drosophila. Evolution, 1,* 1-16.

Epling, C. 1947. Natural hybridization of *Salvia apiana* and S. *mellifera. Evolution, 1,* 69-78.

Ghilarov, M. S. 1945. Influence of the character of dispersal on the ontogenesis of insects. *Jour. Gen. Biol. Moscow, 6,* 36.

Goldschmidt, R. B. 1945. The structure of Podoptera, a homoeotic mutant of *Drosophila melanogaster. J. Morph., 77,* 71-103.

Grinnell, J. 1943. *Joseph Grinnell's Philosophy of Nature.* University of California Press, 237 pp.

Gunter, G. 1943. A "dumpy" croaker, *Micropogon undulatus,* and its significance with respect to rapid species change. *Copeia,* 52-53.

Hubbs, Carl L., and E. C. Raney. 1946. Endemic fish fauna of Lake Waccamaw, North Carolina. *Misc. Publ. Mus. Zool., Univ. Michigan,* No. 65, 30 pp.

Huxley, J. 1942. *Evolution, the Modern Synthesis.* George Allen and Unwin, Ltd. 645 pp.

Jacobi, A. 1900. Lage und Form biogeographischer Gebiete. *Zeitschr. Ges. Erdk. Berlin, 35,* 147-238.

Jahn, H. 1942. Zur Ökologie und Biologie der Vögel Japans. *J. Ornith., 90,* 1-302.

Jones, Arthur W. 1944. *Macrostomum hustedi,* n. sp., a morphological and cytological study of a rhabdocoel turbellarian. *J. Morph., 75,* 347-359.

Kirikov, S. V. 1940. On the connection between the red crossbills and the coniferous trees. *Bull. Acad. Sci. U.S.S.R.* (Biol.), 359-376.

Lorković, Z. 1941. Die Chromosomenzahlen in der Spermatogenese der Tagfalter. *Chromosoma, 2,* 155-191.

Mayr, Ernst. 1942. *Systematics and the Origin of Species.* Columbia University Press. 334 pp.

——. 1947. Ecological factors in speciation. *Evolution, 1,* 263-288.

——. 1948. The bearing of the new systematics on genetical problems. *Advances in Genetics, 2,* 205-237.

Miller, A. H. 1942. Habitat selection among higher vertebrates and its relation to intraspecific variation. *Amer. Nat., 76,* 25-35.

Moore, J. A. 1946. Hybridization between *Rana palustris* and different geographical forms of *Rana pipiens*. Proc. Nat. Acad., *32*, 209-212.

Noll, H. 1934. Die Stammesgenossenschaften unserer Vögel. *Schweiz. Arch. f. Orn., 1*, 176-191.

Patterson, J. T., et al. 1947. Studies in the genetics of *Drosophila*. V. Isolating mechanisms. *University of Texas Publ. 4720*, 184 pp.

Pavan, C. 1946. Observations and experiments on the cave fish *Pimelodella kronei* and its relatives. Amer. Nat., *80*, 343-361.

Rensch, B. 1933. Zool. Systematik und Artbildungsproblem. *Verh. Dtsch. Zool. Ges.*, 1933, 19-83.

Romanes, George J. 1897. *Darwin and after Darwin*. Part 3. Open Court Publishing Co., 181 pp.

Speyer, W. 1938. Über das Vorkommen von Lokalrassen des Kleinen Frostspanners (*Cheimatobia brumata* L.). *Arb. physiol. angew. Ent. Berlin-Dahlem*, 5, 50-76.

Stebbins, G. Ledyard, Jr. 1945. Role of isolation in the differentiation of plant species. *Nature*, *155*, 150-151, No. 3927.

Stegmann, B. 1935. Unterschiede im oekologischen Verhalten als taxonomisches Kriterium. *Orn. Monatsber.*, *43*, 17-20.

Stresemann, E. 1934. Aves, in: Kükenthal-Krumbach, *Handbuch der Zoologie*, VII, 2. Berlin (Walter de Gruyter).

——. 1943. Oekologische Sippen-, Rassen-, und Artunterschiede bei Vögeln. *J. Ornith.*, *91*, 305-328.

Studnitz, G. v. 1935. Geographisch bedingte Unterschiede physiologischer und psychologischer Natur zwischen Vögeln einer Art Bezw. Rasse. *Schrift. Naturw. Verein Schleswig-Holsteins*, *21*, 58-67.

Svärdson, G. 1945. *Chromosome Studies on Salmonidae*. Meddel. Stat. undersökn. sötvattensfisket. Stockholm, Nr. 23, 151 pp.

Turesson, G. 1922. The genotypical response of the plant species to the habitat. *Hereditas*, *3*, 211-350.

Weismann, A. 1872. *Ueber den Einfluss der Isolierung auf die Artbildung*. Leipzig, 108 pp.

White, M. 1945. *Animal Cytology and Evolution*. Cambridge University Press.

——. 1946. The evidence against polyploidy in sexually-reproducing animals. *Amer. Nat.*, *80*, 610-618.

Wright, Sewall. 1943. Isolation by distance. *Genetics*, *28*, 114-138.

Zimmerman, Elwood C. 1943. On Wheeler's paper concerning evolution and the Nemertean Gorgonorhynchus. *Amer. Nat.*, *77*, 373-376.

· 15 ·

THE SIGNIFICANCE OF ECOLOGICAL ISOLATION

BY DAVID LACK[1]

In this paper is presented a brief synthesis of studies by the writer on ecological differences between species and their significance in regard to the origin of new forms. Examples are chosen almost exclusively from birds because, though the writer believes that his conclusions apply more widely, it is dangerous for a specialist to select examples from groups with which he has not worked at first hand. One reason for this paper is to bring the problem to the attention of specialists in other groups. Knowledge of the work on speciation in the synthesis by Mayr (1942) is assumed; indeed the present paper might be regarded as an appendage to Mayr's main thesis.

HABITAT SELECTION

Closely related species of birds living in the same region tend to occupy different habitats. At one time it was naïvely assumed that specific differences in climatic tolerance or food preference were responsible, but birds are homoiothermic animals comparatively independent of their physical environments, and many of them have very generalized diets. When, for instance, one finds two English buntings, *Emberiza schoeniclus* and *E. citrinella*, the former in marshes, the latter in dry scrub, each taking a varied diet of both plants and invertebrates, but the former mainly marsh plants and insects, the latter mainly those of drier country, it is reasonable to suppose that the difference in their diets is a result, rather than a cause, of their difference in habitat (Lack, 1933).

Birds select their habitats, utilizing recognition features which are not necessarily those directly essential to their existence (Lack, 1933, 1937). Originally, the writer suggested that differences in recognition factors might themselves provide a sufficient explanation of the habitat differences between species, but later this view was abandoned (Lack, 1940), the criticism of Miller (1942) being valid. The error arose through a failure, not uncommon among biologists at that time, to distinguish between the proximate factors concerned with internal mechanism and the ultimate factors concerned with survival value. This distinction may be illustrated by reference to an invertebrate which in nature is found only in fresh

[1] Director of Edward Grey Institute of Field Ornithology, Oxford University, England.

waters between certain temperature limits. It might be shown, first, that the animal selects its habitat through a direct response to temperature, and secondly that, under laboratory conditions, it readily survives in temperatures outside these limits. In this case, though temperature is the proximate factor controlling habitat selection, the ultimate factor determining survival is different, perhaps competition for food with another species. A temperature response has been evolved because the animal is thereby brought into the habitat where it can survive.

In the same way, recognition factors proximately determine a bird's habitat, but the writer thinks that, ultimately, the habitat limits have been determined by natural selection. Occasionally a bird breeds outside its typical habitat, and that such irregularities do not persist suggests that they are eliminated by selection. It is also significant that in one part of its range a species may have a more restricted habitat than in another, correlated with the presence or absence of a related species. However, while there is some circumstantial evidence, there is as yet no proof that natural selection is involved in such cases, and it will be very difficult to obtain. Experiment under realistic conditions is impossible, since, when birds are transferred to a strange habitat, they merely fly back home.

Speciation via Ecological Isolation

To account for the habitat differences between closely related species, various writers, formerly including Lack (1933), suggested that where a population is spread over several habitats ecological isolation might lead to subspecific differentiation, and so eventually to speciation. However, Mayr (1942) in his review emphasizes two strong arguments against this view, with which the present writer is in full agreement.

First, in birds, subspecific differentiation is far more pronounced on islands than over continental land masses, though the latter usually provide more varied physical conditions and habitats; i.e. isolation of populations *per se*, and not divergence in their environments, is the major factor in subspecific differentiation. The bird species occupying different habitats in the same region usually have numerous border zones where they come in contact, the degree of isolation is certainly not complete, and it does not seem sufficient for the subspecific differentiation of populations. This view has been criticized by Thorpe (1945), but neither Mayr nor the writer thinks it at all likely that this criticism has validity in birds.

The second objection is much stronger, that in birds there are no known subspecies or incipient species in process of differentiation in adjacent habitats in the same region. All avian subspecies are isolated geographically. Some also differ in ecology, examples being given by Miller (1942), Stresemann (1943), and others, but in all such cases there is also geographical isolation.

In addition to these two negative objections, there is the positive point that the work started by Stegmann and Rensch twenty years ago and summarized by Mayr (1942) has shown conclusively that, in birds, sub-species differentiated in geographical isolation can give rise to new species when they later meet in the same region. Moreover, when the arguments in the next section are admitted, there are no cases known in birds where this method of speciation does not fit the available facts. Rensch queried the Galapagos finches (Geospizinae) in this respect, but the writer has strong reasons for thinking that geographical isolation is the key factor here, as in other birds (Lack, 1947).[2]

When Species Meet

Mayr's review left unexplained the ecological differences between species. Why, if they do not originate in this way, do bird species so often differ in ecology? The answer is, surely, to be found through a considera-tion of what happens when two forms, differentiated in geographical isolation, later meet in the same area. There is first a genetical problem, that of interbreeding, which is not considered here. There is also an ecological problem, that of competition. The chance is negligible that two such forms will be equally efficient, which leaves four possibilities:

First, one form may be so much better adapted than the other that it eliminates it. This will not usually have left any trace for the contemporary observer. Secondly, one form may be better adapted than the other in part of its range, the other in the rest. The result will be geographical replacement. Thirdly, one form may be better adapted than the other in part of the original habitat, the other in the rest. The result will be ecological replacement. In this and the previous case, there may be an area of overlap where both forms are about equally well adapted. Fourthly, one form may be better adapted for taking certain foods, the other for other foods, in which case the two species may be able to live in the same region and the same habitat without competing.

To test these possibilities, the writer has surveyed the ecology of five groups of birds: (i) British passerines (Lack, 1944); (ii) passerines on remote islands (Lack, 1944); (iii) British species of Cormorant (*Phala-crocorax*) (Lack, 1945a); (iv) European birds of prey (Falconiformes and Strigiformes) (Lack, 1946); (v) Darwin's finches of the Galapagos (Geospizinae) (Lack, 1947). In these five groups, nearly every species was found to be isolated ecologically in one of the above ways from all closely related species. The few apparent exceptions may be due merely to inadequate knowledge, apart from the special case of superabundant

---

[2] When this thesis is discussed in relation to small animals, it seems better to replace the term "geographical isolation" by "spatial isolation."

foods, discussed later. The ecological isolation of Darwin's finches is summarized in Table I.

The necessity for ecological isolation was brought to the writer's attention by the statement of Gause (1934) that two species with the same ecology cannot persist in the same region. Gause, who derived his views from the population studies of Lotka and Volterra, explored the manner of competition between species, a study since amplified by Crombie (1945), but the basic postulate is all that is needed for the present argument.

TABLE I

ECOLOGICAL ISOLATION OF DARWIN'S FINCHES

A. On large central Galapagos islands

Species	Main breeding habitat	Main diet	Ecological niche
Geospiza			
magnirostris	semi-arid lowlands*	seeds	large ground-finch
fortis	" " " *	"	medium " "
fuliginosa	" " " *	"	small " "
difficilis	humid uplands	?	humid forest ground-finch
scandens	semi-arid lowlands*	Opuntia	cactus ground-finch
Camarhynchus			
crassirostris	humid uplands*	fruit and leaves	vegetarian tree-finch
psittacula	" " *	insects	large insectivorous tree-finch
pauper	" " *	"	medium " " "
parvulus	" " *	"	small " " "
pallidus	" " *	"	woodpecker-like
heliobates	coastal mangroves	"	mangrove tree-finch
Certhidea			
olivacea	arid lowlands and humid uplands	small insects	warbler-like

*Notes: (i) All the *Geospiza* spp. which breed in the semi-arid lowlands, and all the *Camarhynchus* spp. which breed in the humid uplands, also breed in the extensive transitional zone between the two, so here they overlap widely in habitat.

(ii) On Chatham Island, *G. magnirostris* is absent and *G. fortis* attains an unusually large size, and C. *psittacula* is absent (also C. *pauper*) and C. *parvulus* attains an unusually large size.

(iii) C. *pauper* and C. *heliobates* are very local species.

B. On small outlying Galapagos islands

Note: On the small outlying islands, the only available habitat is semi-arid lowland, and no *Camarhynchus* spp. are known to breed. The number of *Geospiza* spp. is also reduced, with the result that a species sometimes occupies an unusual niche, or combines niches which on the large islands are filled by two separate species. In such cases there are corresponding modifications in beak and size. The reduction in the number of species and of ecological niches, even in the same general type of habitat, on islands as compared with continents, and on small as compared with large islands, seems widespread in birds, and should be studied further.

TABLE I (cont.)

Ecological niche	Tower Island	Wenman Island	Culpepper Island	Hood Island
large ground-finch	G. magnirostris	G. magnirostris	G. conirostris	
cactus ground-finch	G. conirostris			G. conirostris
small ground-finch	G. difficilis	G. difficilis	G. difficilis	G. fuliginosa
warbler-like	C. olivacea	C. olivacea	C. olivacea	C. olivacea

Note how on one island the species *G. conirostris* occupies the cactus-feeding niche, on another that of the large ground-finch, and on a third island it combines the two. Likewise, *G. difficilis* on one island occupies the niche of the small ground-finch, on two others it combines this with cactus-feeding, and on the large central islands its niche is quite different, as it is found not in the semi-arid lowlands but in the humid forest. In all these cases, there are corresponding adaptations in beak. For example, where the species *G. conirostris* or *G. difficilis* feeds on cactus, the beak is modified similarly to that of the species *G. scandens*, which fills this niche on the central islands.

C. Cocos Island

No adaptive radiation. *Pinaroloxias inornata* is the only species. This is a forest form with a beak not unlike that of *Certhidea olivacea*.

The considerations in this and the previous section indicate that, *in birds, ecological isolation is primarily a result, rather than a cause, of speciation.* However, it should be added that if two forms differentiated in geographical isolation are both to persist when they later meet, they must already have evolved some ecological or adaptive difference in their period of isolation, i.e. it is those geographical races that differ in ecology which are the potential new species. But geographical isolation is the primary factor in producing such ecological differentiation. The validity of these views is strongly supported by the recent paper on the fantails of the group *Rhipidura rufifrons* by Mayr and Moynihan (1946).

ISOLATION BY HABITAT

Of particular significance for the views developed here are those cases in which a species has a different habitat in one region than another, correlated with the presence or absence of other species. For instance, the lowland semi-desert of each Galapagos island is occupied by one and only one species of small ground-finch, usually *Geospiza fuliginosa*, but on the northern islands where *G. fuliginosa* is absent, the niche is filled by another species, *G. difficilis*. The latter species also breeds on the large central islands, but here it is confined to the upland humid forest, whereas *G. fuliginosa* breeds only at lower altitudes. So in one part of their range these two species occur in the same region but in different habitats, and in another part they occur in the same type of habitat but are separated geographically. Somewhat parallel, there are cases in Europe where two passerine species breed in different habitats in the same region, but migrate to winter in different geographical regions (Lack, 1944). Hence the ecological isolation of two species is not always achieved in the same way.

Again, while the European Chaffinch *Fringilla coelebs* is in most of its range abundant in both broadleaved and coniferous woods, the race of this species on Tenerife and Gran Canaria does not breed in conifers. On these islands the coniferous woods are inhabited by a related species *F. teydea*, which systematists consider to have been derived from *F. coelebs* by an earlier invasion of the Canary Islands. On another Canary island, Palma, *F. teydea* is absent, and here *F. coelebs* breeds also in conifers. Hence the absence of *F. coelebs* from conifers in Tenerife and Gran Canaria seems clearly due to competition with the other species. A number of similar examples are known, mainly from islands, but also from continents.

The views developed here imply that closely related species which occupy different habitats have associated adaptive differences. In a few cases such adaptations are known, e.g. there is a difference in the length of the hind claw in the European Meadow *Anthus pratensis* and Tree Pipits *A. trivialis*, this being in the same direction as that found between other terrestrial as compared with arboreal birds; but in most cases such adaptive differences have yet to be described. Also, as mentioned earlier, there is not as yet any experimental proof that the habitat restrictions of birds are imposed by natural selection.

COMPETITION FOR FOOD

While closely related bird species often live in different habitats, it is equally striking that, when they occur in the same habitat, they differ in diet. This was shown in all five of the writer's surveys. The case for sympatric speciation through isolation by habitat is, if improbable, at least arguable. But the differentiation of two bird populations living in the same region and habitat but differing in diet is extremely difficult to conceive, as there would be virtually no spatial isolation. On the other hand, isolation by diet and isolation by habitat are likely alternative consequences for species which meet in the same area and tend to compete.

Closely related bird species which live in the same habitat often differ markedly in size. In a number of cases, e.g. Goshawk *Accipiter gentilis* and Sparrowhawk *A. nisus*, a parallel difference has been shown to exist in their prey, and in other cases such a difference probably occurs. Evidently a difference in body-size is one of the easiest ways in which a difference in diet has been evolved. Such size-differentiated species are prominent on oceanic islands but are by no means confined to them, e.g. *Geospiza* and *Camarhynchus* in the Galapagos, *Nesospiza* on Tristan da Cunha, but also *Loxia* in Europe, etc.

Competition for food requires much further study. The mathematics involved has been developed only for monophagous predators, whereas nearly all birds are highly polyphagous. While two monophagous species cannot both persist if they compete for the same food, the polyphagous bird species which live in the same habitat often show an overlap in diet. It is not known how much, and what type of, overlap can be tolerated.

Goshawk and Sparrowhawk show a small overlap in diet probably at all times of year. More interesting is the case of "temporarily superabundant foods" (Lack, 1946). When fruits or caterpillars are seasonally abundant, several passerine species in the same habitat may turn to feed on them, both in Britain and in the Galapagos. Although the food in question may temporarily constitute most of their diet, such species will not be in competition provided that the food supply is excessive. It also seems important that the eventual decrease of the food is not due to the birds, but to some independent factor, such as falling in the case of fruit, and pupation in the case of caterpillars. As already mentioned, the passerine species concerned in these cases differ in ecology at other seasons of the year, though in the case of the Galapagos finches the superficial appearance of overlap in diet was enough to cause a bad misinterpretation of the data in a first analysis (compare the accounts in Lack, 1945b, and by earlier workers, with that in Lack, 1947).

A more striking case of temporarily superabundant foods is provided by the several species of predatory birds and mammals which can be found in the same region and habitat preying on the same species of "plague" rodent, such as the vole *Microtus* or the lemming *Lemmus*. In these cases, the same prey-species provides the bulk of the diet for two or three years, but during this time it would seem to be superabundant, and its decrease is apparently not caused by the predators but by disease or some other factor. Further work is needed to prove whether, as is suggested, each predatory species takes a different alternative prey during the periods when the rodent is scarce.

Two species might also be able to live in the same habitat on the same diet without competition provided that their numbers were controlled by predators or parasites. This situation seems rare or non-existent in birds, but might well be important in small invertebrates, and requires exploration. For instance is it necessary that such species should always, or only usually, be kept below the food limit? Again, is the claim of Nicholson (1933) correct that, if two species are controlled by the same predator or parasite, both cannot persist together? This depends on a parallel argument to that developed for food-competition, but, while it seems logically true if the predator hunts at random, both prey-species might possibly persist if the predator alternated between them, seeking whichever was the more abundant. This situation might be further complicated by polyphagy.

SPECIATION AND ADAPTIVE EVOLUTION

It has sometimes been stated, e.g. by Huxley (1942), that the origin of species has little to do with the main story of evolution, that speciation merely results in irrelevant discontinuities which have no influence on long-term adaptive trends. This view the writer believes to be wrong.

Speciation commonly results in the presence in the same area of two species where formerly there was one. When both persist, the ecology of each is almost certain to be restricted, which in turn allows each to become more specialized. For example, the European Chaffinch cannot become specialized for broadleaved as distinct from coniferous woods, or the reverse, as it is abundant in both types. But the Tenerife form of this species can become specialized for broadleaved woods and the closely related *F. teydea* for conifers, as each is restricted to the habitat in question. These habitat restrictions, and the possibilities of increased specialization, are due to the two forms meeting and persisting in the same area, i.e. to the origin of a new species.[3]

The point under discussion in this section is shown particularly well by Darwin's finches (Geospizinae). The Galapagos archipelago provides admirable opportunities for the geographical isolation of populations and their subsequent re-meeting, and this group of birds has diverged into a multiplicity of species and subspecies. Further, there has been an adaptive radiation, with the evolution of new and quite unfinchlike types, warbler-like, tit-like, woodpecker-like, cactus-feeding, and others. The writer considers that the essential first step in this adaptive radiation has been the geographical isolation of populations, though it has secondarily been greatly assisted by the paucity of other land-birds in the Galapagos. This has allowed greater ecological divergence in geographical races of the same species than is possible on a continent at the present day, where the presence of efficient types in other genera restricts each form to a narrow ecological niche. As already discussed, it is only those geographical races which differ in ecology which can persist as separate species when they later meet in the same area. Such meeting in turn results in a greater ecological restriction of the new species, and this allows the further specialization of each. Any subsequent tendency for increased ecological isolation through their further ecological divergence will also have been assisted by the paucity of other land-birds.

[3] Modern workers seem agreed that *F. teydea* was the original Chaffinch in the Canary Islands and became so distinct in isolation that it was able to keep separate from the much later second derivative from the European stock, i.e. speciation took place allopatrically.

It would seem that, in the Galapagos, this process has been repeated a number of times, the new species in turn spreading over the archipelago, producing geographical races, some of which diverged in ecology, that these later met and persisted in the same area, resulting in further ecological restriction and differentiation, and hence in further specialization, and that in this way an adaptive radiation was gradually evolved. This picture of evolution fits all the known facts about the Geospizinae, and there is no need to invoke some special or unusual type of evolution, as has been thought necessary in the past (excessive inherent variability, repeated hybridization, sympatric speciation, etc.).

One species of Geospizinae occurs outside the Galapagos, on Cocos Island. This bird is so different from the others that it is placed in a genus of its own. This suggests that it has been on Cocos for a long time. Nevertheless, there is still only a single species and subspecies there and, of particular relevance to this section, there has been no adaptive radiation. Cocos resembles the Galapagos in providing varied habitats and in having a great paucity of other land-birds, but it differs in one essential respect: it is a single island, not an archipelago. Hence there has been no opportunity for the geographical isolation of populations and hence no evolution of new species or of an adaptive radiation. There has likewise been no adaptive radiation of an endemic bird species on other single oceanic islands, however isolated. Such radiations have occurred only on oceanic archipelagoes, notably Hawaii, and, further back in time, on the continental land-masses, i.e. only where there has been opportunity for the geographical isolation of bird populations.

The Galapagos finches differ from the passerine birds of large continental regions in that their adaptive radiation is less complex and much more recent, but it is of essentially the same type, differing in degree, not kind. The writer therefore believes that the type of evolution outlined above has much wider application than to the Galapagos alone. The extent to which similar views might apply in groups outside birds is matter for further discussion.[4]

[4] A few points may be briefly mentioned. In invertebrates, particularly insects, ecological isolation requires study, especially to determine the ways in which predator or parasite control might modify views here reached for a group of animals in which control by food supply seems paramount. In smaller animals and also in plants, transference of species to unusual habitats is not impracticable, thus permitting experimental analysis. In plants, competition is greatly affected by the time factor. The situation seems very different in forest trees which, once started, may live for several hundred years, than it is in fast-growing annuals, in which emphasis may be on the rapid exploitation of temporary habitats. Finally, the writer would stress the need for a more complete logical and mathematical treatment of competition, particularly allowing for polyphagy and for composite predator-prey chains.

SUMMARY

1. Birds select their habitats through recognition factors which have been evolved through natural selection, and this is ultimately responsible for the habitat differences between species.

2. Bird species are normally isolated from each other ecologically, either by region, or by habitat, or by diet. This is an inevitable consequence of competition and is a result, rather than a cause, of speciation.

3. Competition for food requires further study and analysis.

4. Speciation is closely associated with adaptive radiation, the links being as follows: (a) geographical isolation of populations, (b) morphological differentiation, (c) partial inter-sterility and partial ecological divergence, (d) re-meeting, with persistence of each form as a new species when both genetic and ecological isolation are sufficient, (e) increased ecological restriction and differentiation, and increased specialization of each form to its modified niche, and (f) further geographical spread of each form, with a repetition of the whole process from (a) to (e).

REFERENCES

Crombie, A. C. 1945. On competition between different species of graminivorous insects. *Proc. Roy. Soc. B.132*, 362-395.

Gause, G. F. 1934. *The Struggle for Existence.*

Huxley, J. S. 1942. *Evolution: The Modern Synthesis.*

Lack, D. 1933. Habitat selection in birds. *J. Anim. Ecol.*, 2, 239-262.

——. 1937. The psychological factor in bird distribution. *Brit. Birds*, 31, 130-136.

——. 1940. Habitat selection and speciation in birds. *Brit. Birds*, 34, 80-84.

——. 1944. Ecological aspects of species-formation in birds. *Ibis*, 1944, 260-286.

——. 1945a. The ecology of closely related species with special reference to Cormorant (*Phalacrocorax carbo*) and Shag (*P. aristotelis*). *J. Anim. Ecol.*, 14, 12-16.

——. 1945b. The Galapagos finches: A study in variation. *Occas. Pap. Calif. Acad. Sci.*, 21.

——. 1946. Competition for food by birds of prey. *J. Anim. Ecol.*, 15, 123-129.

——. 1947. *Darwin's Finches.*

Mayr, E. 1942. *Systematics and the Origin of Species.*

——, and M. Moynihan. 1946. Evolution in the *Rhipidura rufifrons* group. *Amer. Mus. Novit.*, No. 1321.

Miller, A. H. 1942. Habitat selection among higher vertebrates and its relation to intraspecific variation. *Amer. Nat.*, 76, 25-35.

Nicholson, A. J. 1933. The balance of animal populations. *J. Anim. Ecol.*, 2, 131-178.

Stresemann, E. 1943. Oekologische Sippen-, Rassen- und Artunterschiede bei Vögeln. *Jour. f. Ornith.*, 91, 305-328.

Thorpe, W. H. 1945. The evolutionary significance of habitat selection. *J. Anim. Ecol.*, 14, 67-70.

· 16 ·

EARLY STAGES IN ALLOPATRIC SPECIATION

BY E. B. FORD[1]

THERE can be little doubt that in bisexually reproducing organisms sympatric speciation is virtually limited to the establishment of polyploidy, which must itself be a matter of great difficulty in the absence of self-fertilization. It is indeed impossible to be sure that speciation within a freely interbreeding community has never in exceptional circumstances taken place. Yet Mayr (1942), who has made an especially thorough and critical analysis of this subject, holds that such an event, if it occurs at all, is at any rate so rare as to be of negligible significance in evolution, a view that appears to be in full accord with theoretical considerations and with the great bulk of observational data.

Some degree of geographical isolation therefore is an essential for species formation, whether this be achieved by physical barriers, such as mountains or valleys, land or water, or by mere distance, as at the opposite ends of a long cline. A vast body of information is accumulating on this process, but it should be remarked that it may have occurred or be well advanced along its course in many unsuspected instances. For sterility, partial or complete, is sometimes built up between groups which differ so little from one another, when judged by the characters normally used in taxonomy, that its presence may remain unsuspected. Without breeding tests, *Drosophila pseudoobscura* and *D. persimilis*, formerly known as *D. pseudoobscura* Races A and B, would never have been distinguished from one another, nor would it have been supposed that those subspecies of *Lymantria dispar* which give rise to sexual abnormalities on crossing have in fact departed far enough on the road to speciation to do so.

An earlier stage even than incipient reproductive incompatibility may be recognized in allopatric speciation: that in which a sufficiently large number of substitutions have been incorporated in the gene-complex for the genetic adjustments of certain characters to be upset on crossing, while the switch-mechanism controlling maleness and femaleness remains yet unaffected. Indeed this is surely to be anticipated, for the very nature of the sex control suggests that the quantitative reaction involved will have a fairly large "value for safety," the excess of sex-determining substance, at all levels from the primary products of the genes onwards,

[1] University Reader in Genetics, The University Museum, Oxford, England.

{ 309 }

being normally considerable in either direction, since in most forms it ought to be uninfluenced by ordinary environmental and genetic changes.

The point may be illustrated by the results of racial crosses in the moth *Ectropis crepuscularia* Hb. (Geometridae), but as there is some confusion in the literature in regard to this species, its status in the British Isles must first briefly be mentioned. It is single-brooded and occurs throughout England and Scotland and is widespread in Ireland. A deeply speckled semi-melanic form, *delamerensis* White, has become established in Cheshire and the neighboring counties where, in some localities, it is now common. It is inherited as a simple dominant. There also exists a still darker variety, *nigra* Th. Mieg., which is blackish except for a pale submarginal line. It is found sporadically throughout the range of the insect, but is always rare. It is unifactorial and recessive. The very closely related species *Ectropis bistortata* Goeze can only be distinguished from *E. crepuscularia* with difficulty, being on the whole browner, but many specimens are not separable on their visible characteristics. It is double-brooded, is not found so far north in Britain, and seems to be absent from Ireland. No variety comparable with *delamerensis* of *E. crepuscularia* is known in *E. bistortata*, but a recessive blackish mutant, *defessaria* Frr., occurs as a rarity, and this may well be homologous with the dark recessive form of *E. crepuscularia*.

I have bred this latter variety, *E. crepuscularia* var. *nigra*, from a female found in Berkshire, and have reared 73 F_1 specimens and 164 of the F_2 generation (comprising four broods of 63, 56, 34 and 11). The variety behaved as a complete recessive throughout. I also crossed melanics from this stock with normal Irish examples bred from wild larvae, and these did not differ in appearance from the ordinary English form. In two of the families so obtained the dominance adjustment broke down, for the moths of the F_1 generation (broods of 29 and 27 respectively) were distinctly darker than the normal English or Irish insects, and in F_2 (comprising 107 in all) the heterozygotes ranged from a shade approaching, though I think always distinct from, var. *nigra* to that of the normal homozygotes. One more family was reared from a racial cross of the same kind in which, however, var. *nigra* was almost completely recessive (17 F_1 and 38 F_2 specimens) though in each generation two unusually dark individuals emerged, and these may reasonably be ascribed to a slight heterozygous expression of the *nigra* gene. No sexual abnormalities were detected in any of the broods resulting from these racial crosses, and the numbers of males and females closely approached equality in all of them.

Instances of failures in dominance on crossing subspecies or species are of course well known, as in the work of Harland (1933) on *Gossypium*; but in the present example the comparison between that situation and the still normal sex control is a valuable one. Considering the recurrent nature of mutation, it may be assumed that the *nigra* gene exists in the Irish as well as in the English population of *E. crepuscularia*, though I have no definite information on the matter. But it appears that the gene-complex has become adjusted to it in different ways in the two countries (whether *nigra* is fully recessive in Ireland, as is probable, or not), suggesting an early stage in the divergence of the two races.

The obvious possibility of speciation taking place owing to isolation through mere distance, at the opposite ends of a long cline, has been little explored. It may conveniently be illustrated by work on the butterfly *Coenonympha tullia* Müller (Satyridae). This passes through a long cline from Scotland down to Shropshire and Staffordshire, its most southerly habitat in England, which is distinguished by a gradual increase in spotting and darkening in color from north to south, the males being of a deeper shade than the females (Ford, 1946). The butterfly is in Britain an inhabitant of moors and marshes from sea level up to about 1800 feet, but is absent from agricultural land. Therefore it forms colonies throughout its range, and these must now be to a considerable degree isolated from one another, especially in the south. But it is likely that there is some flow of genes between many of them even today, and this must have been much greater before the agricultural improvements of the last half of the eighteenth and early nineteenth centuries. Indeed the north to south cline is rather uniformly expressed, specimens from all localities at a given level within it being very similar. On interbreeding males from Merioneth with females from northern Scotland, I obtained several sexually abnormal individuals, which were restricted to the females; they amounted to 5 out of 36 females bred.

Patches of the darker male coloration were to be seen on the wings of these 5 intersexes. Their prothoracic legs were intermediate between those of normal males and females, which differ rather markedly in the Satyridae, while the internal and external genitalia were abnormal, but were imperfectly developed rather than intermediate in structure. The numbers of these intersexes per brood are given in Table I. I obtained

TABLE I

The occurrence of intersexes among the offspring of Merioneth males and Scotch females of *Coenonympha tullia*.

Brood	Males		Females	
	Normals	Intersexes	Normals	Intersexes
1	25	—	15	4
2	8	—	9	1
3	12	—	7	—
Total	45	—	31	5

only a single successful reverse mating, that between a male from Scotland and a female from Merioneth, and I failed to rear the larvae. It will be noticed that the distribution of these sexual abnormalities conforms with the view expressed long ago by Haldane (1922) that when one sex among the offspring of a cross between species or subspecies is abnormal, rare, or absent, it will be the heterogametic one. This is the female in the Lepidoptera.

Such results, both in their nature and irregularity, are surely of the kind which may be expected sometimes to occur at an early stage in allopatric speciation.

It is clear that evolutionary changes are greatly favored by the subdivision of a species into isolated groups. For example, an isolated colony of the butterfly *Euphydryas aurinia* Rt. (Nymphalidae) in Cumberland, England, was kept under observation for many years (Ford and Ford, 1930). Specimens were very scarce from 1913 to 1919, but from 1920 to 1926 a rapid increase in numbers took place, and by 1925 they had become excessively common and remained so until the observations ceased in 1935. During the period of rarity up to 1920, the imagines were extremely constant in appearance, but an extraordinary outburst of variation took place while the numbers were rapidly increasing, and many of the more extreme aberrations were deformed. When the population became stabilized again at the new and high value, uniformity was restored, yet the constant form which was then established differed in appearance from that which existed before the outburst of variability.

In this instance the process was accelerated by fluctuation in numbers, but whether this occurs or not, colony formation is doubtless favorable to relatively rapid evolution. Evidence is accumulating to show that this is due not, as some have thought, to the effects of random survival in numerous populations of small size, but to selection adjusting them to the varied environments to which they are usually exposed.

The importance of selection and random survival has now been examined experimentally in a colony of the moth *Panaxia dominula* L. isolated in a marsh surrounded by agricultural land about five miles from Oxford (Fisher and Ford, 1947). The area inhabited by the species is about 20 acres, and the number of specimens emerging each year, from 1941 to 1946, has been ascertained by the technique of marking, release, and recapture. It was found that it did not fall below 1000 nor exceed 8000 in any season. This population is one in which a gene has spread in natural conditions during the time that it has been under observation. Since the heterozygote is distinguishable from either homozygote, it has been possible to determine the gene-frequency with considerable exactitude. Up to 1928 it occupied 1.2 per cent of available loci. By 1939 it had risen to 9.2 per cent and in 1940 to 11.1 per cent, after which it has fluctuated between 6.8 and 4.3 per cent, showing no tendency to rise again to the high value reached in 1940 nor to sink back to the low one which it occupied prior to 1929. These gene-frequencies and the population sizes, during the period that both were determined, are shown in Table II.

TABLE II

Percentage frequencies of a mutant gene, and numbers of imagines emerging per season in an isolated colony of the moth *Panaxia dominula.* The size of the samples from which the calculations were made is also given (based on Fisher and Ford, 1947).

Year	Size of sample	% frequency of mutant gene	Total calculated population per season
1941	461	6.8	2000 to 2500
1942	205	5.4	1200 to 2000
1943	269	5.6	1000
1944	496	4.5	5000 to 6000
1945	372	6.5	4000
1946	986	4.3	6000 to 8000

We have here exceptional opportunities for evaluating the parts taken by random survival and selection in the spread of a gene, since both the yearly changes in its frequency and the size of the population in which it was fluctuating are known. It has been possible to show that the chances are less than one in a hundred that the observed variations in the gene-ratio could be produced by random survival, indicating that they must be due to the influence of selection, varying in direction and intensity from year to year. This is the first time that these alternatives have been studied experimentally, and the result gives no support to the view that random survival plays a significant part in evolution in populations of 1000 individuals or more. Moreover, it is likely that colonies of much smaller size are not permanent, being liable to extinction in periods of time which are short from an evolutionary point of view, unless maintained by immigration. Thus though random survival may affect the constitution of such small groups, it does not materially influence the course of evolution. Indeed it has lately been possible to compare the average expectation of life in three colonies of the butterfly *Maniola jurtina* L. (Satyridae), two being much larger than 1000 and one under 500. The results, which are now being analyzed, demonstrate that the survival rate is substantially less in the small population.

A consideration of some of the early stages in allopatric speciation thus suggests that the gene-complexes of isolated populations are gradually modified along distinct lines, a process which usually but not invariably influences the visible characters at an early stage. It may be expected frequently to evoke minor genetic adjustments before the establishment of reproductive incompatibility. Such effects may sometimes be detected by introducing mutant genes when crossing individuals from distinct populations. Mere distance may provide efficient isolation, affecting the balance of the sex genes, even when the forms concerned are connected by an interbreeding series, as in a long cline. The subdivision of a species into isolated groups is favorable to rapid evolutionary change. This is due not to random survival in populations of small size but to selection adjusting them to the varied environments to which such colonies are exposed.

REFERENCES

Fisher, R. A., and E. B. Ford. 1947. *Heredity*, 1, 143-174.
Ford, E. B. 1946, 2nd. ed. *Butterflies* (*New Naturalist Series*), Collins, London.
Ford, H. D., and E. B. Ford. 1930. *Trans. R. Ent. Soc. Lond.*, 78, 345-51.
Haldane, J. B. S. 1922. *J. Genet.*, 12, 101-9.
Harland, S. C. 1933. *J. Genet.*, 28, 315-25.
Mayr, E. 1942. *Systematics and the Origin of Species*, Columbia University Press, New York.

· 17 ·

PATTERNS OF EVOLUTION IN THE GENUS *RANA*

BY JOHN A. MOORE[1]

THERE is no single pattern that will explain evolution in all biological systems. The type of discontinuity that arises is dependent upon a number of variables such as mutation rate, recombination of existing genes, chromosomal pattern, type of reproduction, density of population, degree of panmixia, influence of other organisms, behavior, and the nature of the physical environment. The relative importance of each of these factors may vary from species to species. This variability of the factors involved in speciation necessitates a synthesis of studies on the pattern of evolution in many different species before we can hope for an adequate understanding of evolution as a whole. The data that have already appeared are considerable. Following the pioneer work of Goldschmidt on *Lymantria*, studies have been made on such diverse forms as *Peromyscus*, *Crepis*, the *Gossypium*, and *Drosophila*. These studies have necessarily emphasized one or a few of the factors in evolution, but it is frequently possible to discern the dim outline of a pattern for the species under consideration.

It is my purpose to summarize[2] the available data that are pertinent to an understanding of evolution in the eastern American members of the genus *Rana*.[3] This genus is represented by not more than twelve species in the region under consideration. The majority of the forms appear to have reached a fairly stable evolutionary condition. In marked contrast, *Rana pipiens* seems to be splitting into reproductively isolated subgroups. Thus a single genus affords valuable material for studying the results of evolution at two taxonomic levels. A comparison of the "stable" species will reveal the magnitude and type of the differences associated with the species level. A study of racial variations in *Rana pipiens* will reveal not only the magnitude and type of differences between populations of a single species but also give evidence on the origin of specific differences.

[1] Barnard College, Columbia University, and The American Museum of Natural History.

[2] This paper is essentially a summary of my work on frogs. Some of the data are presented in more detail in Moore, 1939, 1940, 1941, 1942a, 1942b, 1944, 1946a, 1946b, and 1947. The full data on geographic variation in adaptive embryological characters in *Rana pipiens* and on interspecific hybridization of eastern American frogs will be presented in the near future.

[3] These investigations are supported by a grant from the Penrose Fund of the American Philosophical Society. I am indebted to C. M. Bogert, Th. Dobzhansky, and E. Mayr for reading the manuscript.

GEOGRAPHIC DISTRIBUTION

Geographic and ecological distributions are rough measures of adaptation in continental species that have attained equilibrium in space. The failure of a species to extend its range implies the lack of genotypes that could lead to successful colonization of accessible adjacent habitats. This statement should not be construed as implying that each species occupies every suitable ecological niche throughout the world, since barriers of one kind or another may prevent access to appropriate territory.

In general continental species do not have a range equal to the land mass that is available to them. This might be restated in an interpretative way by saying that most species cannot produce genotypes that are suitable for widely different environments without splitting into two or more species. Examples of this restricted distribution can be seen in Figures 1-12. The twelve forms differ considerably in their distribution but not one of them occupies the entire continent. *Rana virgatipes,* for example, is restricted to acid bogs in New Jersey and to similar habitats farther south (Fig. 7). *Rana heckscheri* occurs along the coastal plain from South Carolina to Louisiana (Fig. 12). The two species with the greatest area of distribution are *Rana pipiens* and *Rana sylvatica* (Figs. 1 and 2).

The geographic ranges have been measured from the distribution maps by means of a planimeter. The results are given in Table I. They must be considered tentative and approximate since distributional data are incomplete and the methods of measurement are not precise. It is thought that the values are within 15 per cent of the real area.[4] *Rana sevosa* has

TABLE I
Extent of geographic area occupied by eastern American frogs.

Species	Area in square miles	Relative size of area (*Rana pipiens* = 100)
Rana sevosa	46,000	1
Rana virgatipes	50,000	1
Rana heckscheri	78,000	2
Rana capito	94,000	2
Rana grylio	130,000	2
Rana areolata	306,000	6
Rana septentrionalis	606,000	12
Rana palustris	1,369,000	26
Rana clamitans	1,735,000	33
Rana catesbeiana	1,991,000	38
Rana sylvatica	3,064,000	58
Rana pipiens	5,304,000	100

[4] The species population is not continuous throughout this area but is restricted to suitable habitats. The sum of all habitats actually occupied would be much less than the figure given. I am using "geographic range" as the area encompassing suitable habitats in which the species has been found.

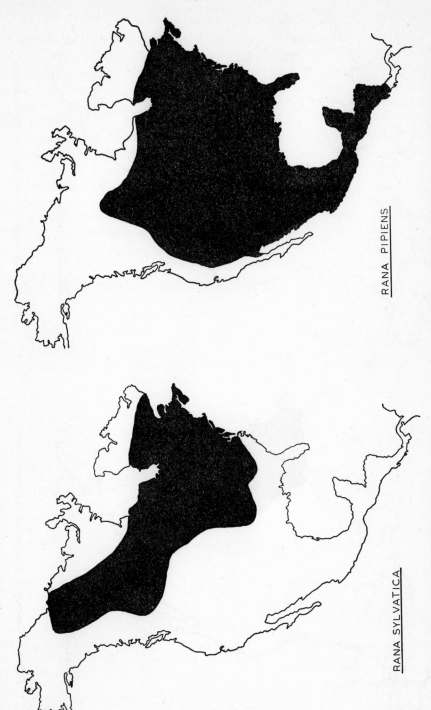

RANA SYLVATICA

Figure 1. Geographic distribution of Rana sylvatica.

RANA PIPIENS

Figure 2. Geographic distribution of Rana pipiens.

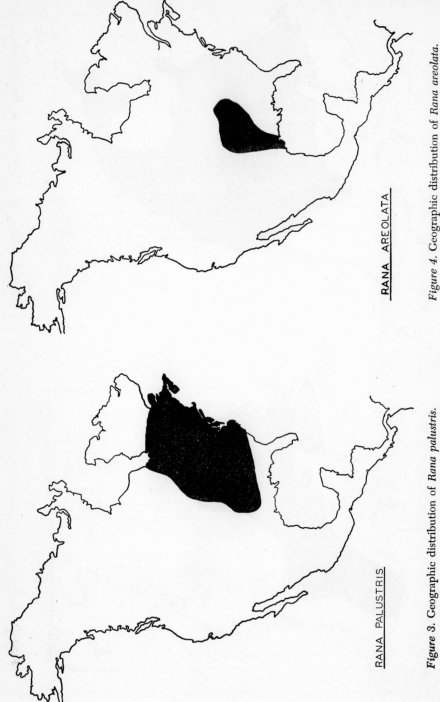

RANA AREOLATA

Figure 4. Geographic distribution of *Rana areolata.*

RANA PALUSTRIS

Figure 3. Geographic distribution of *Rana palustris.*

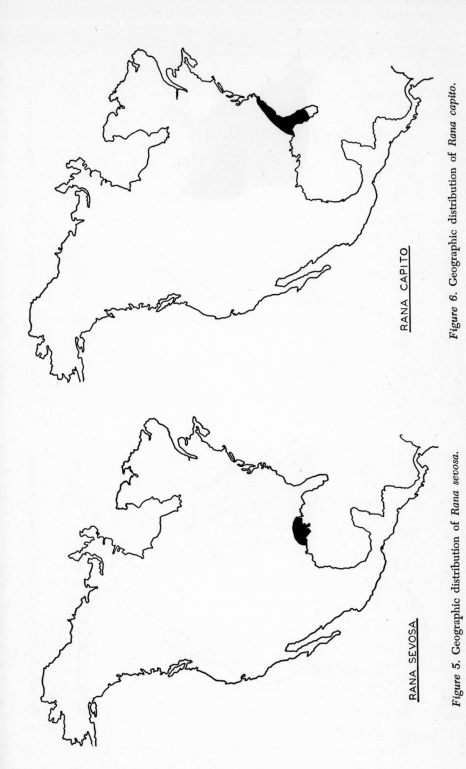

RANA CAPITO

Figure 6. Geographic distribution of *Rana capito*.

RANA SEVOSA

Figure 5. Geographic distribution of *Rana sevosa*.

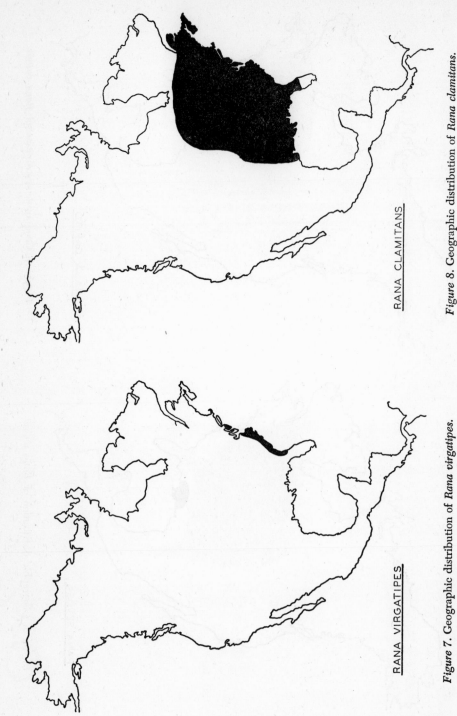

RANA CLAMITANS

Figure 8. Geographic distribution of *Rana clamitans.*

RANA VIRGATIPES

Figure 7. Geographic distribution of *Rana virgatipes.*

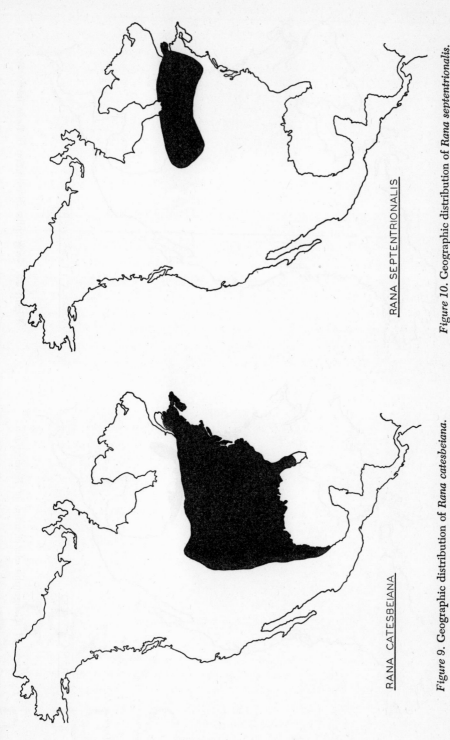

RANA SEPTENTRIONALIS

Figure 10. Geographic distribution of *Rana septentrionalis.*

RANA CATESBEIANA

Figure 9. Geographic distribution of *Rana catesbeiana.*

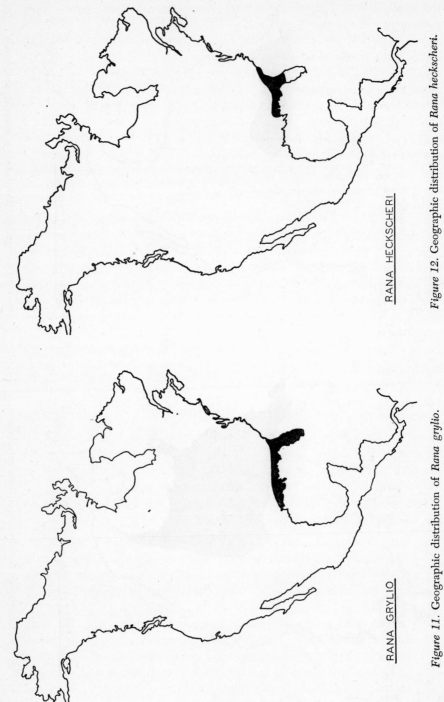

RANA HECKSCHERI

Figure 12. Geographic distribution of *Rana heckscheri.*

RANA GRYLIO

Figure 11. Geographic distribution of *Rana grylio.*

the smallest range, occupying a total area of 46,000 square miles. *Rana pipiens* has the largest range and is found within an area of 5,304,000 square miles. If the range of the latter species is used as a basis of comparison, it will be seen that six of the twelve species each has a range that is less than seven per cent of that occupied by *Rana pipiens*. Five of these species are restricted primarily to coastal areas of the southeastern states. The sixth, *Rana areolata*, is a midwestern form. It is of interest to note that none of these six species with small ranges has extended into regions covered by Pleistocene glaciers. One possible error in Table I concerns the proper taxonomic designation of *Rana areolata*, *Rana capito*, and *Rana sevosa*. These are usually considered valid species, but future study may indicate that they could best be considered as three subspecies of a single polytypic species.

Many of these species, especially those with large ranges, are highly variable. The northern populations of *Rana sylvatica* are frequently considered as separate subspecies. *Rana clamitans* and *Rana catesbeiana* exhibit considerable color variation, but in recent years no one has thought it necessary to name the various local populations. *Rana pipiens* has both the largest range and the greatest amount of morphological variability. Some aspects of its geographic variation are dealt with in Moore, 1944.

The determination of the factors that are responsible for the range of any species presents an enormous problem. The range of *Rana pipiens*, so much greater than that of any other species, raises an especially interesting question. In addition to this extensive geographic distribution, *Rana pipiens* has a wider range of habitats than any other *Rana* with which I have had field experience. In New England it is found in swamps, wet meadows, coastal marshes, lakes, large ponds, and along rivers and large streams. It is the only *Rana* that is successfully established throughout the prairie region. In Mexico I have observed it around the outflow of desert springs and along tropical rivers and streams.

This wide geographic and habitat distribution of *Rana pipiens* could be due to one of several types of adaptation.

1. Individuals of this species might be adapted to a wider range of environments than other members of the genus. Each individual would possess a genotype that is capable of success in any of the habitats and climatic conditions that occur throughout the species' range of distribution.
2. On the other hand, individuals of this species might have the same degree of adaptability as individuals of other species, and the population might consist of a complex of geographic races each adapted to its local environment but incapable of survival in markedly different parts of the species' range.

3. A third, though unlikely, possibility is that *Rana pipiens* consists of a number of ecotypes. Each ecotype might be restricted to a narrow habitat, yet many different ecotypes could spread the species over a wide geographic range. There is no evidence that anything like this occurs and for the present it seems safe to ignore this possibility.

If the first possibility proves to be the correct explanation, no special importance could be attached to the study of speciation in this form, yet a study of its adaptation would be of significance for other evolutionary problems. If the second explanation is correct, this species would be a border-line case in which an originally homogeneous population is becoming divided into different races. In such an event it would be profitable for investigation. In any case it is necessary to ascertain as many as possible of the factors that limit the distribution of *Rana pipiens* and the other species of the genus and to see if these factors vary geographically.

Factors Limiting Geographic Distribution in Frogs

The factors that restrict a species to its characteristic habitat and area of distribution are usually poorly understood. It can safely be said that we do not know why any species of frog has its characteristic distribution, but there is a general feeling that the most important factors are temperature and moisture. Chemical factors, in addition to moisture, appear to play a role in limiting distribution in at least two instances. In the first place no species of amphibians are able to tolerate the high salinity of sea water. The preference of *Rana virgatipes* for bog waters may be a second instance of the role of chemical factors in limiting distribution. Except in such instances the chemical environment seems to be adequate and in no case limiting in eastern North America. There are no known cases in which the absence of a particular type of food is responsible for the absence of a species from a region. The relations of frogs to other organisms is undoubtedly an important factor in distributions, yet relatively little is known of these complex relationships. A possible example is the nearly complete absence in overlap of the ranges of *Rana septentrionalis* and *Rana catesbeiana*. This may be due to the predatory nature of the latter.

The belief in the paramount importance of water and temperature in controlling the distribution of frogs is due in part to our ignorance of other factors, and it seems improbable that these factors are of much influence in limiting species with small ranges, such as *Rana heckscheri*, *Rana capito*, and *Rana virgatipes*. In wide-ranging species, temperature and moisture undoubtedly play a more significant role. The western limits of *Rana palustris*, *Rana clamitans*, and *Rana catesbeiana* appear to be determined largely by the presence or absence of sufficient water for breeding purposes.[5] East of the plains there is ample water to meet the requirements of any species, so this environmental variable is not limiting.

Thus, by eliminating all other factors because they are either unknown or improbable (to be sure a most dubious procedure), we are left with temperature as the principal known factor responsible for the northern and southern limits of distribution of the wide-ranging eastern American frogs. If this is so it should be possible to find among the species physiological differences indicative of adaptations to temperature and correlated with distributions. A form that is able to extend to the Arctic Circle should differ from one reaching its northern limit at the St. Lawrence River.

The search for temperature adaptations has centered largely on the embryonic stages. The reason for beginning investigation with this period of the life cycle is due primarily to the fact that embryonic stages are least resistant to temperature extremes. The effects of temperature would be most pronounced in that part of the life cycle during which the animal is most sensitive. Furthermore the pronounced seasonal nature of the breeding habits suggests the need for special temperature conditions during early life. This is another indication that this part of the life cycle could profitably be studied.

Fairly complete data with reference to the effects of temperature during early development have been accumulated for *Rana sylvatica, Rana pipiens, Rana palustris, Rana clamitans,* and *Rana catesbeiana.* These species have been listed in their sequence of decreasingly extensive northern distribution and, except for *Rana pipiens,* of increasingly extensive southern distribution. The differences in distribution suggest that *Rana sylvatica* possesses the genotype best suited for survival at low temperatures and *Rana catesbeiana* (again omitting *Rana pipiens*) the best equipped for high temperatures. This conclusion is further substantiated by the breeding behavior of the five species in the same locality. *Rana sylvatica* supplies a "northern" environment for its embryos by spawning during the middle of March in the New York region. *Rana catesbeiana* supplies a "southern" environment by breeding in July and August. The other species breed in order of their decreasing northern distribution.

Among these species the main differences (Table II) thought to have an adaptive significance are as follows:

1. EMBRYONIC TEMPERATURE TOLERANCE. Northern species have lower minimum and maximum limiting temperatures for normal development than southern species.

2. RATE OF DEVELOPMENT. In poikilothermic organisms low temperature

[5] *Rana catesbeiana* has been introduced in a number of localities west of its normal range. In some of those places with ample water it has become established.

exerts a retarding effect on physiological processes. The embryos of northern species compensate for this by having a more rapid rate of development than southern species. This difference is most apparent at low temperatures. At temperatures near the upper limit for northern embryos, the rate of development for southern embryos may be the same or slightly exceed those from the north.

3. TEMPERATURE COEFFICIENT. The temperature coefficient for embryonic development is lower in northern than in southern species. This means that the relative influence of different temperatures on the rate of development is less in northern than in southern species.

4. EGG SIZE. The egg size of northern species tends to be greater than in southern species. This phenomenon is frequently encountered in marine invertebrates as well; the cold-water forms endowing their embryos with a greater amount of yolk. Correlated with this large egg size, in frogs the egg complement is frequently smaller in northern than in southern species.

5. TYPE OF JELLY MASS. Northern species deposit their eggs in a compact mass that is usually attached below the surface. Southern species deposit their eggs in a surface film. The submerged mass is laid at a time of the year when subsequent freezing of the surface waters is to be expected. If the embryos were in a surface film at this time they would be killed by the ice. The submerged mass, although well-suited for cold waters, is a decidedly poor type for high temperatures. Under the latter conditions diffusion of oxygen is not rapid enough to supply the needs of the embryo. This results in the embryos in the center of the mass being killed and the

TABLE II

The relation between geographic distribution, breeding habits, and adaptive embryological characteristics.

	Rana sylvatica	Rana pipiens	Rana palustris	Rana clamitans	Rana catesbeiana
Northern limit	67°	60°	51-55°	50°	47°
Southern limit	34°	9°	32°	28°	23°
Beginning of breeding season	mid March	early April	mid April	May	June
Lower limiting embryonic temperature	2.5°	5°	7°	12°	15°
Upper limiting embryonic temperature	24°	28°	30°	32°	32°
Hours between stages 3 and 20 at 20°C.	72	96	105	114	134
Temperature coefficient b.	1.98	2.13	2.30	2.60	2.88
Egg diameter in mm.	1.9	1.7	1.8	1.4	1.3
Type of jelly mass	globular, submerged	globular, submerged	globular, submerged	film, at surface	film, at surface

products of their decomposition have a lethal effect on the embryos of the peripheral portions of the mass.

The adaptive significance of differences in embryonic temperature tolerance and type of jelly mass seems unequivocal. With respect to the other characters studied, that is, rate of development, temperature coefficient, and egg size, this is not so apparent. The best evidence that these differences are of adaptive significance is, first, that they vary in a regular way with geographic distribution and, secondly, totally unrelated forms frequently exhibit these same characteristics when they occur in similar environments. These facts strongly suggest that these characters have become established through the action of natural selection because they confer an advantage on the organism. They are, therefore, adaptive. This method of equating "parallelisms" with "adaptive characters" is probably the most objective means of identifying the latter.

GEOGRAPHIC VARIATION OF ADAPTIVE EMBRYOLOGICAL CHARACTERS

If the embryological differences which were revealed in a comparison of the frog species are important in limiting distribution, they must either be constant throughout the range of the species or show such slight variations that they still remain a limiting factor. A study of *Rana catesbeiana* has shown that these adaptive embryological characters are identical in individuals from the northern and southern portions of the species range. Eggs of a female collected in the Adirondack Mountains of New York were as well adapted to high temperatures as those from southern Louisiana. Limited data for *Rana clamitans* have revealed no geographic variation in these adaptive characters.

Extensive data on geographic variation of adaptive embryological characters are available for *Rana pipiens*. It was thought that this species would be of exceptional interest because of its unusual geographic distribution. Thus, if we compare the maps of distribution with the data of Table II, we would predict a southern limit for *Rana pipiens* near latitude 33°. The New England populations of *Rana pipiens* have embryological characteristics which are intermediate between those of *Rana sylvatica* and *Rana palustris*. If these characteristics are really the important limiting factors then *Rana pipiens* should extend farther south than *Rana sylvatica* but not so far as *Rana palustris*. Instead, in total disregard of the theory, the range of *Rana pipiens* extends southward into Costa Rica. A study of this interesting exception should allow a test of the original hypothesis concerning the relation between distribution and adaptation, and, in addition, throw light on the origin of populations adapted to different climatic regions. The method used has consisted in comparing *Rana pipiens* embryos from widely different geographic regions. The most complete data have been secured on material from Quebec, Vermont,

Wisconsin, New Jersey, Louisiana, central Florida, southern Florida, Texas, and San Luis Potosi.

GEOGRAPHIC VARIATION IN EMBRYONIC TEMPERATURE TOLERANCE. The temperature tolerance of embryos from nine localities is given in Figure 13. The embryos from Quebec, Vermont, Wisconsin, and New Jersey appear to be identical in this respect. Louisiana embryos can survive equally well at low temperatures, but the upper limiting temperature is four degrees

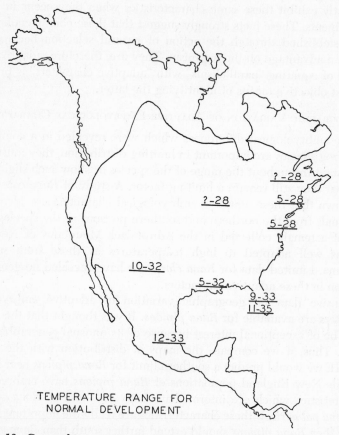

TEMPERATURE RANGE FOR
NORMAL DEVELOPMENT

Figure 13. Geographic variation in embryonic temperature tolerance in *Rana pipiens.* The lower and upper limiting temperatures for the embryonic stages are given. A question mark signifies the absence of data.

above that of northern embryos. The upper limiting temperature for central Florida, Mexico, and Texas is 32-33°. Embryos from southern Florida may possibly have a slightly higher upper limit. These southern embryos, except for Louisiana material, are much less resistant to low temperatures. Such observations are interesting inasmuch as previous work with New England material had shown that *Rana pipiens* possessed the embryological characteristics of a "northern" species. Its extensive southern distribution was difficult to understand, but study of southern material has shown that the embryonic temperature tolerance of these populations is very different from that previously encountered in the north. In fact the southern *Rana pipiens* embryos can withstand temperatures as high as or higher than any southern species of frog or toad that I have studied.

GEOGRAPHIC VARIATION IN RATE OF EMBRYONIC DEVELOPMENT. The rate of development is also subject to geographic variation. Once again the material from Quebec, Vermont, Wisconsin, and New Jersey was uniform. The data are summarized in Figure 14. The method of presentation is as follows. The rate of development of Vermont, Quebec, Wisconsin, and New Jersey embryos at the various temperatures is taken as 0. The data for other localities are expressed as the percentage of acceleration or the

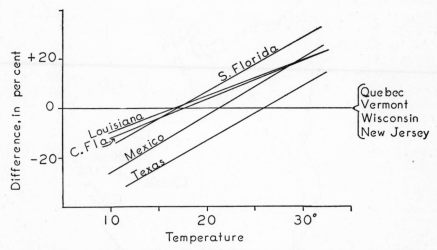

Figure 14. Comparison of rate of development in 9 populations of *Rana pipiens.* The rate of development is identical in embryos from Quebec, Vermont, Wisconsin, and New Jersey. The rate for these embryos is taken as standard, and equal to 0, and the rate of embryos from other regions compared. The comparison is made by determining the percentage acceleration or retardation in terms of the northern embryos.

percentage of retardation in terms of the northern material. In all cases the curves for the southern localities form an angle with the northern base line. Thus, at temperatures above 26° the Texas embryos develop more rapidly than northern embryos, but at lower temperatures the situation is reversed. It should be remembered that the normal breeding temperature for northern populations of *Rana pipiens* is about 12° (Wright,

1914). At this temperature the northern embryos develop more rapidly than any of the southern material tested. The differences in rate of development between northern and southern populations of *Rana pipiens* are of the same type as we find differentiating northern and southern species.

GEOGRAPHIC VARIATION OF THE TEMPERATURE COEFFICIENT. It can be seen from Figure 14 that temperature, acting over a considerable range, has a greater differential effect on the rate of development of the southern *pipiens* than on the northern *pipiens*. Once again we observe the same type of difference previously found between northern and southern species.

GEOGRAPHIC VARIATION IN EGG SIZE. The mean egg diameter for nine localities is given in Figure 15. In the four northern localities the value is large and the differences between means are not significant. In Texas and Louisiana the size is somewhat less and in Florida the smallest

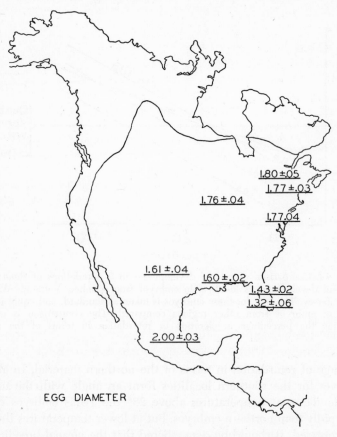

EGG DIAMETER

Figure 15. Geographic variation in egg diameter in *Rana pipiens.*

diameters are observed. This trend is in keeping with the situation in different species, where the southern form has smaller eggs than the northern form. In Mexico, however, the trend is reversed and the egg diameter is the largest recorded for any locality.

GEOGRAPHIC VARIATION IN TYPE OF EGG MASS. The artificial conditions under which eggs are secured in the experiments makes it unwise to compare types of egg mass. Observations have to be made in the field. The only southern *Rana pipiens* embryos that I have observed under natural conditions were near San Pedro, Coahuila, Mexico. The egg masses were very different from those in the northeast. Instead of being found in a single compact mass the eggs had been deposited in a number of relatively diffuse small groups. This may not have been typical for southern egg masses, since Wright (1931) has stated that the egg mass of *Rana "sphenocephala"* (a term used by some for *Rana pipiens* of the southeast states) is the same as that of *Rana pipiens*. The question of geographic variation in egg mass must await additional data.

The original questions asked with reference to the distribution of *Rana pipiens* (page 323) can now be answered. These studies have shown that the greater than expected southern distribution of *Rana pipiens* is associated with a number of adjustments that adapt the embryonic stages to high temperatures. Thus southern populations of *pipiens* resemble southern species in having a greater tolerance to high temperatures, a slower rate of development at low temperatures, and generally a smaller sized egg.

HYBRIDIZATION

Data for approximately one hundred different interspecific and intraspecific combinations of American frogs are available. The interspecific crosses have been made largely among the species found in the northeast. The intraspecific crosses have been among various populations of *Rana pipiens*.

In Table III the results of the interspecific combinations are given in terms of the stage of development reached by the hybrids. The cross *septentrionalis* ♀ × *catesbeiana* ♂ is listed under two categories. Although the majority of these hybrids fail in the early embryonic stages, a few develop beyond transformation. The other types of hybrid combinations are uniform with respect to the time the embryos die.

For the student of evolution these results are of interest in two respects: first, the extent to which interspecific gene exchange is possible; and second, the possibility of correlating ability to hybridize with assumed genetic relationships. With respect to the first point it is clear that gene exchange among the species tested is usually impossible. It is only within the *pipiens-palustris-capito-areolata* group that hybrids are

TABLE III
Extent of development in American frog hybrids.

NO CLEAVAGE

Rana clamitans ♀ × *Rana capito* ♂   *Rana clamitans* ♀ × *Rana palustris* ♂

Rana clamitans ♀ × *Rana catesbeiana* ♂   *Rana clamitans* ♀ × *Rana pipiens* ♂

Rana clamitans ♀ × *Rana heckscheri* ♂   *Rana clamitans* ♀ × *Rana sylvatica* ♂

Rana clamitans ♀ × *Rana septentrionalis* ♂

CLEAVAGE AND BLASTULA STAGES NORMAL, FAILURE AT BEGINNING OF GASTRULATION

Rana areolata ♀ × *Rana catesbeiana* ♂   *Rana pipiens* ♀ × *Rana septentrionalis* ♂

Rana areolata ♀ × *Rana clamitans* ♂   *Rana pipiens* ♀ × *Rana sylvatica* ♂

Rana areolata ♀ × *Rana sylvatica* ♂   *Rana pipiens* ♀ × *Rana virgatipes* ♂

Rana catesbeiana ♀ × *Rana areolata* ♂   *Rana septentrionalis* ♀ × *Rana clamitans* ♂

Rana catesbeiana ♀ × *Rana clamitans* ♂   *Rana palustris* ♀ × *Rana clamitans* ♂

Rana catesbeiana ♀ × *Rana palustris* ♂   *Rana palustris* ♀ × *Rana catesbeiana* ♂

Rana catesbeiana ♀ × *Rana pipiens* ♂   *Rana palustris* ♀ × *Rana sylvatica* ♂

Rana catesbeiana ♀ × *Rana sylvatica* ♂   *Rana sylvatica* ♀ × *Rana areolata* ♂

Rana pipiens ♀ × *Rana catesbeiana* ♂   *Rana sylvatica* ♀ × *Rana catesbeiana* ♂

Rana pipiens ♀ × *Rana clamitans* ♂   *Rana sylvatica* ♀ × *Rana clamitans* ♂

Rana pipiens ♀ × *Rana grylio* ♂   *Rana sylvatica* ♀ × *Rana palustris* ♂

Rana sylvatica ♀ × *Rana pipiens* ♂

EARLY DEVELOPMENT NORMAL, FAILURE DURING NEURULA AND TAILBUD STAGES

Rana septentrionalis ♀ × *Rana palustris* ♂

Rana septentrionalis ♀ × *Rana pipiens* ♂

Rana septentrionalis ♀ × *Rana catesbeiana* ♂

DEVELOP NORMALLY TO ADULTS

Rana pipiens ♀ × *Rana areolata* ♂   *Rana palustris* ♀ × *Rana pipiens* ♂

Rana pipiens ♀ × *Rana capito* ♂   *Rana areolata* ♀ × *Rana pipiens* ♂

Rana pipiens ♀ × *Rana palustris* ♂   *Rana areolata* ♀ × *Rana palustris* ♂

Rana palustris ♀ × *Rana areolata* ♂   *Rana septentrionalis* ♀ × *Rana catesbeiana* ♂

formed that develop normally to the adult stage. The correlation between ability to hybridize and genetic relationship is complicated. The species that hybridize easily, namely the members of the *pipiens-palustris-capito-areolata* group, are thought by taxonomists to be closely related. Similarly *Rana septentrionalis* and *Rana catesbeiana* are thought to be closely related. Species thought not to be closely related form hybrids that invariably fail early in development, but there are some species that appear morphologically to be as closely related as the members of the *pipiens-palustris-capito-areolata* group and yet are incapable of forming hybrids that develop beyond the earliest embryonic stages. Such an example is *Rana clamitans* and *Rana catesbeiana*. These two species are similar in adult structure, embryonic stages, and in general habits but they are incapable of successful hybridization.

The intraspecific crosses among populations of *Rana pipiens* are of interest in demonstrating a gradual development of hybrid inviability with increasing north-south distance between the parent populations. The populations that have been most studied are Vermont, Wisconsin, New Jersey, Louisiana, central Florida, southern Florida, Texas, and San Luis Potosi. The graded nature of the results can be seen when eggs of Vermont females are fertilized with males from the other localities. Hybrids with Wisconsin or New Jersey males are entirely normal. When a Louisiana male is used some irregularities are noticed. There is a slight retardation in the rate of development and the embryos exhibit morphological defects. These are not extensive enough to result in a significant mortality. When males from Florida are used there is a marked retardation in the rate of development and morphological defects are so great that many of the embryos die. Incompatibility is even greater when Texas males are used. In addition to retardation in rate, the morphological abnormalities are extensive and in some experiments the mortality has been 100 per cent. If we reverse the direction of the cross and use southern females and progressively more northern males the degree of incompatibility increases with distance. The crosses Texas ♀ × central Florida ♂, central Florida ♀ × Texas ♂, central Florida ♀ × southern Florida ♂ result in normal embryos. In the Texas ♀ × New Jersey ♂ cross there is a slight retardation in the rate of development and some morphological defects. The crosses Texas ♀ × Wisconsin ♂ and Texas ♀ × Vermont ♂ result in very abnormal embryos and, as is the case in the reciprocal crosses, the mortality may be 100 per cent. The most abnormal intraspecific hybrids thus far obtained have been in a cross between a Mexican female and a Vermont male. In this case most of the hybrids died in the gastrula and neurula stages.

A paradoxical situation appears when we compare the results of these *Rana pipiens* intraspecific crosses with the results of interspecific crosses between *Rana pipiens* and *Rana palustris* or *Rana areolata* or *Rana capito*. *Rana pipiens* can be crossed with any of these species and the resulting embryos are perfectly normal, yet northern and southern individuals of *Rana pipiens* form very defective hybrids. In these cases intraspecific "hybridization" is less successful than interspecific hybridization.

DEGREE OF ISOLATION OF THE SPECIES

The importance of isolation in maintaining separate species has been reemphasized in recent years by geneticists. There are many ways by which contemporaneous[6] populations of sexually reproducing species can be prevented from exchanging genes. Following Dobzhansky

---

[6] Since we are dealing with populations living at the same time level we do not have to consider temporal isolation (in the geological-time sense).

(1937) and Mayr (1942), these methods could be outlined as follows.

1. *Geographic isolation.* During the period of breeding the two populations occupy different geographic regions.

2. *Habitat isolation* ("ecological" isolation of many authors).[7] During the period of breeding the two populations occupy different habitats or niches. The distinction between geographical and habitat isolation is merely quantitative.

3. *Seasonal isolation.* The periods of breeding of the two populations are different.

4. *Sexual isolation.* Individuals of one population will not mate with members of the other population even if the opportunity presents itself.

5. *Failure of fertilization.* The exchange of genes between the two populations is prevented by the failure of the egg of one and the sperm of another to form a zygote.

6. *Hybrid inviability.* The hybrid formed from gametes contributed by the two populations is incapable of reaching maturity due to developmental failure at some stage in the life cycle.

7. *Hybrid sterility.* Free genic exchange between the two populations is prevented by the failure of the hybrids to produce gametes normally.

These isolating mechanisms may be partial or complete in their effectiveness. Two populations may be separated by one, several, or all.

In Table IV an attempt is made to measure the effectiveness of some of the isolating mechanisms that prevent gene interchange among the six species of frogs found in the northeast. No data are available that serve to measure sexual isolation or hybrid sterility (in those cases where the hybrids reach the adult stage). The absence of development in hybrids formed from *Rana clamitans* eggs is probably due to some failure in the fertilization process, but since this is not definitely known, all cases in which normal development does not occur are listed as developmental incompatibility.

All of these species are sympatric to some extent, so geographic isolation is always less than 100 per cent effective. The degree of geographic isolation becomes complex when the ranges of the two species overlap. This can be brought out by a consideration of the case of *Rana palustris*. The entire range of this species is included within the range of *Rana pipiens*. Inasmuch as all female *Rana palustris* would be found in areas with *Rana pipiens* males, the extent to which geographic isolation is effective is zero. On the other hand *Rana pipiens* has a much greater range. The possibility of the cross *Rana pipiens* ♀ × *Rana palustris* ♂ taking place will be limited to that part of *Rana pipiens'* range where *Rana palustris* males

---

[7] It does not seem appropriate to restrict a broad term, such as ecological, to one of its particulate aspects. Geographical, seasonal, and habitat isolation all have an ecological basis.

occur. Since in only 26 per cent of *Rana pipiens'* range are *Rana palustris* males to be expected, the degree of geographic isolation between *Rana pipiens* females and *Rana palustris* males is 74 per cent.[8] This method of measuring geographic isolation is based on the assumption that the species have fixed ranges and that the two species have an equal and uniform distribution throughout their ranges. The first assumption is probably

TABLE IV

Estimations of the magnitude of geographic isolation (G), habitat isolation (H), seasonal isolation (S), and developmental incompatibility (D). Complete isolation = 100. Absence of isolation = 0.

Females \ Males	Rana sylvatica	Rana pipiens	Rana palustris	Rana clamitans	Rana catesbeiana	Rana septentrionalis
Rana sylvatica		G 29 H 70 S 60 D 100	G 61 H 40 S 100 D 100	G 59 H 30 S 100 D 100	G 68 H 70 S 100 D 100	G 80 H 60 S 100 D ?
Rana pipiens	G 59 H 70 S 60 D 100		G 74 H 70 S 40 D 0	G 67 H 70 S 100 D 100	G 62 H 85 S 100 D 100	G 88 H 80 S 100 D 100
Rana palustris	G 13 H 40 S 95 D 100	G 0 H 70 S 40 D 0		G 3 H 60 S 95 D 100	G 23 H 70 S 100 D 100	G 72 H 50 S 100 D ?
Rana clamitans	G 28 H 30 S 100 D 100	G 0 H 70 S 100 D 100	G 24 H 60 S 95 D 100		G 18 H 30 S 50 D 100	G 22 H 20 S 0 D 100
Rana catesbeiana	G 51 H 70 S 100 D 100	G 0 H 85 S 100 D 100	G 47 H 70 S 100 D 100	G 29 H 30 S 50 D 100		G 93 H 30 S 50 D ?
Rana septentrionalis	G 0 H 60 S 100 D ?	G 0 H 80 S 100 D 100	G 37 H 50 S 100 D 100	G 36 H 20 S 0 D 100	G 79 H 30 S 50 D 95	

correct. The second is undoubtedly incorrect. Thus *Rana pipiens* probably does not reach the same density in the arid portions of the west that it does in the more humid east. The value for geographic isolation of *Rana pipiens* females from *Rana palustris* males may be somewhat too large for this reason.

The values for developmental incompatibility can be given in more exact terms. In the *Rana pipiens* and *Rana palustris* combinations where normally developing hybrids are formed it is zero. In the cross *Rana*

[8] These values were determined from measurements of the area of overlap of the ranges of distribution that are shown in Figures 1-12. Area was determined with a planimeter. The data are, therefore, approximate.

septentrionalis ♀ × *Rana catesbeiana* ♂ approximately 5 per cent of the hybrids reach the adult stage. Developmental incompatibility is thus 95 per cent effective. In all other combinations developmental incompatibility is 100 per cent, affording complete isolation.

The values for habitat and seasonal isolation are tentative. They are based on my impressions of the extent to which these factors operate in the northeast. Zero habitat isolation between two species would signify that they always occur in the same habitats at the time of breeding. If the value was 100 per cent it would signify that there was no overlap in breeding sites. From the data in the table it is apparent that habitat isolation is never complete. The extent of seasonal isolation is highly variable since it depends on the climate of each year. In some years there is no overlap in the breeding periods for *Rana sylvatica*, *Rana pipiens*, and *Rana palustris*. Seasonal isolation would then be 100 per cent. In other years, characterized by a retarded spring and a subsequent rapid rise in temperature, there may be considerable overlap of breeding season. It is probable that the extent to which seasonal and habitat differences separate two forms varies in different geographic regions. These difficulties mean that the data in Table IV are to be considered as first approximations that can be revised on the basis of subsequent data.

DISCUSSION

An effort can now be made to relate the data to problems of evolution. It is invariably found in studies of this sort that evolutionary theory contributes more to the understanding of the data than the data contribute to an understanding of evolution. The present studies are no exception.

In the introduction it was stated that evolution could be studied at two levels in the genus *Rana*, namely, the specific and the subspecific. This can now be considered.

The gaps between the various species in northeastern America are now so extensive that little can be deduced concerning their origin. Effective isolation is attained through differences in breeding habitats, breeding seasons, and by hybrid inviability. Even in the closely related *Rana pipiens* and *Rana palustris* there is no evidence of hybridization under natural conditions. To me the most interesting data derived through study at the species level are those showing adaptive differences between the species. It is usually assumed that adaptive differences between species must exist but they are rarely demonstrated. The nature of the adaptations encountered suggests that they are important factors in the geographic distribution of the species. The origin of these adaptations is, therefore, a most important problem. The data strongly suggest that they are inherited characteristics of the species. With respect to the manner of origin, the very fact that these adaptations are correlated with environmental temperature differences suggests that the various species originated in different climatic zones. This is inference, not fact; nevertheless it may indicate that divergence was associated with allopatric rather than sympatric distributions. Another observation might appear, at first sight, as evidence of sympatric speciation. *Rana palustris* is found throughout much of eastern North America (Fig. 3). Its range is entirely encompassed by that of its closest relative, *Rana pipiens* (Fig. 2). A number of hypotheses could be advanced to explain this case, the simplest of which would be to assume sympatric speciation; but evidence from other sources suggests that sympatric speciation would be unusual, if not impossible, in an organism such as the frog. An alternate explanation, for example allopatric speciation with subsequent invasion of the territory of one species by the other, is more likely.

The improbability of obtaining much insight into the dynamics of speciation from studies of different species necessitated a change in the intraspecific level. The data accumulated through observations on different populations of *Rana pipiens* revealed a method by which speciation *could* occur in the genus *Rana*. *Rana pipiens* was found to consist of a series of populations adapted to different temperature regions. This is the only species so far examined in which temperature-adapted races have been formed. The differences in temperature tolerance and rate of development between the extreme temperature races in this species are of the same magnitude as those found between many species of the genus *Rana*. This suggests that the adaptive characters now differentiating any two closely related species *could* have arisen from allopatric populations of a common ancestor. But speciation implies the splitting of a population into reproductively isolated groups in addition to adaptation. It is of exceptional interest, therefore, to find that the extreme temperature races of *Rana pipiens* are isolated to a high degree through the inability of their hybrids to develop. The data suggest that adaptation to widely different environmental conditions can in itself lead to genetic isolation. The pattern of evolution in *Rana pipiens* consists of the formation of temperature races in allopatric populations through the action of natural selection. This in itself can lead to barriers of the type separating species-groups.

REFERENCES

Dobzhansky, Th. 1937. *Genetics and the Origin of Species*. Columbia University Press.
Mayr, E. 1942. *Systematics and the Origin of Species*. Columbia University Press.
Moore, J. 1939. Temperature tolerance and rates of development in the eggs of amphibia. *Ecology*, 20, 459-478.
——. 1940. Adaptive differences in the egg membranes of frogs. *Amer. Nat.*, 74, 89-93.
——. 1941. Developmental rate of hybrid frogs. *J. Exp. Zool.*, 86, 405-422.

——. 1942a. The role of temperature in speciation of frogs. *Biol. Symp.*, *6*, 189-213.

——. 1942b. Embryonic temperature tolerance and rate of development in *Rana catesbeiana*. *Biol. Bull.*, *83*, 375-388.

——. 1944. Geographic variation in *Rana pipiens* Schreber of eastern North America. *Bull. Amer. Mus. Nat. Hist.*, *82*, 345-370.

——. 1946a. Incipient intraspecific isolating mechanisms in *Rana pipiens*. *Genetics*, *31*, 304-326.

——. 1946b. Hybridization between *Rana palustris* and different geographical forms of *Rana pipiens*. *Proc. Nat. Acad. Sci.*, *32*, 209-212.

——. 1947. Hybridization between *Rana pipiens* from Vermont and eastern Mexico. *Proc. Nat. Acad. Sci.*, *33*, 72-75.

Wright, A. A., and A. H. Wright. 1933. *Handbook of Frogs and Toads*. Comstock Publishing Co.

Wright, A. H. 1914. *Life-histories of the Anura of Ithaca, New York*. Publication 197. Carnegie Institution of Washington.

· 18 ·

INCREASED VARIABILITY IN POPULATIONS FOLLOWING NATURAL HYBRIDIZATION

BY WILLIAM HOVANITZ[1]

THE genetic consequences of occasional crossing between the members of distinct populations depends upon the ability of the hybrids to cross freely with the parental types and with other hybrids so that segregation and assortment of genetic factors may occur. Where no physiological barrier to such crossing exists, an increased variability in the participating populations is the usual result. Such an event might occur at the time of hybridization between diverse populations of the *same* species (races or subspecies), or in the hybridization between totally *different* species. In either case, the increased variability arises due to the segregation and independent assortment of the various genes and alleles by which the populations differ.

Hybridization between distinct species is considered a rare phenomenon. Generally speaking, it must remain a rare phenomenon, for otherwise the genes by which two species differ would be interchanged and the two species would blend into one.

Hybridization between subspecies usually occurs geographically in the sense that two geographically discrete subspecies can blend together in a geographical area where the two populations are in contact. In this case, the blending between the two subspecies occurs in a series of steps by means of intermediate subpopulations. True hybrids between different individuals of the two subspecies in contact are rarely formed; instead, the hybridization is accomplished by means of the intermediate populations the individuals of each of which differ from individuals of the next adjacent population by a few of the many genes by which the two subspecies differ.

The difference between species hybridization and subspecies hybridization as thus described is a matter of degree—the degree to which crossing occurs accompanied by Mendelian assortment and segregation. Intermediate cases may be expected to be found, cases in which a small amount of crossing occurs. The crossbreeding is insufficient in these instances to eliminate the distinctive character of the participating species, nor, on the other hand, enough to allow them to become highly inbred and homozygous for the genes for which they are specific. One result of this small

[1] Department of Biology, Wayne University.

amount of crossing is to introduce the alleles of one species into the genome of the other with resulting heterozygosity and observed variability in visible characters of both. Hybridization of this sort can be an effective aid in the development of parallel variation gradients as have often been described (Hovanitz, 1941).

Some examples of natural hybridization in American butterflies to illustrate this increase in variability are given in this paper.

The Genus Basilarchia

Butterflies of the genus *Basilarchia* occur throughout North America from central Mexico to the barren lands of Canada and Alaska. There are five distinct species recognized by most systematists although for reasons given below occasionally these are reduced to two.

Basilarchia archippus occupies the area from central Mexico north to southern Canada, west to the Sierra Nevada and Cascade Mountains and east to the Atlantic Ocean (Fig. 1). Through this area there is a remarkable uniformity in coloration of the wings but some subspecies have been described, one in Florida, one in the southeastern deserts and another in Mexico.

The remaining four species occupy discrete but adjoining geographical areas (Fig. 2) covering the territory of the North American continent south of the barren lands of Canada and Alaska to the southeastern deserts, south along the Mexican plateau, west to the Pacific ocean and east to the Atlantic. These four species are *arthemis* of the north, *astyanax* of the east and south, *lorquini* of the Pacific coast and *weidemeyeri* of the mountain states.

Much information on the interrelationships between these species exists for only *astyanax* and *arthemis*, and *lorquini* and *weidemeyeri*. The detailed map of the contact zone between *astyanax* and *arthemis* (Fig. 3) shows that these two species actually overlap from New England to Pennsylvania and west through northern New York, central Michigan, Wisconsin and Minnesota. In this zone of overlap there is no belt of intermediate populations. Both species exist largely in their typical form. The typical forms are distinctive enough, for *arthemis* has a wide white band on a black background across the wings while *astyanax* lacks this white band and has instead a blue band along the margin of the hind wing (Plate I).

Nearly all the butterflies collected in the field, whether in the zone of overlap or elsewhere in the distributional range of the species, are either one or the other of these two types. The form with the white band (*arthemis*) is shown by the dots in Figure 3 while the type lacking it (*astyanax*) is shown by the triangles. North and south of the zone of overlap intermediates between the two types are not found at any considerable

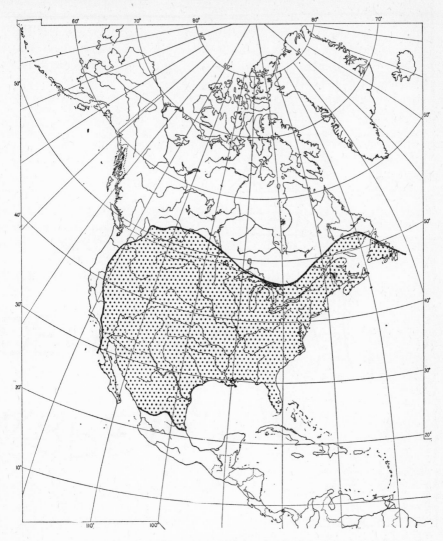

Figure 1. Distribution of *Basilarchia archippus.*

distance. They are, however, frequently encountered along the belt indicated by wavy lines and by crossed circles on the map. Unfortunately, quantitative data on the relative frequencies of the different forms are almost nonexistent, even though these facts have been known for seventy years. Mead (in Edwards, 1879) states of the situation in the Catskill Mountains of southern New York: "When I collected every *Proserpina* (intermediate) I could find, I took 110. Of *Arthemis*, I actually did take about 200, and could have taken a thousand without any difficulty."

{ *341* }

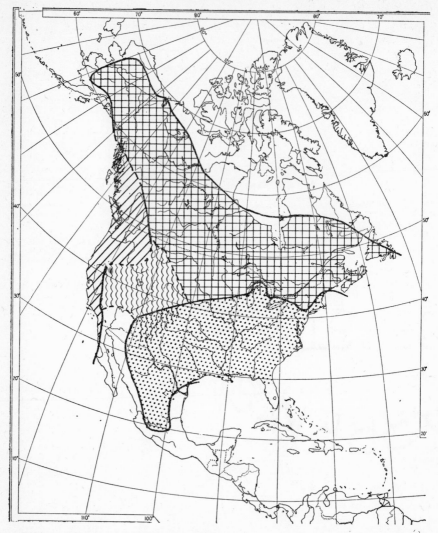

Figure 2. Distribution of *Basilarchia arthemis* (cross-hatched), *B. astyanax* (dotted), *B. weidemeyeri* (wavy-lines), and *B. lorquini* (lines slanting to the left).

Edwards (1879) states that he has had the same results in the same area. Information written by Edwards in 1879 is especially interesting because of the long time that contact hybridization has been prevalent, and his remarks are repeated here. When he mentions *ursula* he refers to *astyanax* and when *proserpina* he refers to intermediates of one type or another.

    . . . in the Adirondacks of northern New York, where *Arthemis* abounds, Mr. W. W. Hill, in four seasons collecting, has seen no example of *Proserpina*. So Mr. A. E. Graef states that he found *Arthemis* abundant in the Adirondacks, but saw no *Proserpina*.

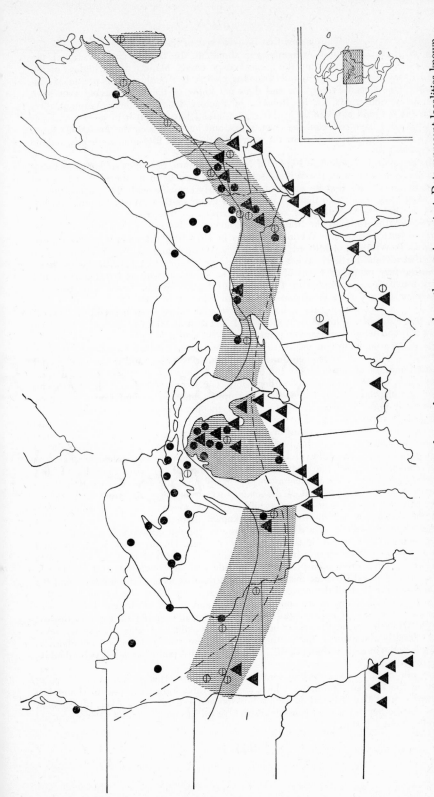

Figure 3. Distribution of *Basilarchia arthemis* and *astyanax* in the northeastern states where they are in contact. Dots represent localities known for *arthemis*, triangles for *astyanax*, crossed circles for intermediates of one sort or other. The shaded area represents the zone where intermediates are often found. Locality data are obtained from many published sources.

Professor S. H. Peabody writes that he collected in the Hoosac Mountains the last week of June, 1873, and *Arthemis* was abundant. In 1875, was in Vermont the middle of July, and walked up the western slope of Mt. Mansfield, the highest of the Green Mountain range. He found *Arthemis* plenty, but neither there nor in Massachusetts has he seen *Proserpina*, and does not know of the latter having ever been taken in Vermont. Mr. C. H. Roberts, of Factory Point, southern Vermont, says "*Arthemis* is found abundantly in this region, and I have taken it in several counties of this State. I have collected for seven years, and have not seen the *Proserpina* form. I have twice bred *Arthemis* from the egg, with the result fifty-nine *Arthemis*, but no *Proserpina*."

Mr. Scudder, in Geological Report of New Hampshire, describes *Arthemis* as being exceedingly abundant in the White Mountains, as well as in northern New England generally, and states that its southern limits nearly coincide with the northern limits of *Ursula* [*Astyanax*]; also that it has not been taken south of Massachusetts, and but rarely in that State. Nothing is said of *Proserpina* in this report, showing that the presence of this form in the State was unknown to the author. Mr. Morrison, who collected butterflies in the White Mountains in 1875, did not meet with *Proserpina*.

Mr. C. P. Whitney, of Milford, southern New Hampshire, says that *Arthemis* is rare in his district, and further: "What I have called *Proserpina*, that is, with a white band across the fore wings, or traces of it, is fully as abundant here as *Ursula*, which last varies much from examples of *Ursula* found further south. I am sure that my *Proserpina* are a variety of *Ursula*—a northern form. A few weeks ago I received a letter from a friend saying he had seen an *Arthemis* raised from a brood of *Ursula*." With this letter Mr. Whitney sent me 8 ♂ 1 ♀ taken at Milford. One of these males shows a broad white band across primaries below, and a macular stripe across same wings above; no white on either side of secondaries. Another shows a cluster of whitish scales in each interspace quite across primaries below, and a clear white spot at costal margin of secondaries; but beyond this there is no trace of a band on secondaries, or on upper side of either wing. The female also has a slight band on under side of primaries, and faint traces on upper side; but no white on secondaries. Three other males have very slight traces of the band on under side of primaries, restricted to small clusters of scales in the two or three posterior interspaces. The remaining examples have nothing of this. The first three spoken of I have no doubt are true *Proserpina*, and probably all the others are, though they cannot be distinguished from some examples of *Ursula* taken in certain districts where *Arthemis* is never known to fly. All these Milford examples, and all from the Catskills which I have ever examined, have this common peculiarity, that the general coloration of the under surface is similar to that of *Arthemis*, varying as this varies from cinnamon or ferruginous-red to chocolate-brown, exhibiting many shades of color. Now in *Ursula* from the districts in which *Arthemis* is unknown there is almost always a flush of blue-black or of green over a dark brown ground, though occasionally an example is ferruginous or light brown, just as some *Arthemis* are. On the other hand, now and then an example of *Proserpina* from the Catskills has a flush of blue-black. I have in my cabinet such a *Proserpina* placed side by side with an *Ursula* taken at Coalburgh, W.Va., in which last the blue flush is much less than usual in examples here, and the two are scarcely if at all distinguishable from each other. Therefore I cannot say that all these Milford examples are not *Proserpina*; and indeed I do not know where *Proserpina* ends and *Ursula* begins, though a typical example of each is distinct enough. Mr. Scudder, in the report before cited, speaking of *Ursula* [*Astyanax*], says: "It is tolerably abundant in the southern parts of New England, and occurs about as far north as the annual isotherm of 45°, the northernmost points recorded being Dublin and Milford, N.H."

Arthemis must rarely cross the southern line of New Hampshire, or of Vermont except at the Hoosac Mountains, which are a continuation of the Green Mountains. Dr. Harris states that it is rare in Massachusetts; and Prof. H. W. Parker, of Amherst, writes that he has never seen it in his district, or on Mounts Tom and Holyoke, or on the hills about Chester.

Plate I. A, *Basilarchia arthemis.* B, *Basilarchia astyanax.* C, An intermediate specimen showing part of the characteristics of *arthemis*, part of *astyanax* but the wide band of *arthemis*. D, An intermediate showing a part of the characters of each of *arthemis* and *astyanax* but an intermediate band. This form would be known as *proserpina*.

Mr. Anson Allen, of Orono, central Maine, says, "*Arthemis* is common here, but I have never known of *Proserpina* being taken. *Ursula* is not found here."

Mr. H. H. Lyman, *Can. Ent.*, VI., p. 38, speaks of *Ursula* (*Ephestion*) as having been taken at Portland, Me.; but I learn from him that he is now satisfied that the butterflies were *Proserpina*.

To the eastward, *Proserpina* is recorded by Rev. C. J. S. Bethune, *Can. Ent.*, II., p. 55, as having been taken in Nova Scotia.

Mr. Robert Bunker, of Rochester, N.Y., says that *Proserpina* has not been taken in that part of the State, so far as he knows, but that *Arthemis* is taken about Rochester every summer. Also that *Ursula* is not common.

At Albany, N.Y., which is nearly in the latitude of the southern line of Vermont and New Hampshire, and is half a degree north of the Catskills, and not more than thirty miles from them, *Arthemis* is usually rare, but in some seasons has appeared in considerable numbers, according to Mr. Lintner. He has sent me two males of undoubted *Proserpina*, with traces of the band on both surfaces, and another like these, but with no trace. As these graded from *Proserpina* to what seemed to be *Ursula*, Mr. Lintner was led to the same conclusion that other observers reached, that *Ursula* originated with *Arthemis*, through *Proserpina*. This apparent *Ursula* is precisely like the unbanded examples from Milford, with the coloration of under surface as in *Proserpina*.

Mr. Robert M. Grey, residing at Kenwood, near Albany, writes that he has taken examples of *Proserpina* three miles below Albany in company with *Ursula*. And of three males sent me by Mr. Grey, one was somewhat banded, while the other two showed no trace of the band, and were of same type as the supposed *Ursula* of Mr. Lintner. Mr. Grey states further that he has taken *Proserpina* in the Heldeberg Mountains, fifteen miles back of Albany, in company with *Arthemis*. An example sent from that locality was *Proserpina*, slightly banded. A fifth male, taken five miles back of Albany, in "company with *Arthemis* and *Ursula*," as Mr. Grey states, also showed traces of the band. It is evident in all these cases that what has passed as *Ursula* is only distinguished from *Proserpina* by the absence of the band. Both these types in districts inhabited by *Arthemis* probably come from the same brood of larvae. With the examples sent by Mr. Grey was a very interesting one of *Disippus*, considerably melanized, so that there was sufficient approach to the black species to suggest hybridism between the two.

Mr. Adolph Conradi, of Bethlehem, Penn., writes: "*Arthemis* is common in Monroe and Pike counties, northeastern Pennsylvania, and in pine swamps. *Proserpina* I have never taken myself, but a friend took one in Monroe County last summer. This had the white band on primaries entirely wanting, whereas on secondaries it was fully developed. I have been a collector of lepidoptera for the last eighteen years and have taken *Ursula* in at least twenty counties of this State, but I have never taken one which varies from the ordinary type."

Going westward, Dr. R. M. W. Gibbs, of Kalamazoo, Mich., writes that *Arthemis* is not a common species. That *Proserpina* has been taken in Wexford County in the northwest (lat. 44°).

Prof. A. J. Cook, of Lansing, says that *Arthemis* is found in the very north of the State, but is rare, so much so that no examples of it are in the cabinet of the Agricultural College. *Proserpina* is found in the middle counties, and *Ursula* in the south.

Mr. Charles E. Worthington, of Chicago, has collected extensively for several years in northern Indiana and Illinois, but has not met *Arthemis* or *Proserpina*, though *Ursula* is frequently seen.

Dr. J. P. Hoy, of Racine, Wis., writes that *Arthemis* was formerly quite common in his neighborhood, but of late years has become very rare, and that *Proserpina* in certain localities was numerous; and he sent me a well-marked example of the latter form, male.

Rev. J. D. Hulst collected in Minnesota, near St. Cloud, and at Duluth and Sault St. Marie: found *Arthemis* everywhere, but saw no *Proserpina*.

As to the northern limits of *Proserpina*: Mr. Wm. Brodie, of Toronto, writes that his experience is based on acquaintance of thirty years with *Arthemis*, mostly in the central parts of County of York, about thirty miles north of Toronto. *Arthemis* was very abundant, but he never saw a Canadian specimen of *Proserpina*.

On the other hand, Mr. W. Murray, of Hamilton, Ontario, says: "For the last seven or eight years I have found *Proserpina* in company with *Arthemis*, but they are never plenty. Four years ago, 2d July, I tried sugaring in the daytime, and among the insects which came to the sugar were four *Arthemis* and one *Proserpina*. On the tree one of the *Arthemis* was trying to mate with the *Proserpina*, when I disturbed them." Hamilton is about fifty miles to the south of Toronto, and nearly in line with the southern boundary of Vermont. So in *Can. Ent.*, IX., p. 140, Mr. Moffat states that *Proserpina* has been taken near Hamilton occasionally, and always in company with *Arthemis*.

In *Can. Ent.*, VII., p. 208, is a list of butterflies taken at Godbout River, on the north side of the lower St. Lawrence, in the seasons 1873 and 1874, in which *Arthemis* is included, and said to be common, but neither *Proserpina* nor *Ursula* are mentioned.

The conditions as described in 1879 by Edwards are apparently unchanged today. In check lists of the butterflies of the different states, authors vary in their treatment of these intermediate forms; some do not differentiate them from the typical in their lists while others do note their distinctness. As Edwards found, the range of variation may be continuous from one species to the other but the parental types and the F_1 hybrid types are the more abundant. Moore (1939) states under *arthemis* in his listing of localities for the two species in Michigan: "There seems to be little doubt but that this and the preceding [*astyanax*] are the same species. Intermediate forms intergrade completely. The records above include all intermediate forms as well as the typical *arthemis*."

In addition to the intermediate form *proserpina* of *arthemis* there is the form *albofasciata* of *astyanax* (Newcomb, 1907). The difference between these two is that *proserpina* presents most of the characteristics of *arthemis* except the broader white band, while *albofasciata* presents most of the characteristics of *astyanax* and has a portion at least of the white band. Also, *proserpina* is largely found in the southern part of the range of *arthemis*, while *albofasciata* is found in the northern part of the range of *astyanax*.

Field (1910) reared the offspring of a wild captured female *proserpina* and obtained nine *proserpina* and seven *arthemis*. Edwards (1877) likewise bred the offspring of a female *proserpina* from the Catskills and obtained three *arthemis* and one *proserpina*. These added together give ten *arthemis* to ten *proserpina* as the offspring from *proserpina* wild females, each of which most likely had mated with *arthemis* males because they were obtained in an area where *astyanax* were extremely rare. If the difference between the banded form and the non-banded forms were differentiated by alleles of a single gene, the allele controlling the banded form might be designated b_p (meaning band present) and for the non-banded form b_a (meaning band absent). The fully banded forms then might be considered homozygous, b_p/b_p. Likewise, the fully non-banded forms might then be considered homozygous b_a/b_a. The partly banded forms, *proserpina* and *albofasciata*, would then be heterozygotes without dominance, b_p/b_a, as they are intermediate in the characteristic. With respect to this hypothesis, both *proserpina* and *albofasciata* are then alike as to genotype for this pair of alleles. They are not alike in appearance, however, for *proserpina* is more like *arthemis* in other characteristics and *albofasciata* is more like *astyanax*. Since *proserpina* is northern and *albofasciata* is southern it would be expected that each would carry genes typical of the species from their respective districts. This would alter the heterozygote in the direction of that species. The occurrence of *proserpina* far to the north of the area where *astyanax* often flies (in Nova Scotia) and of *albofasciata* far to the south of *arthemis* territory (in Virginia) suggests that the alleles may be carried considerable distance as a heterozygote. The result is that the populations of the two species exhibit a zone of variability decreasing outward from the belt of overlap.

The ratio of 10:10 for the offspring of the heterozygotes is anticipated for the backcross to either parental type. Since both females were taken in *arthemis* territory, the 1:1 ratio of equal numbers *arthemis* and *proserpina* is expected. Similar ratios of equal numbers of *astyanax* and *albofasicata* are expected from *albofasciata* females if they mate with an *astyanax* male. One fully banded *albofasciata*: two half-banded *albofasciata*: one non-banded *astyanax* would result from crossing two half-banded *albofasciata*. I have found no record of the existence of these fully banded *astyanax*, but they would be very rare.

Similar ratios would be expected for the *proserpina* crosses because *proserpina* × *proserpina* should give one banded *arthemis*: two half-banded *proserpina*: one non-banded *proserpina*. Such varieties have been taken in the wild populations along the southern range of *arthemis*.

The above hypothesis might be summarized as follows:

genotype	band	*arthemis* genome	*astyanax* genome
b_p/b_p	full	arthemis	albofasciata
b_p/b_a	half	proserpina	albofasciata
b_a/b_a	none	proserpina	astyanax

The cross *arthemis* × *astyanax* according to this hypothesis should give all half-banded individuals blending as one *arthemis* and *astyanax*. The hybrids arising from the cross would be b_p/b_a in genetic constitution for this pair of alleles but would also share equally the other genes for which the species differ. Thus they would be intermediate in appearance. Field (1914) made such a cross in the laboratory between a bred female *astyanax* × a wild male *arthemis*. Eight offspring were obtained which he called *proserpina* and which, judging from his figures of a male and female, were exactly intermediate in all characteristics.

The two species *lorquini* and *weidemeyeri* seem to hybridize on the line where their ranges overlap along the eastern edge of the Sierra Nevada, Cascade, and northern Rocky Mountains. *B. lorquini* is distinguished from *weidemeyeri* most obviously by an orange patch at the apex of the fore wings and by a more orange color generally. In the zone of juxtaposition of these two species at Mono Lake and Mammoth Lakes in the Great Basin, intermediates have been taken which have been named *fridayi*. I have collected all three forms in the same willow grove. No breeding has been carried out on these forms but it is possible that the relationships will be found as simple as in the case above. Both species have the white band across the wings as in *arthemis*.

The species *archippus* seems quite distinct from each of the other four species in the genus *Basilarchia* and overlaps or bounds the range of each of them. It is generally brown in color instead of black. Hybridization seems to occur at quite infrequent intervals between *archippus* and the other species and hybrid or varietal names have been given to the results, such as *arthechippus*, *rubrofasechippus*, *weidechippus*, and *rubidus*. Few of these, however, are based upon anything more than circumstantial evidence, namely, the fact that they are intermediate between the other species, that they were found in company with them, and that they are rare. Field (1914), however, has some definite information that the species do cross. He reared *Basilarchia archippus* in captivity and mated a female with a wild *arthemis* male. Eight males were bred through to maturity and these were all found to be intermediate between the parents and similar to the form *arthechippus*, which is occasionally taken in the wild where these two species overlap. These F_1 were not all alike; and although they were intermediate between the parents, they showed considerable variation. This might be an indication that the parents were not completely homozygous for different alleles; for if so, the heterozygotes which resulted should have been alike. It seems likely that enough interbreeding occurs between these different species so that none of them is able to reach a state of complete homozygosis for the genes by which they differ. Thus the hybrids are never all alike.

The Genus *Colias*

Evidence seems to point toward the fact that nearly all species of the genus *Colias* will cross with any other species of the genus if given favorable circumstances in the natural environment or in the laboratory. At present the laboratory evidence of hybridization is restricted to two species but in the wild many populations which may involve in a ring nearly all North American species have indicated cross-hybridization either directly or through circumstantial evidence. Many of these data are now in the process of accumulation and only a general idea of the magnitude of the hybridization can now be indicated.

The two species *eurytheme* and *philodice* (which I earlier called the orange and yellow races of *chrysotheme* due to their hybridization) occur over a large part of North America, overlapping much of the territory of the United States. *Colias philodice*, however, occurs much farther north than does *eurytheme*. In the area of overlap of the two species as shown by the double hatched lines on the map (Fig. 4), the two species

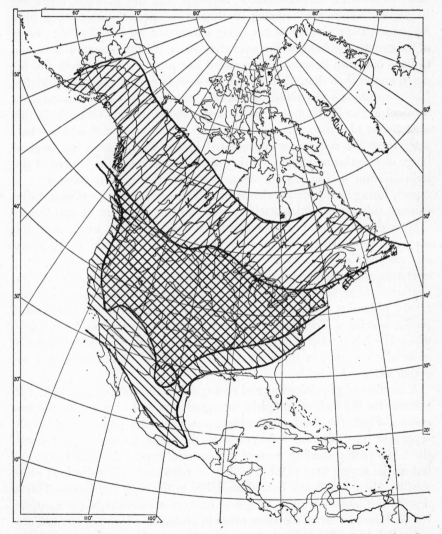

Figure 4. Distribution of *Colias philodice* (lines slanting to the left) and *Colias eurytheme* (lines slanting to the right). Where the lines overlap, hybridization occurs between these species.

hybridize to such an extent that in long-standing populations approximately ten per cent of all the individuals taken in wild populations are intermediates of one sort or another. Copulating pairs consisting of the two parental types have been taken in the wild and, likewise, hybrid pairs have been mated in the laboratory. The genetic difference between the two species is multifactorial as shown by the F_1 being intermediate and the F_2 giving a swarm of all variations ranging from the one species to the other. Wild individuals have been taken, the progeny of which indicate that backcrosses between the F_1 hybrids and the parental types are frequent. Despite the crossing of these two species with such a high frequency, their identity is not being eliminated by the blending effects of the genetic mechanism. For over sixty years, the hybridization is known to have occurred in some places and it has probably been occurring for much longer than that. Throughout the eastern part of the United States, *Colias eurytheme* is a recent immigrant, although it is now a permanent resident in the fields opened up by man's deforestation. Throughout this area *Colias philodice* was represented by a subspecies different in character from the subspecies represented in the west, where the original range of *eurytheme* overlapped that of *philodice*. Since the advent of the hybridization in the eastern area, however, the eastern subspecies is rapidly losing its distinctive character and may soon become similar to the western subspecies which itself approaches the character of *eurytheme*.

Hybridization has been intensively studied in three areas over the range of these two species, in New Hampshire by Gerould, in Michigan and eastern California by the present author. In each of these places the circumstances connected with the hybridization are the same, although the characters of *philodice* are different in each zone. In Michigan and California, *philodice* is especially abundant in areas where the larval food plants, species of *Trifolium*, grow; and *eurytheme* is especially abundant where the larval food plants, species of *Medicago*, grow. Hybridization is especially common in those areas where the food plants are grown together in the same fields.

A number of physiological and ecological circumstances are evident to account for the lack of complete intergradation and blending of the two species. First, the food plant differences keep the populations largely separated into different fields even in the same general area. Second, there is a partial sterility even of the parental types when the larvae are fed on the wrong food plant. Third, even notwithstanding the food plant sterility, there is a heavy hybrid mortality in the eggs and larvae. This is despite the fact that the F_1, F_2, and backcross individuals are normally fertile. Fourth, a larval diapause exists in *philodice* which permits individuals of that species to overwinter in cold areas better than *eurytheme*. Indirectly this diapause also regulates the periods of butterfly flight quite closely so that the adults of the two species may have different flight periods in the same region.

It might be thought that excessive hybridization between two species would be deleterious and that mechanisms would be developed to act toward its elimination. Such does not seem to be the case. On the other hand, there is a definite advantage for both species because of the hybridization. The hybrid individuals would have the advantage of increased heterozygosity and accompanying hybrid vigor as well as a store of gene material available for selection which is greater than that possessed by either species alone. Neither species seems to have lost out in the struggle for existence. On the contrary, the evidence indicates that both species are now much more common than formerly over much of the territory. This fact is probably connected with the increased habitat now available due to the elimination of the eastern hardwood forest.

Other species within the genus *Colias* also give evidence of hybridization. These include the following pairs:

Colias christina × *Colias gigantea* (Alberta plains)
Colias hecla × *Colias nastes* (Arctic coast)
Colias christina × *Colias philodice* (Alberta mountains)
Colias interior × *Colias philodice* (Michigan)
Colias alexandra × *Colias philodice* (Idaho)

The two species *christina* and *gigantea* occupy overlapping ranges throughout the northern Great Plains area in southern Canada. The larval food of *gigantea* is a dwarf willow which lives in muskeg bogs and that of *christina* includes a number of leguminous plants such as *Astragalus* and *Hedysarum*. *Colias gigantea*, therefore, inhabits bogs or the low-lying areas and *christina* the uplands or the hilly areas where the drainage is good. These areas overlap to a certain extent and because of this it is possible for the males of one species to find the females of the other before the latter have had much chance to fly. The latter occurrence is important because the females mate but once and will mate with the first available male.

Changes in the natural habitats made by man have probably been of some importance in increasing the natural hybridization of the two species by the increase in the overlap between the bog and the upland habitats. The construction of roads has brought *Hedysarum* along the roadsides into the midst of the bogs, for example. But nevertheless, the hybridization is of natural occurrence and appears in areas where the primitive conditions have not been altered at all. In these areas, the orange color characteristic of the wings of *christina* may be found in small quantity on some specimens of normally yellow *gigantea*.

Colias hecla and *nastes* are two Arctic species which overlap over a part of their geographic range along the northern coast of North America

(Fig. 5). *Colias hecla* exists in the Arctic archipelago and Greenland south to Southampton Island and east in the barren grounds of Alaska and south along the plains of the Mackenzie drainage basin to southern Alberta. In the southern area it is a very early flyer, being found as the adult as early as May. In the north it is found in July and August. *Colias nastes* does not occur so far north as *hecla* but is found along the north coast of North America, Southampton Island, Labrador, Churchill, and

Figure 5. Distribution of *Colias nastes* (lines slanting to the right) and *Colias hecla* (lines slanting to the left). Where the lines overlap, *Colias boothi* as well as *nastes* and *hecla* occurs. It is intermediate in characteristics between *nastes* and *hecla*.

south from the barren lands along the tops of the Rocky Mountains to Montana. It flies during late July and August both in the north and south.

In the southern areas there is no possibility of *nastes* coming in contact with *hecla* owing to the two months difference in flying time and the elevation differences at which they occur. In the north, however, they fly in the same place and at the same time in the narrow belt of country from northern Alaska and the mouth of the Mackenzie River to Southampton Island. Now, in this area a species of *Colias* named *boothi* is found which combines the characteristics of *hecla* and *nastes*. This species is found only in the area of overlap of the two species *hecla* and *nastes*. Further information concerning the exact relationship between *boothi* on the one hand and *hecla* and *nastes* on the other awaits further field work and will be reported on later. At any rate, when a long series is obtained, the range of variation in the populations is from *nastes* through *boothi* to *hecla*. Here, however, instead of the parental types being the more numerous, the species *boothi* is more numerous than the two presumed parental species.

The remaining examples of hybridization all involve *Colias philodice* and may be affected by alterations in ecological conditions aided by agriculture. *Colias philodice* occupies clover pastures or fields in either the mountains or the plains. Many of these fields have been created by men for the pasture of range animals by the cutting and clearing of the natural vegetation. Therefore, the habitat of *philodice* can impinge very closely upon that of other species which may have been living in the natural areas. *Colias christina* lives in the open woods in the foothills of Alberta and this area may be dotted with clearing occupied by *philodice*. In this area, specimens are found which seem to be intermediates between these two species. They are not abundant. The fact that a dominant white gene is very abundant in populations of *christina* and nearly absent in populations of *philodice* suggests how weak the results of the hybridization are.

Colias interior occupies the open sand barrens of northern Michigan where there is a dominant ground cover of low *Vaccinium* (blueberry). It is very abundant in this area. Open fields of clover pasture have been cut in the same area but are not abundant and in these fields *philodice* are not rare. Likewise, clovers have come in along roadside cuts followed by *philodice*. There is evidence of hybridization between these two species as evidenced by a long range of intermediates. These, however, are not common. A white genetic form of the *interior* population is very rare here while in *philodice* it is very common. The responsible allele thus is not exchanged from one species to the other frequently.

Colias alexandra probably is a geographical division of the *christina* species. It exists throughout the western mountains of the United States in various forms such as have been given the names *astraea, edwardsi, chrysomelas, harfordi,* etc. It lives on the uplands and is never in the meadows or open fields where *philodice* is found. Nevertheless, the habitats overlap to a certain extent in the Great Basin semi-desert irrigated lands and in one population there is considerable evidence of complete crossing between the forms in the same manner as that between *christina* and *philodice.*

In all these cases of hybridization the first evidence of the intercrossing is the great increase in the variability of the species concerned in the area of overlap. These variations tend in the direction of the characters of the species with which they are hybridizing. In the one case of *Colias boothi* it appears as if the two parental species may be disappearing in favor of the hybrid in the area of overlap.

Another type of increase in variability as a result of hybridization is that of breaking down a set of modifiers of dominance for a given gene. Each species of *Colias* has two color phases in the female, the normal yellow or orange, and a white form. The latter is usually controlled by an allele which is dominant over that for the yellow or orange so that the white individuals are either homozygous or heterozygous for the dominant allele and the yellow or orange are all homozygous for the recessive. The segregation between these two color forms is usually very sharp. That is, the dominance of the white is usually complete. However, in the population in Alberta where *christina* is hybridizing primarily with *occidentalis* a series of forms can be obtained which range from orange to yellow and various grades of white. These intermediate forms may be explained by postulating a breakdown of the different system of modifiers for dominance of the white allele which had been developed in the two species. Thus, intermediates would be formed.

A similar situation has been found in the hybridization between different geographical subspecies which differ by single characters in the genus *Argynnis* (Hovanitz, 1943). The single character differences seem to be controlled by single pairs of alleles, but at the zones of overlap intermediates occur, and these tend to simulate a hybrid swarm. An explanation which now may be postulated is that the difference between any two races is largely that of a single pair of alleles as suggested then, but that different modifiers have been developed to act with the allele present in any one subspecies. These modifiers are assorted by crossing at the zone of hybridization and lead to the series of intergrading forms present only at that zone. Such an explanation is applicable also for the variations in the forms *proserpina* and *albofasciata* of the species *Basilarchia arthemis* and *astyanax* previously discussed.

SUMMARY

Examples of natural hybridization between species within the butterfly genera *Colias* and *Basilarchia* are illustrated. In each case the hybridization has resulted in an increased variability in the populations directly participating in the hybridization. In most examples the hybrid or intermediate forms are less common than the parental types; in one presumed case of hybridization between *Colias hecla* and *Colias nastes* the hybrid type (*Colias boothi*) appears to be more abundant than either parental type in the area of hybridization. In another case, the dominance of one allele over its contrasting allele seems to have been changed as a result of the hybridization.

REFERENCES

Edwards, W. H. 1877. Notes on Limenitis proserpina and arthemis. *Canad. Entomologist*, 9:114.

——. 1879. *Butterflies of North America*, 3 vols. Privately printed.

Field, W. L. W. 1910. The offspring of a captured female Basilarchia proserpina. *Psyche*, 17:87-89.

——. 1914. Hybrid butterflies of the genus Basilarchia. *Psyche*, 21:115-117.

Hovanitz, W. 1941. Parallel ecogenotypical color variation in butterflies. *Ecology*, 22:259-284.

——. 1943a. Hybridization and seasonal segregation in two races of a butterfly occurring together in two localities. *Biol. Bulletin*, 85:44-51.

——. 1943b. Geographical variation and racial structure of Argynnis callippe in California. *Amer. Nat.*, 77:400-425.

Moore, Sherman. 1939. A list of the butterflies of Michigan. *Occ. Papers Museum of Zoology*, No. 411, 1-23.

Newcomb, H. H. 1907. Description of a new variety of Limenitis ursula. *Psyche*, 14:89-91.

· 19 ·

EVIDENCE FOR THE GENETIC SUBMERGENCE OF
PINUS REMORATA

BY HERBERT L. MASON[1]

An example of natural genetic processes operating in the development of present day floras is afforded by the fossil and recent history of the Insignes section of the genus *Pinus*. Here is presented a situation about which we may erect an hypothesis with a view to developing a method to demonstrate its validity. The Insignes section of *Pinus* includes the so-called "closed cone pines" of the Pacific coast of North America. Genetically they are a group of closely related species as is indicated by the ease with which they can be made to produce fertile hybrids, as well as by the fact that wherever two species occur together in nature, occasional natural hybrids between them may be found. All have twelve pairs of chromosomes. This western group of pines includes *Pinus attenuata* Lemmon, the knob cone pine; *P. radiata* Don, the Monterey pine; *P. muricata* Don, the bishop pine; and *P. remorata* Mason, the island pine. Subspecific races have been described in both *P. radiata* and in *P. muricata* as taxonomic varieties. With the exception of *P. attenuata* all are members of the maritime and insular floras of California and Lower California. *P. attenuata* occurs discontinuously in the coast ranges and the Sierra Nevada to the Cascades from northern Lower California to central Oregon. It is typically an interior species but reaches the coast at Año Nuevo point where it hybridizes with *P. radiata*. It is authentically recorded in the Pleistocene (1) from California as is also *P. linguiformis* Mason (2). In the Pliocene is reported *P. pretuberculata* Axelrod (3). These three closely related pines probably represent a continuum of the genetic lineage of *P. attenuata* in time.

Pinus radiata is a discontinuous maritime species that occurs along the southern shores of Monterey Bay in Monterey County, and at San Simeon and Cambria along the San Luis Obispo County coast, California. The southern colonies are characterized by very large cones and it is possible that this character might have taxonomic significance. A two-needled colony on Guadalupe Island off the west coast of Lower California has been described as *P. radiata* var. *binata* Engelmann. *P. radiata* is well represented from the Pleistocene (4, 5) in several deposits from Santa Barbara County to Mendocino County in California. Notable are the

---

[1] Department of Botany, University of California.

Carpinteria flora and the Tomales flora. A Pliocene occurrence is represented by two cones in a private collection taken from a deposit that is now paved over by road work within the city of Santa Barbara. The collection belongs to Dr. Ouzdel, a surgeon of Santa Barbara. The remaining two species, *P. muricata* and *P. remorata*, form the basis of the present discussion and will now be treated in greater detail.

Pinus muricata is a highly discontinuous and highly polymorphic species of coastal and insular California. A few isolated individuals occur near Crescent City in Del Norte County, California. A considerable colony occurs in the redwood forest just north of Trinidad Head in Humboldt County. The main mass of the species ranges from Ten Mile Creek in Mendocino County to near Fort Ross in Sonoma County. Another colony occurs on Inverness Ridge in Marin County with a few scattered individuals on San Geronimo Ridge in the same county. An isolated colony occurs in the vicinity of Monterey and Carmel in Monterey County. This is entirely surrounded by *P. radiata*, and what appear to be hybrids between them occur in the zone of contact of the two species. The smooth cone character of these putative hybrids suggests the botanical origin of the enigmatic *P. insignis* Loudon (6) of the early literature. Other colonies occur in the Pecho hills in San Luis Obispo County, from where the type upon which the name *P. muricata* rests is presumed to have come, and on La Purisima Ridge in Santa Barbara County. The species occurs also on Santa Cruz, Santa Rosa, and Cedros islands, the latter in Lower California. A colony reported from "near San Quentin," Lower California, and described in the literature as *P. muricata* var. *Anthonyi* Lemmon (11) and based on a collection by A. W. Anthony in 1889, probably came from San Vicente canyon about 32 miles north of the point. Point San Quentin seems an unlikely habitat for the pine, and several botanists have attempted to locate it here and have not only failed to find it but those who were familiar with the species throughout its range report the habitat unsuitable for it. In 1925 I noted a single half-dead specimen near a building in this decadent village, giving every evidence of having been planted by man. Recent investigators have failed to note even this specimen. When considering the nature of cone variation in the species it is probable that the colony of pines of Cedros Island which have been described as *P. muricata* var. *cedrosensis* J. T. Howell (7) is the same genetic stock as that on the mainland and hence the name should be reduced to synonymy with it. On Santa Cruz Island hybrids between *P. muricata* and *P. remorata* occur. Major geographic breaks in the distributional pattern of *P. muricata* occur as a 45-mile gap between Crescent City and Trinidad Head; a 110-mile gap between Crescent City and Ten Mile Creek; 35 miles between Fort Ross and Inverness Ridge; 120 miles between Point Reyes and Monterey; 75 miles between Carmel and San Simeon; 50 miles between San Luis Obispo and Purisima Ridge; 50 miles from Purisima Ridge to Santa Rosa Island; and 550 miles from Santa Cruz Island to Cedros Island. Mileages expressed are approximate airline distances. Many of these gaps were less extensive in Pleistocene time as is indicated by fossil records in some of the intermediate areas where the species no longer occurs. Like *P. radiata* this species has left an extensive fossil record. It is recorded from the Pleistocene asphalt deposits at Rancho La Brea (1) and at Carpinteria in southern California, from the Tomales flora and from the Point Arena flora of northern California. In the Pliocene Pico formation of southern California as well as in the Merced sandstones (8) and the Santa Clara lakebeds (9) of the San Francisco Bay area, *P. Masoni* Dorf occurs. It is so close to *P. muricata* as to represent a continuum in time with the Pleistocene and modern forms.

The trees in the colonies north of San Francisco Bay differ from those to the south both as to stature and as to the nature of the habitat in which they occur. These northern individuals are massive trees with large trunks and heavy blue-green foliage. They occur on good soil that is often deep and sometimes also wet. Where the habitat is rocky, the bed rock is usually shattered or covered with deep pockets of soil. However, these northern trees at times extend into poorly drained winter-wet pine barrens. The cone scales of the northern type, although well developed, are not on the average so massive as those of the southern type. In the south the trees are smaller, the foliage is a lighter blue-green hue than the northern type, and the plants occur on shaley or decomposed dioritic ridges as well as on diatomaceous earths in habitats suggestive of pine barrens. These differences in form and aspect as well as in habitat preference may well indicate that the entities merit subspecific taxonomic separation.

Pinus remorata is an insular endemic confined to Santa Cruz and Santa Rosa islands, and it is possible that it occurs also on Cedros and Guadalupe islands, although the evidence for this is far from clear. It differs from *P. muricata* in its symmetrical cones, the scales of which bear smooth, rounded, scarcely raised umbos when mature, in its thicker needles, and also in some of the details of the internal anatomy of the needles. In stature the trees resemble the southern California members of the *P. muricata* complex.

On Santa Cruz Island there is abundant evidence that *P. remorata* and *P. muricata* are actively hybridizing. Much intergradation occurs, suggesting complete genetic compatibility between the two. The extent of this intergradation led J. T. Howell (7) to the belief that *P. remorata* as such had no taxonomic reality but was only a minor expression of *P. muricata*. He gave no hint of his interpretation of the causes of so high a degree of polymorphism as characterizes these variable populations. Repeated rumors suggested the occurrence of *P. remorata* at La Purisima Ridge on the adjacent mainland. Investigation of the entire colony at this locality disclosed many intermediates between *P. remorata* and *P. muricata*. There were, however, no pure *P. remorata* individuals to be found. There is reason to doubt that any of the Pleistocene type of the *P. muricata* complex now exists on La Purisima Ridge, since these trees all give evidence in their stature of being close to *P. remorata* from Santa Cruz Island. Furthermore, at La Purisima Ridge they occur only on diatomaceous soils or other pine barren sites such as do not exist near the localities where abundant Pleistocene records of the species have been obtained, immediately to the south of Pt. Conception, where the species does not occur today. That *P. remorata* is a pure-breeding genetic entity is exemplified by the fact that seed gathered on Santa Cruz Island by Dr. Carl Wolf and planted in an extensive grove at Rancho Santa Ana Botanic Garden came true to type. On the other hand, trees in Tilden Park, Berkeley, from seed from intermediate types from Santa Cruz Island give ample evidence of genetic instability, as shown by the great range of variation of cone and needle characters. Further evidence that in times past *P. remorata* was a distinct morphological and taxonomic type may be derived from the fossil record. In the Santa Cruz Island flora, Chaney and Mason (10) reported *P. remorata*. The numerous fossil specimens are all essentially uniform and are clear examples of *P. remorata* as it still exists on Santa Cruz Island. In the several lenses containing the Pleistocene flora that were investigated no specimens of *P. muricata* were discovered. All of the lenses contained needles, cones, and wood referred to *P. remorata*. This led to the conclusion that *P. remorata* at least dominated the flora and probably existed to the complete exclusion of *P. muricata* in that area during that part of the Pleistocene. This interpretation is strengthened by our findings in the apparently contemporaneous Carpinteria flora just across the 30-mile-wide Santa Barbara Channel. Here we found, in the Pleistocene flora, both *P. radiata* and *P. muricata* in great abundance. There were two water-worn cones of *P. remorata* found imbedded among cobblestones on what was evidently a former beach. This is taken as evidence that the cones may have been transported across the channel and deposited on the Pleistocene beach. The very prolific way in which *P. remorata* bears its cones would seem to demand that if it grew near enough to the Carpinteria site for two cones to enter, many more cones would certainly have entered with them and their preservation would have been insured by the asphaltum matrix of the deposit. The usual mode of occurrence of pines in these deposits is for branches with several whorls of attached cones to be imbedded in the matrix. From three to seven or eight cones occur in each whorl. It must be admitted that the absence of *P. muricata* from the Pleistocene of Santa Cruz Island is negative evidence, but its abundance in other Pleistocene deposits tends to support the conclusion that its absence from the record here may be significant. Such discrepancies between mainland and insular floras are consistent with many such occurrences between Santa Cruz Island and the adjacent mainland today.

Pinus remorata was observed by Chaney and Mason (10) in the fossil record of the Pleistocene flora of Santa Cruz Island. During the investigation of the floristics involved in this study, the pine was discovered still living on Santa Cruz Island. There had been previous reference to it in the literature (11) but here it was confused with *P. radiata* var. *binata* Engelmann, an endemic on Guadalupe Island some 650 miles to the south.

The situation as it exists between *P. muricata* and *P. remorata* today on the one hand, and as is suggested by their fossil record on the other, presents some interesting evidence of the role of certain genetic processes in the history of the genetic lineages that make up our floras. Here is a case where two species apparently closely related and probably not very anciently separated from one another developed independently through genetic processes under the sanction of geographic isolation. This isolation was apparently complete as far as *P. remorata* is concerned on Santa Cruz Island. But there is evidence that possibly even in Pleistocene time genetic disturbances, involving gene infiltration of *P. remorata* into the southern population of *P. muricata* were operating toward the differentiation of the northern and southern populations of the latter species. However, since the migration of *P. muricata* to Santa Cruz and Santa Rosa Islands in Late Pleistocene or post-Pleistocene time, complete and uninhibited gene flow between these two species is apparently taking place, resulting in a third type of pine. This new type has cone characters largely influenced by *P. muricata*, but the stature of the tree and the habitat requirements have been influenced by *P. remorata*. *P. remorata* is now doomed to extinction by complete genetic submergence. *P. muricata*, because of its discontinuity, will be enabled to maintain distinctive populations in the north as well as on Cedros Island to the south for considerable time to come; already the stands from Monterey to Santa Barbara County give evidence of increasing relationship with *P. remorata* as one moves southward. This apparent infiltration of genes of *P. remorata* into the mainland populations is evidenced particularly in the stature of the trees and in habitat preferences. The situation at La Purisima Ridge suggests a key to the problem. This grove of trees lies in the path of the prevailing wind from Santa Cruz and Santa Rosa islands. *P. remorata* pollen could readily be carried the 30 or 40 miles from the islands and function to pollinate the ovules of *P. muricata*. Likewise pollen from the hybrid swarms now on Santa Cruz Island will serve to further speed the processes operating on La Purisima Ridge. It should be recalled that the population of La Purisima Ridge is an evident hybrid swarm without any of the parent *P. remorata* being present as a tree in this locality. It is here suggested that the flow of genes of *P. remorata* into the adjacent mainland populations of *P. muricata* via wind-borne pollen began in Pleistocene time and was able slowly to build up an effect on the population of *P. muricata*. Due to the continued isolation of the insular colony of *P. remorata* it could continually exercise its influence upon *P. muricata* without in turn being submerged by that species. Today with *P. muricata* on Santa Cruz and Santa Rosa islands, the situation is different. The gene flow is now in both directions, a situation that will lead to the complete submergence of *P. remorata* as a distinct entity.

I have deliberately avoided any discussion of species concepts as involving this group of plants, preferring not to formulate judgments in the light of any of the current ideas on this subject but rather to await further investigation into the nature and behavior of the entities within the complex. To make a decision at this time would be premature. To shift the groups up or down the taxonomic hierarchy or to merge them will in no way alter their relationships nor will it at all alter the problem. There is, however, in this problem an interesting example of the futility of nomenclatorial rigidity in the field where modern botany impinges upon paleobotany. If we assume that our deductions in this case are correct and that *P. remorata* and *P. muricata* were distinct species during Pleistocene time but today through gene infiltration have already resulted in the partial submergence of *P. remorata* and a differentiation in the present population of *P. muricata*, then what name and relative categories must be used for such an entity as *P. remorata* both as a fossil species and as a living intergrade with *P. muricata*? The science of taxonomy must rest upon realized facts and not upon potential facts, simply because potentialities are not always realized. This will demand recognition of a changed status for this entity through time. Continuity with genetic change is bound to plague the nomenclaturist and tend to point up the inadequacy of our present taxonomic structure to fit the facts derived from genetic studies.

A program of genetic study of this complex designed to test the above hypothesis is now under way under the joint auspices of the University of California and the Institute of Forest Genetics of the California Forest and Range Experiment Station of the United States Forest Service. These species lend themselves well to genetic study since they mature cones when only 4 to 5 years old. With the techniques developed at the Institute of Forest Genetics, crosses within this group of pines are easily made. Many of the preliminary crosses have been completed and in some cases first generation hybrids are already established in the nursery.

REFERENCES

1. Mason, Herbert L. 1927. *Fossil Records of Some West American Conifers.* Carnegie Institution of Washington Pub. 346:139-158. 6 pls.
2. ——. 1932. *A Phylogenetic Series of the California Closed-Cone Pines Suggested by the Fossil Record.* Madroño 2:49-55.
3. Axelrod, Daniel I. 1937. *A Pliocene Flora from the Mount Eden Beds, Southern California.* Carnegie Institution of Washington Pub. 476:125-183. 6 pls.
4. Chaney, Ralph W., and Herbert L. Mason. 1933. *A Pleistocene Flora from the Asphalt Deposits at Carpinteria, California.* Carnegie Institution of Washington Pub. 415:47-79, 9 pls.
5. Mason, Herbert L. 1934. *Pleistocene Flora of the Tomales Formation.* Carnegie Institution of Washington Pub. 415:81-179. 11 pls.
6. Loudon, John C. 1838. *Arboretum et Fruticetum britannicum.* 4:2265. figs. 2170-2172. London.
7. Howell, John Thomas. 1941. *The Closed-Cone Pines of Insular California.* Leaflets of Western Botany. 3:1-8.
8. Dorf, Erling. 1933. *Pliocene Floras of California.* Carnegie Institution of Washington Pub. 412:1-112. 13 pls.
9. Scott, Flora Murray. 1927. *On Certain Fossil Cones from the Pacific Coast.* Bull. Torrey Botanical Club. 54:7-11.
10. Chaney, Ralph W., and Herbert L. Mason. 1930. *A Pleistocene Flora from Santa Cruz Island, California.* Carnegie Institution of Washington Pub. 415:1-24. 7 pls.
11. Lemmon, John G. 1892. *Handbook of West American Cone Bearers.* 24 pp. Oakland, California.

PART VI

ADAPTATION

· 20 ·

ADAPTATION AND SELECTION

BY SEWALL WRIGHT[1]

THE process of adaptive evolution is one of central interest from both the philosophical and scientific points of view. As with other natural phenomena there is probably both an internal and an external aspect. To avoid possible duplication of the same factor under different aspects, an attempt at scientific analysis must be restricted to the latter. In the present discussion, no consideration will be given to hypotheses which attribute evolution to inscrutable creative forces whether these be supposed to bring about gradual orthogenetic advance (Nägeli, Osborn), abrupt emergence (Lloyd Morgan) or are assigned to individual organisms (Lamarck). The discussion will also be restricted to factors for which there is a substantial basis in genetics. This consideration excludes the hypothesis that evolution is an extension of individual physiology (Lamarck, Eimer, Cope, etc.). Mutations of chromosomes and genes, and recombinations of these, are with minor qualifications the only known sources of hereditary change. The available evidence indicates that these occur independently of physiological adaptations of the individual. We are left with the hypothesis that phylogenetic adaptation is ultimately preadaptive. The variations come first, the organisms do the best they can with them, and natural selection is the arbiter (Darwin). Under any hypothesis, the results of natural selection may be considered as the measure of adaptation, and some degree of guidance of the course of evolution is virtually inevitable. It appears now that natural selection is the only verifiable factor making for cumulative adaptive change. This statement, however, by no means exhausts the possibilities of analysis.

EVOLUTION FROM SINGLE MUTATIONS

The earliest hypothesis along Mendelian lines was that significant evolutionary change is due to the occasional occurrence of mutations of such a nature as to give rise to new species (or higher categories) at once (deVries, Goldschmidt).

The abrupt origin of species by mutation requires that the most essential feature of the mutation be an isolating effect. This hypothesis has in its support the evidence that polyploidy has been important in the multi-

[1] Ernest D. Burton Distinguished Service Professor of Zoology, The University of Chicago.

plication of species, especially in cases in which it has occurred in a sterile hybrid, converting the latter into a fertile amphidiploid.

It is, however, impossible to base all evolution on the addition of chromosome sets. There is no other class of mutation which combines the properties of full fertility by itself, the production of sterile hybrids with the parent form or forms, a balanced organization favorable to adaptation, and (in amphidiploids) striking novelty. The other balanced types of chromosome mutation (translocation, inversion) result, when viable, in minor variants within the species of origin, often recognizable only by examination of the chromosomes themselves. Simple aneuploidy may bring complex character changes, suggestive of those distinguishing species, but not isolation. Most such changes are indeed incapable of existence except as heterozygous segregating varieties. Compound aneuploidy may, however, be a rare species-forming process (Darlington). Small duplications have no doubt been very important in evolution in increasing the number of genes, but hardly in the abrupt origin of new species. Such minor chromosomal changes can be treated statistically for the most part as gene mutations.

Evolution by Gradual Transformation

The most obvious alternative to abrupt origin of species by mutation is the conception of gradual transformation through the occurrence, orderly increase in frequency, and ultimate fixation of mutations that give a selective advantage to the individuals that carry them. Haldane has developed mathematically the nature of this process in a great variety of cases (1924 and later). Fisher (1937) has investigated the properties of the wave of diffusion from a portion of a population in which a mutation has become fixed.

Acceptance of any hypothesis of evolution by statistical transformation of populations permits differences of opinion as to whether it is the fixation of rare major adaptive mutations or the accumulation of a large number of minor ones that is usually responsible for a new species, whether by transformation of the entire parent species or of an isolated portion of the latter. This issue is somewhat confused by the ambiguity of the term bigness as applied to a mutation. The most literal sort of bigness is in the degree of physical change in the chromosomes. There is, however, no consistent correlation between this sort of bigness and conspicuousness or complexity of the effects on characters. There may be extensive rearrangements of the material of the chromosomes without conspicuous effect, and conversely single gene mutations may produce abnormalities of the most extreme sort. Again mere conspicuousness (as of many color mutations) may have little relation to morphological or physiological complexity. Finally bigness in any of these ways is far from being positively correlated with ecological potentiality.

Analyses of the actual genetic differences between related species have demonstrated all of the viable types that have arisen in the laboratory (cf. Dobzhansky, 1941). Changes in chromosome number and rearrangements are common but appear to have only minor importance, where any, with respect to distinguishing characters other than of fertility of hybrids. Conspicuous unitary differences are sometimes found especially with respect to color. The mode of segregation for most characters, however, indicates a multiplicity of genetic changes with effects that are either individually slight, or (if the character itself is of an all-or-none sort) of low penetrance.

The view that these species differences are largely due to mutations that were not only adaptive from the first but were carried directly to fixation by favorable selection is undoubtedly too simple, as indeed has probably been recognized in some degree by all who accept the general hypothesis of transformation. It makes the occurrence of adaptive mutations the limiting factor in evolution to an extent that severely restricts the possible rate of evolutionary change. There is evidence that evolution can proceed with great rapidity, given an adequate ecological opportunity.

It is necessary to examine the genetic properties of populations to find whether these may not provide a basis for rapid exploitation of opportunities without waiting for the accidental occurrence of the right mutation.

GENE FREQUENCY

The basic concept of statistical genetics is gene frequency. Because of the symmetry of the Mendelian mechanism, gene frequencies tend to persist unchanged from generation to generation. The state of the species with respect to a particular locus can be described in such a form as

$$\Sigma_{i=1}^{k}(q_i A_i)$$

where the A's designate k alleles and the q's are their frequencies.

The random unions of eggs and sperms, each with the array of alleles characteristic of the species, give a stable genotypic array at each locus of the type

$$[\Sigma_{i=1}^{k}(q_i A_i)]^2$$

(Hardy, 1908; Weinberg, 1908). The frequencies of combinations among loci are in the long run those of random combination, in a random breeding population, irrespective of linkage, unless the latter is complete (Weinberg, 1909, 1910; Robbins, 1918; Geiringer, 1944, 1948). The array may be represented by

$$\Pi_{L=1}^{n}[\Sigma_{i=1}^{k}(q_{Li} A_{Li})]^2$$

{ *367* }

where L is any one of n different loci. Thus 4 alleles (10 combinations) at each of 100 loci provide the potentiality for 10^{100} different genotypes.

A genetic description of a population can obviously be given much more economically in terms of gene frequencies than of genotypic frequencies. Moreover the tendency toward persistence of gene frequencies insures relative persistence of the statistical properties of the population, if the system of mating remains the same, even though no genotype is ever duplicated.

A change in the system of mating changes the array of genotypic frequencies and consequently the statistical properties of the population, but does not in itself tend to change the arrays of gene frequencies. Thus a tendency toward mating of relatives, whether sporadic or from a breaking up of the population into more or less isolated groups, gives a genotypic array at each locus of the type

$$(1-F)[\Sigma(q_iA_i)]^2 + F\Sigma(q_iA_iA_i)$$

where F is the inbreeding coefficient, defined as the correlation between uniting gametes with respect to additive gene effects (Wright, 1921, 1922). The increased homozygosis, measured by F, gives rise to the well-known effects of inbreeding, but the q's are not changed, and a return to the original system of mating is followed by return to the original genetic situation. Similarly, pure assortative mating with respect to any character causes departures from randomness of combination among the loci and consequent changes in the statistical properties of the population, but again the process does not in itself affect the gene frequencies and random combination is gradually restored on resumption of random mating (Wright, 1921).

THE ELEMENTARY FACTORS OF EVOLUTION

The elementary evolutionary process in a reasonably large homogeneous population may be considered to be change of gene frequency. It is convenient for the present purpose to distinguish three primary modes of change according to the degree of determinacy in the changes which they bring about. First are modes of systematic change, termed the evolutionary pressures (Wright, 1929, 1931). These are capable at least in principle of precise mathematical formulation which would make possible prediction of evolutionary trend if there were no processes of an indeterminate nature. Second are the random fluctuations in gene frequency, of which only the variance is determinate. Finally, it is convenient, although somewhat arbitrary, to distinguish from both of these, events that are unique or nearly so in the life of the species.

Modes of Immediate Change of Gene Frequency

1. *Systematic change* ($\triangle q$ determinate in principle).
   A. Pressure of recurrent mutation.
   B. Pressure of immigration and crossbreeding.
   C. Pressure of intragroup selection.
2. *Random fluctuations* (δq indeterminate in direction but determinate in variance).
   A. From accidents of sampling.
   B. From fluctuations in the systematic pressures.
3. *Nonrecurrent change* (indeterminate for each locus).
   A. Nonrecurrent mutation.
   B. Nonrecurrent hybridization.
   C. Nonrecurrent selective incidents.
   D. From nonrecurrent extreme reduction in numbers.

Back of these processes are all factors that cause secular changes in mutation rates, conditions of selection, size and structure of the population and the possibilities of ingression from other populations.

Mutation Pressure

Mutation pressure refers to the tendency of known genes to mutate to known alleles at definite rates. In the two-allele case, the net rate per generation obviously may be written

$$\triangle q = \frac{dq}{dt} = v(1-q) - uq$$

where u is the rate of mutation from the gene in question (frequency q) to its allele, v is the rate of reverse mutation, and time is measured in average generations. Haldane (1926) has shown that the effects of overlapping of generations are of only secondary importance in the transformation of populations. $\triangle q$ may be treated as dq/dt in order to obtain the approximate amount of change in a given number of generations (t) by integration.

The extents of systems of multiple alleles, known at many loci in many organisms, make it probable that each locus is capable of evolutionary change through a branching system of indefinitely great extent, and that many alleles normally coexist at many loci in any large population. Taking cognizance of this, the description of mutation pressure requires a system of simultaneous equations of the type

$$\triangle q_c = \frac{\partial q_c}{\partial t} = \Sigma(u_{ci} q_i) - (\Sigma u_{ic}) q_c$$

where u_{ci} is the rate of mutation to allele A_c from one of its alleles A_i, u_{ic} is the rate of reverse mutation and summation applies to all alleles of A_c.

It is obvious that the distinction between recurrent mutation and non-recurrent mutation must be arbitrary.

IMMIGRATION PRESSURE

Immigration pressure refers to the effects of recurring invasion of the territory under consideration by individuals, capable of producing cross-breds that enter into the population. Here

$$\triangle q_c = -m(q_c - q_{c(I)})$$

where $q_{c(I)}$ is the frequency of the gene among the immigrants and m is a coefficient measuring the amount of replacement of population by the immigrants per generation. The theory is closely similar to that of mutation pressure because of the linear nature of its effect. As with mutation pressure there is no sharp line between recurrent immigration and a type of hybridization so infrequent in the history of the species that each occurrence is best treated as a unique event.

SELECTION PRESSURE

Immigration pressure may be considered as a process of intergroup selection, less drastic than expulsion or extermination. We shall, however, use the term selection pressure, where not qualified, as relating only to intragroup selection. Selection pressure in this sense may be defined so as to include exhaustively all systematic modes of change of gene frequency which do not involve physical transformation of the hereditary material (mutation) or introduction from without (immigration). It includes the effects of differences in mating rate, fecundity, mortality rate, rate of attainment of maturity, and emigration rate. It differs mathematically from the pressures of mutation and immigration in being nil for either $q = 0$ or $q = 1$. There can be no selection in the absence of alternatives.

The general formula for selection pressure is

$$\triangle q_c = \partial q_c / \partial t = q_c\,(W_c - \overline{W})/\overline{W}$$

where W_c is the momentary selective value of the gene in question, giving due weight to the frequencies and selective values of all types of zygote into which it enters, and

$$\overline{W}\,(\, = \Sigma^k_{i=1} W_i q_i)$$

is the mean selective value for the population as a whole.

The selective value of a given type of zygote (fertilized egg) is assumed to be measured by its average contribution under the prevailing conditions to the array of zygotes produced a generation later in such a way that $\overline{W}$ is the ratio of the effective size of the population in the following generation to that in the one under consideration.

$$\overline{W} = \Sigma Wf$$

in terms of the selective values (W) and frequencies (f) of genotypes.

It is important to distinguish two kinds of selection: that in which the selective values of genotypes are constant under standard conditions, and that in which they are functions of the relative frequencies of genotypes. Relative constancy is to be expected where selection depends directly on a constant environment external to the species. Secular changes in both absolute and relative values of the selective values may indeed be expected to occur with changes in the density of the population but these are independent of the relative frequencies of genotypes in this sort of selection. If, however, there is selection based directly on the relations of different kinds of individuals of the species to each other, the selective values are necessarily functions of the frequencies of these genotypes. In the following discussion, random mating is assumed unless otherwise specified.

CONSTANT SELECTIVE VALUES. SINGLE LOCI

It is convenient to take up first the case in which the selection coefficients for genotypes of the locus in question are independent of frequencies at other loci and are constant and alike in the sexes. In this case the rate of change in frequency of gene A_c is as follows (Wright, 1937, 1942).

$$\triangle q_c = \partial q_c / \partial t = q_c(1-q_c)(\partial \overline{W}/\partial q_c)/2\overline{W}$$

It is assumed that the frequencies of all alleles of the gene, A_c, are expressed in the form

$$q_i = r_{ic}(1 - q_c)$$

in $\overline{W}$ before differentiating. Here r_{ic} is the frequency of A_i among the alleles of A_c. Thus

$$\partial q_i / \partial q_c = -r_{ic} = -q_i/(1 - q_c).$$

The composition of the population relative to a series of alleles may be represented by a point in a $(k-1)$ dimensional space. Thus in the case of three alleles, the gene frequencies may be represented by the distances from the sides of an equilateral triangle of unit height. The mean selective values $(\overline{W})$ for populations with given sets of gene frequencies, corresponding to points within this, may be represented by ordinates from the plane of this figure, defining a surface. Similarly in the case of four alleles the gene frequencies may be represented by distances from the four faces of a regular tetrahedron of unit height. The mean selective values of populations require an additional dimension $\overline{W}$ which may be indicated by shells of equal selective value, the contours of a "surface" in four-dimensional space.

This "surface" of selective values may be of various sorts. There may be a continuously upward gradient leading from each point toward a single peak value. If this is at one of the corners, it means that selection leads inevitably to fixation of the corresponding homozygote, except in so far as mutation or immigration maintains other alleles. If it is on an edge, or face, or in the interior of the figure, it is implied that selection by itself leads to a condition of stable equilibrium among two or more alleles. A depression from which gradients lead up in all directions implies a position of unstable equilibrium. There may also be saddle points, toward which selection drives the set of gene frequencies from certain directions but from which selection tends to cause ever-increasing departure, after a slight initial departure in certain other directions.

All alleles are maintained in equilibrium, if all heterozygotes (A_iA_j) are alike in selective value and are superior to all of the homozygotes $(A_iA_i, A_jA_j$ etc.). Let

$$W_{ij} = a, W_{ii} = a(1 - s_i), W_{jj} = a(1 - s_j):$$
$$\overline{W} = a[1 - \Sigma_{i=1}^k s_i q_i^2]$$
$$\triangle q_c = aq_c(\Sigma_{i=1}^k s_i q_i^2 - s_c q_c)/\overline{W}$$
$$\hat{q}_c = (1/s_c)/\Sigma_{i=1}^k(1/s_i)$$

where $\hat{q}_c$ is the value of q_c at equilibrium all $\triangle q$'s equal 0.

If the heterozygotes differ in selective value, the conditions for maintenance of all alleles are somewhat restricted. Thus if all homozygotes (k alleles) have the same selective value, a, and all of the heterozygotes except one have the value $a (1 + s)$ with s positive, and that one (A_1A_2) has the value $a (1 + t)$

$$\overline{W} = a[1 + s(1 - \Sigma_{i=1}^k q_i^2) + 2(t - s)q_1 q_2]$$
$$\triangle q_1 = aq_1[s(\Sigma_{i=1}^k q^2 - q_1) - (t - s)(2q_1 q_2 - q_2)]/\overline{W}$$
$$\triangle q_3 = aq_3[s(\Sigma_{i=1}^k q^2 - q_3) - (t - s)2q_1 q_2]/\overline{W}$$
$$\hat{q}_1 = \hat{q}_2 = s/[ks - (k - 2)(t - s)] \text{ if } 0 < t < 2s$$
$$\hat{q}_3 = \hat{q}_k = (2s - t)/[ks - (k - 2)(t - s)] \text{ if } 0 < t < 2s$$

All alleles are maintained in equilibrium if t is between 0 and $2s$. If t is negative, equilibrium is unstable; either A_1 or A_2 is eliminated according to the initial composition. If t is greater than $2s$, all alleles other than A_1 and A_2 tend to be eliminated.

It is possible for a gene that would be eliminated if only certain alleles were associated with it in a population to be maintained if others also are present. The conditions are decidedly restricted, however.

In many cases, some of which have been indicated above, there may be two or more peak values. Obviously any homozygote that is superior to all of the heterozygotes in which its allele enters is at a distinct peak. Which allele becomes fixed depends on the initial composition of the population. Any two or more alleles may form a group capable of stable equilibrium within itself but in unstable association with other such groups.

The rate of change in the mean selective value of the whole population is given approximately by the following formula, if the selective differentials are small.

$$\triangle \overline{W} = \Sigma_{i=1}^{k} [(1 - q_i)(\partial \overline{W}/\partial q_i) \triangle q_i]$$

It is assumed, as before, that the frequencies of all alleles are expressed in the form $q_j = r_{ji}(1 - q_i)$ in $\overline{W}$, before differentiating with respect to any frequency, q_i.

Constant Genotypic Selective Values

The treatment of selection as acting on single loci independently of all others is however highly artificial. Selective value, in a given setting, is a property of the organism as a whole and hence of its whole genotype. A gene is likely to be more favorable than an allele in some combinations, less favorable in others. The composition of the species may be thought of as located in a space of $\Sigma^n(k - 1)$ dimensions, assuming n loci and a variable number (k) of alleles at each locus. If the selective value, W, for each genotype as a whole is constant, and if the frequencies at the loci are combined at random (as is approximately true under long continued random mating and small net selection coefficients of the genes), the formula for rate of change of gene frequency per generation is still

$$\triangle q_c = q_c(1 - q_c)(\partial \overline{W}/\partial q_c)/2\overline{W}$$

under the same convention as before but $\overline{W}(=\Sigma Wf)$ is here a function not only of the gene frequencies at the locus in question but of the genes at all other pertinent loci.

It is again convenient to add another dimension to the geometric model: mean selective value $(\overline{W})$ of populations. The "surface" defined by $\overline{W}$ may be expected to be a very rugged one with innumerable peaks and subpeaks, corresponding to different harmonious combinations of genes.

These peaks may be of three sorts phenotypically: (a) peaks centering in different genotypes that give the same phenotype (as under the conventional multiple-factor hypothesis for quantitative variability and an intermediate optimum), (b) peaks that center in phenotypes that differ but give adaptation to the same conditions, and (c) peaks that center in adaptations to different conditions within the array of conditions to which the population has access, corresponding to the different adaptive zones and subzones of Simpson (1944).

The formula for $\triangle \overline{W}$ is the same as that above except that summation applies to all genes at all loci. The control by the gradient is obviously qualified by the term $q_c(1 - q_c)/2\overline{W}$ in the formula for each $\triangle q_c$. With constant genotypic selective values, the species tends to move toward one of the peaks, though not, as carelessly stated previously, up the steepest gradient in the surface $\overline{W}$ from the point at which it is located. The peak toward which it moves is not likely to be the highest one.

Effects of Deviations from Assumed Conditions

The situation is altered more or less by various types of deviation from the idealized case to which the preceding formulae apply. If there are very large differences between the sexes in selection, special formulae must be used; but even with moderately large differences the results are almost as if the average selective coefficients for each genotype applied to both sexes as shown (with a different mathematical formulation) by Haldane (1926) (cf. Wright and Dobzhansky, 1946). If there are moderate deviations from random mating due to inbreeding, and the net selection coefficients of genes are small, the expression $\partial \overline{W}/\partial q_c$ of the preceding formulae may be replaced by $\partial(\overline{W} + F\overline{W_I})/\partial q_c$ where $\overline{W_I}$ is the mean selective values of genotypes that are homozygous at the locus in question. The expression $\overline{W_I}$ is identical with $\overline{W}$ at loci at which there is no dominance but otherwise is different (Dobzhansky and Wright, 1941).

Selective mortality at different ages, and selective fecundity have diverse effects on observable frequencies. These must be carefully considered in analysis of concrete cases and are likely to make it necessary to go back to the basic formula.

Selection itself always produces departures from complete randomness of combination among loci if there are nonadditive interactions, but these are negligible for most purposes unless selection or linkage is strong (cf. Wright, 1942). Assortative mating, however, may produce very great departure from randomness (Wright, 1921) which requires considerable increase in complexity in its treatment. Subdivision of the population into nearly isolated strains also has effects which alter the situation drastically and are best treated under the head of intergroup selection by means of differential migration pressure. In view of a criticism by Fisher (1941) it should be emphasized that the formula for $\triangle q$ above, to which he referred, was explicitly based on the assumption of random mating of diploids and of constancy of genotypic selection coefficients. Other formulae had been used for other conditions.

Fisher (1930, 1941) himself has developed a different mode of approach for dealing with selection apart from other factors. According to his "fundamental theorem of Natural Selection": "The rate of increase in fitness of any organism at any time is equal to its genetic variance in fitness at that time." Genetic variance here refers only to the additive effects of genes. There is approximate agreement between our formulae for small selective differences and constant selective values, the difference being that Fisher's method does not introduce the term $\overline{W}$ in the denominator. The application of this theorem to cases in which there are variable genotypic selection coefficients is not, however, clear.

VARIABLE GENOTYPIC SELECTIVE VALUES

With variable genotypic selection coefficients, but otherwise the same assumptions as above and the same convention with respect to differentiation,

$$\triangle q_c = q_c(1 - q_c)\Sigma[W(\partial f/\partial q_c)]/2\overline{W}$$

where the f's are frequencies of genotypes, in general involving many loci, and the summation applies to all genotypes. The term $\Sigma[W(\partial f/\partial q_c)]$ may be written

$$[(\partial \overline{W}/\partial q_c) - (\overline{\partial W/\partial q_c})]$$

(Wright, 1942). In this, $\partial \overline{W}/\partial q_c$ measures the effect of change in the frequency of the gene in question on the average selective value of the population as a whole, while $(\overline{\partial W/\partial q_c})$ measures the average effect on the selective values of all genotypes and is of course absent if these selective values are constant.

An important case is that of competition between members of the same species such that the relative degree of competitive success of each of the genotypes is constant but the net rate of increase of the population is unaffected by changes in the relative frequencies. This situation can be represented by writing $W_c = aR_c/\overline{R}$ when a is a general constant, R_c is a constant pertaining to the particular genotype, and $\overline{R}(=\Sigma R_i f)$ is the variable average value of R. The surface of selective values for the population as a whole is constant $(\overline{W} = a)$ in accordance with the hypothesis, but gene frequencies change according to the rule:

$$\triangle q_c = q_c(1 - q_c)(\partial \overline{R}/\partial q_c)/2\overline{R}$$

The surface $\overline{R}$ is not level and selection pressure tends to drive the species toward a peak value of $\overline{R}$.

If there is a combination of both kinds of selection, we can write

$$W = a[(R/\overline{R}) + s]$$
$$\overline{W} = a(1 + \overline{s})$$

$$\triangle q_c = aq_c(1 - q_c)\frac{\partial(\log \overline{R} + \overline{s})}{\partial q_c}/2\overline{W}$$

The surfaces $\overline{W}$ and $\log \overline{R}$ may both be rugged and the peaks and valleys need not agree. The species moves toward a peak in the resultant surface $[(\log \overline{R}) + \overline{s}]$. If $\log \overline{R}$ and $\overline{s}$ are systematically opposite in sign and $\log \overline{R}$ is numerically greater, selection leads to a deterioration of the species in relation to its environment. This puts in symbolic form an interpretation of apparently orthogenetic trends toward extinction given by Julian Huxley. The special case considered by Huxley was that of selection for characters useful to males in competition but somewhat deleterious in relation to the environment.

A case that is similar in its consequences although somewhat more complicated from the mathematical standpoint is that of competition among members of the same brood. If there is no relation to success of the population and W_{11}, W_{12} and W_{22} are the selective values of A_1A_1, A_1A_2 and A_2A_2 when present in the same brood, $\overline{W} = a$

$$\triangle q_1 = aq_1(1 - q_1)\left[\left(\frac{W_{22} - W_{12}}{W_{22} + W_{12}}\right) q_1^2 + \left(\frac{W_{22} - W_{11}}{W_{22} + 2W_{12} + W_{11}}\right)\right.$$
$$\left. 2q_1(1 - q_1) + \left(\frac{W_{12} - W_{11}}{W_{12} + W_{11}}\right)(1 - q_1)^2 \right]$$

If there is a negative correlation between success in intrabrood competition and success in meeting the external environment, the process may lead to deterioration of the species. This case has been treated from a different mathematical viewpoint by Haldane (1924a).

Where advantages with respect to social relations and external environment are negatively correlated but closely balanced, it is possible for the opposing selection pressures to maintain alleles in equilibrium.

A genotype may have qualities that are of advantage to the species in proportion to some function of the frequency of such individuals but of no additional advantage to these individuals themselves. If this is the case, all selective values (W) are to be multiplied by the same term $[1 + \Psi(q_c)]$ in which $\Psi(q_c)$ is the function of the frequency of the genotype in question. If the W's are otherwise the same, $\overline{W} = a[1 + \overline{\Psi(q_c)}]$ with a peak or peaks corresponding to one or more values of q_c. There is, nevertheless, no tendency for q_c to change at all ($\triangle q_c = 0$). If the gene has a deleterious effect on its possessors it will tend to be eliminated in spite of its advantage to the species, still assuming random mating (cf. Haldane, 1932; Wright, 1945a).

The relative as well as the absolute selective values of genotypes may change with changes in their frequencies. It must suffice here to consider a few simple cases involving only one series of alleles. It will be assumed that the selective values of heterozygotes are always exactly intermediate between those of the corresponding homozygotes to avoid complications due to dominance or superdominance of the sorts that occur also where the selection coefficients are constant.

First consider the case in which the selective value of a homozygote rises in proportion to the frequency of its allele in the population. This may hold where the individuals of each type receive a social advantage from the presence of others of their own kind or are injured by the presence of other types. Let

$$W_{11} = a(1 + 2s_1q_1), W_{12} = a[1 + s_1q_1 + s_2q_2], W_{22} = a[1 + 2s_2q_2], \text{ etc.}$$

$$\overline{W} = a[1 + 2\Sigma_{i=1}^{k} s_i q_i^2]$$

$$\triangle q_c = aq_c[s_c q_c - \Sigma_{i=1}^{k} s_i q_i^2]/\overline{W}$$

There is unstable equilibrium (s's all positive) at the set of values

$$\hat{q}_c = (1/s_c)/\Sigma_{i=1}^{k}(1/s_i)$$

One allele or another tends to become fixed according to the initial composition of the population.

The selective advantages of genotypes may, however, decrease as the corresponding allele increases in frequency. This occurs if there is a division of labor among types to their mutual benefit, or if the population occupies a heterogeneous territory in which rare genotypes can always find a favorable niche but abundant ones are forced to live in part under unfavorable conditions. In this case the s's in the above formula are negative. There is stable equilibrium at the values $\hat{q}_c = (1/s_c)/\Sigma(1/s_i)$, exactly as if all heterozygotes had the same constant selective value and each of the homozygous types had a certain disadvantage $[W_c = a(1 - 2s_c)]$ etc. In the case with variable selection coefficients considered here, gene frequencies move in exactly the same type of surface $\overline{W}$ in the same way except that the rate is only half as great in relation to the slope as with constant coefficients (Wright and Dobzhansky, 1946).

A somewhat similar case which has been analyzed in detail in a previous paper (Wright, 1938) is that of self-sterility alleles in plants. Alleles are favored when rare and opposed when common, but as the selection depends on a relation between male gametophyte (haploid) and female sporophyte (diploid), it is more complicated mathematically than cases in which selection depends on relations among diploids, and is symmetrical or nearly so with respect to sex.

There may be cyclic movement of gene frequencies under certain limiting conditions which are probably of more mathematical than evolutionary interest. Thus if the selective values are as follows, and s is very small, there is an approach to perpetual cyclic motion although the surface of values is completely flat ($\overline{W} = a$)

$$W_{11} = a[1 + 2s(q_2 - q_3)] \qquad W_{12} = a[1 + s(q_2 - q_1)]$$
$$W_{22} = a[1 + 2s(q_3 - q_1)] \qquad W_{23} = a[1 + s(q_3 - q_2)]$$
$$W_{33} = a[1 + 2s(q_1 - q_2)] \qquad W_{31} = a[1 + s(q_1 - q_3)]$$
$$\triangle q_1 = sq_1(q_2 - q_3)$$
$$\triangle q_2 = sq_2(q_3 - q_1)$$
$$\triangle q_3 = sq_3(q_1 - q_2)$$

With the slightest departure from the limiting situation the species tends to move in a spiral in the field of gene frequencies either toward or away from a peak, if there is one, or toward or away from a depression to a point at which all $\triangle q$'s are zero. Somewhat similar cases may involve more than one locus.

The formula for $\triangle \overline{W}$ is the same as with constant selection coefficients.

Net Systematic Pressure

The net effect of all of the systematic pressures on the frequency of a gene is the sum of the various components. Thus in a random breeding population of diploids, the rate of change in the frequency of a gene A_c as one of a system of simultaneous equations is approximately as follows:

$$\triangle q_c = \Sigma(u_{ci}q_i) - (\Sigma u_{ic})q_c - m(q_c - q_{c(I)}) + \frac{q_c(1 - q_c)}{2\overline{W}}\left[\frac{\partial \overline{W}}{\partial q_c} - \left(\frac{\partial \overline{W}}{\partial q_c}\right)\right]$$

This type of pressure on all of the genes tends to carry the species to some position at which $\triangle q = 0$ for each of them (except in certain limiting cases referred to above). This position tends to be in the neighborhood of a peak in the surface of mean selective values in so far as due to selection related to the environment, but this is not likely to be the highest peak. Mutation and immigration pressure, if present, keep the population from attaining the exact peak. The position of stability may indeed not even be near a peak in cases in which selection depends on certain types of social relations. We have here a theory of stability of species type in spite of constant mutation, extensive variability at all times, constant action of selection, and substantial possibility of improvement if the species could arrive at certain combinations of genes already present, other than the combinations that prevail.

Accidents of Sampling

Accidents of sampling may cause fluctuation from the position of stability, but these are negligible in a large random breeding population. They become important in small populations where they are responsible for the well-known effects of inbreeding. They may be responsible for nonadaptive differentiation of small island populations but are more likely to lead to ultimate extinction in a small population, completely isolated from its kind, than to evolutionary advance (Wright, 1931 and later). These conclusions follow from the chance of fixation of a completely indifferent gene which is $1/(2N)$ where N is the effective size of population, and from the chance of fixation of a deleterious gene (selective disadvantage s in heterozygote, $2s$ in homozygote) which is $2s/(e^{4Ns} - 1)$.

NONRECURRENT MUTATIONS

Stability in a species living under constant conditions may be upset by the occurrence and establishment of a favorable mutation that has never occurred before or has previously been lost by accidents of sampling if it ever has occurred. Even a mutation with a considerable selective advantage is likely to be lost by accidents of sampling when present in only a few individuals, although it is practically certain to reach its equilibrium frequency if it ever reaches moderate frequencies in a large population. The chance of fixation of a semidominant mutation with selective advantage s in the heterozygote is $2s/(1 - e^{-4Ns})$, or approximately $2s$ as given by Haldane (1927b). A recessive mutation with selective advantage s has a chance of fixation given by Haldane as of the order of $\sqrt{s/N}$ and by Wright (1942) as $\sqrt{s/2N}$. With v the rate of recurrence of a mutation, the chance that all recurrences within a period of T generations are lost by accidents of sampling is $P = (1 - 2s)^{2NvT}$ in the former case, $P = [1 - \sqrt{s/2N}]^{2NvT}$, in the latter. The line between recurrent and nonrecurrent is necessarily arbitrary. A type of mutation with an even chance of becoming established within 1000 generations must be considered recurrent from the standpoint of a species with a life (T) of hundreds of thousands of generations; but if there is an even chance only in 100,000 generations, the mutation may be considered nonrecurrent in this case. Putting $P = \frac{1}{2}$ in the period T generations, rate $v < 0.69/4NsT$ may be used to define nonrecurrent mutations with dominant favorable effect and $v < 0.69/\sqrt{2NsT}$ for recessives with favorable effect. Thus in a population of 10^{10} and $T = 10^4$, mutation rates above about 10^{-13} would be considered recurrent for mutations with $s = 0.01$ in the heterozygote and mutation rates above 10^{-8} in the case of recessives with $s = 0.01$.

The likelihood of disturbance of stability by nonrecurrent mutations probably increases indefinitely with increase in size of population. The number of alleles maintained in equilibrium at each locus by one of the mechanisms discussed earlier should obviously increase with increase in the size of population and thus give a broader base for new mutations. It was suggested in earlier papers (Wright, 1931 and later) that there might be a certain optimum size for evolution in the case of a homogeneous population living under constant conditions, but this probably does not give adequate weight to the likelihood of indefinitely extended allelic series.

Evolution from novel favorable mutations is obviously limited by the rate at which these occur, in so far as dependent on these mutations themselves. However, the process of establishment of a novel mutation would tend to upset the system of selective values among genes that have been maintained within the species (Fisher, 1930). The readjustments in the system required to set off to best advantage the effects of a novel favorable major mutation might be extensive. They would be less extensive with the more frequent favorable minor mutations. Even so a single novel mutation might start a chain of evolutionary changes that would continue long after the mutation itself had reached either fixation or an approximately stable frequency. Evolution by this mechanism is therefore far from being completely limited by mutation rate.

In terms of the geometric model, the establishment of a novel favorable mutation in the species adds a new dimension. If minor in effect, it may be thought of as slightly elevating the adaptive peak to which the species has been bound, thus making possible slow evolutionary advance along the established line. If, however, a novel mutation brings about a new adaptive type at a step, this means the formation of a bridge to a higher peak across what had been an impassable valley.

Changing Environment

So far we have assumed constancy of external condition. But climatic conditions change, food species and enemy species increase or decrease in numbers and change in character. A portion of the species may move to a region in which such environmental conditions are different from those hitherto encountered. Under such changes of condition, the whole system of selective values of genotypes in the species changes. Peaks in the surface of selective values may be depressed and low places elevated. With too rapid a change the location of the species in the system may be carried to such a low point that it becomes extinct, but with less extreme changes the species may move sufficiently rapidly to keep up with the changing position of the peak to which it is attached, by drawing on the store of variability provided by loci in which multiple alleles have been maintained in equilibrium. Very great changes in character may be brought about without waiting for the occurrence of any novel favorable mutation and without elimination of any established genes, merely by a shift in the equilibrium frequencies at many loci. The number of combinations of frequencies may be so great, if there are many such loci, that evolutionary adjustment to a continually changing environment may theoretically proceed indefinitely without limitation by mutation rate. However, as the system of gene frequencies changes, mutations which have been so rare as to be classified as nonrecurrent may be expected to become recurrent. While the process as a whole has the aspect of a struggle of the species to hold its own in the face of a continually deteriorating environment, rather than of evolutionary advance, there can be no doubt that a large part, perhaps the major portion of evolutionary change, is of this character (Wright, 1932).

GENOTYPIC SELECTION

In the reaction of a homogeneous species both to novel favorable mutations and to changes of environment, the course of the changes in frequency at each locus is governed largely by the net effects of change in the frequency of each gene in all of the genotypes in which it occurs. The real objective of selection is the genotype as a whole (or even a harmonious system of genotypes); but under random mating exceptionally adaptive genotypes are broken up by the reduction division immediately after they are formed, making selection by genotype impossible. Effective selection by genotype requires that these multiply as such.

This occurs most simply if there is uniparental reproduction. Selection among competing clones is indeed so effective that an array of such clones tends to be reduced to a single clone very rapidly in a homogeneous environment. Thereafter evolution can proceed only by the occurrence of favorable mutations, with no amplification through readjustments in a store of variability. If, however, there is a properly adjusted alternation of predominant uniparental reproduction with occasional crossbreeding, and sufficient isolation and local heterogeneity to mitigate the effects of selection in the uniparental phase, the situation would seem favorable for a very effective and indefinitely continuing evolutionary process based on genotypes (Wright, 1931). This system is, of course, characteristic of many species, especially ones in which there are great cyclic variations in numbers and has no doubt provided effectively for their evolution. It is less favorable in species in which population size remains relatively constant.

POPULATION STRUCTURE

This brings us to consideration of the effects of population structure in species in which there is exclusive or at least predominant biparental reproduction. The mathematical theory depends on the inbreeding coefficient F (Wright, 1943, 1946). If a species is divided into numerous local populations which are partially isolated from each other and which may become genetically differentiated from each other for any reason, the store of variability in the species as a whole is obviously much greater than in a random breeding population of the same size. Moreover the store of variability in any local population should be much greater than in a completely isolated population of its size because the postulated immigration from the rest of the species may have very much greater effects than recurrent mutation at observed rates without breaking down the basis for local differentiation. Any local population that acquires a genetic complex of exceptional adaptive value tends to increase in numbers and become a major source of immigration into neighboring populations. If this adaptation is only of local value, selection pressures may be set up against its spread that tend to isolate it and split the species, but if the adaptation is of general value it tends to transform its neighbors in this direction. There is here the basis for an extensive trial and error mechanism within the species by which the species as a whole may advance. It is to be noted that the unit of selection here is not the gene and not even the genotype as a whole but the entire system of gene frequencies of a local population.

It is important in this connection to compare the various mechanisms by which local populations may become differentiated. The most obvious is difference in the pressure of different local environments on the direction of selection. Appreciable differentiation occurs if the difference in the net selection coefficient s of a gene is greater than the immigration coefficient m (Wright, 1931). Otherwise differentiation tends to be swamped by crossbreeding. Strong differentiation of this sort belongs in the category which tends more toward splitting of the species than of promoting its evolution as a single group. Nevertheless if differentiation is not too extreme, the increase in the store of variability both locally and in the species as a whole is favorable for evolution of the species as a whole and occasionally selection directed by local conditions may lead to adaptations of general value.

Where structure is sufficiently finely divided, the effects of local accidents of sampling provide a mechanism of differentiation complementary to the preceding, since it affects all loci in which there are no important differences in selection pressure between localities. The sampling variance of gene frequencies in one generation is

$$\sigma_{\delta q}^2 = q(1-q)/2N$$

where N is the effective size of the local population (in general much smaller than its actual size).[2] The variance of the frequencies among local

[2] Random fluctuations in the systematic pressures have effects somewhat similar to those due to accidents of sampling. Formulae for the variance, $(\sigma_{\delta q}^2)$ in each case, and the resulting frequency distribution $\phi(q)$ of gene frequencies, have been published (Wright, 1948) since this was written.

populations tends to increase by this amount in each generation but is counteracted by the effects of the systematic pressures toward the equilibrium frequency. The result is a frequency distribution through which the local populations tend to drift at random. If q represents a gene frequency and $(q + \delta q + \triangle q)$ its value after a random fluctuation (δq) and a systematic change $(\triangle q)$ has occurred, the frequency distribution $\phi(q)$ of the gene frequencies should be such that all moments of deviations from the mean before and after the above changes remain the same.

$$\int_0^1 \int_{-q}^{1-q} (q + \delta q + \triangle q - \bar{q})^n \phi(q) d(\delta q) dq = \int_0^1 (q - \bar{q})^n \phi(q) dq$$

For cases in which $\triangle q$ is of the same or lower order than $\sigma_{\delta q}^2$, it can be shown that this is satisfied by the equation

$$\phi(q) = (C/\sigma_{\delta q}^2) exp[2 \int (\triangle q / \sigma_{\delta q}^2) dq]$$

This was demonstrated in earlier papers for the mean and second moment (Wright, 1937, 1938). The same proof can be extended at once to all higher moments. Various special cases have been derived by other methods (Wright, 1931). A method, used by Kolmogorov (1935) in confirming one of these, leads to the partial differential equation of the general case (Wright, 1945), of which the preceding equation is the solution for the case of a stable state.

$$\frac{\partial \phi(q,t)}{\partial t} = \frac{1}{2} \frac{\partial^2}{\partial q^2} [\sigma_{\delta q}^2 \phi(q,t)] - \frac{\partial}{\partial q} [\triangle q \phi(q,t)]$$

I am indebted to Dr. L. J. Savage for calling to my attention that this same formula (Focker-Planck) has been used in physics in the analysis of Brownian and allied types of random movement.

In the case of an array of local populations of effective size N, all subject to the same conditions of selection of the type with constant coefficients, and each replaced to the extent m by a random sample from the total population, the rate of change of gene of gene frequency is

$$\triangle q_c = -m(q_c - \bar{q}_c) + \frac{q(1-q)}{2} \frac{\partial \log \overline{W}}{\partial q_c}$$

The distribution of frequencies of the gene A_c for a given set of frequencies at other loci is

$$\phi(q_c) = C \overline{W}^{2N} q_c^{4Nm\bar{q}_c - 1} (1 - q_c)^{4Nm(1-\bar{q}_c)-1}$$

The joint distribution for multiple alleles at a locus, still assuming that the frequencies at other loci are given, is

$$\phi(q_1 \cdots q_k) = C \overline{W}^{2N} \Pi_{i=1}^k q_i^{4Nm\bar{q}_i - 1}$$

{ 383 }

The joint distribution for genes at all loci under the assumed conditions is of the same form except that q_i applies to any gene at any locus and there are Σk terms in the product, the summation here relating to all loci. It should be emphasized that it is assumed in these formulae that effective m is the same for all alleles, which is not necessarily the case.

Returning to the case of one pair of alleles and assuming that selection and mutation pressures are negligible, the variance of the distribution of gene frequencies is approximately (Wright, 1931)

$$\sigma_q^2 = q(1-q)/(4Nm+1)$$

Somewhat severe isolation is necessary to permit extensive random local differentiation. Nevertheless it can be shown that even in a large population with full continuity of interbreeding throughout its area, a slow rate of diffusion permits extensive random differentiation not only of neighborhoods but of large regions (Wright, 1943, 1946). The rate of diffusion must be such that the parents of any individual are drawn from an adult population of not more than a few dozen. If the effective population of the neighborhood (parental population) is in the hundreds random differentiation is relatively slight, while if it is in the thousands the situation is practically equivalent to random breeding, even though the species as a whole is indefinitely large (still assuming no differential selection). The possibilities of random differentiation are, however, much greater if there is merely linear continuity as along a shore line or river or if there are obstacles to interbreeding other than distance.

The continually shifting random differentiation of local populations is especially significant because it occurs at all variable loci. If there are hundreds of unfixed loci in the species, the number of substantially different genetic complexes that may arise by chance among local populations becomes indefinitely great.

This sort of differentiation cannot be expected to continue independently of selection, however, even though conditions are uniform throughout the species. Genetic complexes may be expected to arise in different localities that give adaptation to these same conditions in somewhat different ways and thus create differential selection where it had not existed before.

In certain cases such joint effects of selection and chance are exceptionally great. Any character that is affected by multiple factors with more or less additive effects and which is optimum at an intermediate grade (as is usually the case) necessarily has many peak combinations of genes. For example if capitals are used for plus factors and small letters are used for minus factors, *AABBccdd, AAbbCCdd, AAbbccDD, aaBBCCdd, aaBBccDD*, and *aabbCCDD* may determine six peaks representing the same phenotypic optimum. Stability is reached in a large random breeding population at approximate fixation of one or another of these types. On subdivision of the population into partial isolated local populations, every type may be expected to predominate somewhere. The transition from one to another may arise from slight fluctuations in the position of the optimum or else merely by accidents of sampling (Wright, 1935a, b). Such a species is obviously in a position to utilize to advantage any favorable secondary interactions of such genes with others in which local populations come to differ.

Certain conditions were referred to earlier as leading to the maintenance of two or more alleles at subequal frequencies in a random breeding population. The opposite conditions favor differentiation among partially isolated populations and hence maintenance of multiple alleles. Such differentiation is to be expected in cases in which homozygotes are superior to the corresponding heterozygotes. An important example is that of reciprocal translocations. In plants, heterozygotes for reciprocal translocations are usually semisterile and thus very strongly selected against, while the balanced homozygotes may be equally vigorous. The situation is similar though somewhat more complex in animals. The establishment of a new arrangement requires accidents of sampling in exceedingly small local populations, probably ones in which there is frequent extinction of the population and restoration from very small numbers of migrants (Wright, 1941). In this case the process obviously has more significance for ultimate splitting of the species than for its evolution as a single group.

A locus in which genes become increasingly favored as they increase in frequency has, as noted earlier, a point of unstable equilibrium. Genes with social effects favorable to their own kind come here. Recognition marks are an example. Again differentiation of local populations on such a basis tends toward splitting of the species, but less than in the case of reciprocal translocation, and in contributing to the store of variability may contribute to the evolution of the species as a whole.

The evaluation of the actual importance of the various evolutionary processes depends on the determination of values of the various coefficients. Determinations of mutation rates from a number of very different sorts of organisms (men, flies, corn plants, bacteria) indicate that genes with recurrence rates of the order of 10^{-6} per generation are not uncommon but that few have rates higher than 10^{-5}. No lower limit can of course be set. The value of m can be anything from 0 (complete isolation) to 1 (no isolation whatever), but much remains to be learned of the structure of actual populations. The observations of Dubinin, Dobzhansky, and others on the occurrence of lethals in nature have demonstrated that genes with the highest possible selection coefficient are common. Such studies as those of Dobzhansky and associates on *Drosophila pseudoobscura* indicate the existence of abundant selective differentials of high order (greater than 0.10) relating to physiological characters. These strongly indicate a shifting state of balance among selection pressures of far higher magnitude than had previously been believed to be the case. Accidents of sampling can of course be of little importance for such sets of genes except where there is isolation of very small populations. This, however, does not preclude and indeed favors the existence of a still larger number of sets of genes with much smaller selective differentials.

The general conclusion seems warranted that a certain degree of sub-division of a species into partially isolated groups provides the largest store of variability both locally and within the species as a whole, and by providing for selection in which whole genetic complexes are the objects, frees evolution most completely from dependence on rare favorable muta-tions and makes possible the most rapid exploitation of an ecologic op-portunity (Wright, 1931 and later).

THE EVOLUTIONARY PROCESS

Under this interpretation, a continual kaleidoscopic shifting of the statistical characteristics of the local populations is to be expected within any species that occupies, not too densely, a reasonably large range. A similar but slower shifting of character is to be expected among the larger and more differentiated groups recognized as subspecies. The net result should be a gradual shifting in the characters of the species as a whole until the change becomes so great that a new species must be recognized. Subspecies on this view are only rarely incipient species.

In the occasional splitting of species to form two, the critical event seems necessarily to be complete or nearly complete interference with exchange of genes. In some cases, especially in higher plants, the primary isolation is undoubtedly genetic in origin (autopolyploidy, amphidiploidy, compound aneuploidy). In most cases, at least in higher animals, it seems however to be geographic, less frequently if ever purely ecologic (cf. Mayr). If splitting occurs by the extinction of intermediates in a chain of subspecies, it is possible for one species to become two without any current genetic change whatever in these. At the other extreme, a portion of a species which does not differ appreciably in any respect from the parent stock may become completely isolated. In the course of time the accumulation of random and selective differences in genetic composition may be expected to lead to clear-cut character differences and also to ones that prevent exchange of genes on renewed contact. The question as to the time at which two species are present instead of one is here somewhat arbitrary. The critical event however is the isolation rather than any particular genetic changes. The majority of cases are perhaps intermediate.

Similarly the multiplication of species relatively rarely leads to generic differences and still more rarely to families and higher categories by a gradual cumulative process. There seems to be a large measure of truth in the contention of Willis and Goldschmidt that evolution works down from the higher categories to the lower rather than the reverse. Nevertheless the critical event in the appearance of a higher category seems to be a major ecological opportunity rather than any sort of mutation. Such an opportunity may arise in various ways. Two extreme cases may be distinguished (1) A form, in the course of its gradual evolution, may acquire a character or character complex that happens to be of general rather than merely special significance and which thereby opens up the possibility of a relatively unexploited way of life. In many cases such an "emergence" turns on the possibility of using an organ evolved apparently for one purpose for a different purpose. (2) A form which reaches relatively unoccupied territory also has before it a major ecological opportunity independently of any character differences from its parent form. David Lack has made a most illuminating analysis of such a case in his recent study of the ground finches of the Galapagos Islands. In terms of our geometric model, the first case is one in which the genetic composition of the species manages by any means to cross a difficult valley in the surface of selective values and reaches a system of peaks higher than the single peak to which it has been bound. In the second case, the surface of selective values of the isolated portion of the species is itself changed abruptly by the elimination of competition and in many cases by changes in environmental conditions. The effect, however, is the same as in the first case; a single peak is replaced by a higher system of peaks.

Beyond a certain threshold in degree of success in the achievement of a major adaptation, improvement should be as rapid as the store of variability permits. When decisive superiority is attained or unoccupied territory is reached, a very extensive and rapid adaptive radiation should follow under the divergent selection pressures toward exploitation of the various special ecological niches, opened up by the general adaptation (in the first case) or the mere absence of competition (in the second). The most favorable conditions are those in which the population is sufficiently sparse and the territory sufficiently extensive and interrupted to permit a fine-scaled subdivision grading into complete isolation in many places. Differentiation of two forms must ordinarily start in geographically isolated regions but may be accelerated by competition if one form reinvades the territory of the other after genetic isolation has been reached. This rapid evolution in the origin and adaptive radiation of a higher category constitutes the tachytely of Simpson.

The primary adaptive radiation may be expected to be followed by secondary and tertiary radiations of progressively lower scope, and by extensive selective elimination of other higher categories especially in the case in which an original general adaptation has outmoded older forms in a great variety of ecological niches. As this process continues, the time comes when each of the successful forms has only one line of advance open to it, a single ridge in our model. There is slow and more or less orthogenetic advance, the horotely of Simpson. There may be extensive diversification of genera and species, but these are rarely of significance in starting new trends. Ultimately forms may become bound each to a single peak, with no other peak attainable and evolution virtually ceases, the bradytely of Simpson. While the sizes of the steps in such a cycle tend continually to fall off until they reach the vanishing point, a step may occasionally be larger, and on very rare occasions, much larger, initiating a new higher category and new evolutionary cycle of emergence, adaptive radiation, selective elimination of higher categories, orthogenesis and stability.

REFERENCES

Darlington, C. D., and A. A. Moffett. 1930. *J. Genet.*, 22:129-151.

Dobzhansky, Th. 1941. *Genetics and the Origin of Species.* 2nd ed., Columbia University Press, 446 pages.

——. 1946. *Genetics*, 31:269-290.

Dobzhansky, Th., and S. Wright. 1941. *Genetics*, 26:23-51.

Dobzhansky, Th., A. M. Holz, and S. Spassky. 1942. *Genetics*, 27:463-490.

Dubinin, N. P., M. A. Heptner, Z. A. Demidova, and L. I. Djachkova. 1936. *Biol. Zhur.* 5:939-976.

Fisher, R. A. 1930. *The Genetical Theory of Natural Selection.* Oxford, The Clarendon Press, 272 pages.

——. 1937. *Annals of Eugenics*, 7:355-369.

——. 1941. *Annals of Eugenics*, 11:53-63.

Geiringer, Hilda. 1944. *Ann. Math. Stat.*, 15:27-57.

——. 1948. *Genetics*, 33:548-564.

Goldschmidt, R. 1940. *The Material Basis of Evolution.* New Haven, Yale University Press, 436 pages.

Haldane, J. B. S. 1924. *Trans. Camb. Phil. Soc.*, 23:19-41.

——. 1924. *Proc. Camb. Phil. Soc.* (Biol. Sci.), 1:158-163.

——. 1926. *Proc. Camb. Phil. Soc.*, 23:363-372.

——. 1927. *Proc. Camb. Phil. Soc.*, 23:607-615.

——. 1927. *Proc. Camb. Phil. Soc.*, 23:838-844.

——. 1932. *The Causes of Evolution.* London, Harper & Bros., 235 pages.

Hardy, G. H. 1908. *Science*, 28:49-50.

Huxley, J. S. (editor). 1940. *The New Systematics.* Oxford, Clarendon Press, 583 pages.

——. 1942. *Evolution, the Modern Synthesis.* London, Harper & Bros., 645 pages.

Kolmogorov, A. 1935. *C. R. de l'Acad. des Sciences de l'U.R.S.S.*, 3(7):129-132.

Lack, D. 1947. *Darwin's Finches.* Cambridge, Cambridge University Press, 208 pages.

Mayr, E. 1942. *Systematics and the Origin of Species.* New York, Columbia University Press, 334 pages.

Morgan, C. Lloyd. 1933. *The Emergence of Novelty.* London, Williams and Norgate, 207 pages.

Osborn, H. F. 1917. *The Origin and Nature of Life.* New York, Charles Scribner's Sons, 322 pages.

Robbins, R. B. 1918. *Genetics*, 3:375-389.

Simpson, G. G. 1944. *Tempo and Mode in Evolution.* New York, Columbia University Press, 237 pages.

de Vries, Hugo. 1905. *Species and Varieties. Their Origin by Mutation.* Chicago, Open Court Publ. Co.

Weinberg, W. 1908. *Jahresheft Ver. f. vaterländische Naturkunde im Württemberg,* 64:368-382.

——. 1909. *Zeit. ind. Abst. u. Vererbungslehre,* 1:277-330.

——. 1910. *Arch. Rass. u. Ges. Biol.,* 7:35-49; 169-173.

Willis, J. C. 1940. *The Course of Evolution.* Cambridge, Cambridge University Press, 207 pages.

Wright, S. 1921. *Genetics,* 6:111-178.

——. 1921. *Amer. Nat.,* 56:330-338.

——. 1922. *Bull. No. 1121 U.S. Dept. Agric.,* 59 pages.

——. 1929. *Amer. Nat.,* 63:274-279.

——. 1931. *Genetics,* 16:97-159.

——. 1932. *Proc. 6th Internat. Congress of Genetics,* 1:356-366.

——. 1935. *Jour. Gen.,* 30:243-256; 257-266.

——. 1937. *Proc. Nat. Acad. Sci.,* 23:307-320.

——. 1938. *Ibid.,* 24:253-259, 372-377.

——. 1939. *Genetics,* 24:538-552.

——. 1941. *Amer. Nat.,* 75:513-522.

——. 1942. *Bull. Amer. Math. Soc.,* 48:223-246.

——. 1943. *Genetics,* 28:114-138.

——. 1945. *Ecology,* 26:415-419.

——. 1945. *Proc. Nat. Acad. Sci.,* 31:382-389.

——. 1946. *Genetics,* 31:39-59.

——. 1948. *Evolution,* 2:279-294.

Wright, S., and Th. Dobzhansky. 1946. *Genetics,* 31:125-156.

· 21 ·

PROGRESSIVE ADAPTATIONS
AS SEEN IN THE FOSSIL RECORD

BY EDWIN H. COLBERT[1]

It is perhaps a commonplace to say that the geneticist studies the mechanisms of evolution while the paleontologist studies the results of evolution. This statement of fact needs no reiteration to paleontologists and geneticists, yet it must be constantly borne in mind if the students working in these two branches of evolutionary factual and interpretive research are to meet for an exchange of data and ideas on a common ground. It is because of this basic fact that the common ground is so difficult to find; there is no getting around it, a meeting of minds between scholars in these two scientific disciplines is not easy.

In spite of this difficulty it behooves the geneticists and paleontologists to work together, with due regard on the part of each for the work of the other, if progress in the two fields is to avail itself of the fullest opportunities. The paleontologist must base his interpretations of evolution not only upon the fossils before him but also upon the facts of genetic mechanisms as revealed by recent researches in this branch of zoology. The geneticist must always give proper attention to the facts of paleontology in the interpretation of his data; his theories must not contravene the fossil record.

Perhaps there has been in the past a tendency on the part of some geneticists to ignore, or at least to minimize, the role of adaptation in the study of evolution. This has been the result of too great a preoccupation with the mechanisms of evolution as revealed by experimental work in the laboratory, and not enough appreciation of the results of evolution as revealed by structural adaptations seen in the recent organisms living around us and the extinct organisms seen in the fossil record. Adaptations cannot be ignored, and this is a fact of which the paleontologist is well aware. The record of evolution as revealed by paleontology is largely a record of adaptations—adaptations as correlated with environments.

The particular contribution of paleontology to evolution is the possibility for a long view of life on the earth. It is the dimension of geologic time, the projection back through vast epochs of time by means of the record of the fossils and of the rocks in which they are contained, that gives to the field of paleontology a value that is unique among the various

[1] The American Museum of Natural History and Columbia University.

branches of evolutionary studies. The paleontologist can journey through the ages, he can see climates changing, as revealed by the records of the rocks, and he can see the responses of organisms to these changing climates. Thus he has a record of what actually happened as a result of genetic plasticity as controlled by ecological opportunity, and the record is definite.

Consequently there can be no doubt in the mind of the paleontologist about the importance of adaptations in the evolution of life. He sees adaptations in the fossil record, and what is more, he sees progressive adaptations correlated with geological changes—which is to say, with environmental and ecological changes. The question that confronts him is this: how are these environmental changes and the correlated adaptations in the evolving organisms to be interpreted?

INTERPRETATION OF THE FOSSIL RECORD

Various interpretations can be brought forward to explain the close correlation of adaptations with environmental conditions through geologic time. In the light of modern work in genetics and paleontology it is possible to picture the interrelationships of adaptations and environment during long stretches of geologic time as the result of natural sequences of events in earth history and evolutionary history. It is possible to explain trends in adaptations, for there certainly are directional trends, in terms of mutations and natural selection, without resort to vitalistic theories of orthogenesis or other explanations that have been invoked in the past to account for evolution as seen in the fossil record. Perhaps the sequence that brings about a directional trend in adaptations can be outlined somewhat as follows.

1. EQUILIBRIUM OF ENVIRONMENT AND ORGANISM. This is the state of affairs that may hold at any particular, limited time in the history of the organism and its environment. Actually equilibrium either of organism or of environment probably is relatively rare, geologically speaking. The earth is constantly changing; this is evolution. Of course the biologist looking at modern plants and animals gets the impression of stability and equilibrium, because the experience of Man as a scientist in the geologic time scale is limited to an almost instantaneous impression.

2. A CHANGE OF ENVIRONMENT OF DEFINITE GEOLOGIC DURATION. Earth changes in geologic history are of varying magnitudes and speed. At some stages changes are very slow and relatively small, at other times very rapid and great. At the present time we are living in a period of rapid and profound geologic changes.

3. BUILDING UP SELECTION PRESSURES DURING THE ENVIRONMENTAL CHANGE. This point needs no elaboration; it is obvious that changes in environment will result in selection pressures along definite lines.

4. REACTION OF ADAPTATIONS TO THE CHANGE. A favorable interaction between the adapting organism and its environment will of course result in the continuation and even the expansion of a phyletic line. An unfavorable interaction may very well bring on extinction.

5. A CONSEQUENT EVOLUTIONARY TREND. Naturally, if the environment is changing in a definite direction, the adaptations through mutation and natural selection will be controlled in definite directions also. Thus there are definite trends in adaptations, trends which in many cases may follow very narrow lines. Adaptations under conditions of changing environments certainly are not random.

6. NEW ADJUSTMENTS AND A NEW STATUS OF EQUILIBRIUM. Again, complete equilibrium and adjustment probably is not very common in the long view of evolution.

THE SEQUENCE OF CHANGES DURING TRIASSIC TIMES

The Triassic period in earth history is of particular interest to the student of vertebrate evolution, for it marks the era of reptilian dominance. It is of interest because it was a period of change, a period during which old vertebrate types that had become well established in Paleozoic times and had held over into the Triassic suffered extinction, a period during which new vertebrate types that were destined to dominate the earth for more than one hundred million years were becoming established. One might say that the Triassic was a period of transition.

It was definitely a period of continental emergence over a great portion of the earth's surface. Of course there were epeirogenic fluctuations within the Triassic in some areas; for instance in Europe there was a marine incursion during the Middle Triassic in contrast to emergent conditions at both the beginning and the end of the period. On the whole, however, lands were high and areas that in Late Paleozoic times had been shallow seaways were now dry continental regions. The climate was probably generally rather uniform with tropical or subtropical conditions prevailing over much of the earth's surface.

Naturally these environmental conditions, which were changing during the development of the Triassic, had their effect upon the evolution of continental animals and plants of that time. Faunas and floras, which at the beginning of the Triassic period were in many respects similar to life of the Late Paleozoic, were by the end of the period quite changed in their aspects, for in this time most of the Mesozoic groups became established, to set the pattern for a long subsequent course of evolution. Vegetation was rich in many areas, but there was a decrease during the Triassic of Paleozoic plant types and there was a development of characteristic Mesozoic forms, such as the cycads, the conifers, and the ferns.

In this period the holostean fishes went through a phase of great expansion and became widely adapted to marine environments. On the land certain characteristic Paleozoic tetrapods held over into, and in some cases persisted through, the Triassic period. But by the end of the period these ancient types had become extinct. Such were the labyrinthodont amphibians, as represented by the large and secondarily aquatic stereo-spondyls, the cotylosaurian reptiles as represented by the small specialized procolophonids, and the therapsids or mammal-like reptiles. Among the therapsids, the theriodonts offer a special and interesting case of extinction, for some of them disappeared through transformation into the first mammals, which appeared in the upper portion of the Triassic sequence.

The establishment of the characteristic Mesozoic reptilian groups was a very important development in the evolution of Triassic life. Thus, we see during the course of this geologic period the appearance of the great and highly varied group of archosaurian reptiles; the thecodonts, the crocodiles, and the dinosaurs, which were to be so completely dominant during later Mesozoic times. We see also the appearance of other dominant Mesozoic groups, especially the marine ichthyosaurs, the sauropterygians or plesiosaurian reptiles, and the first turtles.

It may be useful at this place to outline the adaptations that took place among two groups of Triassic reptiles, one group representative of a characteristic Paleozoic order that held over into the Triassic period, the other representative of one of the new archosaurian orders that appeared in this period of geologic history. The first of these groups to be considered is the family Procolophonidae, constituting a persistent Triassic branch of the order Cotylosauria, the stem reptiles characteristically of Late Paleozoic age. The second group to be considered is the family Phytosauridae, an archosaurian family of the order Thecodontia, representative of the new progressive reptiles that appeared during Triassic times.

Progressive Adaptations in the Triassic Procolophonids

The procolophonid reptiles are found in South Africa, various parts of Europe, and North America. The Procolophonidae are essentially of Triassic age, although the first members of the family are found in sediments of Late Permian age. As pointed out above, they belong to the primitive reptilian order known as the Cotylosauria, the order of stem reptiles from which most if not all other reptiles evolved.

The first procolophonids were essentially primitive reptiles, not far removed either in age or in structure from the point of reptilian origin. They were of small size, no larger than good-sized lizards, and were rather elongated, ground-living reptiles. Indeed, they must have been considerably like some of our modern lizards in appearance and in habits, even though they preceded the origin of the lizards by many millions of years.

The legs were relatively short, so that the early procolophonids must have been for the most part crawling animals. The skull was rather flat and triangular, and around the edges of the upper and lower jaws there were numerous small, sharply pointed teeth. In most respects the skull was similar to the stem reptile skull, as exemplified in certain primitive cotylosaurs, but it was specialized in that the orbital openings were inordinately large. Evidently these first procolophonids had very large eyes. Moreover, the pineal opening, so characteristic of the primitive reptiles, was also large. Because of these structural developments, it has been suggested that the early procolophonids were nocturnal or crepuscular.

It would seem that these early procolophonids, as typified by the genus *Nyctiphruretus*, found in the Late Permian of northern European Russia, were small, inoffensive animals, perhaps living in the underbrush along streams, or in swampy areas, probably preying for the most part upon insects or upon other very small reptiles.

Because the ancestral procolophonids of Late Permian times have retained most of the primitive characters found in the Early Permian stem reptiles, it can be assumed that they were probably in a fairly stable stage of equilibrium in relation to their ecological environment. In other words, these were conservative reptiles, with a long conservative heritage behind them, a heritage marked by but minor genetic changes during a considerable lapse of geologic time.

From these beginnings it is interesting to trace the ecological relationships and the structural development of the procolophonids through Triassic times.

For instance, there was no definite trend toward increase in size, as is so common in phylogenetic lines represented by good paleontological materials. There were, of course, sporadic size increases that affected certain genera in this family of reptiles, but such increases were not part of a general trend. Indeed, selection pressures probably were against an increase in size, for these reptiles seemingly were inoffensive and timid animals that sought safety from the contemporary large predatory reptiles by hiding under plants or rocks. Thus the very specialized procolophonids of Late Triassic times were essentially no larger than their primitive Permian forebears.

Evolution in the procolophonids was a matter of definite changes in certain structural characters as correlated with changes in living habits. During the extent of the Triassic period these animals showed a marked development of and increase in spinescence, with the result that in the end stages of their evolution the skull was armed with numerous spines or points in contrast to the spineless skull of the ancestral types. In a superficial way the skull of Middle and Late Triassic procolophonids foreshadowed what subsequently and quite independently was to take place in the skull of the horned lizard, *Phrynosoma*. Although we do not have any evidence as to the nature of the skin in the later procolophonids, it is reasonable to think, in the light of the development of horns or spines on the skull, that the skin also was covered with spines as it is in the modern horned lizard or the moloch.

Even more interesting evolutionary trends in the procolophonids are to be seen in the changes brought about in the skull and dentition, obviously as adaptations to a shift in the diet. The skull of the primitive procolophonid has been described briefly above. To repeat, it was rather flat on top and triangular in outline. The long lower jaws, which were hinged at the extreme posterior border of the skull, and the upper jaws too, were armed with numerous sharp, conical teeth. The orbits were very large and the pineal foramen was large.

During Triassic times the following evolutionary trends are to be seen developing in the skull, jaws, and teeth of the procolophonids.

1. Development and increase of spines on the skull (discussed above).

2. Shortening of lower jaw, with a consequent anterior migration of the jaw articulation from the back to the middle portion of the skull.

3. Lengthening of the orbital openings.

4. Reduction in number of teeth.

5. Enlargement of premaxillary and anterior mandibular teeth.

6. Enlargement and transformation of maxillary and posterior mandibular teeth to form broad interlocking chisels.

What is the meaning of these changes? By analogy with other tetrapods it seems fairly clear that the evolutionary trends in the procolophonid skull represent a shift from a carnivorous or insectivorous diet to a predominantly herbivorous diet. A shortening of the lower jaw in relation to the skull is a general trend among herbivorous tetrapods, and can be seen taking place independently time and time again in numerous phyletic lines. The transformation of the teeth from sharp points to broad chisels, working against each other, is again an herbivorous or frugivorous adaptation that is seen among many different lines of land-living vertebrates. Finally, the lengthening of the orbital opening is an adaptation for increased strength in the jaw muscles. It is probable that the eye occupied only the forward part of the elongated orbital opening, and that the portion of the opening behind the eye was developed as a sort of pseudo-temporal fenestra, to allow for the bulging of the short and powerful capiti-mandibularis muscles.

In the post-cranial skeleton the evolutionary trend was toward a relative shortening and broadening of the body. Thus, while retaining the primitive crawling habitus, the procolophonids were transformed from elongated animals with considerable lateral flexion of the backbone during the various phases of locomotion, to rather short, flat, stubby animals in which there probably was very little bending of the backbone from side to side. Here again we see an analogy with the horned lizard, *Phrynosoma*, and if analogies mean anything we very probably see a shift from life in semi-aquatic or moist habitats to an upland dry-land mode of life. Perhaps the sequence of correlated adaptations and the evolutionary changes in the procolophonids can be outlined according to the process described above, in the following manner:

1. Equilibrium of organism and environment.
   Swamps, streams. Animal elongated; carnivorous. Late Permian, *Nyctiphruretus*.
2. Change in environment.
   Gradual increase in dry-land conditions. Consequent changes in botanical associations. Early to Late Triassic.
3. Building up selection pressures.
   Pressures brought on by the changes in environment and ecological conditions and biotic factors. A decrease of opportunity for life in moist areas; an increase of opportunity for upland life. Presence of active predators favoring selection against size increase. Safety was sought by an obscure mode of life, by hiding in the sand or in undergrowth.
4. Adaptations to environmental changes and selection pressures.
   Genetic changes controlled by these selection pressures; therefore oriented in the direction of upland life and an herbivorous diet.
5. Evolutionary trend.
   Adaptations along a definite line and for the most part not random. Adaptive trend toward persistent small size, spinescence, shortening of the body, flattening of the skull, increase of the orbital openings, shortening of the lower jaw, decrease in the number of teeth and transformation of the teeth from sharp points to broad chisels. These trends can be followed through the extent of the Triassic period, about 30 million years.

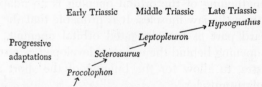

6. New adjustments and a new status of equilibrium.
   A true status of equilibrium may or may not have been attained before the group became extinct.

PROGRESSIVE ADAPTATIONS IN THE TRIASSIC PHYTOSAURS

The phytosaurs are reptiles characteristically found in Late Triassic sediments in the northern hemisphere, particularly in central Europe and in eastern and western North America. Most of the known phytosaurs are limited to the Late Triassic, but a primitive genus is found in the Early Triassic of Europe, and through this form we can project the history of the group back to their earlier, pre-phytosaurian ancestors. Thus it will be seen that the knowledge of the phytosaurs depends to a large extent upon the specialized end forms, so that the course of the evolutionary history in this group must be to a considerable degree inferred, in contrast to the rather well-documented history of the procolophonids that runs through the extent of Triassic times. Nevertheless, upon the basis of the highly adapted end forms and the more primitive Early Triassic ancestor, a valid picture of the evolutionary trends in this group of reptiles can be drawn with a reasonable degree of exactitude. And in reconstructing this picture it is interesting to contrast the development of the progressive, new archosaurian phytosaurs with the development during the same time of the persisting Paleozoic cotylosaurian procolophonids, already outlined on the preceding pages.

The phytosaurs belong to the reptilian order Thecodontia, being one of the highly adapted suborders within this larger taxonomic division. As such, it is to be supposed that the phytosaurs eventually were descended from some of the primitive thecodont types, which are well known to us in the fossil record. These primitive thecodonts appear in Early Triassic times and are characterized by such genera as *Euparkeria* of South Africa or *Ornithosuchus* of Europe.

These were small reptiles, generally no more than two or three feet in length. They were lightly built and evidently very active, for they habitually walked and ran in a semi-upright posture on strong elongated hind limbs. The front limbs and hands were relatively small and evidently were used for grasping. Since locomotion was essentially bipedal the pelvis was very strong, for it served as a fulcrum upon which the body was suspended. It had a typical triradiate structure, with the pubic bones directed forwardly and the ischia to the back, and there was a strong sacral connection with the backbone. The tail was elongated and served as a counterbalance to the body. The skull like the post-cranial skeleton was lightly built yet relatively strong. It was deep and narrow, and as seen from the side or the top it consists of a series of arches or bars surrounding various openings. In front of the large eye and behind the nasal opening there was a large preorbital foramen, while behind the eye there were two large temporal fenestra, one on the side of the skull and one placed dorsally. In addition there was a large opening in the side of the mandible.

All of these openings made the skull light in weight without sacrificing essential strength. The articulation for the lower jaw was placed at the posterior limits of the skull, thus giving a wide gape to the mouth. Both upper and lower jaws were armed with sharply pointed, conical teeth, obviously well adapted to the grasping of prey.

Such was the primitive thecodont—evidently an active, predatory reptile, well adapted to catching other reptiles as well as vertebrates of other classes. This small swiftly-moving predaceous animal set the pattern for early thecodont evolution, and from it as a central type evolved not only the highly specialized thecodonts such as the phytosaurs, but the later archosaurian reptiles as well. These were the crocodilians, the pterosaurs or flying reptiles, and the dinosaurs. They were, however, largely of post-Triassic development, and it is with the Triassic phytosaurs that we are concerned at this place.

The earliest phytosaur, the genus *Mesorhinus* from the Early Triassic, shows a very great shift in its adaptations from the presumed thecodont ancestry. It is obviously far along on the evolutionary road toward the most advanced phytosaurs of the Late Triassic, so one must conclude that there was a short phase of explosive evolution, or what Simpson has called "quantum evolution," in Early Triassic times, during which all of the essential phytosaurian adaptations were established. From that point on, evolution in the phytosaurs was a matter of perfecting the details.

In the evolution of the phytosaurs from ancestral thecodont types there was a complete shift away from the upland mode of life, away from very active cursorial adaptations as exemplified by the bipedal pose, and toward an aquatic existence in which the animal was secondarily completely quadrupedal. Thus in the phytosaurs the fore and hind limbs became subequal in size and relatively small, for these were above all swimming reptiles, spending a greater part of their time in the water. It is probable that in the water the limbs were used very little, as is the case in the modern crocodilians, propulsion being effectuated largely by undulatory movements of the tail. The main use of the legs in these animals was for crawling about and walking on river banks or on the shores of lakes.

Along with this reversion from dry land to the water, there was a distinct trend toward size increase in the phytosaurs. As is so common among aquatic vertebrates the phytosaurs became large—and often times huge. The body was long and rather cylindrical; the tail was deep and powerful, a strong scull for pushing the animal through the water.

In the evolution of the skull and jaws the phytosaurs showed a very marked trend away from the basic thecodont skull pattern. The facial part of the skull became greatly elongated to form a long rostrum armed with numerous sharp teeth. There was a correlated elongation of the lower jaw.

Thus the jaws of the phytosaur became extraordinarily long and well armed, an adaptation of great effectiveness for an animal of predaceous habits. The nostrils did not take part in the forward growth of the rostrum, as might be expected, but rather they retreated and became elevated to a position immediately in front of and above the eyes; indeed in many phytosaurs the nostrils are elevated above the level of the skull roof on a crater-like eminence. The advantage to an air-breathing aquatic animal of having the nostrils on the top of the head is obvious.

Such were the general trends of phytosaurian adaptations, yet in spite of this phyletic shift away from the basic thecodont structural pattern the phytosaurs retained many of the fundamental characters that show them to be essentially thecodont in their organization. Thus the cranial portion of the skull, even though modified, was still thecodont. The various openings in the skull, described above as typical of the ancestral thecodonts, were retained. In these reptiles, in spite of their aquatic adaptations, the structure of the pectoral and pelvic girdles was very similar to that for the ancestral thecodonts. And in other respects, throughout the skeleton, characteristic patterns retained from the primitive thecodont ancestor are to be seen in the advanced phytosaurian descendant.

Perhaps these trends in the evolution of the phytosaurs can be summed up as follows:

1. A secondary trend toward complete quadrupedalism, involving a relative reduction in the size of the hind limbs.

2. Increase in size.

3. Elongation of the rostrum and of the lower jaw.

4. Increase in the number of teeth.

5. Retreat and elevation of the nostrils to a point on the top of the skull, just in front of the orbit.

The ecological implications of these changes are clear. The phytosaurs left the upland habitat that had been the home of their ancestors and became completely adapted to life in the streams and lakes of the Triassic landscape. But in doing this they retained the predaceous habits of their ancestors; in fact predaceousness was accentuated in these animals so that they became very aggressive beasts of prey. It is probable, from the development of the long slender snout and lower jaw, that the phytosaurs preyed largely upon fishes, but there is every reason to suppose that they may have eaten such land-living vertebrates as they could catch.

Thus their evolutionary history may be contrasted very sharply with that of the procolophonids, described above. The procolophonids evidently shifted from a moist to a dry upland environment; the phytosaurs did the opposite. In the evolution of the procolophonids there was no distinct trend toward size increase, which was the case in the phytosaurs. The procolophonids lost the carnivorous habits of the ancestral cotylosaurs and seemingly became adapted to plant-eating, whereas the phytosaurs retained and accentuated the predaceous mode of life that was characteristic of the primitive thecodonts. The evolution of the procolophonids was a rather steady process of progressive development continuing through the Triassic period, whereas evolution in the phytosaurs was marked by an explosive phase taking place at the beginning of the period, during which most of the phytosaurian adaptations were established, followed by a long, rather even phase at a high level of advanced adaptations, during which evolution was mainly a matter of the perfection of details. The whole process can be outlined in the same manner that was used for illustrating the evolutionary adaptations of the procolophonids.

It will be seen, however, that the order of events is not quite the same in the evolutionary adaptations of the phytosaurs as it was for the procolophonids. It seems likely that in the evolution of the procolophonids a change in environment was involved in the building up of selection pressures that brought about adaptations. In the phytosaurs, on the other hand, it appears that primary selection pressures were dominant in bringing about a shift of the developing phyletic line from one type of environment to another.

1. Primary equilibrium of organism and environment.

   Uplands. Animal bipedal, very active, carnivorous. Basal Triassic. Primitive thecodont reptiles.

2. Building up of selection pressures.

   Pressures probably the result of intense competition between predaceous forms in upland environment.

3. Change in environment.

   A shift of the phyletic line from one environment (uplands) to a new environment (rivers and lakes). This probably was independent of general changing environmental conditions in the Triassic.

4. Adaptations to new environment.

   Genetic changes oriented in the direction of increased adaptations to an aquatic mode of life and a new food supply. Aquatic vertebrates instead of upland vertebrates.

5. Evolutionary trend.

   Adaptations toward quadrupedalism, increased emphasis on tail as propulsive organ, increase in size, elongation of the skull and jaw, and increase in the number of teeth to form a fish-catching mechanism, elevation of the nostrils to the top of the skull. These changes took part largely at the beginning of Triassic times.

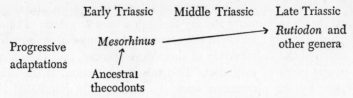

6. New adjustments and a new status of equilibrium.

The adjustments were made very rapidly in the early part of the Triassic, and a status of equilibrium then persisted over a long time range, until the close of the period.

EXTINCTIONS AND SUBSEQUENT REPTILIAN PARALLELS

At the end of the Triassic period both the procolophonid and phytosaurian phyletic lines became extinct. The extinction was sudden and complete, and coincided, so far as can be determined, with the termination of the Triassic period and the initiation of the Jurassic period.

Why these extinctions should have taken place is one of those difficult problems of paleontology to which no satisfactory answer can be given. The procolophonids were an evolving line throughout the extent of the Triassic period, and it is difficult to see why the line should not have continued into later Mesozoic periods. The phytosaurs, though they had attained their full evolutionary status at an early stage in the Triassic, seemingly were well adjusted to their environment; they were a highly successful and a very dominant group of reptiles in the final phases of Triassic history. But for some reason both of these lines failed to survive the transition from Triassic to Jurassic conditions.

Yet both of these lines were imitated by later reptiles. So far as the procolophonids are concerned, the imitators did not appear until late Mesozoic and Cenozoic times in the forms of the lizards. It may be that environmental conditions during the Jurassic were not favorable to small ground-living reptiles of this type, but this point cannot be settled definitely for the early history of the lizards is as yet quite unknown. At any rate, when the lizards did become established, they went through a wide range of adaptive radiation that included types quite similar in many respects to the long-extinct procolophonids. The specialized end forms of an archaic line of reptilian evolution were replaced by specialized members of a new and perhaps progressive phylogenetic line.

The imitation of the phytosaurian adaptive trend by the crocodilians is one of the most striking examples of parallelism to be seen in the fossil record. After the phytosaurs had become extinct, the crocodilians evolved in Jurassic and subsequent geologic periods to imitate almost completely the line of adaptive trend that had been followed earlier by the phytosaurs. Indeed, from the beginning of the Jurassic to the present day the crocodilians have been a highly successful group of reptiles, and they have continued their evolutionary history through a long sequence of time during which many other reptilian lines and many groups of mammals have arisen, reached the culmination of their development, and then have declined to the point of extinction. This raises a question. If the adaptive trend taken by the phytosaurs could be successfully paralleled by the crocodilians, why was it not continued by the phytosaurs? Why did this adaptive trend ultimately fail for the one group, and why was it so successful for the other?

In Late Triassic times, when the phytosaurs were at the height of their dominance as aquatic predators, the first crocodilians were making their appearance as small upland-living reptiles. While the phytosaurs were dominant these ancestral crocodilians were limited by selection pressures to their initial upland mode of life, a mode of life not greatly different from that earlier enjoyed by the ancestors of the phytosaurs. But with the extinction of the phytosaurs a new habitat was opened to the primitive crocodiles, and within a remarkably short duration of geologic time these reptiles shifted from one environment to another, just as the phytosaurs had done at the beginning of the Triassic period, to become during Early Jurassic times fully adapted aquatic predators, fulfilling in every way the same ecological role that had been fulfilled during the Triassic period by the phytosaurs. Here we see adaptations to environment taking place according to the same pattern in two successive geologic periods. The pattern was established by the phytosaurs in the Triassic period. It was repeated by the crocodilians in the Jurassic period, and this time the pattern held, to continue into Recent times.

CONCLUSION

Two examples of progressive adaptations as seen in the fossil record have been outlined. These examples have been selected to show differing types of adaptations taking place side by side in geologic history. They illustrate the importance of adaptation and selection in evolution.

Natural selection is the keystone in the arch of evolutionary principles; it is the main evolutionary process. As the result of natural selection the evolving organism becomes adapted to the conditions under which it must exist. Thus adaptation is a process of prime importance to the evolving animal or plant, for without adaptation through selection there would be no evolution. This fact is especially brought out through the study of fossils, because the paleontological record brings the time factor into the evolutionary picture. In the fossil record we can see progressive adaptations taking place through definite periods of geologic time; we can see the manner in which organisms change as their environments change. The fossil record leaves no doubt as to the importance through geologic time of adaptation and selection in evolution.

PART VII

HUMAN EVOLUTION

· 22 ·

HUMAN EVOLUTION: PAST AND FUTURE

BY J. B. S. HALDANE[1]

I AM asked to speak on one of the great problems of human biology. I do so gladly, but with one important reservation. I am going to treat of man from one point of view, the biological. This is wholly justifiable provided I do not leave you with the impression that this is the only point of view that matters. Only evil can come from forgetting that man must be considered from many angles. You can think of him as a producer and a consumer. This is fully justifiable provided that you do not think that the economic angle is the only angle. You can treat him as a thinker, as an individual, as a member of society, as a being capable of moral choice, as a creator and appreciator of beauty, and so on. Concentration on only one of these aspects is disastrous. I make these obvious remarks for the following reason. Hitler and his colleagues believed that the history of the human past could be interpreted, and the history of the human future created, on biological lines. Now the Nazis degraded most of the German people morally, and brought death and misery to a whole continent. Their biological ideas were grossly incorrect. But supposing they had been as accurate as any which we possess today or will possess a century hence, I believe that any attempt to reduce ethics and politics to biology would have involved a moral degradation.

A biologist can do two things besides discovering facts, such as the facts of human evolution and genetics. He can tell his fellows how to achieve ends which they desire already, such as the cure or prevention of a disease. He can tell them of possibilities at which they had not guessed, such as the possibility of making childbirth painless, or some of the possibilities of which I shall speak later. But he can never tell them what is worth doing. That is always an ethical, not a biological, question. In what follows, I shall say that I think certain things are worth doing, that it is better to be born with a normal mouth than a harelip, with a normal color sense rather than color-blind, and so on. These are my opinions as a human being. If you disagree with them, I cannot, as a biologist, persuade you to change your opinion. But if you agree, then, as a biologist, I may be able to help you to work for the ends on which we are agreed.

Perhaps you think I have taken too long over these preliminaries. But

[1] Department of Biometry, University College, London. Address delivered: January 1947. Subsequently published in the *Atlantic Monthly*, March 1947.

there are those who say that any attempt to apply biology to human affairs is mere Hitlerism. To my mind, that is as stupid as to say that when a tailor wants your measurement he is treating you as a mere lump of matter and no more. However that may be, I have felt it necessary to safeguard my rear. Now let us go forward.

We have been discussing evolution as something which has happened in the past, and is happening now. I may add in parentheses that we are all convinced that it has occurred, though we differ a good deal as to how, and still more as to why, it has occurred. The very first point I want to make is the time scale of the process. Forty years ago we knew the sequence of events in our evolutionary history, but could only guess at their dates. It is as if we knew that Washington lived before Lincoln, but did not know whether Washington was born 200 or 2000 years ago. Now, thanks to the study of radioactive minerals, we know our dates with an error generally under 10 per cent when we are dealing with dates between about 30 million and 500 million years back. We know that somewhere around 350 million years ago our ancestors were fish, 270 million years ago amphibians somewhat like salamanders, 200 million years ago reptiles not very like any living forms, and 70 million years ago, mammals something like shrews.

Curiously enough we cannot date the last few million years quite so accurately, until we get to the last 20,000, when we have layers of mud laid down each year in water from melting ice. But we can say that *Sinanthropus*, the so-called Pekin man, lived about half a million years ago, and almost surely less than a million and more than 200,000 years. Further we can say that at that time there were no men of the modern types; so our ancestors must have been a good deal less human than any existing race, even though, as they used tools, they probably deserved the name of man.

CONTROLLED EVOLUTION AS AN IDEAL

These Pekin men had queer-shaped heads, broadest about the level of the ears instead of much higher up, brow ridges, no chins, and so on. In half a million years we have changed a bit. Certainly the difference between *Sinanthropus* and modern man is as great as that which separates many nearly related animal species (for example the coyote and wolf). It is doubtful whether it is as great as that between two nearly related animal genera (for example dogs and wolves on the one hand, and various kinds of fox on the other). In fact it has taken about half a million years for a change large enough for zoologists to give it a name with full certainty. Other animals, such as horses and elephants, of whose ancestors we have a far better record, have been evolving at about the same rate.

These facts suggest that, if we did not try to control the evolutionary process in any way, our descendants half a million years hence might differ from us, for better or worse, about as much as we differ from Pekin man, or a cat from a puma. Now at present I do not think we know how to control our evolution, even if we wanted to, or if biologists were granted all the powers which Hitler exercised for twelve years. But supposing a thousand years hence we know how to direct our evolution, and further that the vast majority of men accept this ideal, as the vast majority of Americans accept the idea of sanitation today, what then?

The answer is rather curious. An unaided man can walk 20 miles a day with a fair load, and keep it up indefinitely. I have walked over 50 with a rifle and a few extras, but I couldn't keep it up. At present one can easily fly 2000 miles a day, but a 5000-mile flight is more difficult. Roughly speaking, science has increased our speed of travel a hundredfold. It is reasonable to hope that we might speed up evolution a hundredfold if we knew enough. If so, we might achieve a change as large as I have indicated in 5000 years, or 200 generations. This is a long time. The earliest date in human history is 2283 B.C., or just over 4000 years ago. This is the date of a total eclipse of the sun which immediately preceded the capture and destruction of Ur by the Elamites. Five thousand years ago civilization had started in Egypt, Iraq, and maybe a few other areas, but most men were savages.

Is it worth while even talking about a change which we do not yet know how to bring about, and which would take 5000 years to accomplish if we did? Yes, it is worth while talking about it, for three reasons. In the first place we ought to discuss the right and wrong ways of using a power before we get it. The world would be a far safer and happier place today if we had discussed how to use nuclear, or so-called atomic, energy for a century, or even a generation, before we got it. If so, very likely almost all decent people would be agreed as to the rights and wrongs of this matter, which they certainly are not today. About 2500 years ago, the prophet Isaiah got the idea that one day all the nations of the earth would be at peace. Isaiah's idea of universal peace was something like a Jewish world empire. Ours is an association of friendly democracies. The ideal has only just become possible of accomplishment because world-wide transport has been achieved. But if visionaries had not been talking about it off and on since Isaiah's time, there would be no chance of achieving it now, when the alternative is, quite literally, destruction by fire from heaven. Now Hitler's idea of the desirable biological transformation of man was very crude indeed. Mine may be a little less crude. Mr. Olaf W. Stapledon's ideas, or Prof. H. J. Muller's ideas, may be better than mine, and so on. But we shall only get at better ideas by putting up our own to be shot at, as I am doing here.

Secondly, we shall not get the required knowledge in a hurry. Even now we can do a little to alter the inborn capacities of the next generation. Let us begin to think about what sort of changes we want, and criticize one another's ideas, as democrats should.

Thirdly, if we put the ideal of controlling evolution before us, and try to accumulate the necessary knowledge, we may find out something even more important on the way. Columbus set out to find a sea route from Europe to China. A ship can get from Europe to China through the Panama Canal, but the discovery of America was a vastly more important result of his voyage than the opening of this route.

Slow Development as a Major Evolutionary Trend

Our first task will be to take a glance at human evolution, and to see how man differs from the other mammals, his nearest relatives, and how these differences have arisen. Man is an exceptionally brainy animal. The whale has a heavier brain, and the mouse has a brain which is a larger fraction of its body weight. But if we take a series of closely related animals, such as the cat, ocelot, puma, and lion, we find that their brain weight is roughly proportional to the square root of their body weight. If we rate animals on the ratio of brain weight to square root of body weight, the great and small cats, for example, are about equal, and man comes out well ahead of any other animal.

We use our brains for thinking, but it is a mistake to suppose that the brain is primarily a thinking organ. Thinking is mainly, if not wholly, performed with words and other symbols, as the Greeks recognized when they used the word logic—from *logos*, a word—for the study of thought processes. From the study of the effects of brain injuries we know what parts of the brain are most concerned in thought and language. These areas are usually in the left cerebral hemisphere in the neighborhood of the area which controls the right hand. The human brain has two super-animal activities, manual skill and logical thought. Manual skill appears to be the earlier acquisition of the two, and the capacity for language and thought has grown up around it. If we bred for qualities which involved the loss of manual ability, we should be more likely to evolve back to the apes than up to the angels.

We develop far more slowly than any other mammal. Most mammals are mature at one year or less, a chimpanzee at about 7 years, a human being at 15 or more, while growth is not complete till over 20 years, and the skull sutures are often open till nearly 30, so that the brain can still grow. We are much more like baby monkeys than adult ones. In biological language we are neotenic, like the axolotl, a Mexican salamander which, unlike most salamanders, never comes out of the water, but breeds without shedding its larval gills. Since a little thyroid hormone will make it grow up, and for other reasons, we may be pretty sure that

its ancestors came out of the water. An obvious advantage of this neotenic tendency has been that man has a very long period of learning. As
regards behavior he is the most plastic of all the animals. His behavior
patterns are less fixed by heredity than theirs and more dependent on his
environment.

If this tendency continues, whether by natural processes or human
design, we should expect our remote descendants to have an appearance
which we should describe today as childish. We should expect their
physiological, intellectual, and emotional development to be slower than
our own. We should not expect them to be born with an overpowering
urge to any particular kind of conduct, good or bad.

For example, some birds are monogamous, others polygamous. Monog-
amy is just one of a series of fairly stereotyped behavior patterns. Man
has evolved away from stereotyped behavior patterns, and can be
monogamous, polygamous, or celibate. How he will behave depends
largely on the impact of society on him. Even a cat is comparatively plastic
in its behavior. A kitten which is brought up with mice, and does not
see other cats kill mice in its first few months of life, will rarely kill them.
But a child's behavior is far less fixed in advance than a kitten's.

This feature, which is so highly developed in man, and which we call
plasticity of behavior when we look at it from outside, is called the
freedom of the will when we look at it from inside. In any evolution
which could be called progressive we are likely to develop it still further.
Bernard Shaw, in *Back to Methuselah*, shows us a young lady emerging
from an egg some thousands of years hence, and spontaneously talking
very good English. She is like those birds which, without education,
produce a fairly complex song characteristic of their species. I can
imagine human beings bred for stereotyped behavior patterns. Perhaps
if the Nazis had won they would have tried to do so. But any such step
would be a step backwards.

Man is not only the brainiest species of mammal. He is the most polymorphic and polytypic if we exclude domesticated species such as the dog.
Let me explain these words. We say that a species is polymorphic when
in the same area there are several different types breeding together, the
differences being genetically determined. For example, the fox *Vulpes
fulva* of eastern Canada has three color types: the red, cross and silver
foxes. A polytypic species has different types in different areas. Your deer
mouse, *Peromyscus maniculatus*, has a gray form inland, and nearly
white forms on the white beaches of the Gulf of Mexico.

HUMAN DIVERSITY DESIRABLE

Man is polytypic. For example, the peoples of tropical Africa have
very dark skins and kinky hair. Those of Europe have light skins and

wavy or curly hair. The pre-Columbian peoples of North America have intermediate colored skins, but straighter hair than the Europeans. Man is polymorphic. And at least as regards to color, the European, the most successful of the human races at the present time, is also the most poly-morphic. If anyone thinks that I am exaggerating this polymorphism, he will perhaps tell me of another mammalian species apart from domestic animals in which the hair color in a single geographical area ranges from black to pale yellow, the eye color from dark brown to pale blue.

This polymorphism is not necessarily, or even probably, due to race mixture in the past. For example, there is no reason to think that there was ever a race all of whose members had red hair. And the skull shape is as variable in cemeteries of 6000 years ago as in modern cemeteries.

Human polymorphism certainly extends to innate abilities as well as physical and chemical characters such as stature and hair color. For example, I am tone-deaf. I cannot distinguish between quite well-known tunes. I am pretty sure that this defect is congenital. I am also a better mathematician than the average, and have little doubt that I have ab-normally high congenital ability for mathematics. No doubt I had good opportunities of learning mathematics, but so I had in the case of music. We know very little about the reasons for variation in human achievement, but we know enough to be reasonably sure that inborn differences play a great part in determining very high and low levels of achievement.

I believe that this psychological polymorphism has been a major reason for the success of the human species, and that a full recognition of this polymorphism and its implications is an essential condition for its success not only in the remote future but in our own lifetime. Let me make my meaning clearer. One of my colleagues, a man of greater manual ability than myself, and very likely of equal or greater intellectual ability, is also a musical executant who could have been a professional musician. If I had his musical gifts I might devote as much time as he does to music, at the expense of my scientific output. It is quite possible that my tone-deafness is an advantage not only for society but even for myself; though such a limitation would almost certainly be undesirable if my probable span of socially useful life were 400 years instead of 40.

The Political Implications of Human Diversity

I will now make a definition. Liberty is the practical recognition of human polymorphism. I hasten to add, because I recognize that your brains work differently from my own, that few of you will accept this definition. That society enjoys the greatest amount of liberty in which the greatest number of human genotypes can develop their peculiar abilities. It is generally admitted that liberty demands equality of opportunity. It is not equally realized that it demands a variety of opportunities, and a tolerance of those who fail to conform to standards which may be culturally desirable but are not essential for the functioning of society. If I lived in the Soviet Union I should not find its political and economic system irksome. I should be, and have been, irked by the assumption often made there that any cultured man enjoys listening to music and playing chess. If a nation were a pure line there would be little scope for liberty. Everyone between 45 and 50 would want so many hours a week at the movies, so much (or so little) liquor per week, and so on. These would be provided by rationing, as our needed food calories are provided in England, and everyone would be equally happy. There would be no freedom, no deviants, and no progress.

We are polymorphic not only in our aesthetic but in our intellectual abilities. Ways of describing the world as different as analytical and projective geometry may be equally true, even if at present one human mind cannot accept more than one of them at a time. Last year I saw for the first time Rubens's and Breughel's great picture of Paradise at The Hague. As a geneticist I noted with interest that the guinea pig had been created with at least three genes recessive to the wild type. But I was even more struck by the fact that the Tree of Knowledge was infested by only one serpent but no fewer than four parrots. Maybe in the long run the parrots are more dangerous than the serpent. Certainly we must so far recognize polymorphism as to realize that our own formulations of knowledge are not unique.

Domesticated animals such as dogs are more polymorphic than man. But greyhounds and sheep dogs differ only because they are reproductively isolated. The Indian caste system was an attempt to divide society into a set of reproductively isolated groups each with its peculiar function. This system broke down, as I believe and hope that any such system would break down. I believe that when our descendants plan the genetical future of man they will have to plan for high polymorphism without reproductive isolation. I don't know how they will do it. Fortunately I shan't have to do the planning.

Man is also polytypic. This does not mean that any two races differ as much in intellectual, aesthetic, or moral potentialities as they do in color. The darkest European has lighter skin than the lightest Negro. There is no overlap. But even in a society where Negroes have poor opportunities of education the most cultured Negro is far more cultured than the average European, let alone the least cultured one. Nevertheless polytypicism has so far been an advantage to humanity. Without postulating any over-all superiority of one race to another, we can be fairly sure that some desirable genotypes are commoner in one people than in others and that this difference is to some extent reflected in its achievements. For example, the genotype needed for long-distance runners is relatively frequent among Finns, that needed for short-distance runners among American Negroes. Doubtless the same is true for the genotypes needed for cultural achievement.

In the past a given people at a given time has usually specialized in a few fields of culture. Thus, potential mathematicians had little chance in medieval Europe, but potential architects had a good chance. Very likely the contributions of a people to our common culture depend considerably on the genotypes available in it. If so, it is certainly desirable that, until all peoples have reached such a stage of liberty that rare but desirable genotypes can develop their faculties everywhere, man should remain polytypic.

If, however, 10,000 years hence we combine extreme tolerance with a psychology which will enable us to pick out human abilities at an early age, then I can see no need to foster or preserve polytypicism—though it may be desirable to do so for reasons which are not obvious at the present time. In discussing polymorphism we must not forget sex dimorphism—that is to say, the innate differences between the sexes. It is curious that in our existing society most men try to diminish them by removing their beards, while women try to exaggerate them by the use of cosmetics and other devices. *Sinanthropus* and related types seem to have been much more sexually dimorphic than ourselves. So it looks as if men conformed better than women with the evolutionary trend. It is not clear whether this trend should be encouraged to go much further. It is essential that the sexes should understand each other, but a certain difference in intellectual and emotional reactions may well be sociably desirable.

THE EVOLUTION OF THE MEEK

To sum up, I think that in the last million years man has become more cerebral, more neotenic, and more polymorphic. I think it probable that these are desirable evolutionary trends, while I suggest that judgment should be reserved concerning polytypicism and sexual dimorphism. Others will doubtless say that I have left out the one essential: namely, a bias towards their own canon of behavior, whether moral, religious, or political. However, I have at least given reasons why I believe that any hereditary fixation of behavior patterns is undesirable.

Even this moderate list of desirable qualities gives us food for thought. If it were shown, for example, that the median intellectual performance of English children at the age of 15 were diminishing, and that this was not due to environmental changes, this fall could be due either to the fact that, on the whole, we were reaching a lower intellectual level at maturity, which would be undesirable; or that we were reaching the same level as our ancestors, or a higher one, but reaching it more slowly, which would be desirable.

How are we to achieve these ends? I do not know. We do not know in detail for what human characters we want to breed. The experience of animal husbandmen will not help us much, for several reasons. We do know that the domestic breeds have been selected for highly specialized performances. But in gaining desired qualities they have lost others which would be desirable in a different context. The greyhound cannot hunt by smell, the dachshund is a poor runner, the husky is ill adapted for city life, and so on.

I also think that the history of man's ancestry, as revealed by the geological record, should make us a little cautious. If a Martian zoologist who knew no more than we do now about evolution had been asked to pick the most progressive vertebrate at any time in the past, I think he would very rarely have picked on the line which was destined to give rise to man. During most of the last quarter-billion years they have been pretty small, inconspicuous, and unspecialized animals. Looking at the Jurassic and Cretaceous mammals, and most of the Tertiary Primates, one might be inclined to summarize the evolutionary story as "Blessed are the meek, for they shall inherit the earth," and perhaps to suggest that peoples such as the British in the nineteenth century and the American in the twentieth, who have been successful in war, are dead ends from the evolutionary point of view.

However, if we go back to the Permian, we find that our ancestors were large and progressive reptiles. No one who looks at the skeleton and particularly the teeth of such a beast as *Cynognathus*, which was not far from our own ancestral line, could possibly class it as meek. Why the descendants of large predatory theromorphs became small and vegetarian is very far from clear. It is possible that the giant forms discovered by Dr. von Koenigswald were actually our ancestors. If so, our ancestors a million years ago were monsters who could have torn up a tiger with their bare hands. In that case there was a second occasion on which our ancestral line tried physical dominance and gave it up again. It is also possible that the giants of Java and China were side branches from the human line, and represent an unsuccessful evolutionary experiment.

Negative Eugenics

After all this caution, I believe we can make a start. Whatever else we may want our descendants to be, we do not want them to be blind, deaf, paralyzed, or brittle-boned. Now these conditions are sometimes due to dominant genes, which can be prevented from spreading further by negative eugenics. At first sight it might be thought that these genes could be eliminated. For example, in many pedigrees of juvenile cataract, affected persons pass on the gene for cataract to about half their children, and it very rarely skips a generation. It has been said that were they all sterilized, these conditions would be abolished. This was one of the ideas behind Hitler's racial hygiene laws.

The idea is false, because these harmful genes constantly reappear as the result of mutation. Occasionally two normal parents will have a child with a harmful dominant gene, which is then handed on until natural selection or negative eugenics puts an end to its career. The two processes are roughly in equilibrium. Thus, achondroplastic dwarfs have about one fifth the fitness of normal people. That is to say, they produce on an average about one fifth as many children. So only one fifth of the dwarfs alive at any time are the progeny of dwarfs, the others being the progeny of normal parents. If all dwarfs of this kind were sterilized we could only cut down the number of dwarfs by one fifth.

With hemophilia we could cut down the frequency to about one half by preventing the breeding of hemophilics and heterozygous women. With hereditary cataract we could cut down the frequency to much less than one half—perhaps to one tenth. Some, though not all, types of mental defect could be considerably reduced; so could harelip and many other physical defects. This would be well worth doing, but the battle would never be finally won, the race never finally purified.

We could, however, cut down the incidence of a great many congenital maladies to a large extent. Others, such as neonatal jaundice, or *erythroblastosis fetalis*, and perhaps mongoloid idiocy, are due to gene differences between father and mother. We could only abolish them by forbidding unions between people of different genotypes. A closed mating system based on skin color is bad enough, in the sense of making for the division and perhaps the instability of the community. One based on blood antigens, in which an Rh-negative woman might not marry an Rh-positive man, would perhaps be even worse. I should be the last to recommend it, even if it saved the lives of a few babies.

Nor at the present time can we do much to diminish the frequency of undesirable recessive conditions, whether they are lethal, like fetal ichthyosis, or merely a slight handicap, like albinism. The most efficient eugenic method is the introduction of good road transport into backward rural areas, thus encouraging outbreeding.

It may be that, if we knew enough, 1 per cent or even rather more of the population would be found to carry undesirable dominants or sex-linked recessives, which any sound eugenic policy would reduce. How should we do it? Many people believe that carriers should be sterilized, either voluntarily as in Denmark, or compulsorily, as in Nazi Germany. I do not, for the following reasons. Laws for compulsory sterilization are liable to gross abuse. Those for voluntary sterilization are only rather less so. I recall the case of a laborer in one of your Western states who was given an indeterminate sentence up to five years' imprisonment for theft. The judge suggested that he be voluntarily sterilized. He agreed, and was not imprisoned. His agreement can only be called voluntary in a Pickwickian sense. However, I might be in favor of sterilization if it would finally rid us of these undesirable genes. But it would not.

There is another reason, perhaps worthy of consideration. If we are ever to control our evolution we shall certainly have to overhaul our whole mating system. By this I do not mean that we shall have to abolish marriage or adopt polygamy. I do not know what we shall have to do. We shall only do what is right if people realize that we have a duty to beget and bear the best-endowed children possible.

It is of the utmost importance that the idea should not be spread abroad that we can improve the human race to any serious extent by sterilizing individuals who do not come up to certain standards. In England we are already beginning to persuade people with harmful dominants to refrain from reproduction, either by chastity or by contraception. We shall not improve the human race by compulsion. A prerequisite for doing so is the moralization of our sexual behavior—that is to say, making it subordinate to ideal ends, not to impulse on the one hand or superstition on the other.

DIFFICULTIES OF POSITIVE EUGENICS

What about positive eugenics? In many human societies those types which are most admired are bred out. The Middle Ages admired holiness and courage. The holy men and women were celibate, the courageous men killed one another. Our age admires money-making. The men who make most money have least children. I am less worried by this than many of my contemporaries. I am not convinced that a business executive is a higher type than a saint or even a feudal knight. In any case, a differential birth rate lasting over a century need no more permanently affect the gene frequencies of a race than selection of certain chromosome orders for a few months per year affects a *Drosophila* species. And in Sweden the tendency has already reversed itself, and the poor breed rather more slowly than the rich.

Why, it may be asked, should we not encourage the breeding of rare and desirable genes as we can discourage the breeding of rare and undesirable ones? The answer is that we do not know of a single rare gene in man whose frequency we should increase. I have no doubt that such exist. But our analysis of the genetic basis of human abilities is so utterly rudimentary that we know nothing of them. Their discovery will need a vast program of collaboration between geneticists, physiologists, and psychologists. Until even one such gene is known, it seems to me rather futile to talk about a program for positive eugenics.

I would, however, suggest that among the genes whose spread we would want to encourage are those for the non-development of teeth, particularly wisdom teeth. Our cerebral development has caused a good deal of overcrowding of our teeth. I hope also that we shall do something about our noses, which are one of our weak points. (I have a nasal infection at the moment. No other organ lets me down so frequently.) The nose has of course been squashed out of shape by the growth of the brain. In consequence, while a sneeze takes a straight path in a dog or a horse, it has to take a hairpin bend in our own species. In a century or so we may know of detailed changes in our psychological make-up which are equally desirable.

In fact, while we can begin with negative eugenics, we cannot begin on positive eugenics until we have got a great deal more knowledge and a wider diffusion of the eugenic attitude. Probably the first requisites for the development of this knowledge are, on the one hand, the mapping of the human chromosomes, a task to which I have devoted some effort, and on the other, an attempt to analyze the psychological make-up of people judged to be exceptionally gifted, as Spearman in England and the Chicago school in America have tried to analyze that of more normal people. When these are accomplished it will be time to start research on the genetics of great intellectual or moral endowment. Much of it may turn out to be due to heterosis, and as unfixable as the good points of a mongrel dog, but I have little doubt that many rare and desirable genes for these characters exist.

So far I have assumed that our descendants will take over the control of evolution in an intelligent manner. Let us consider the other possibilities. In the next century the human race may largely destroy itself. From the genetic point of view a war using atomic energy would be worse than one using old-fashioned weapons, or even pestilences. For the survivors of Hiroshima and Nagasaki have been so affected that their descendants will show a variety of abnormalities. Some will appear in the first generation and disappear within ten or so. Others will be recessive, and first appear after several generations, their evil (and very rarely good) effects continuing for many thousand generations. The killing of 10 per cent of civilized humanity by atomic bombs might not end civilization. The vast crop of abnormalities produced by another irradiated 10 per cent might do so, and even render recovery very difficult.

I hope that we shall avoid such an international war, or, what seems to me just as likely, a civil war in which a small group get control of some atomic bombs and hold up a whole nation. If so, we may settle down to some peaceful world order, but do nothing about our evolution. In such a case we might stay put for a very long time. Sewall Wright has shown that, on certain assumptions, which seem to me thoroughly sound, evolution goes on quickest in a species divided up into many groups of a few score or hundred individuals nearly, but not quite, sexually isolated from other groups. This was the human condition for thousands of centuries during the Old Stone Age. With agriculture and industry the community has grown, and evolution has probably slowed down. For some time there was heavy selection against crowd diseases, but the progress of hygiene has checked this tendency.

I do not know what we are selecting for now. Let me take an example. Until two generations ago large families were respectable in my country. Anyone who voluntarily restricted his or her family was a deviant. Selection favored genes making for conformity to mores in this respect. Now it is a deviation from the norm to have a dozen children. We are selecting in favor of deviation, instead of against it.

We may be favoring genes which make for high sexual activity, low intelligence, or lack of susceptibility to propaganda, to mention only three possibilities. Most eugenists regard the parents of large families as, on the whole, undesirable genetically. This may well be true. It is certain that on the whole they are economically unsuccessful. Before we equate economic success and long-term biological value, however, it might be desirable to read the Sermon on the Mount or the record of the dinosaurs. I do not know if the trend described is desirable or not, and I contend that no one else does.

Another possibility is that we shall control our evolution and choose the wrong path. If I had had to pick hopeful ancestors for a rational and skillful animal from past faunas I doubt if I should ever have got the right answer between the Pennsylvanian and the Miocene. I should certainly have picked *Struthiomimus*, a Cretaceous reptile like an ostrich, standing on its hind legs, but with arms in place of wings. I am equally sure that I should go wrong today. Dr. H. J. Muller has suggested a method for the radical improvement of the human race, involving the widespread use of artificial insemination. I guess that if I were made eugenic world dictator I should have one chance in a hundred of choosing the right path. Dr. Muller is ten times as good a geneticist as I, so he might have one chance in ten, but not, I think, much more.

I am convinced that the knowledge required, both of past evolution and present genetics and cytology, is considerably greater than the whole body of scientific knowledge on which our present civilization is based. We can get this knowledge if we want it. We may say that God is now enlarging the sphere of human choice, and therefore giving us new duties. Or we may say that the evolutionary process is now passing from the stage of unconsciousness to that of consciousness. But we have not yet got the knowledge.

Our immediate task is the remodeling of human society. This can be done in a few generations. The great men who founded your Republic based it on principles which had never before been applied to human societies but which nevertheless worked in practice. The great men behind the French and Russian revolutions made somewhat different but comparable experiments. No society is perfect, and the time scale of social change is so vastly less than that of evolutionary change that the duty to reform society is far more urgent than that to control evolution. The two duties must and will go together. But it would be fatal to think of the man of the future as one who would fit into contemporary American, British, Russian, or Chinese society, or into any society which we can even imagine today.

If I am right he would probably be regarded as a physical, mental, and moral defective. As an adult he would probably have great muscular skill but little muscular strength, a large head, fewer teeth than we have, and so on. He would develop very slowly, perhaps not learning to speak till 5 years of age, but continuing to learn up to maturity at the age of 40, and then living for several centuries. He would be more rational and less instinctive than we are, less subject to sexual and parental emotions, to rage on the one hand and so-called herd instinct on the other. His motivation would depend far more than ours on education. In his own society he would be a good citizen, in ours perhaps a criminal or a lunatic. He would be of high general intelligence by our standards, and most individuals would have some special aptitude developed to the degree which we call genius.

But just as, were we transported to the past, we should be unlikely to win the admiration of *Sinanthropus*, so, were one of these products of planned evolution brought back to our own time, we should probably judge him an unpleasant individual. This thought need not distress us. We shall not meet him.

PART VIII

SUMMATION

· 23 ·

REDINTEGRATION OF THE SYMPOSIUM ON GENETICS, PALEONTOLOGY, AND EVOLUTION

BY H. J. MULLER[1]

THE CONVERGENCE OF EVOLUTIONARY DISCIPLINES

HALDANE, in the preceding chapter, has called attention to the fact that one of the features of importance in human evolution is man's polymorphism. A striking illustration of this (though by no means mainly on a genetic level!) is the coexistence of those two peculiar types known as paleontologists and geneticists. Fortunately there is a related feature, even more important—plasticity. This not only allows the change of any type, but the fusion of types, leaving new and higher types formed by their synthesis, and this is a process which we are witnessing now. We may, of course, expect the synthetic types in due course to split again, along different lines of cleavage than before, as the evolutionary process continues. A third feature which according to Haldane is advantageous, namely, slow development, has evidently been retarding the process of change and of fusion, making it slower but, we hope, surer, by allowing the elements to settle into more harmonious configurations than might otherwise be attained. Many of us geneticists can remember an analogous process of merger which occurred in our own earlier history, when the forms known as cytology and genetics combined to give rise to a higher type, which was given the name of "cytogenetics," or, as is now more usual, simply "genetics" again. We need expect no such terminological foul play on the part of geneticists in the present instance, however, for there are still the good old terms "evolution" and "evolutionists" waiting to be promoted to their higher meanings here. It has been one of the chief functions of the present symposium to assist in this promotion.

That great complex beast called Life, which is so subject to both inner and outer conflicts, has left behind him a long and devious though often ill-marked trail. Poring over the footprints, the marks where he has lain down or struggled or undergone digressions or reverses, the paleontologists have tried to reconstruct the story of his wanderings and to interpret what features of his nature and what characteristics of the terrain led to his following the routes that he did. On the other hand the geneticists, coming upon the creature himself apparently slumbering (his motions

[1] Department of Zoology, Indiana University.

being so much slower than theirs), have tried, together with the taxonomists and physiologists, to penetrate into his present nature and therefrom to infer the manner of his movement, what paths he is likely to have taken and why, and what future directions of travel might be expected of him. On each method alone, it is evident, the complexities and uncertainties of the problems are very great, and far better results could be achieved by a pooling of the evidences.

Fortunately the two groups of investigators, after years of turning their backs to each other, are now coming to a common point of view and system of interpretations which promise to be mutually helpful. Both have been recovering from that reaction against Darwinism which set in with the closing years of the last century. Among geneticists this had led some over-zealous "mutationists" to set up large mutations against natural selection as a method, or the method, of evolutionary change, and it had also led some, such as Bateson, to conclude that genetics cannot reach any interpretation of evolutionary splitting whatever. Among paleontologists considerable credence had been given both to the idea of inheritance of acquired characters and to that of an inner evolutionary urge. The latter was supposed to lead on the one hand to increasing perfection and on the other to what might be called willful waywardness, decadence, and suicide. But along with the more recent realization that these hypotheses are not justified by the evidence, both disciplines have been attaining a common ground of theory, wherein evolution is based on the natural selection of, mainly, minute variations, taken out of a great store of hereditary variations occurring in numerous directions. This conception is entirely in harmony with those features of Darwin's own interpretation which distinguished him from most earlier evolutionists. In the course of time this conception has become greatly sharpened, elaborated, and implemented, so that now it constitutes a really vigorous "neo-Darwinism," incorporating within it the principles of Mendelism and of mutation as at present understood, as well as, in its longer ranges, the processes dealt with by the paleontologists.

THE RELATION OF GENE CHANGES TO CHARACTER CHANGES

The genetics of today traces the fact of evolution back to the existence of ultramicroscopic bodies, the genes, which not only reproduce themselves but, more important, reproduce their own changes, or mutations, and which can continue thus to change without losing the power of reproducing their changes, to an unlimited degree. At the same time there are mechanisms whereby the genes can become bound into an aggregate, and whereby the number in an aggregate can become increased ("duplication"). Following such increase in number the component genes can and eventually will undergo mutations different from one another, and thus not only the degree of compoundness but the complexity of the gene aggregate becomes increased, and with it its potentialities of forming a complex organism as a result of the interactions of the different genes of an aggregate with one another. In this way it has been possible for what we call living matter to advance from the stage of one or a very few kinds of genes, at first separate from one another and naked, to that of a large constellation, individually differentiated from one another within the group, which by their common activities result in that prodigious, stupendously intricate working system evident to us as the soma.

In higher organisms the different genes are numbered in the thousands and their interactions are so complex that, as Stern has pointed out in this symposium, there is hardly a trace of a one-to-one relation between the outward characters of an organism and its genes. First, many or most of the individual genes affect more than one, sometimes very many, outward characters, being as geneticists say "pleiotropic." Put in another way, we may say that the developmental and physiological reactions initiated originally by the genes are branching ones, so that there are commonly many end-twigs to a given gene's effects as seen in the organism. Second, not only do the reactions initiated by one gene branch, but the reactions initiated by different genes are apt to run into one another, with the result that various different genes cooperate in the production of most observed characters of the organism. Taking both the branchings and the anastomoses into account at the same time, we see that the processes of development as well as those of physiology constitute a complicated network of biochemical paths, leading from the genes at one side of the net to the observed or phenotypic characters at the other side. Hence a change in a given character can usually be caused by a mutation in any one of a considerable number of genes, some of these having much and others little influence on the character, and some being obviously qualitative in effect while more of them are detectible only as differences in the degree or quantity of expression of the character.

There is evidence that any individual gene is usually exceedingly stable, that is, that new mutations take place in it with great rarity, often of the order of 10^{-5} or even 10^{-6} per reproductive cell per generation. Nevertheless, because of the multiplicity of genes affecting a given character, the frequency of new mutations affecting that character may be not inconsiderable (e.g. of the order of 10^{-4} to 10^{-2}). Moreover, it must be remembered that in most natural crossbreeding populations there has occurred a great accumulation of mutations that have arisen through the course of hundreds of preceding generations and that have not yet become established but with regard to which the population is still heterogeneous. Thus there may be a very considerable amount of hereditary variability of that character in the population, allowing its plasticity in response to selection in virtually any direction, and this again despite the fact that mutation in any individual gene is so exceedingly rare.

As data on mutational occurrences accumulate, students of the subject become more and more convinced that there is no relation between the kind of natural circumstances (e.g. type of climate or prevailing physiological state) under which given mutations arise and the direction of phenotypic change which these mutations result in; still less is there any adaptive relation between them in the sense of the phenotypic changes tending to be of types that would be more useful under the circumstance that prevailed when they arose. There are, to be sure, a few genes known which tend to change with a high frequency in a given direction when in a certain genetic or non-genetic environment, but this is not common enough in nature to affect our thesis, especially when all mutations affecting a given character, rather than a given gene, are taken into account. In general, the natural mutations are sporadic, and one gets about the same range under one type of condition as under another. It is further evident that the vast majority of natural or "spontaneous" mutations, being in this sense blind, must be to some degree harmful in their effects upon the organism's functioning. When we compare them with the gene mutations produced by radiation, which certainly must be the result of ultramicroscopic accidents, we find that the spontaneous mutations cover about the same range, are in general similar in type, and are, on the whole, no more harmful than the radiation mutations. This shows clearly that the spontaneous mutations likewise are accidental, in a similar sense; the accidents upon which they depend, however, are usually effects of thermal agitation rather than of natural radiation.

As a natural consequence of this situation, those mutations which have smaller effects should, on the whole, be less harmful than those with more marked effects. The smaller ones should therefore have more chance of getting established in the course of evolution, as Stern has stated. The correctness of this inference is indicated, among other things, by the finding that most of the phenotypic differences between organisms of different systematic categories that can be crossed and subjected to genetic analysis prove to be due to individually small and usually fairly numerous gene differences that act cumulatively upon the given character. It is, however, to be expected that occasionally a mutation causing a large change will become established, but in such a case it will be accompanied by a number of the smaller gene differences which, as Huxley has termed it, "buffer" its effects, that is, bring them into harmony with the rest of the organism.

It is important to note that, although a picture of apparently continuous variability is thereby given, and of a gradually sliding evolution, nevertheless even the minimal changes in the genes are individually rare, and are discrete. They arise by sudden mutations, just as the big changes do, and they are subject to the Mendelian, i.e. chromosomal, rules of inheritance. Thus it still remains necessary to make a sharp theoretical distinction between the effects of the environment on the soma, which are not inheritable and usually show a really continuous variation, and the effects caused by the accidental changes in the genes, which are inheritable with regularity and with high stability.

As for the question to what extent the organism may be affected by changes in non-nuclear genes, it must be recognized that such genes certainly do exist, both in the plastids of plants and also to some extent even outside the plastids proper, in the cytoplasm of plants and of at least some animals (all, as yet observed, unicellular). It is clear that between different species the number of such differences is usually extremely small, as compared with the number residing in the chromosomal genes. An important reason for the limitation of the number of different genes that lie free from one another in the protoplasm, as compared with that of the genes which are bound together in linear order in the chromosomes, must lie in the fact that for the former it would be very much more difficult to establish a system whereby their relative numbers remain fixed, i.e. to prevent one kind from displacing another through random distribution and through competition. And even if such a stable equilibrium had on occasion become established, it would still be susceptible of being upset when one of its genes underwent a mutation. An increase in the number of kinds of such genes would thus entail great difficulties, since here again delicate chemical adjustments would be necessary for establishing the new equilibrium. Furthermore, the establishment of stable recombinants following crossing would be far less likely to occur than for chromosomal genes, especially in view of the fact that the male gamete usually carries far fewer of the non-nuclear genes than the female gamete.

CRYPTIC GENETIC CHANGE

It has been pointed out that, owing to the phenotypic equivalence of numerous mutations, characters which appear very similar to one another in related species may nevertheless have a somewhat different genetic basis, the close similarity thus being deceptive and constituting a sort of phenotypic façade. This must certainly be true in those species in which crossing gives rise to a hybrid in which the given characters are different from those of the parents. The sterility of many interspecific hybrids furnishes good examples of this fact in the field of the physiology of reproduction.

On the other hand, the findings of Sturtevant that many of the conspicuous mutations retain the same distribution among chromosome arms in rather diverse species of *Drosophila* give evidence that these genes have largely retained the same general functions in these different species. Since it seems likely that those genes whose changes affect a given character more conspicuously would usually, in their normal form, play a more important role in the production of that character than do the genes whose changes seem to affect the character less, this result is rather to be expected, in the light of the conception that evolution tends to proceed by small steps. But it would probably still remain true that, if a more detailed examination were made, considerable differences would be found in the genes having a more accessory or supporting function, and that even the major genes for the character would differ to some extent in their degree and direction of expression.

The differences found by Stadler between the representatives of the R gene in different varieties of maize, when minutely examined, have given a good illustration of this phenomenon. And Spencer's finding of the rarity of mutations to the Minute bristle condition in *Drosophila hydei*, as compared with *melanogaster* and other species, shows how the mechanism of development may change so that a given character (long bristles), though still appearing the same, comes to rest on a rather different genetic and developmental basis. Probably the extent to which such invisible genetic differences creep in, behind a relatively permanent phenotypic façade, differs a good deal from one group of organisms to another and even from one character to another in the same group of organisms, depending upon genetically determined characteristics of the mechanism of development. This is indicated, for example, by the relative ease with which species crossing in animals leads to genic disharmonies in the first-generation hybrid resulting in its sterility, as compared to the situation in plants, where most of the apparent hybrid sterility seems to be due simply to the non-matching of chromosomes at meiosis and to the formation of inviable recombinants in the second diploid generation, or in the haploid gametophytes just antecedent to the latter. The degree to which the genetic basis changes underneath a given façade must also depend upon the extent to which a given population is panmictic or broken up into many relatively isolated groups, for, as will be discussed later, the latter situation gives opportunity for a much greater amount of genetic change even while the same phenotype is being retained as a result of its usefulness.

THE EFFECTIVENESS OF SELECTION

That given phenotypes are maintained over long periods as a result of natural selection, and therefore must also have become established by such selection, is evident from the very fact of their long continued existence, and in many cases of their coexistence in different species, in fact sometimes even in very distantly related ones where the conditions of life are similar, as in the case of the fish-like form of aquatic vertebrates belonging to different orders and classes. Were the phenotypes not held in place, so to speak, by a selective process, most of them would be bound to decay into other phenotypes by mere mutation pressure, since enough is known about mutation rates to make it certain that this pressure usually is more than sufficient to change the phenotype over the course of a geological period unless it is counteracted by selection pressure. Here the combination of genetics and paleontology is a very fruitful one in confirming the conclusions of either alone concerning the importance of selection.

Further evidence from genetics in the same direction lies in the data which show the high stability of the normal phenotype as compared with most mutant phenotypes. This stability depends upon groups of so-called modifying genes operating in conjunction with the genes of major effect to render their expression more resistant to both environmental and genetic influences that would tend to change the major genes' effectiveness. It is this principle which results, very probably as a by-product, in normal genes usually having far greater dominance than mutant ones. Another manifestation of the same principle is seen in the phenomenon known as dosage compensation. In this kind of case modifying genes have been preserved that are of such a nature as to compensate for the difference between the dosage of major sex-linked genes present in male and female, even though such dosage differences without the modifiers are usually insufficient to produce a phenotypic effect visible to our unaided eyes. In other words, in the practically identical phenotypes of male and female with regard to these sex-linked genes, we do have examples of like façades which are brought about by different genetic mechanisms acting in the two sexes, and these mechanisms must have come into existence as a result of selection operating in favor of a given phenotype, and operating with a nicety of discrimination that considerably surpasses our own visual powers.

Despite the exactitude with which a given advantageous phenotype can be attained, as shown by such evidence, the organism cannot be considered as infinitely plastic and certainly not as being equally plastic in all directions, since the directions which the effects of mutations can take are, of course, conditioned by the entire developmental and physiological system resulting from the action of all the other genes already present. An illustration of that is seen, for instance, in the dearth of Minute bristle mutations in *Drosophila hydei* already referred to, and in the dearth of body color mutations in *Drosophila robusta* to which Spencer has called our attention. Similarly, in paleontology, it is well known that given characteristics, such as horns, are much more prone to arise and evolve, again and again, within the different lines of certain large groups, rather than within those of other large groups which apparently would have found them as useful. As Stern has pointed out, even intra-nuclear conditions, such as gene positions, the presence of heterochromatin in certain places, etc., tend to set limitations on variation, not to speak of the interior structure of the genes themselves, that conditions their individual mutability. Hence certain kinds of qualitative mutations will be absent and others may be so exceedingly rare (like the porcupine boy mentioned by Haldane) as to make such mutations practically not recurrent but indeterminate, so far as their furnishing a handle for selection is concerned. Nevertheless, despite these restrictions, there is necessarily a big leeway for selection, i.e. a pressure of mutation in many different directions. Thus when it comes to changes in size, proportions, and patterns in general, which affect the dimensions and degrees of development of already present structures, the organism may be regarded as exceedingly plastic and correspondingly responsive to selection, and predominantly determined by the latter.

But even the change in degree of a given character, under the guidance of natural selection, cannot be as simple and easy a process as sometimes supposed. Since any given species has hundreds of millions of years of natural selection behind it already, it tends to have attained optimal degrees of development of its characters in relation to one another and to the conditions of life under which it lived. And any recurrent mutation having the frequency of origination dealt with in most genetic data would already have become selected and established in that species had it been advantageous under the conditions for which that species had been selected. If, however, the outward conditions themselves (under which we include of course the biological environment, constituted of other species) undergo some sort of shift, then some mutations formerly disadvantageous become advantageous and we may expect our given species gradually to change *pari passu*, giving the appearance of orthogenesis. Even if the outer change be a relatively sudden one, the change in the given species may lag far behind, again proceeding gradually through an orthogenetic-seeming process. This is because all parts and characters of the organism are so nicely intercoordinated that a major change in one character, even though considered separately it might represent a better adjustment to the new outer environment, causes trouble until many other characters can be brought into harmony with it. Hence a small step in the character in question is for a time more advantageous, and then has to be followed up by small changes in the other characters before a further step in the same direction can become established. Therefore the progression will tend to be gradual in this case also, although of course not nearly so slow as if the change in conditions had itself been less sudden. And the fact that not only do the different characters of the given species have to be brought into relation with one another but that there is also an interaction between those of different species, a reciprocal ecological interplay, acts as a brake on the changes of both. But in the end this may result in the changes going much further than they otherwise would, as each gradually responds, and this, too, will be seen to favor a more or less prolonged orthogenetic effect. All this can happen even in large panmictic species, through the gradual spread and establishment of (in the main at least) recurrent mutations. The importance of sexual reproduction is to be noted here, in allowing various mutations to spread simultaneously within a species, interpenetrating one another, so to speak, as a result of Mendelian recombination and crossing over, rather than having to wait in line as in asexual organisms.

It has been pointed out by several students of the subject, but especially by Haldane, that there are often various different selective tendencies, some of them conflicting to a greater or lesser degree, acting at once on a population. Some of these tendencies are more shortsighted than others, in the sense of favoring characters which may help the immediate spread of the individuals or genes concerned but which are harmful to the population as a whole or in the long run. This is particularly apt to be the case with the characters that help an individual in its competition with others of the same species immediately around it rather than in its struggle with the rest of nature. Among such characters would be the increased rate of multiplication allowed by a return to asexual reproduction, or, in a social species especially, characters of social parasitism. In such cases there is, of course, in the end, a longer-sighted natural selection operating also, either in the form of intergroup competition within the same species or, if the species is practically panmictic, then only in the forms of interspecific competition or of the general struggle against nature to keep alive at all. The latter forms may not be effective enough, however, to prevent extinction on a large scale. This is one reason why the existence of numerous small semi-isolated groups in a species is favorable to its evolutionary advance.

It is also very important to note that when for any reason some character or part of the organism has undergone a change which introduces that organism to a new mode of life of any kind, this circumstance at once begins to operate in the same way as a change in the outer conditions themselves, throwing many other parts or features out of adjustment and making mutations in them advantageous which previously were not. Hence this sort of change might well be followed by a long orthogenetic progression in a certain direction. Seeing how intricate and delicate the balance of parts in an organism is, it is easy to see that the process might be started by some relatively small change. And such a change could, of course, come about more easily in a small semi-isolated section of a species exposed to special conditions of selection, and subject also to drift, than in a large panmictic population.[2]

Wright has pointed out the various advantages of the division of a population into small partially independent but ultimately competing units. In general these advantages all derive from the fact that numerous experiments, if we may call them so, in diverse directions, are thus made possible on the part of species, experiments which involve the temporary establishment of whole combinations of genes rather than the trying out of single genes on their individual average merits as happens chiefly in panmictic populations. It seems probable that many genes which in the population as a whole would have a net disadvantage and so would fail to gain an evolutionary foothold would be successful in local combinations, which they would not have had a chance to form effectively except (for some cases) through the accidents of small numbers (drift), and (for other, more numerous, cases) through the vagaries of the selection applying under local and often temporary conditions. Genes are thereby enabled locally to pass through the stage of combinations which in the species as a whole would have been effectively selected against, and thence on to combinations in which they can succeed on a wider longer-range scale, thus traversing "troughs" and arriving at "peaks" of advantage, as Wright puts it. Then, in the intergroup competition that gradually follows, they may finally be found successful even for the species as a whole. Probably this (temporarily at least) non-orthogenetic progression is more frequent on the biochemical and physiological level than on the morphological one, yet there is enough relation between the two kinds of characters, both ontogenetically and ecologically, for the process to have important morphological repercussions also. And since local conditions are so varied and unpredictable, an element of indeterminacy is

---

[2] Some surprise was expressed at the symposium that the present author should defend the thesis that evolutionary rates are chiefly determined by selective factors rather than by mutation rates. Just because my own experimental work has dealt largely with the latter does not mean that I have ever considered them to be the dominating factors in this respect. Over twenty-five years ago I taught my classes in evolution that the keys to evolutionary spurts and radiations were to be found in (1) the appearance (without preadaptation) of character complexes which happened to open up major new modes of life and opportunities for living, and (2) changes in the physical and biological environment which had a similar effect; and I have retained these views on this subject. In explaining this point of view, I repeatedly resorted to the expression that, at any such critical time, many of the mutations which had previously been occurring but which till then had proved disadvantageous, because of the temporary "optimum" that had been reached, became advantageous at that point because of the changed needs of the organisms, and in this way allowed a faster evolution, even without any speeding up in the occurrence of the mutations themselves. The point was also made at that time, with such illustrations as that of genetically conditioned social parasitism, that a shortsighted natural selection would sometimes lead to the establishment of characters that were not of benefit to the species as a whole.

thereby introduced into the evolutionary process which is probably considerably greater than that due to the exceedingly rare (non-recurrent) types of mutations of individual genes previously referred to. For in this way those corners may more easily be turned which lead to changes in mode of life and which thus set the species going along a new direction of evolution, as pointed out in the preceding paragraph, than in the plodding conservative mode of progress of large, thoroughly interbreeding species.

Species Divergence

Among the changes to which the presence of numerous small local populations thus gives rise are those leading to the formation of gene combinations that are inharmonious when crossed with those of the original population or with those of other local populations. If the disharmony is great enough to limit the interflow of genes to the level where it can be counteracted by the differential selections and drifts operating on the groups in question, speciation has been started on its way, i.e. the splitting of an original species into two or more groups which are effectively isolated genetically from one another. These will necessarily tend thereafter to undergo genetically divergent evolution, even though phenotypically they may sometimes run largely parallel.

There is good reason to infer that the establishment of groups which are in a state of nature unmixable even if brought together (in other words, of separate species, if we may for present purposes at least define species in this way) ordinarily requires to begin with an isolation, that is enforced from without, of one group from another. This implies some form of "geographical" isolation, using this term in a broader sense than usual.

To be sure, occasional individual mutations are conceivable which by themselves would be so drastic in their action and of such a nature as to render the individuals inheriting them uncrossable with the original type, although still fertile with one another. These would not seem to require spatial isolation, although (except in selfing organisms) it would have to be postulated that several such identical mutants had arisen at once, and, presumably by virtue of some feature conferred upon them by the same mutation, succeeded in finding one another effectively enough and over a long enough period to establish a permanent line. This might be supposed to happen if, for example, the mutation led to sufficiently different food habits, sex preferences, time of breeding, or other peculiarities of reproductive behavior, provided the mutation was one of those very rare ones which had a large effect but was nevertheless well enough adjusted for indefinitely long survival. However, even in such a favorable *ad hoc* case, it is to be expected, except in the relatively rare case of polyploids, that mutants of the same general nature as the "isolating" ones but of a less extreme nature would also be present in the population. In the great majority of cases in which large gene mutations of a given sort are found, others deviating in the same direction but to a lesser degree are more frequent, and various grades of intermediates usually coexist. In other words, the more extreme mutants simply form one end of a curve. The intermediates then would serve as a bridge to allow intercrossing between the more extreme type and the usual, and there would be no real isolation. For this reason this process could seldom lead to speciation.

Ordinarily, then, for genetic isolation to be effective at least two mutational differences working together, and in this sense complementary to each other in their action, are required to differentiate two groups of organisms in such a way as to make them non-crossable. Either difference taken alone would allow crossing—a fact which would explain how each step, occurring separately, had been able to breed sufficiently to get established in the first place. Organisms of the two genetically isolated groups would however differ regularly in both respects at once, otherwise they could intercross indirectly by way of those individuals of the two groups that differed by only one step, and thus the isolation would become more and more broken down. But for the two groups thus to have come to differ regularly by both established gene differences would have required a prior isolation imposed from without since, as we have seen, there would by no effective genetic isolation before *both* the differences had become established, and since Mendelian recombination (or crossing over) would have prevented their getting sorted out into the separate groups so long as interbreeding was allowed. On the other hand, given the outwardly imposed isolation, the complementary mutations, producing the mutually inharmonious but self-harmonious gene combinations, would have been bound to occur in the course of time, as mutational differences accumulated between the isolated populations. For so long as the groups could not mix, there would be no selective hindrance to the establishment within either group of mutations inharmonious with the other group only. After this genetic isolating mechanism had once become established, however, the groups could safely be brought into contact without danger of their merging, and this must often have happened, so as to give sympatric species.

It is interesting that the above interpretation of geneticists should be in such complete agreement with the conclusions arrived at by Mayr as a result of his studies of systematics. Geographic isolation, he finds, in the great majority of cases at least, is the factor which initiates the splitting; it has been necessary for most of the evolutionary divergence which we see in crossbreeding organisms. Sympatric species thus become secondary phenomena, resulting from the later removal or overcoming of the geographic barriers. It is to be understood that geographic differences are to a certain extent associated with ecological ones, and that unless two species that were originally isolated geographically have become somewhat different ecologically, both cannot later survive in the same area because there could be no stable equilibrium between them, short of the extinction of one or the other.

Without this primary possibility of divergence, there could have been no evolutionary radiation, whether adaptive or not. By a repetition of such a process of divergence, however, a group may be enabled to branch out into various geographical and so, eventually, ecological niches, and if these afford it good opportunities for further development, the result will be "adaptive radiation."

EVOLUTIONARY SPEED AND GENETIC SYSTEMS

We have seen that the direction and speed of evolution will be determined largely by selection pressure, that is, by the molding factors of the outer environment acting in relation to the possibilities of the organism for further change in advantageous directions. It must be remembered at the same time that the speed of genetic change is limited by various features of the given breeding system. Thus, we have seen that non-crossing organisms suffer from a serious disadvantage as compared with those that can have Mendelian recombination of mutations arising in separate lines of descent. There are many other characteristics of the breeding system that can influence evolution, such as the extent of polygamy or polygyny, the degree to which crossing over may be restricted to given chromosome regions, the existence of haploid generations, or of considerable haploid portions of the genotype, polyploidy, the wideness of crossing consistent with interfertility, etc.

It may here be asked: Is not the mutation rate itself a basic limiting factor of great importance? No doubt in an ultimate sense this is true, but even the mutation rate is known to be influenced by the kind of genes present and therefore it itself must have come under the influence of selection. Obviously those species with a rate more nearly optimal for themselves would, other things being equal, have succeeded better. This optimal rate is, of course, not the maximal one, since very high rates exceed the power of selection to maintain an equilibrium between the origination of harmful mutations and their elimination, and thus lead to genetic degeneration. On the other hand, as Sturtevant once pointed out, the selective tendency which acts to keep the mutation rate low by reason of the harmful effect of most mutations is probably more effective than that working in the opposite direction, which tends to raise the rate because of the occasional advantage that a few mutations do give the species in its evolution. The former tendency is more effective because its process of selective elimination, by acting sooner and more constantly, is more apt to weed out the very individuals which contain the genes that caused the difference in mutation rate in question. In consequence, we should expect most species to have mutation rates rather below than above the optimal, although the amount by which they were less than the optimal would depend in considerable measure upon characteristics of their system of breeding, including on the one hand the amount of division into small local populations, this favoring a higher rate, and on the other hand the amount of dominance of mutant genes and the relative size of the X chromosome, these factors favoring lower rates. Some artificial speeding up of the mutation rate then might not in the end be a disadvantage to most species, and in this sense mutation rate might in truth be to some extent a limiting factor in evolutionary speed.

Present genetic knowledge shows the hereditary basis of every higher organism to be exceedingly complex, the number of genes lying in the thousands at least. But most individual genes are, in all probability, themselves very complex, and if our interpretation is correct they attained their present state through a succession of numerous small mutations. Most of these individual small mutations seem to have conferred only a very small selective advantage and therefore took a considerable time to become established in the species as a whole, over which they had to spread after originating in a very few individuals. All this must have required an exceedingly great length of time, even when we take into consideration the telescoping of the process allowed by the recombining of genes in sexual reproduction. Making any plausible assumptions concerning the quantitative aspects of these several facts, we find a period of time measured in the hundreds of millions of years at any rate, a period far beyond that allowed by geologists of Darwin's day.

EVOLUTIONARY TIME

Modern physics and geology combined have come to the rescue of Darwinism, or, if you like, neo-Darwinism, by giving the great extension of time needed.

As Knopf has explained in Chapter 1, the eon-glass found in the running down of the radioactive elements to helium and lead can now be read in an increasing number of cases without those grave errors which marred its use at first. Even where the chief source-substance, uranium, has been partly oxidized and washed away, another, actinium U, can sometimes be used, provided its own end-substance, its characteristic lead isotope, is isotopically identified. And for the determination of the end-substances from the running down of uranium, not only its lead but also helium, as Hurley has shown, can now be used where the mineral magnetite is present, since unlike most other minerals which tend to lose their helium and thus throw off the calculation, magnetite holds all the helium generated within it. Unfortunately it has been possible so far to make only four accurate time readings of strata which can be placed precisely in the chart of geological succession by means of the usual geological criteria, since the strata holding most of the radioactive deposits are not geologically satisfactory for placement. But these four have been enough to give good landmarks for the Late Paleocene, Early Permian (confirming each other accurately from two places), and Late Cambrian—fairly strategically spaced points, as it happens. With the working out even of micro-methods along these lines (which, though not so well checked, have on the whole shown considerable consistency) and with the increasing ease of conducting isotope determinations, it is to be expected that our knowledge will be considerably more abundant and precise in the not too distant future.

As it is, from the fact that the Late Cambrian shows an age of 460,000,000 years, and that some other strata, though not placed geologically with any precision, are at least 2,000,000,000 years old, we see that there has been as much time for the evolution of higher forms as anyone had thought necessary, while there has been considerably more allowed for the earlier parts of evolution. (In fact, according to Arthur Holmes in an article which appeared in *Nature* on January 25, 1947, there is good evidence from radioactive deposits that the earth has existed for about 3,300,000,000 years.) All this agrees with the evidence from biochemistry and physiology that even the bacteria have protoplasm about as complicated as that of higher organisms, and that therefore a great many more biochemical complications had to develop in the time between the origin of the first genes and that of bacteria than in the whole time elapsing from that stage to the present.

Even at its best, the radioactive clock can be expected to give us only a relatively few definite landmarks, but other methods are being worked out for the determination of shorter sequences, particularly through the finding of "varves" or annual markings. These allow us to count the years in these deposits almost as in sections of tree trunks, and they are thus helping to fill out our knowledge of the between-times, even though little has yet been done along these lines as compared with estimates based on the much more variable and uncertain measures afforded by thickness of deposits.

INTERPRETATIONS OF OBSERVED DIFFERENCES IN EVOLUTIONARY RATES

Although a more nearly absolute time scale is thus being set up gradually, most studies of evolutionary rates have been relative to the thickness of strata or to one another, criteria which must be used with caution. Moreover, as Simpson has pointed out, the paleontological rates, necessarily dealing with morphological changes, are not necessarily proportional to genetic rates (see, for instance, the above strictures about phenotypic façades). And the rate of morphological change within a given line can vary quite differently from the rate of morphological splitting, in other words from taxonomic diversification.

Nevertheless, despite all these limitations, it is quite evident that the time-rate of change within individual lines and also the rate of diversification of lines has for some large groups been exceedingly different during some portions of geological history than during others; there have been unquestionable spurts and bursts, and contrasted long periods of relative stasis. There has been no convincing evidence for ascribing these evolutionary accelerations, as a general principle, to such inanimate factors as earth crustal movements or outpourings of radioactivity, except in so far as the rearrangement of terrain may alter the conditions of selection and of isolation. Despite the apparent suddenness of many of the evolutionary events, the spatial as well as temporal imperfections of the records have been so great as to make the interpretations of migration and of lost intervals much more plausible than that of major coordinated changes occurring in a really discontinuous fashion ("quantum evolution"), especially when the gradualness of the record in practically all cases where the record itself has been continuous over a sufficient area is taken into account.

Many examples of changes in rate of evolutionary progression as well as in rate of diversification have been presented, especially by Chaney and by Stebbins in plants, and by Romer, by Watson, and by Newell in animals. Our attention has been called, for instance, to the burst, combined with spurt, in land plant structure in the later Paleozoic, in flower structure in the Cretaceous, followed by relatively very slow development in both cases, to the burst of bivalves in the Ordovician with their subsequent slowing down, to that of mammals in the Early Tertiary, and to the vacillations in the rates of change of nautiloids and ammonoids, not paralleling each other but with many intra-group parallels. Although the details of the causal factors concerned are largely lost to our view because of the difficulties in learning the minutiae of ecology and physiology of extinct organisms, many of these bursts and spurts involve the common feature that a new structural system (and/or a biochemical one, but in any case one genetically conditioned) had recently arisen, giving rise to a new mode of life that offered further opportunities of living, in varied directions not open to these organisms before (or at any rate not open to nearly the same degree). This not only raised these organisms above much of the previous competition but in some cases, as in the land plants especially, even opened comparatively virgin fields within which selection, pursuing new courses, must have favored both diversification and progression. Of course, if you ask what caused the new structural or other genetic complex to arise here in the first place, you cannot give an exact answer, and the thing may even have been to a certain extent indeterminate, but it is evident in various cases that the pre-existing structures happened to come close enough to the new ones to afford a basis for the development of the latter, as we should have expected. This, however, is by no means the same as saying that there was some principle of preadaptation, for evolution can take advantage only of its inherent possibilities when it proceeds from step to step. It has already been mentioned that, following the initial turning of a corner with its immediately ensuing burst, there should be a slower and slower selective approach towards new optima, as both the intra-organismal and more especially the inter-organismal reciprocal adjustments will be very intricate, with minor corners again occurring here and there. Thus too there is ever and again the possibility of once more upsetting the main balance and starting off anew.

Even in following a relatively complete story which has been supposed to show practically steady progression, as in the case of the horses, as Romer has pointed out, things are not usually very simple. So, for example, though the growth of face length seems to have been practically linear, the face-to-cranium and face-to-cheek-teeth ratios have gone first down and then on the whole up, with branchings, while the tibia-to-femur ratio has shown several reverses. Yet on the whole the longer and most characteristic central line has undergone a development which is not only fairly constantly oriented but which in this case, because of our knowledge of the "regularities" of vertebrate anatomy and ecology, is very understandable. As Watson has pointed out, it represents an obviously increasing adjustment to a herbivorous grass-eating life, at a time of the spread of the grasses, in an animal profiting by the advantages of increase in size while maintaining or increasing the cursorial ability forced upon it by the presence of increasingly fast and formidable carnivores. Here then, given the original structure and mode of life of the animal, we need only grant it the plasticity in morphological proportions allowed by general genetics to explain its major changes as a result of the selection imposed by outer conditions.

The importance of the outer conditions, taken in relation to the organism's own endowment, in bringing about evolutionary spurts and bursts or, contrariwise, periods of relative stasis, was demonstrated by Stebbins. What can be the meaning, for example, of the fact that in typical temperate forests, throughout a great range of angiosperm types, including both woody and herbaceous species, there has been practical stagnation in their evolution since Miocene times, together with a similar rate of extinction for both the woody and herbaceous forms, whereas in the drier regions of the western Cordilleras with their newly diversified habitats and comparative isolation of localities, there are varied examples of more recent change and diversification, more especially in the herbaceous but also to some extent in the longer-lived forms? What can be the meaning here except that the comparatively recent changes in environmental conditions, acting on what was originally the same collection of material, led to the establishment of adaptations to those conditions (including adaptations to the changes in other species that were also occasioned by these conditions), whereas in the original environment there was little or no selective pressure to alter the optima which had already been attained?

On the other hand, in tropical forests, which have more local diversifications and barriers than typical temperate ones, there seem to be more examples of comparatively recent changes. Especially instructive in tropical forests, as showing the influence of outer selective conditions, are the remarkable flower developments found in the epiphytes there. Being able by reason of their partial parasitism to survive and flower in a dark submerged habitat where insects are scarce, there is a premium here on attracting and making the most of insects, and this must be far more pronounced than in the ordinary habitats of flowering plants, where insects are abundant. Surely the varied and remarkable flower fantasies of the orchids have been a result of the selection pressure thus engendered (whereas this in its turn is in part to be ascribed to the new mode of life brought about by their genetically conditioned parasitism). Now in a general sense these flower developments, though so diverse, have run parallel to one another, from the point of view of function. One cannot explain this result, however, by a tendency to vary in a given direction, since the result is so polymorphic, and so one is led to interpret it as an effect of outward selection pressure working in all the lines towards the same end, although through means that are subject to accidental deviations—unless indeed one would endow the germ plasm here with a very versatile and knowing entelechy! Other striking evidences of a widely operating activity of selection were the evolutionary changes in flora of varied species attendant on the recession of glaciation and, in most recent times, on the radical disturbances in nature's economy made by man.

In judging what organisms would be likely to evolve furthest in response to changing outer conditions or to the changed conditions of life brought about by some prior change of their own in a structural or physiological complex. Stebbins has called attention to considerations recently put forward by the Russian vertebrate embryologist Schmalhausen. The latter has pointed out that, in a general way, the evolutionary rate may be expected to be higher for organisms standing higher in what he terms the nutritive hierarchy. The lowest stage of this hierarchy consists, according to Schmalhausen, of the organisms that are eaten but whose species survive primarily by reason of their very active growth and reproduction. Second come those which passively protect themselves, third those which try to escape, and finally the predators. Since most of this is inapplicable to plant evolution, Stebbins would add that there is, similarly, a reproductive hierarchy there, in which the lowest stage gets by through sheer quantitative multiplication, the second engages in passive protection of its stages of dispersal, and the third achieves dispersal by having these stages become attached to actively moving animals. These hierarchies, if taken too literally, are of course oversimplifications, since one would hardly put a predatory *Stentor* above an escapist horse, nor put a juniper, with its edible berries, above some anemophilous hardwood tree. However, in so far as they are true to fact, they represent the well-known principles that in the competition for holozoic nutrition there is a chance for success in ever greater elaborations of mechanism working to gather more elusive and/or resistant prey, while for non-holozoic organisms, lacking contractile and nervous systems, there have been great advantages in the development of machinery to protect their dispersal stages (especially under terrestrial conditions) and to effect their transportation. For these are among the major general problems for the two respective groups of organisms, as any good elementary course in biology should bring out.

Organisms standing in a more primitive position in one of these series have failed to turn the major corners, i.e. to develop the major innovations of their series, and, representing in the main an archaic type of organization, find themselves now surrounded by a wealth of forms that have long been diversified in innumerable minor ways, i.e. that have turned minor corners. Hence there is usually not much room for their further evolution, and they find themselves largely confined to their present niche. On the other hand, some of those that have taken part in the great developments and turned one major corner after another are not yet so effectively hemmed in, and so there are more apt to be opportunities for their still further development. In other words, "There's always more room at the top"—for those already there, and so major steps as well as minor steps of evolution are to be expected more often on the part of organisms which have already advanced far than in those which have stayed behind. This makes it appear as if the germ plasm of one line had been more progressive than that of another on account of some inner urge; but differences in fundamental genetic plasticity are not required, since an organism that has through historical accident remained behind tends to find itself in a selective rut. If, however, the competition of other forms is somehow removed or lessened later, as by placing it in an isolated region of great enough extent to allow active evolution, it may now be found taking advantage of this by adaptive radiation, as Lack has pointed out in the case of certain finches. On the other hand, even the achievement of major advances often fails to protect an organism from getting into a rut of specialization, and it is almost a truism to add that further evolution may be expected mainly from those forms which have remained more functionally versatile.

It is evident that to get at rational specific interpretations of how or why the major innovations which led to the great evolutionary spurts came about, we must attempt to get more detailed knowledge of the organisms concerned, as they existed in their ecological settings. Such ecological knowledge is often very imperfect, as Newell has pointed out for the bivalves. Moreover, an understanding of why a given key structure or system arose in one group rather than another may involve us in minutiae of physiology, developmental mechanism, or biochemistry. Why was it, for example, that tracheae arose at least twice independently among land arthropods but nowhere else? Wherever there are parallelisms of evolution (and where are there not?) there is evidence of deterministic processes of some kind, and the causes involved represent actual problems to be worked out, which are not to be solved by referring to inner urges. On the other hand, as has been pointed out above, some unique turning points may never be completely soluble because of the appearance of practically non-recurrent mutations or, more likely, of practically non-recurrent combinations of mutations that chanced somewhere to become locally established. Naturally, however, science seeks to reduce the postulation of such occurrences to a minimum, though not denying their possibility. In the meantime, it would be presumptuous to try to attribute evolutionary changes which we cannot at present explain, such as the apparent "overdevelopment" of a certain character in numerous parallel lines, followed by their extinction, to such mysterious processes as racial senility, inwardly conditioned orthogenesis, or even developmental correlation of a harmful character with a useful one (there being few correlations which cannot be overcome when it is to the advantage of the organism to do so). For we must bear in mind how very rudimentary our knowledge usually is of the ecology and physiology of existing organisms, not to speak of long extinct ones.

It may seem as though, in laying emphasis on the primary importance of selective factors in evolution, we had gone back on our thesis that genetic plasticity is itself a variable, through variations both in the mutation rate itself and in all sorts of factors concerned in the system of breeding. These factors do remain important. Thus, higher organisms which develop exclusively asexual reproduction or which by too unmitigated inbreeding or other limitations seriously curtail the advantages of sexual reproduction, although they sometimes do well for a while because of the advantage that their speedier and more convenient method of reproduction gives them, are seldom destined to survive long geologically, except perhaps in the lowest groups, where further evolution at this late date would seem to be least advantageous. The more evolving lines have been those possessing the various characteristics (including that of division into small local populations) necessary for optimal genetic plasticity. In most major groups, and more particularly the higher ones, this combination of reproductive features is in fact to be found, in some of the members at least, even though there may be reproductively decadent side-branches; and it has itself been maintained by a long-term natural selection. Granting this, however, the questions whether and what evolution will occur in these reproductively progressive groups, and at what rate, must be decided mainly by selective factors, dependent upon the relation of the structure of the organism to the opportunities afforded by its environment.

At the same time, we must recall that there remain certain rather permanent features of the system of reproduction, widespread throughout whole groups and not easily changed, which must have evolutionary repercussions on these groups. The implications of some of these features, such as the relative extent of haploid versus diploid phases, would bear considerable discussion. Darlington, and later Stebbins, have elsewhere considered some of these matters, but most of them would take us too far afield to allow entering into them here. We will consider only one feature, namely, the length of the generation, as this was mentioned several times in this symposium, where the question was raised whether it is better to measure evolutionary rate in terms of time itself or of number of generations.

Doubtless the answer to this question will vary with the purpose of the measurement; but it is to be observed that the number of steps of recombination, of multiplication, and of selection all depend upon the number of generations, and that these processes therefore tend to be slowed, proportionately, by longer generations, other things being equal. Of course they are not really equal, since, for one thing, survival and reproduction tend to be more selective and less accidental for higher organisms, which tend to have longer generations, and that is probably true more especially in higher forms of animals in which conditioned responses of the nervous system may play an important role. As for mutation frequency, if this were, as some students of the subject formerly thought, proportional to absolute time, then the latter should be our index so far as this factor is concerned. However, longer-lived organisms have probably been selected more effectively for a lower mutation rate than have short-lived ones, and, if our recent results on flies could be extended to other forms, there may also be a physiological mechanism which tends to keep the mutation rate much more nearly constant per generation, when the time is varied, than it would be according to a time-proportionality rule, even in organisms of the same or related species. Furthermore, what limited data are available on mutation frequency from varied kinds of organisms tend to confirm the inference that the frequency per generation is much more alike for species of widely different lengths of life cycle than would be expected if a fixed time-proportionality rule applied. All this is in keeping with Stebbins's observation that on the whole longer-lived species tend to evolve more slowly than their shorter-lived relatives, even though the speed would, according to our present considerations, vary somewhat less than proportionately to the number of generations in a given time. If, then, a situation were observed in which, on the contrary, the evolution of related groups having widely different lengths of generation seemed to proceed at a similar time-rate, despite the difference in length of life (as in some cases referred to by Stebbins), we would be justified in suspecting that this rate was primarily a reflection of the rate of change in outer conditions and that these furnished the limiting factor in the evolutionary speed in these cases, rather than intrinsic features of the organisms themselves.

ON THE POSSIBILITY OF FORECASTING EVOLUTION

If the task of working out the causes of past changes is in many cases such a difficult and uncertain one, how much more so must be that of predicting future events in evolution? While in some cases it would seem safe to extrapolate, orthogenetically, we must beware of the treacherous corners and remember that they occur especially often when there are sudden and profound changes in general conditions, such as have undoubtedly taken place *par excellence* in most recent times. Yet, while preserving our caution about making predictions in our present state of unreadiness, we must recognize that it is nevertheless one of the aims of science in every line to get to the point where it can make predictions, and that it must gradually arrive at both surer and more distant ones.

It has been noted above that the interference of man, even of primitive man, has already resulted, unintentionally, in considerable changes, not all of the nature of extinction, in our "wild" flora and fauna. To judge the possibilities arising from a continuance of this interaction, we should first take into account the relevant peculiarities of man himself. Haldane has outlined some of these to us. Practically everyone will agree that the most important, and the dominating, change distinguishing man's evolution has been the development of his brain power far beyond that of his predecessors and of all other organisms, even though this may in turn have been occasioned by the selection attendant upon certain other innovations, such as an erect predatory life involving use of the hands for manipulation, acting on a basis of organization already advanced in appropriate directions and furnishing an opportunity for further such development. It should be recognized that this increase of brains reached a critical turning point when it became quantitatively and qualitatively adequate for allowing the continued development of tradition, whereby the process of learning by experience was enabled to unite the experiences of coexisting individuals and extend over countless generations. Very recently we have in a sense reached a further turning point with the development of mechanisms for the betterment and increase of tradition itself, mechanisms which may be largely summed up in the word "science." Thereby we are clearly becoming the dominating influence throughout living nature. Hereafter our interference with the evolution of other organisms will not have to be guided only by our immediate needs, unconscious of the long-range effects, as it has in the main been until now, but can increasingly take the latter into account in an ever more far-seeing way. It is to be expected, therefore, that if we make use of our own potentialities, the job of finding out what will happen to other organisms will not be only that of determining how the by-products of our activities will chance to affect them. It will rather be that of determining what we ourselves wish, on the assumption that we will be able largely to carry our wishes into effect, provided these wishes are in harmony with biological possibilities. In other words, the world of plants and animals should be increasingly ours to remold as we choose. Here, of course, the question of ethics, raised by Haldane, cannot be ignored, but I submit that ethics itself cannot be divorced from the biological realities which brought it forth and which must continue to condition it.

But what of the further evolution of man himself? It seems unthinkable that if man brought under his control the evolution of the major species about him he would wish to leave his own nature to the play of uncontrolled forces. Particularly is this true since in his own case the development of his tradition has resulted in certain peculiarities of his system of breeding which, without his so intending it, are markedly antagonistic to, or at the best grave hindrances to, such further biological evolution as could be considered progressive under any reasonable meaning of the term. For there are no longer any other, non-human, species offering serious competition, to whet the knife of such selection as still operates on mankind. Neither is he himself divided into separate species which could give play, among them, for a trial and error process, with reserve types to fall back upon in case of evolutionary errors. And within his own single species he is now rapidly approaching the condition of one immense panmictic population, which will be practically devoid of those numerous semi-isolated local groups that were previously so important in his evolutionary progression, particularly in regard to the selection of those invaluable characters which favored intra-group cooperation. The selective forces which do remain, moreover, must be to a considerable extent different in their direction from those which brought these characters to their present point, and they are evidently weaker, if not in some respects even reversed, in regard to their former action of putting a premium on greater intelligence. That is, most signs indicate strongly that one effect of modern civilization is to bring about a higher rate of multiplication on the part of those with lower intelligence, no matter whether that lower intelligence is chiefly of environmental or of genetic origin, and there is evidence that this phenomenon exists in the U.S.S.R. just as in the other major industrialized countries. Despite these unfavorable tendencies, however, mankind has so far shown marked resistance to having his reproductive behavior modified further, or guided in any way.

Reproducing as a single panmictic species, man has, so to speak, thrown all his eggs into one basket. Unquestionably dominant though he now is, this is a risk in which the chances would be all against him, since only a very small proportion of evolutionary twigs can ever be expected to form the indefinitely continuing lines. Despite natural selection within the lines, there is too much likelihood of failure for any single one. Therefore the only chance of avoiding ultimate decline must eventually be the foreseeing of the biological pitfalls, and the exercising of some form of conscious guidance over his processes of multiplication. This would certainly involve a very great amount of genetic and evolutionary knowledge indeed. Yet I am not pessimistic enough to think that humanity will in the end balk at the application of such knowledge, when the realization of it has become sufficiently widespread. And when such knowledge has once been put to use for the prevention of degeneration, the next step, that of applying it so as to bring about actual progression, would surely be on the way also. It is true that here again we would come into questions of ethics and of social science in general, but these cannot be disengaged from the biological factors which largely underlie them. Such "biological engineering" is no doubt in its major features far distant; it is one of the highest activities in which an organism can conceivably engage. But we have at least made a significant beginning in our very recognition of the existence of natural biological evolution and of the kinds of factors whereby it operates. It is also possible at this stage to see clearly one thing regarding the goals thereby to be achieved: that is, that whatever else happens we must strive for an increase in intelligence and in those characteristics which help intelligence to operate for the benefit of the species as a whole.

It may seem absurd to be optimistic about these distant possibilities just when we are at our most critical moment of indecision, standing at such a portentous parting of the ways in regard to our physical control of the environment. We do not know whether higher life on earth is about to be destroyed, or to be empowered to spread to other regions of the cosmos. It is only on the assumption that we shall successfully surmount the dilemma of having discovered means of using overwhelming violence for which our social structure is not yet ready that we can talk about further developments for our species at all. But if we do survive this dramatic episode, there will remain for us our own inherent biological problem, of a nature no less grave, though infinitely slower in its coming on. Even greater potencies of injury or benefit will depend on our treatment of this problem than on that of our immediate socio-physical problem. For we now see that there is no inexorable law of evolution, after all, which spells "onward and upward forever," and that despite the fact that the highest species have the best chance of going further still, there is no necessity that any given species do so, and nothing can take the place of the multitudinous trials and errors of nature except the most consummate intelligence. Yet, theoretically at least, this can. And conceivably we may gain such intelligence. If, then, we wish evolution to proceed in ways that we consider progressive, we ourselves must become the agents that make it do so. And all our studies of evolution must finally converge in that direction.

GLOSSARY AND INDEX

GLOSSARY

acarpy. Lack of carpels in inferior ovary, also lack of fruit.

aceratheres. A group of extinct (Oligocene to Pliocene), hornless, Old World rhinoceroses.

achene. A small, dry and hard one-seeded fruit which remains closed at maturity.

achondroplasia. In man, a hereditary developmental defect resulting in dwarfs with abnormally short limbs and with trunk and head disproportionately large. (The statement by Wood in this volume that the amynodont rhinoceros skull "tends toward achondroplasia" presumably does not imply equivalence with the pathological human condition and may refer to normal increase in relative size of the head of these animals.)

Actinopterygii. The great group (commonly ranked as a subclass), that includes all the true, bony fishes except the Crossopterygii and Dipnoi (q.v.).

adaptation. Correlation, in a way useful to the organism, between structure, function, and environment. Also, the progressive changes bringing about increase in such relationships in organisms.

adaptive peaks. A figurative representation (especially in work by Sewall Wright) of an organism-environment situation such that the top of the peak represents the highest possible degree of adaptation, and change downhill from this point represents lessened adaptation.

adaptive radiation. The spreading or phyletic ramification of a group of animals from a common ancestral type into divergent descendent types, each with distinct and characteristic adaptive status and ecological relationships.

adaptive zone. A figurative representation of organism-environment situations such that a zone represents a given type of adaptation, broader or narrower as the structural and functional relationships involved are few and loose or many and rigid. A zone may be pictured as including subzones each with a particular sort of adaptation as a variant of or in addition to the adaptation common to the whole zone.

Adelospondyli. Another name for the Microsauria (q.v.).

agglutination. The aggregation of cells, or other particulate material into groups. When an antigen is present at the surface of cells or particles, they may be agglutinated by the specific antibody.

allele. Any of the alternate expressions (states) of a gene.

allometric. Referring to the relative growth of two parts of an organism such that their proportions may change but the ratio of their growth rates (as percentage increases) remains approximately constant. Specifically, growth patterns of two variables x and y, such that $y = bx^a$ where b and a are constants. (Or, $y = bx^k$.)

allopatric speciation. Speciation during spatial isolation or segregation.

allopolyploid. A polyploid (q.v.) having one or more of its chromosome sets derived from a distant or unrelated strain or different species, and with chromosome association at meiosis often largely or entirely between homologous chromosomes of like origin; hence a triploid allopolyploid tends to form n bivalents $+ n'$ univalents, certain tetraploid allopolyploids tend to form $n + n'$ bivalents, etc.

alveolus. The socket in a bone into which is inserted the root of a tooth and its surrounding soft tissues.

ammonites. A large, extinct group of molluscs related to the living chambered nautilus. They are generally distinguishable by the fact that the sutures (lines of attachment of the chamber partitions to the outer shell) are complex and angular whereas they are straight or simply curved in the nautilus and its relatives (nautiloids).

amniote egg. An egg in which the developing embryo is surrounded by a thin double membrane, the amnion, characteristic of the reptiles and their derivatives, the birds and mammals.

amorph. A gene that fails to produce the effect of its wild type allele.

amynodonts. A group of extinct (Late Eocene to Early Miocene), hornless, hippopotamus-like, probably amphibious, North American and Eurasian rhinoceroses.

anamestic. Term applied (by Westoll) to small, highly variable bones (specifically in fish skulls) which seem to arise in a haphazard manner in individual ontogeny and to fill in space left between larger, more constant, topographically fixed bones.

aneuploid. With a chromosome number which is not a multiple of the haploid number; the opposite of euploid.

angiosperms. The class of flowering plants having seeds enclosed in carpels or ovary.

antheres. The pollen bearing parts of the stamens.

anthesis. The time of opening of a flower.

anthracosaurs. Members of a small family of Paleozoic (Carboniferous) primitive amphibians (labyrinthodonts, q.v.).

antigen. A substance, usually protein, but sometimes polysaccharide or lipopolysaccharide, which is capable of evoking the formation of antibodies in the animal organism, which can be collected in the blood serum and which will react specifically with the antigen.

antimorph. A gene that produces the opposite effect of wild type.

apomict. A plant which produces viable seed without fertilization.

Archegoniatae. Group designation embracing bryophytes and pteridophytes and characterized by flask-shaped female sexual organ (archegonium).

archegonium. Female sexual organ of bryophytes, pteridophytes, and some gymnosperms, typically flask-shaped with egg cell in venter (bulblike base) surrounded by sterile multicellular outer wall and with prolonged narrow neck.

archosaurian reptiles. Members of a large group (usually taken as a subclass) of reptiles characterized in part by having two openings and two bony arches in the posterior part of the skull. The group is mainly extinct and includes pterodactyls and dinosaurs, but also includes the crocodiles and the ancestors of the birds.

Arthrodira. A group of placoderms (q.v.), abundant in the Devonian, with heavily armored heads which are movably jointed to similar armor covering the anterior part of the body.

assortative mating. The mating within a population of individuals of similar phenotype or any other form of nonrandom mating.

astrapotheres. A group of extinct (Eocene to Miocene), tusked, herbivorous, ungulate mammals, confined to South America.

autopolyploid. A polyploid originating by a doubling of a chromosome set.

autosomes. Chromosomes ordinarily existing in identical numbers in both male and female of species having heterogametic modes of sex determination; i.e. not X- or Y-chromosomes (q.v.).

awn. A slender bristle at the end or back of an organ, usually on the principal flowering bract of grasses.

back-cross. A mating between a first generation hybrid ("F_1") with one of the parental types.

baluchitheres. A group of extinct (Late Eocene to Early Miocene), hornless, Asiatic rhinoceroses which attained enormous size and include the largest known land mammals.

basalt. An igneous rock composed essentially of gray feldspars and dark minerals, in fine grains of uneven size.

bauriamorphs. A group of advanced, Triassic, South African mammal-like reptiles, paralleling the cynodonts (q.v.).

belemnites. A group of extinct Mesozoic molluscs closely related to the squids and resembling them, but with the internal shell more complete.

bennettitalean. Of or pertaining to Bennettitales (Cycadeoidales), an extinct Mesozoic group of gymnosperms.

biogenetic law. The so-called "law" of recapitulation (q.v.).

biotype. All individuals of the same genetic constitution.

brachiopods. A very large group of marine invertebrates, often classed as a distinct phylum, abundant in the fossil record since the Cambrian and now surviving in diminished numbers. The animal is enclosed in two shells or valves which differ from each other and in which (with rare exceptions) each valve is bilaterally symmetrical.

brachyodont. Referring to teeth, low-crowned.

brachyopids. Members of a widespread Old World family of Triassic amphibians (late labyrinthodonts, q.v.).

bradytelic. Of evolution, proceeding at rates so slow as to simulate cessation of evolution or casual and slight fluctuation about a norm; rates below any of those shown in the inferred usual distribution of rates for the group in question. (*See* horotelic.)

Bryophytes. Moss-like plants, true mosses and liverworts.

buffer. Subsidiary genes that help to integrate a gene into a harmonious gene complex.

bunodont. Referring to teeth, with distinct cusps, not or not fully merged into crests or developed into crescents.

callus. The hardened, pointed base of the flowering bract and fruit of certain grasses.

carnassial teeth. Teeth adapted to shearing or scissor-like cutting, especially of flesh.

carpel. In flowering plants technically equivalent to megasporophyll of lower vascular plants and comparable to a leaf; either developed as a simple pistil or element of compound pistil; bearing ovules.

caytonialean. Of or pertaining to the Caytoniales, an extinct Mesozoic group of gymnosperms.

centromere. A chromosomal region or organelle attaching the chromosome to the spindle at mitosis; a synonym for *kinetochore* or *spindle attachment body*.

cephalaspids. An extinct group of ancient (Silurian and Devonian) fish-like but jawless vertebrates, remote allies of the living lampreys, with flattened, armored heads.

ceratopsians. A group of quadrupedal Cretaceous dinosaurs with posterior skull bones forming a frill over the neck and usually with horns.

chaparral. A dense plant formation of hard-leaved evergreen shrubs.

chelonians. Members of the reptilian order Chelonia, the turtles and their allies.

chromatin. An ambiguous term originally denoting nuclear or chromosomal constituents which stain intensely with basic dyes, thus contrasting with other weakly basophilic nuclear and chromosomal constituents. By tacit understanding today, "chromatin" is often more explicitly employed to designate chromosomal materials rich in desoxyribonucleoprotein.

chromosome limb (or arm). The entire portion of a chromosome lying to one or the other side of the centromere. Most chromosomes have a single interstitial centromere, and accordingly possess two limbs.

cingulum. On teeth, a ridge or shelf, generally basal in position, along some part of the tooth borders.

clone. All the individuals derived by asexual reproduction from a single sexually produced individual.

coelacanths. Members of an ancient (Devonian to Cretaceous as fossils and with one Recent species) group of true or bony fishes, belonging to the Crossopterygii (q.v.), allies of the lungfishes and near the ancestry of the amphibians.

coriaceous. Leathery in texture.

corm. The broadened, bulb-like fleshy base of a stem from which the new growth starts in spring, as in a gladiolus.

cormophyte. Plant differentiated into axis and foliage, as all vascular plants.

cosmine. A hard, enamel-like substance in the outer parts of scales and dermal bones of certain fish (especially Crossopterygii, q.v.), with numerous canals or pulp cavities, in distinction from the denser but otherwise similar ganoine of ganoid fish scales.

cricetine rodent. A member of the Cricetidae or Cricetinae, a very large group of rat- and mouse-like rodents, including the field mice and native rats of the New World, along with some Old World forms, but excluding the house mouse, house rats, and their Old World allies.

crossing-over. Ordinarily an exchange at meiosis of homologous genes between two homologous groups of linked genes (or chromosomes).

Crossopterygii. A large group of true fishes, Devonian to Recent (only one known living species), including among others the osteolepids and coelacanths (q.v.), the early members ancestral to amphibians and related to lungfishes.

cryptic species. *See* sibling species.

cycloid. In reference to fish scales, rounded in shape and broadly overlapping, like shingles.

cynodonts. A group of advanced mammal-like reptiles, Permian to Triassic, known mainly in South Africa (but also South America).

cytogenetics. That branch of genetics (and of cytology) that studies the structures of the cell, in particular the chromosomes that are involved in inheritance, and analyzes the effect these structures have on the modes of inheritance.

Deinocephalia or Dinocephalia. A group of relatively primitive, Permian, Old World mammal-like reptiles.

diabase. An igneous rock essentially similar to basalt (q.v.) in composition but with a "meshwork" or felted texture.

diapause. A temporary interruption of growth in the embryo or larva of insects, usually during hibernation or aestivation.

dicotyledon. A member of that subclass of angiosperms having usually two cotyledons (seed leaves), vascular tissue in a hollow cylinder of a single ring of bundles, and netted veined leaves.

dictyostele. A type of vascular (woody) cylinder in the stem, net-like in structure.

diphycercal. In fishes, referring to a type of tail in which the tapering end of the body and its vertebral column run straight to the end, with fins symmetrically developed above and below this.

diploid. Having a double set of chromosomes, as is characteristic for most cells derived from a fertilized egg cell.

Dipnoi. The lungfishes.

dolerite. A general term for dark colored to black igneous rocks containing some feldspar and with the grains of fairly even size and large enough to be distinguished with the naked eye.

Dollo's Law. *See* irreversibility.

dominant. A genetically controlled character that is expressed in the phenotype, whether the gene producing it is in the heterozygous or the homozygous state.

dosage. In genetics the quantity of a given gene in a zygote.

dosage compensation. The effect produced by modifying genes that compensate for the difference between the dosage of major sex-linked genes present in male and female.

double dose. The presence of two identical alleles in the germ plasm.

Downtonian. In Europe, a stage transitional from Silurian to Devonian and assigned by students sometimes to the latest Silurian and sometimes to the earliest Devonian.

echinoids. The sea urchins and their close allies.

ecotype. A term used in botany for ecological races or for subspecies that owe their most conspicuous characters to the selective effects of local environments. Many plant species have pronounced ecotypes on the sea coast, on sandy soils, in the mountains, or in other localities characterized by special climatic or edaphic conditions.

edaphic. Affected by properties of the soil rather than by other extrinsic factors.

Edentata. An order of mammals including the armadillos, true anteaters, sloths, and allied extinct groups.

effective population size. The total number of individuals of an interbreeding local population which contribute genes to the next generation, in other words, which are the parents of the next generation.

elasmobranchs. A subclass of fish-like vertebrates including the sharks and their allies.

elasmotherine. Referring to a group of extinct, Old World rhinoceroses in which the teeth became extremely high-crowned and one large horn boss developed on the forehead.

embolomerous. Referring to vertebrae of certain primitive amphibians, in which each vertebral segment consists of two circular, nearly equal discs surrounding the notochord.

embryo sac. Female gametophyte in flowering plants; a large thin-walled cell in nucellus of ovule, in which egg and eventually embryo are formed.

endocranium. The internal part of the skull around the brain and associated sensory organs, formed by cartilage or by bone. In this sense, essentially = neural cranium (q.v.). (So used by Westoll in this book, following good precedent. The term is, however, more commonly used for the internal surface of the brain cavity or for the membranes lining this.)

entelechy. The nonmechanical agency held responsible by vitalists for the phenomena of life and growth.

environmental niches. Local and narrowly defined ecological situations having specific requirements with respect to adaptation (q.v.).

enzyme. Protein catalyst produced by living organisms, typically consisting of a protein part (apoenzyme) which confers specificity and a non-protein part (coenzyme) which is required for action.

epeirogenic. In geology, referring to broad, mainly vertical, movements of the earth's crust, such as those lowering regions on continents and causing their invasion by shallow *epeiric* seas.

epharmonic. Perfectly adapted to environment; adaptive.

epigenesis. The theory that individual development consists not of expansion of structure performed in the egg but of the entirely new creation of individual structure, guided more or less rigidly by an inherited developmental system or series of determinants. Also, the process of development in this way.

epigenotype. The set of organizers and organizing relations to which a certain piece of tissue (or organism) will be subject during development. (The appearance of a particular organ [or organism] is the product of the genotype and the epigenotype, reacting with the external environment.)

epiphysis. A terminal part or process of a bone that ossifies separately and usually later fuses with the main body of the bone. (General only in mammals, for instance at the articular faces of the vertebrae or the ends of the long bones of the limbs.)

epiphytes. Plants growing upon other plants without being parasitic.

equids. Horses in the broadest sense, members of the horse family, Equidae.

euchromatin. Regions of chromosomes or whole chromosomes are said to be composed of euchromatin when they undergo the customary alternations of coiling, condensation, and basophily in a mitotic cycle more or less simultaneously with the other chromosomes of a set; euchromatin stands in contrast to heterochromatin (q.v.).

euploid. A chromosome number which is an exact multiple of the haploid number.

explosive evolution. Relatively rapid splitting of a group into numerous different lines of descent within a period of time geologically short (but which may, nevertheless, run into some millions of years).

Fissipedia (or Fissipeda). A suborder of progressive, terrestrial, mammalian carnivores, including all the nonaquatic, living Carnivora.

fitness. In terms of natural selection, fitness is sometimes defined by the number of offspring an individual leaves as compared with individuals of different genetic constitution or as compared with the average for the population of which it is a member.

fusion. The more or less permanent union of unrelated chromosome arms or fragments following breakage by natural or artificial means. The term is often used more explicitly to indicate the joining, generally by an unknown process, of two rod-shaped chromosomes to give a V-shaped chromosome.

galactozymase. Enzyme system required for the fermentation of (production of carbon dioxide from) the sugar galactose.

gametophyte. The gamete (egg and sperm) bearing generation of higher plants, usually haploid in chromosome number.

gene frequency. The percentage of a given gene in a population.

genetic drift. Genetic changes in populations due to random fixation ("Sewall Wright effect").

genome. The sum total of genetic material in the chromosomes of a zygote.

genotype. In genetics, the genetic constitution of an organism. In taxonomy, the type species of a genus.

geochronology. The study of time in relationship to the history of the earth, or a system of dating developed for this purpose. Absolute geochronology involves dating of geological events in years. Relative geochronology involves the system of successive eras, periods, and epochs used in geology and paleontology.

gephyrocercal. In fishes, referring to a tapering tail, symmetrical above and below, and so resembling the diphycercal (q.v.) tail, but generally with upper and lower fins confluent around the end of the vertebral column and secondarily derived from some other type of tail, such as the heterocercal (q.v.).

Gestalt morphology. Proposed in 1937 by Agnes Arber for modern school of plant morphology (W. Troll) which aims to determine principal structural types of main organs or whole plants irrespective of their taxonomic relationships and wide range of individual variants.

gnetalean. Of or pertaining to Gnetales, the highest group of gymnosperms with many angiosperm characteristics.

Gymnophiona. An order of limbless, worm-like, burrowing, tropical amphibians. (Also called Apoda.)

haemophilia (hemophilia). A heritable defect in which blood does not clot under conditions in which clotting is normal.

haploid. Having only a single set of chromosomes, hence having the basic chromosome number for the species. Gametes are usually haploid; somatic cells, ordinarily diploid.

heterocercal tail. In fishes and fish-like vertebrates, a tail in which the vertebral axis at the end of the body bends upward and tapers to a point, while a fin is asymmetrically developed below this.

heterochromatin. Regions of chromosomes or whole chromosomes are said to be composed of heterochromatin, rather than of euchromatin (q.v.), when their alternations in coiling, condensation and basophily in a mitotic cycle either take a different course from the majority of chromosomes, or are wholly dissynchronous with respect to them.

heterogametic. The sex which is heterozygous for the sex chromosomes.

heterogonic. Referring to relative growth, same as allometric.

heterosporous. Producing two distinct kinds of spores.

heterozygote. An individual with unlike alleles of one or several genes.

heterozygous. Having different alleles at one locus.

holostean fishes. Members of a large group of relatively primitive bony fishes, especially characteristic of the Mesozoic but also including the living bowfin (Amia).

holostylic. Referring to a type of jaw suspension in vertebrates in which the cartilaginous element (palatoquadrate) of the upper jaw is fused to the cranium and the lower jaw articulates directly with the cranium.

holozoic nutrition. With the mode of nutrition characteristic for an animal.

homeosis (or homoeosis). The assumption, by one member of a series of structures in an individual organism, of a form usually characteristic of another member of the same series.

homeostatic system. A developmental process or regional control involved in modification or differentiation of a series of generally similar structures in an individual organism.

homoiothermy (or homeothermy). Maintenance by an animal of more or less constant body temperature by physiological mechanisms independent of or resistant to environmental temperatures. Contrasted with poikilothermy (*see* poikilothermic).

homology. Essential similarity between structures in different groups of organisms, interpreted as due to inheritance of these structures from a common ancestry. An alternative usage bases homology on similarities of position, development, etc., without implication as to common ancestry.

homoplastic. Similarly adapted through parallel but independent evolution.

homosporous. Having the asexual spores all alike, as in most ferns.

homozygous. Having like alleles at one or more specified loci.

horizon. In stratigraphy, an exact plane or limited zone in sedimentary rocks defined essentially as representing a point (or span of imperceptible duration) in time. Definition is commonly by names of fossils diagnostic of the time in question.

horotelic. Referring to rates of evolution included in the distribution of rates usual in a given group for lines evolving normally and over considerable periods of time. Contrasted with tachytelic rates during short, exceptional fast evolutionary shifts or spurts, and bradytelic rates in lines evolving unusually slowly or showing virtual cessation of progressive change.

hybrid flock or hybrid swarm. A local population consisting largely or entirely of hybrids between two species.

hypomorph. A gene that produces a smaller effect than its wild type allele.

hypsodont. Referring to teeth, high-crowned.

ichthyosaur. Any member of a large order of extinct Mesozoic (Triassic to Cretaceous) reptiles, completely aquatic and shark-like in body form.

immigration coefficient. A term in population genetics denoting the percentage within a population of those individuals which have become members of the population by immigration.

inflorescence. The flowering part of a plant and in particular its mode of arrangement.

intersex. An individual showing characters intermediate between those of male and female. This intermediacy may affect either the sex organs or other morphological differences between the two sexes.

inversion. Reversal of the linear order in a segment of a linkage group or chromosome; e.g. the *c-e* interval in *abedcfg* is inverted with respect to the original sequence *abcdefg*.

inversion, paracentric. An inversion that does not include the centromere, hence an inversion restricted to one limb of a chromosome.

inversion, pericentric. An inversion that includes the cetromere within the inverted segment, and thus involves both limbs of a chromosome.

irreversibility. Of evolution, the principle or belief that an evolving group of organisms (or a part of an organism) does not return to an ancestral condition. Also known as "Dollo's Law."

isoalleles. Alleles which, although they are not identical, produce such slight phenotypical differences that special techniques are required to reveal them.

isolate. An isolated population or group of populations.

isolating mechanism. Any intrinsic factor that inhibits interbreeding between two populations (mostly species).

isopods. A group of mostly terrestrial crustaceans including the so-called wood lice or sow bugs.

isotopic. Relating to isotopes, which are elements of identical chemical properties but different atomic weights.

karyogenetic. Heritable, not subjected to direct environmental influences.

Keweenawan. A series of rocks, mainly of late pre-Cambrian age, in the Great Lakes region. Also, the time when these rocks were formed.

labyrinthodonts. Members of a large group of extinct amphibians, including most of the Paleozoic forms (also occurring in the Triassic), defined mainly as primitive amphibians in which the vertebrae ossified from blocks or arches of cartilage.

lateral line system (or organs). In primitive aquatic vertebrates, a series of canals or pores along the sides of the body and on the skull, lodging special sense organs, sensitive to movement, pressure, or vibrations in the surrounding water.

latero-sensory canals. Canals within or on the superficial (dermal) skull bones of primitive aquatic vertebrates, lodging the anterior part of the lateral line system (q.v.).

least squares. In statistics, a method of fitting a line to a graphic series of observations in such a way as to make the squares of their distances from that line minimal.

lemma. The principal flowering bract or scale of grasses, which encloses the fruit at maturity.

lethal. A gene or genotype that produces the death of its bearer.

lethal, homozygous. A gene, or genetic condition, which in homozygous condition produces the death of its bearer.

limulids. King or horseshoe crabs. Members of an ancient family of crab-like animals, more nearly related to the spiders (Arachnida) than to the crabs (Crustacea). *Limulus* is the typical living genus.

lingulids. Members of an ancient family of brachiopods (q.v.) with simple shells. *Lingula* is the typical living genus.

linkage. The tendency of several distinct genes or loci to be inherited together due to residence in the same chromosome.

locus. The position of a gene on a chromosome.

lodicules. Small organs at the base of the grass flower, probably reduced petals.

lophs. On teeth, especially of mammals, elongated crests in the enamel pattern.

loxommids. Members of a family of Paleozoic (Carboniferous) European and North American primitive amphibians (labyrinthodonts, q.v.).

M. Symbol for a molar tooth in mammals. M^2 is the second upper molar, M_3 the third lower molar, etc.

macroevolution. Evolution of higher categories than that of local differentiation in interbreeding populations; origin of species, genera, etc. The term is used particularly by Goldschmidt, in whose work it reflects his belief that such units arise by saltation, by a process supposedly distinct from the "microevolution" studied by experimentalists in interbreeding groups.

maltase. Enzyme which hydrolyzes the sugar maltose into its glucose components.

mass spectograph. A device for separating elements of identical chemical properties but different atomic weights (isotopes, *see* isotopic).

meiosis. Two consecutive modified mitotic divisions, characterized by pairing and segregation of homologous chromosomes, and consequently ordinarily resulting in cells or gametes having haploid or reduced sets of chromosomes.

meristem. Formative (embryonic) tissue capable of giving rise to permanent (differentiated) tissues; either *primary* at growing points (tips of roots and stems) or *secondary* found in thin layers in association with permanent tissues.

mesophyte. A plant adapted to intermediate conditions of moisture.

metaphase. The stage of mitosis at which the chromosomes lie in the equatorial plane of the spindle prior to their disjunction and movement to the spindle poles.

metapodial. In land vertebrates, the long foot bones between the toes and the wrist or ankle. The metapodials of the forefoot (or hand) are metacarpals and those of the hindfoot are metatarsals.

metatarsal. *See* metapodial.

Microsauria. A group of relatively rare, small, long-bodied, rather salamander-like extinct amphibians from the Late Paleozoic (Mississippian to Permian).

modifier. A gene which affects the action or expression of a gene at a different locus; such modifying genes often have no other known effects.

monocotyledon. A member of that subclass of angiosperms having one cotyledon, vascular tissue in scattered bundles, and usually parallel veined leaves.

monophagous. An animal that feeds on a single type of food (host plant or species of prey).

monotypic. A taxonomic category which contains only a single unit of the next-lower category, e.g. a monotypic genus contains only a single species.

multifactorial. Controlled by several gene loci.

mutant. The bearer of a mutation.

natural selection. The natural process favoring "the survival of the fittest" and the elimination of less adapted genotypes.

negative eugenics. Improvement of the genetic make-up of a population by prevention of reproduction in individuals with undesirable heritable characteristics.

Neo-Darwinian. A somewhat equivocal term which until recently was applied particularly to the school of Weismann in antithesis to the Neo-Lamarckians. Many recent students, including some of the contributors to this volume, call the recent synthesis of (mainly) mutationist and selectionist evolutionary theory "Neo-Darwinian," although it differs radically from Darwinism or from Weismannian Neo-Darwinism.

Neo-Lamarckism. The theory that evolutionary change is directly caused by the influence of the environment on the organism and the reaction of the organism to the environment. (This theory differs radically from Lamarckism, strictly speaking.)

neotenic. Characterized by prolongation of juvenile or larval stages of development. Applied especially to amphibians (such as the living axolotl) that do not metamorphose but breed in the larval form.

neural cranium. The part of the vertebrate skull that is laid down as cartilage in the embryo and that surrounds the brain and closely associated sensory organs.

neuromast. A cluster of sensory cells, with connecting nerve fibers and surrounding supporting cells, constituting a unit sensory organ in the lateral line system (q.v.).

nominate subspecies. The first named subspecies of a species which therefore gives its name to the species.

obligatory hermaphrodite. A self-fertilizing individual with both male and female sexual organs.

Occam's razor. In logic and scientific methodology, the principle that "entities are not to be multiplied without need," or that the simplest sufficient hypothesis is to be preferred, even though others are possible.

occlusal surfaces. On teeth, the surfaces of upper or lower teeth that come into contact with opposing surfaces, lower or upper, when the jaws are closed.

ontogeny. Development of the organism throughout its individual existence.

oogamy. Sexual reproduction by means of a large type of gamete, the egg, and a small type, the sperm.

oreodonts. Extinct mammals confined to North America and common there during most of the Tertiary, forming an independent group of even-toed hoofed mammals with adaptive similarities to both pigs and ruminants.

orthogenesis. Evolution continuously in a single direction over a considerable length of time. Usages differ greatly, but the term usually carries the implication that the direction is determined by some factor internal to the organism or, at least, is not determined by natural selection.

orthoselective. Pertaining to natural selection acting continuously in the same direction over long periods, a phenomenon often called orthoselection. (Compare "orthogenesis.")

osteolepids. Members of a family of extinct, Paleozoic (Devonian to Permian), true or bony fishes belonging to the Crossopterygii (q.v.), allies of the lungfishes and near the ancestry of the amphibians.

palaeoniscids. A Pennsylvanian to Jurassic family of true fishes, typical of the palaeoniscoids (q.v.).

palaeoniscoids. A large group of early (mainly Paleozoic, some in the Jurassic) very primitive Actinopterygii (q.v.), forerunners of and broadly ancestral to most of the abundant groups of higher bony fishes.

palaeotheres. Extinct, Early Tertiary relatives of the horses, which evolved independently in Eurasia while the main early horse line was evolving in North America.

palea. The inner flowering scale of grasses.

paloplotheres. Extinct, Early Tertiary, European relatives of the horses, allied to the palaeotheres (q.v.) and usually included in that group. In particular, members of the genus *Plagiolophus* Pomel, 1847 (= *Paloplotherium* Owen, 1848).

panmixia. Random interbreeding among the members of a species.

pappus. A series of hairy, scaly, or hook-like appendages on fruits of members of the family Compositae.

pegmatite. A coarse-grained rock, occurring only in dikes or veins cutting across other rocks, with a great variety of mineral constituents but usually mainly composed of quartz, feldspar, and mica.

Pelycosauria. The most primitive order of mammal-like reptiles, Pennsylvanian to Early Triassic, especially characteristic of the North American Permian but also known in the Old World.

penetrance. The frequency with which a gene manifests itself in the phenotype; most genes have a 100 per cent penetrance, other genes, though dominant, have only low penetrance.

perianth. The outer envelope of the flower either undifferentiated or consisting of calyx and corolla.

phenotype. Observable appearance of an organism due to the interaction between the genotype and environment.

phosphatase. An organic catalyst (enzyme) involved in the utilization of phosphates in animals.

phyletic evolution. Evolution within a phyletic series (q.v.). More particularly, evolution occurring within a broad phyletic series, or group of such lines, at moderate rates, without marked change of adaptive type.

phyletic series. A line of ancestors and descendants. (Compare "phylogeny.")

phylogeny. The line, or lines, of direct descent in a given group of organisms. Also, the study or the history of such relationships.

placoderms. A heterogeneous assemblage of ancient (Silurian to Permian), fish-like vertebrates possessing bone and jaws but more archaic in structure than the shark-like fishes or the true bony fishes.

poikilothermic = "cold blooded." Animals in which the body temperature fluctuates with the temperature of the environment.

polymorphic. Of a population, including two or more recognizably different sorts of individuals within a single, interbreeding group.

polyphagous. Feeding on many types of food.

polyploid. A cell, tissue, or organism is said to be polyploid when its nuclear complement of chromosomes is some integral multiple (greater than 2) of the haploid chromosome set; if the haploid set is n chromosomes, the diploid set $2n$, then *triploids* ($3n$), *tetraploids* ($4n$), etc., are polyploids.

polytypic. Of a taxonomic category, including several units of the next lower category, e.g. a species with several subspecies.

population. In statistics, the universe of discourse, the theoretically infinite group represented by the finite body of data derived from a sample. In biology, broadly the whole (finite) group of existent organisms of a given kind. More narrowly or more explicitly in systematics and in population genetics, a local population, the essentially homogeneous group of actually or potentially interbreeding organisms at a given locality.

porphyry. An igneous rock with visible grains or crystals scattered in a matrix that is glassy or very fine-grained; the term refers only to the texture and a wide variety of minerals may compose the rock.

positive eugenics. Improvement of the genetic make-up of a population by increasing reproduction of individuals with desirable heritable characteristics.

preadaptations. Characteristics, especially new characteristics arising by mutation, which have no usefulness as regards the preceding, ancestral adaptation, but which become adaptations in a new and available relationship between organism and environment.

Proboscidea. An order of mammals including the elephants, mammoths, mastodons, and their allies.

propagule. Any structure adapted to propagating the plant, whether asexually or sexually.

protostele. A primitive type of vascular (woody) cylinder in the stem, solid in structure.

pteridophytes. Ferns and fern allies.

quantum evolution. Relatively rapid evolution, under strong selection pressure, from one type of adaptation to another distinctly different.

radiogenic. Said of an element derived from another element by atomic disintegration. Thus lead derived from associated uranium is radiogenic and is to be distinguished from lead which may also be associated with it but which was not derived from the uranium.

Radiolaria. Microscopic animals consisting of a single mass of protoplasm, not divided into cells, usually with an internal skeleton composed of silica.

recapitulation. The theory (now rejected in large part and profoundly modified) that the individual development of an organism passes through stages resembling the adult conditions in its successive ancestors.

rectilinear evolution. Continued change of the same sort and in the same direction within a line of descent over a considerable period of time. Similar to orthogenesis (q.v.), but with no implications as to how the direction of evolution is determined and maintained.

reduction division. An obsolete term formerly used to indicate one of the meiotic divisions at which homologous chromosomes from opposite parents were believed to be segregated to the poles of the spindle. In most organisms both meiotic divisions are reductional for some portions of the chromosome set, depending upon the relations of these portions to centromeres and to crossing-over proximal to them.

reverse mutation. A mutation, affecting a previously mutated locus, which reestablishes the original genotype, often a return to wild type; some reverse mutations lead only part way to the original genotype.

Rh [factor]. Heritable presence in the blood of a certain chemical substance (a particular antigen). Those having the factor are Rh-positive; those lacking it, Rh-negative.

rhipidistian. A member of an extinct (Devonian to Pennsylvanian) group of true fishes, members of the Crossopterygii (q.v.) and including, among others, the osteolepids (q.v.).

rhizome. Any subterranean, most horizontal, stem, usually rooting at the nodes and becoming erect at the apex, differing from true roots by the presence of buds and scale-like leaves.

rhizomorph. A root-like structure, usually applied in plants which lack true roots.

salivary chromosome. In many somatic nuclei of larval flies homologous chromosomes uncoil to a marked degree, pair side by side, and undergo growth in length and girth. The resulting giant chromosomes are called "polytene chromosomes," but as they have been especially studied in salivary glands of larval flies they are commonly referred to as "salivary gland chromosomes" or, inelegantly, "salivary chromosomes."

saltatory evolution. The theory that new types and groups of organisms arise by abrupt and radical change from parent to offspring, without transitional intervening generations and populations.

sauropterygians. Members of an extinct (Triassic to Cretaceous) order of marine reptiles, including the plesiosaurs.

sclerite. A hardened area in the integument of an arthropod, usually separated from adjacent sclerites by sutures or membranous areas.

scutellum. A sclerite in the dorsal portion of a thoracic segment of an insect.

selection coefficient. The increase in fitness (above 1) produced by a gene. A selection coefficient of .01 denotes a 1 per cent increase in fitness.

selection pressure. The degree of systematic bias or enhanced probability in favor of increase, from one generation to the next, of the frequency of a given genetic factor or type of genetic system.

selfing. Self-fertilizing, in hermaphrodite or monoecious organisms.

semi-dominant. A character in which the heterozygote is intermediate between the two homozygotes.

serial homology. The resemblance between different members of a single series of structures within an individual organism, for example, between fore and hind limbs or between different vertebrae.

sex chromosome. A chromosome which does not occur in identical number in both sexes, and which consequently is usually involved in sex determination. (See autosomes).

sex-linked. Of genes, located in a sex chromosome.

shale. A general term for a rock compacted and hardened from what was originally a soft sediment consisting of very fine grains, usually clay or fine silt, commonly with a tendency to split along the bedding planes.

sibling species. Pairs or groups of morphologically nearly or completely identical species.

single-brooded. Producing a single brood per year.

single dose. The presence of only a single one of a given allele in a genotype.

siphonostele. A type of vascular (woody) cylinder in the stem of a plant, tubular in structure.

spermatheca. An organ in the female reproductive tract of most insects and many other invertebrates which stores sperm. In Drosophila the spermatheca is a sclerotic capsule of characteristic shape.

sphenacodonts. Mammal-like reptiles, a group of pelycosaurs (q.v.).

sphenodonts. Members of an ancient (Triassic to Recent) family of reptiles including the relict, living, lizard-like Sphenodon or Hatteria of New Zealand.

sporangium. A spore-case.

sporogenous axis. Fertile axis capable of producing spores.

sporophyte. Independent or parasitic generation arising from fertilized egg and eventually terminating with production of asexual (haploid) spores.

stage. In stratigraphy, the ensemble of rocks within a single province of deposition deposited during a defined span of time, generally shorter than an epoch and designated as a provincial age.

standard deviation. In statistics, a measurement of the scatter of observations around their mean value: the square root of the mean square of their deviations from that value.

stock. In geology, a circular or irregular body of igneous rock, up to a few miles in diameter, that has been intruded as a molten mass upward into the crust of the earth.

sympatric. Coexisting in the same geographical area.

sympatric speciation. The splitting of one species into two, without spatial segregation of the involved populations.

symphysis. The immovable or only slightly movable, usually sutural or fused, union of paired bones at the midline of a vertebrate; for example, the union of lower jaws anteriorly at the mandibular symphysis.

tachytelic. Of evolution, proceeding at rates more rapid than any involved in usual or long-continued evolution of the group in question. (See horotelic.)

talonid. The posterior, usually lower, part of the lower premolars and molars of many mammals, posterior to the trigonid (q.v.).

teleology. The principle that a given occurrence or construction arises in response to a purpose and is directed toward an end. In evolutionary studies, specifically the belief that evolution is finalistic, has followed the purpose of a Creator, and is directed by Him toward His determined goal.

telome. Terminal (ultimate) division of plant axis above point of union with other telomes; characteristic of primitive vascular plants; either sterile or fertile.

terebratuloid. Pertaining to a particular, long-lived (Devonian to Recent) group of brachiopods (q.v.), in the superfamily Terebratulaceae, with loop-like internal supports and generally with rather smooth shells.

testa. The outer usually hard seed coat.

tetrapod. A vertebrate animal with four feet, or descended from an ancestor with four feet; an amphibian, reptile, bird, or mammal.

Thallophyta. Collective term for all lower plant groups such as bacteria, algae, fungi, and lichens.

thecodonts. Members of an extinct (Triassic) order of reptiles including the most primitive archosaurian reptiles (q.v.) and the crocodile-like phytosaurs.

therapsids. A large order of mammal-like reptiles, Permian and Triassic in age, including among others the Deinocephalia, cynodonts, and bauriamorphs (q.v.).

thrust. In geology, a result of local compression of the earth's crust by which one segment of the crust has broken from the next and has been pushed forward over the latter.

translocation. A transfer of a portion of a chromosome to a new location in the same chromosome, in a corresponding chromosome, or in a non-homologous chromosome, that results in new linkage relations.

translocations, reciprocal. The interchange of chromosome sections between two chromosomes.

trigonid. In mammalian teeth, the anterior triangle of three main cusps on lower molars (sometimes also premolars) of primitive marsupials and placentals, and homologous structures derived from these in specialized forms.

trilobites. Primitive, extinct crustaceans, occurring throughout the Paleozoic and abundant in its earlier periods, characterized by segmented bodies divided by longitudinal grooves into three lobes.

triturating dentition. A dentition adapted to grinding and crushing, usually consisting of teeth forming large, flat or ridged plates.

turbellarians. The class of flatworms to which the planarians belong.

umbo. In plants, a protuberance bearing a spine.

ungual. In vertebrate feet, the last joint of the toes, a joint bearing a claw or hoof.

unifactorial. Controlled by a single gene.

uniformity, principle of. The principle that the past history of the earth and of life is correctly interpreted as caused by or subject to the same influences, physical laws, and properties of matter and of life that exist and operate today, and no others.

Ursidae. The bear family.

variance. In statistics, the square of the standard deviation, or the mean square of deviations from an average value.

varve. A layer or layers representing the deposition of one year in a fine-grained, laminated sediment. Sediments with recognizable annual laminae are said to be varved.

viable. With the capacity for growth or development.

wild-type. The sum total of the normal alleles of a species or of those usually found in nature.

X-chromosome. Ordinarily a chromosome in diploid heterogametic forms normally represented twice in the chromosomal set of one sex, but once only in the chromosomal set of the other. Usually the female is XX in constitution, the male XY.

GLOSSARY

xerophyte. A plant adapted to dry conditions.

Y-chromosome. Ordinarily a chromosome normally present in but one sex of diploid heterogametic forms; e.g. only the male has a Y-chromosome in humans.

zygote. A cell or individual resulting from a union of two gametes; in the higher animals and plants a fertilized egg.

Geological Time Table
(Younger divisions above, older below)

ERAS	PERIODS	EPOCHS
	Quaternary*	{ Recent or Holocene { Pleistocene
Cenozoic	Tertiary*	{ Pliocene Miocene { Oligocene Eocene Paleocene
Mesozoic	{ Cretaceous { Jurassic { Triassic	(No world-wide system for epochs earlier than the Paleocene is in general use.)
Paleozoic	{ Permian Pennsylvanian† Mississippian† { Devonian Silurian Ordovician Cambrian	

Pre-Cambrian

* Some authors reject the terms "Tertiary" and "Quaternary" and consider the whole Cenozoic as a single period.
† European authors (e.g. Watson in this volume) do not use the American terms "Mississippian" and "Pennsylvanian" but include the corresponding time in a single period called "Carboniferous."

INDEX

Acarpy, 90
Accipiter gentilis, 304; *A. nisus*, 304
Acoustico-lateralis system, 163
Adamson, R. S., 95
Adaptation, 402; altered direction, 83; and comparative anatomy, 66, 78; definitions, 78; degree of, 80; diverse, leading to genetic isolation, 337; in embryonic temperature tolerance, frogs, 325; in fossils, 103; generalizing vs. specializing, 80-81; and geographic distribution in *Rana*, 336; interpretation in extinct types, 77, 103; major, genetic changes leading to, 273-275, and ontogenetic change, 181, origin of, 68, 274, 387, 430, sudden emergence, 74, 76, 81, 114; measured by geographic and ecological distribution, 316; at nuclear level, 19; origin of, 80ff., and comparative anatomy, 82; and paleontology, 76; in plants, 235-238; and population structure, 75; progressive, in fossil reptiles, 390ff.; reality of, 78; selective extension, 83; shift in vs. evolutionary rate, 224; specializing, in taeniodonts, 269; and speciation, 284; and standardization, 96; successive shifts in direction, 87
Adaptive changes, major, genetic changes leading to, 273-275
Adaptive characters, embryonic, geographic variation in *Rana*, 327-331; identification via parallelisms, 327
Adaptive differences in closely related species, 304
Adaptive evolution and speciation, 306
Adaptive peaks, 79, 373ff., 430
Adaptive radiation, 114, 387, 433, 439; on Galapagos vs. Cocos, 307; in Galapagos finches, 306
Adaptive shift and origin of major adaptive types, 87, 274
Adaptive trends, sequence leading to, 391-392
Adaptive type, modes of origin, 82ff.
Adaptive zones, 79; in taeniodonts, 267
Adelospondyli, 62
Age composition tables, 215
Age of the earth, 4, 435
Algae, blue-green, 239; green, 239
Alleles, multiple, maintenance, 385; self-sterility in plants, 377; species specific, 14
Allen, G. S., 94

Alligator, relative intelligence of, 186
Allometric equation, 212; growth, 52, 208
Allometry, genetic base, 213
Amadon, D., 84
Amentiferae, 234
Ammonites, 47
Amorph, 18
Amphibia, major trends in resemble labyrinthodont pattern, 62
Amphidiploidy, 386
Amphiploidy and origin of species, 366
Amynodonts, evolution, 188-189
Analogy, 23, 80
"Anamestic" bones, 135
Anas, 289
Anchitherium, 48, 49
Aneuploid, 233
Aneuploidy, compound, 386; and origin of species, 366
Angiosperm flower, interpretation, 90
Angiosperms, origin and evolution, 191ff.
Animal distribution and earth history, 226
Anomodontia, 60
Anser, 289
Anteaters, 81
Anthracosaurs, 56
Anthus pratensis, 304; *A. trivialis*, 304
Antigens, 14
Antimorph, 18
Apatemyids, 270
Aplodontidae, 269, 274
Aptenodytes forsteri, 83; *A. patagonicus*, 83
Arber, A., 91, 94
Archaeohippus, 49, 111
Archegoniatae, 96
Archeria, 55
Archosaurs, 393
Argynnis, 354
Aromorphosis, 224
Artiodactyls, 52
Autopolyploidy, 386
Aves, 16
Axolotl, 408

Bacteria, 238
Badger, 85
Baluchitheres, 186
Barrell, J., 224
Barriers, to gene flow, 286; mechanical vs. intrinsic factors, 288
Basilarchia, natural hybridization, 340-348; *B. archippus*, 340ff., vars., 348; *B. arthemis*, 340ff.; var. *proserpina*,